Ore Deposits

A SERIES OF BOOKS IN GEOLOGY

EDITORS: James Gilluly, A. O. Woodford

CHARLES F. PARK, Jr.

Stanford University

AND

ROY A. MacDIARMID

State University College at Fredonia, New York

Ore Deposits

W. H. FREEMAN AND COMPANY

San Francisco and London

Preface

ORE DEPOSITS is designed to present to the student of economic geology the principles and data basic to understanding the genesis and localization of the metallic ores and the nonmetallic ores associated with them. It is assumed that this student has at least an elementary knowledge of chemistry and physics, as well as of mineralogy, petrology, and structural geology.

Modern civilization's dependence upon minerals makes the search for new mineral deposits continually more challenging—the demand for ores increases as the number of undeveloped near-surface deposits decreases. If the future geologist is to meet this challenge he must be given a broad and thorough training; he must develop a blend of ingenuity, imagination, and optimism that will enable him to face the many problems that remain unsolved; and he must be encouraged to make use of every bit of available knowledge in undertaking the search for new deposits. A knowledge of prospecting techniques is, of course, essential; but to understand, to use, and to improve exploration methods, the student must first become fully acquainted with the principles of ore deposition. The geologist who understands why an ore body has been deposited in a certain environment has made real progress toward the discovery of a new deposit or a new mineral district. It is the purpose of this book to present in an orderly fashion the ideas and principles that will aid the student in reaching this understanding.

The book is based on the premise that ores are transported and deposited by fluids of magmatic, metamorphic, or meteoric origin, and contains brief sections on the nature of these fluids and on the ways in which the fluids travel—on the surface, at shallow depths, and at great depths in the earth. A large part of the book is taken up with discussion of where and why ores are concentrated. An attempt has been made to correlate the physical and chemical characteristics of various ores with environments and conditions of deposition. In order to clarify the subject of ore deposition, there are chapters on structural and chemical controls, depositional textures, replacement, wall-rock alteration, gangue, paragenesis and zoning, and geothermometry. The chapters on theory are followed by a chapter on the classification of ore deposits, which includes examples taken from the field. Each Lindgren category of ores is treated in a separate chapter, in sequence from deep-seated to near-surface. The last three chapters deal with the behavior of ore minerals in environments of weathering and metamorphism.

The ore deposits described and the illustrations included have been selected to encourage three-dimensional thinking and to emphasize structural and chemical controls. In chapters dealing with particular classes of ore deposits, we have chosen to describe a few carefully selected deposits in detail rather than offer a brief description of every important deposit. References to additional examples are given at the end of each of these chapters, but no attempt has been made to include references to all large mining districts. Special attention has also been given to the many useful developments in experimental geochemistry that can be applied to field geology: throughout, the chemistry of ore genesis and localization is emphasized.

Many of the ideas discussed in this book are controversial. We have made no attempt to settle these controversies. Because ideas about the chemistry of metal-bearing fluids, the techniques for determining temperatures and environments of deposition, and the accepted classification of ore deposits are constantly changing, all sides of the major issues have been presented. Untested hypotheses, although given, have been approached conservatively, and reflect our preference for the field evidence.

Throughout the book we have made free use of the literature, and have made an effort to acknowledge the contributions of colleagues. Of the many geologists with whom we have had helpful discussions, we are especially indebted to K. B. Krauskopf and Adolph Knopf: it is impossible here to extend individual recognition to the many others who have contributed valuable ideas and suggestions. Parts of the manuscript dealing with geochemistry were read by J. J. Hemley and H. L. Barnes; the chapter on geothermometry was read by Kurt Servos; and our descriptions of Magma, Arizona, and Potosi, Bolivia, were read by R. N. Webster and F. S. Turneaure, respectively. The excellent photographs taken by Professor W. J. Crook, Ruperto Laniz, and C. M. Taylor require special acknowledgment and thanks. Financial assistance was given to the junior author by Tulane University. Each of these contributions is gratefully acknowledged.

December 1963

Charles F. Park, Jr.

Roy A. MacDiarmid

Contents

Introduction

Besides, what we are pleased to call the riches of a mine, are riches relatively to a distinction which nature does not recognize. The spars and veinstones which are thrown out in the rubbish of our mines, may be as precious in the eyes of nature, as conducive to the great object of her economy, and are certainly as characteristic of mineral veins, as the ores of silver or gold, to which we attach so great a value.

John Playfair, 1802

ORES ARE ROCKS AND MINERALS that can be recovered at a profit. In a strict sense, *ore* refers only to metals or metal-bearing minerals, but in common usage it includes a few of the nonmetallic minerals, such as sulfur and fluorite. Building stone and industrial materials, such as abrasives, clays, refractories, light-weight aggregates, and salts, are not considered ore; they are classified as industrial rocks and minerals or as *economic minerals*—a term that includes both ore minerals and industrial materials. *Ore minerals* are compounds valued for their economic content of metals. Accordingly, not all minerals containing a given element are classified as ore minerals. For example, simple iron oxides, such as magnetite and hematite, are ore minerals, but most iron silicates, such as fayalite and ferrosilite, are not mined for their iron and therefore are not ore minerals. An ore may be a rock containing veinlets, disseminations, or small amounts of useful minerals. Ores—either metallic or nonmetallic minerals—are widely distributed in the rocks of the earth's crust, but are concentrated in amounts sufficient to be of economic value, and in a form that permits their recovery, only under exceptional circumstances. Most ore minerals are associated with valueless material called *gangue,* and many ores grade into *protore*—mineralized rock that is too lean to yield a profit. As Playfair stated so lucidly in 1802, the economic value of the ore does not set it apart genetically from the worthless pyrite, sericite, calcite, or other gangue and rock with which it is associated. The study of ore deposits is thus a specialized phase of the broader field of petrology.

The tremendous expansion of world population in recent years, combined with a slowly improving standard of living throughout the world, has resulted in greatly increased demands for mineral products of all types. These demands will certainly continue to grow; hence the economic geologist's responsibility for finding more ore will also increase. In order to obtain sufficient supplies in the future, new ideas and techniques must be devised to supplement the old. The search for ore is becoming increasingly complex; more and more, ore is being sought under cover and at greater depths. Recovery and mining techniques need to be improved so that large bodies of near-surface mineral of grades lower than those that are now economic can be developed. For these reasons the truly successful economic geologist must be able to understand and to use all phases of his broadening science. He must possess imagination, ingenuity, and a degree of optimism in order to develop "exploration thinking." The successful student of ore deposits must be thoroughly grounded in structural geology. He must understand and be able to use stratigraphy, petrology, and mineralogy, and he should have a knowledge of how fluids migrate underground. Geophysics and geochemistry are becoming increasingly useful in the search for buried deposits, and the modern economic geologist should be familiar with their fundamental techniques.

An economic geologist should seek the answers to several pertinent questions. Under what conditions, and as a result of what processes, are ores formed? What are the factors that lead to concentration of the useful elements in a particular environment and not in another? What causes the localization of ore? Probably the best way to obtain answers to these questions, and hence the best way to search for new orebodies, is to study the structure and genesis of known mineral concentrations and then explore the geologically favorable areas.

Owing to the complex nature of the earth, and because many of the processes involved in ore deposition cannot be observed, it follows that the study of ore deposits and ore genesis is not an exact science. This does not mean that precise laboratory and experimental data are not desirable and useful, but it does mean that such data should be viewed critically and must be used with caution. Laboratory data unsupported by field evidence frequently lead to erroneous conclusions. Geology, especially the study of ore deposits, is basically a field science. The final test of all theories and hypotheses is their applicability and validity in the field.

CHAPTER 1 **The Development of the Modern Theories of Ore Deposition**

EARLY MAN was acquainted with ore deposits, and worked many of them. He used cinnabar and soft red hematite as pigments long before smelting was devised. Gem stones and native copper, gold, and silver were highly valued as ornaments and as materials for making simple implements. Essentially nothing was understood of the origin of minerals, however, and even in the days of the Greek and Roman civilizations, the hypotheses about ore genesis were postulated by philosophers, none of whom had firsthand knowledge of ores in the ground. From the time of Greco-Roman supremacy until the eighteenth century, many imaginative theories were advanced to explain the presence of minerals and metals in the earth's crust. Some philosophers envisioned an animated earth that breathed ores or gave off metallic exhalations as a regular function of metabolism; others considered the ores themselves to be alive, growing from seeds or ripening from base metals into precious metals. A popular conception among such "naturalists" was that the ores existed in the form of a subterranean "golden tree" whose twigs and branches were various kinds of metals and whose roots led down to the center of the earth. In a metaphorical sense, some of these concepts were not as fantastic as they may seem, and many modern ideas can be traced to them. Alchemy flourished during the sixteenth and seventeenth centuries, and the general belief held among alchemists was that ore deposits were generated by such celestial powers as the sun's rays or planetary influences. These fanciful ideas were not restricted to alchemists; their proponents included some of the world's most renowned thinkers: Aristotle,

Pliny, Avicenna, Albertus Magnus, Thomas Aquinas, Robert Boyle, Roger Bacon, and Georges de Buffon.

The early hypotheses are of interest in the study of ore deposits principally because their shortcomings emphasize that the study of ore-forming processes must be based upon field observations. This point is occasionally accentuated by modern writers who attempt to theorize about ore deposits without a thorough knowledge of field relationships; their hypotheses too often resemble theories discredited in the past.

In view of the religious attitudes and rampant superstitions of the early days of civilization, it is not at all surprising that mysterious forces were called upon to explain ore deposits and to detect buried minerals. Even today the ancient practice of dousing, or witching, for ore deposits is employed by many of our less sophisticated prospectors. The ancient Egyptians and Greeks used divination rods for predicting future events, but it was not until the fifteenth century that forked twigs were used to locate mineral deposits. Credit for the adaptation of a divination rod to prospecting has been given to the Germans of the Harz mining region, who in turn "enlightened" the English (Gardner, 1957). As the theories of ore genesis improved, however, so did prospecting techniques, with the result that advanced geophysical methods (de Wet, 1957) and geochemical methods (Hawkes and Webb, 1962) have nearly replaced the hazel stick.

A solid base for the modern theories of ore deposits was formulated in the sixteenth century by Georg Bauer, who is generally known by his Latinized name, Georgius Agricola. Agricola's observations about ore deposits were remarkable for a man of his time, and for this reason he is considered the father of economic geology. He lived in the Erzgebirge region of Saxony and gained an intimate firsthand knowledge of the mines in that district. He wrote many treatises on geology and mining, the most significant of which was his comprehensive and pioneering work, *De Re Metallica* (1556). In spite of the fact that most of Agricola's publications were in Latin, and as a consequence generally unusable by all but the scholars, his writings gave a significant, though premature, stimulus to the science. Present-day fundamentals of ore deposits bear the stamp of his influence. Agricola's principal contribution was his attempt to classify ores, for without classification no great progress would be possible. His classification was based upon genesis—whether the deposits were alluvial or in situ— and upon form. Thus the in situ deposits included fissure veins, bedded or horizontal deposits, impregnations, stringers, seams, and stockworks; and a vein or seam might be straight, curved, inclined, or vertical.

According to Hoover and Hoover, translators of Agricola's *De Re Metal-lica*, two fundamental principles have been attributed to Agricola in addi-tion to his classification of ore deposits. These principles are (1) that ore channels are secondary features, younger than the country rocks, and (2) that the ores are deposited from solutions circulating in these channels. Agricola thus marks the transition between speculation and observation; he brought geology into the field. The hazel twig first came into use in the search for ore deposits during Agricola's time, and it is a tribute to this great geologist that he argued against such a prospecting technique like a twentieth-century scientist.

From the time of Agricola until the middle of the eighteenth century, little advancement was made in the study of ore deposits. During this period, as before, many people throughout the world looked upon mining as dangerous work—and, what was worse, as degrading. Mining was work for convicts and slaves; it could not compete with the elite and more lucrative professions of ministry, medicine, and law. Moreover, mining was closely controlled by governments, which collected the profits. Since most mining was done in remote parts of the world and communications were primitive or nonexistent, working in the mines was equivalent to being banished from civilization. These conditions did not change until the begin-ning of the nineteenth century. With improved means of communications and increasing demands for metals, scientists gradually became interested in geology and mining.

In spite of the general lack of interest in science that prevailed following Agricola's generation, a few noteworthy works were published, and consider-able field knowledge was accumulated. Nicolaus Steno—Latinized name of Niels Stensen, a Dane who worked in Italy—stands out in the seventeenth century as a scientist of great perception; responsible for many contributions to general geology, he argued that ores are a product of condensation from vapors ascending through open fissures (Steno, 1669)—a remarkably ad-vanced concept, and one that has been retained in modern theory.

By the eighteenth century, many trained scientists were puzzling over the problems of ore genesis. Most of the early progress was made in Ger-many, as a result of activities in the Erzgebirge mining district. Henkel (1725, 1727) and Zimmermann (1746) acknowledged the importance of hydrothermal solutions, or vapors of deep-seated origin, which they cor-rectly reasoned should contain dissolved rock materials; they even recog-nized the products of ore deposition by metasomatism (replacement). In 1749 von Oppel made the important distinction between veins and bedded deposits, the former being cross-cutting features of secondary, open-fissure origin, and the latter being conformably interbedded with the stratified sediments.

It must have been difficult for a student of ore deposits to differentiate between fact and fancy in those days, because the scientific method had not been established and because some of the leading scientists were guilty of proposing theories that did not acknowledge all of the field data. The product of such practice was a mixture of positive contributions and imaginative ideas, and it is only in retrospect that we are able to distinguish between the two and give credit where it is due. A good example of the sometimes observant, sometimes fanciful scientist is Delius (1770, 1773), who was first to recognize the superficial alteration of ores by atmospheric agents. He also observed the development of secondary minerals in the alteration zone as well as a zone of supergene enrichment beneath the altered layer. Yet he reasoned erroneously that the development of alteration products requires heat from the sun.

A few years later, Charpentier (1778, 1799), a professor at the Mining Academy at Freiberg, Germany, published two small but well-written books. His writings were based upon astute observations made during many years of study in the Freiberg mines. He believed that the veins in these mines were formed by alteration of the country rock, and he showed as supporting evidence how some of the veins grade into wall rock. He likened this process to the silicification of wood and, as did Henkel and Zimmermann, proposed that one material had been altered to another. On the other hand, Gerhard (1781), a contemporary German author, considered the veins to be open fissures filled by minerals leached from the country rock. From Charpentier's and Gerhard's writings has come the theory of lateral secretion, which considers that the contents of an ore deposit are leached from the adjacent wall rock by waters that are usually, but not necessarily, of meteoric origin. The theory of lateral secretion was apparently neglected for almost 100 years, and not until Sandberger (1882) published his *Untersuchungen über Erzgänge* (*Investigations Concerning Mineral Veins*) did the theory become generally known and widely accepted. Sandberger attempted to show that most mineral deposits were formed according to this theory, and his publications profoundly influenced contemporary thought. Actually the theory has much to commend it; parts of many ore deposits are considered by careful workers today to have formed in this manner.

During the latter part of the eighteenth century, two outstanding men of diametrically opposed views dominated geological thought: James Hutton, a Scot, and Abraham Gottlob Werner, a German. Their ideas have had a far-reaching effect on the science of ore deposits. Hutton—a "plutonist" —thought that both igneous rocks and ore deposits were derived from molten magmas at depth and were transported in the fluid state to their present positions (1788, 1795). He was impressed by the similarity between metallic ores and the products observed in smelters. Arguing against the idea of ore deposition from hydrothermal solutions, he suggested that ore materials solidified from the molten state, the ore magma having been injected into fissures of tectonic origin. Massive, mixed sulfides were assumed to have an origin similar to that of an igneous rock, as evidenced by the mutually interpenetrating mineral grains, but Hutton went too far with his magmatic theory of rocks when he insisted that metals could not have been precipitated out of aqueous solutions.

The suggestion that ores are direct magmatic products or are formed as products of differentiation was also advocated by Joseph Brunner (1801), a Bavarian mine official. He developed the idea to help explain the origin of some of the puzzling Bavarian ores. Scipione Breislak (1811) an Italian geologist, also called upon the process of magmatic segregation to explain how ore minerals became concentrated in definite layers within igneous rocks. The theory remained essentially unchanged until Joseph Fournet revived it in about the middle of the nineteenth century. Fournet was an able advocate of the theory of ore magmas, and his ideas, with little modification, were revived in recent times by Spurr (1923). Today ore magmas are widely accepted as the origin of certain types of ore bodies.

In contrast to Hutton, Werner was a "neptunist." He argued that all rocks and ore deposits were formed as sediments in a primeval ocean. In 1791 Werner published a résumé of his ideas in the *Neue Theorie von der Entstehung der Gänge* (*New Theory of the Formation of Veins*). He pictured veins as originating as cracks formed on the bottom of a primeval ocean by slumping or earthquakes; the cracks were subsequently filled with chemical precipitates, as evidenced by the symmetrical banding observed in veins of the Erzgebirge. Werner's personal charm and gift of oratory, as well as his comprehension of mineralogy and local stratigraphy, gained him a devoted following and a reputation as an outstanding teacher and logician; both directly and indirectly he had great influence on the entire science of geology.

We are dependent upon the students and followers of Hutton and Werner for the amplification of their theories. Hutton lacked the ability to present his ideas in a lucid style, and if it had not been for John Playfair (1802), who popularized Hutton's contributions shortly after he died, this great pioneer's influence would not have been so widespread. Probably the best explanation in English of Werner's hypotheses was published by Charles Anderson in 1809.

Heated arguments and discussions between advocates of the plutonist and neptunist theories were conducted by disciples of Hutton and Werner for many years. Observant men were quick to discredit both principles as all-inclusive generalities. It was readily shown that lavas are not sedimentary formations. Similarly, it was readily shown that minerals, including those that contain metals, are soluble and may be transported in and deposited from aqueous media. Even today, however, this argument between plutonists and neptunists—or as they are now known, magmatists and syngeneticists—has not been resolved. Some geologists maintain that banded sulfide ores similar to those in the Rammelsberg district, Germany (see Fig. 17-12, p. 386), are sediments; other geologists do not accept this theory, because it is not clear how the large amounts of unusual minerals present could have originated in ordinary sources of sediments.

Many mines were examined and operated during the early part of the nineteenth century, but in retrospect it seems as though few advances were made in the theories of ore transportation and deposition. Mining methods were improved by technical advances and by the development of such mechanical devices as the hoist. One of the greatest steps forward was the invention of the Cornish pump, which permitted operations to be carried on well below the water table. Detailed geological observations were recorded by such careful scientists as J. L. Heim, Alexander von Humboldt, and D'Aubuisson de Voisins. Their observations later provided the basic field data for many theories and conclusions. One of the results was the demonstration of a spatial relationship between certain types of ore deposits and intrusive rocks. Recognition of this association helped to establish the foundation for modern theories concerning the origin of hydrothermal ores. It was during this period that geologists began to distinguish between ore deposits of igneous affiliation and those of sedimentary origin.

The field data accumulated during the previous century or two showed clearly that many large ore deposits are localized in areas of structural complexity and igneous activity, a fact that is used extensively in exploration. Most evidence cited to show that ores are associated with igneous sources is circumstantial and somewhat tenuous, though nonetheless convincing. Certain types of ore are so commonly found in and around igneous masses of a particular composition, and so seldom elsewhere, that it is natural and reasonable to associate the presence of these ores with definite types of igneous activity. For example, nickel ores are associated with norites and peridotites; disseminated copper deposits are almost always found in monzonite or quartz monzonite stocks; and tin is associated with siliceous plutonic rocks, such as granite and siliceous pegmatite. This close association has strengthened the assumption that a genetic relationship exists between igneous rocks and many ores. The arrangement of minerals in zones around igneous centers likewise suggests that ore-bearing fluids spread out from channels that tap deep-seated sources, presumably magma chambers. As the fluids rise and spread throughout the rocks, they deposit their minerals in favorable structural and stratigraphic environments. Much of the evidence used to relate ores to igneous activity has been obtained from the studies of fumaroles and hot springs, where many constituents of ore deposits have been recognized, either in the hot fluids or in the wall rocks of the channelways.

In the middle of the nineteenth century Élie de Beaumont made several contributions that are still generally accepted. In addition to his many ideas concerning general geology and structural geology, de Beaumont thought that hydrothermal solutions played a part in the formation of ore deposits. Although this suggestion had been made previously, de Beaumont emphasized and developed it. Besides hydrothermal deposits, he recognized and described magmatic segregations and replacement ores formed in the contact metamorphic zones of intrusive igneous rocks. It was also during the period of de Beaumont's activity that chemical principles began to influence geologists' ideas about ore genesis, thanks to such men as K. G. Bischof and Bernhard von Cotta.

The latter half of the nineteenth century found many eminent scientists contributing to the theories of ore transportation and deposition. Among the best known of these men were von Cotta, F. Sandberger, and A. W. Stelzner in Germany; A. Daubrée, and later L. de Launay, in France; and F. Posepny in Bohemia; J. A. Phillips in England; J. H. L. Vogt in Norway; and S. F. Emmons in the United States. The science was coming of age. Enough field facts had been collected and described by impartial and independent observers to withstand even reasonable generalizations of too broad a nature. Geologists were able to understand clearly that no single theory will explain the genesis of all ore deposits.

Louis de Launay, J. H. L. Vogt, Waldemar Lindgren, R. Beck, C. R. Van Hise, F. L. Ransome, W. H. Emmons, J. F. Kemp, W. H. Weed, and other scientists formulated and stated many of our modern theories early in the present century. Owing to the host of careful field observations made throughout the world and to an expanding need for minerals, economic geology began to shape into an important branch of science. It slowly became obvious that structure plays a vital role in ore localization by guiding ore-bearing fluids into areas favorable for their deposition. The process of replacement was widely recognized, and knowledge of the more simple chemical changes that take place in nature was gradually extended.

Not until the first decades of the twentieth century was the genetic classification of ore deposits greatly improved upon. Nearly everyone who works with ore deposits recognizes the need for a systematic arrangement of the data in such a way that differences among deposits will be made most apparent. Some of the most prominent geologists in the world have gathered for symposia to discuss this problem, and their efforts laid the groundwork for our present classification scheme. One such symposium (Rickard, 1903) was attended by Waldemar Lindgren (Fig. 1-1), whose endeavors in subsequent years produced the popular form of our genetic classification (Lindgren, 1907, 1913, 1922). Lindgren classified the deposits according to whether they are products of mechanical or chemical concentration and, if chemical, whether they were deposited from surface waters, from magmas, or within bodies of rock. The major controversy involved the classification of hydrothermal veins, which fit into Lindgren's group of chemical deposits introduced into bodies of rock by igneous processes. Within this group Lindgren included both pyrometasomatic (igneous-metamorphic) and hydrothermal deposits. The *pyrometasomatic deposits* form as high-temperature replacement bodies near the border zones of igneous intrusives. The *hydrothermal deposits*—the ores formed by hot, aqueous solutions—were further subdivided according to temperature and depth of formation. Hydrother-

FIGURE 1-1. *Waldemar Lindgren.*

mal deposits formed at great depth and high temperature (about 300–500°C) were termed *hypothermal;* those formed at intermediate depths and temperatures (about 150–300°C), *mesothermal;* and those formed at shallow depths and relatively low temperatures (50–150°C), *epithermal.* By 1933 Lindgren had increased the mesothermal-epithermal temperature boundary from 150°C to 200°C, but this change merely reflects advances made in geochemistry rather than a flaw in his classification system. Subsequent additions have been made to Lindgren's genetic classification, though only two of them have been universally accepted. In 1933, Graton introduced the term *telethermal* to include deposits formed at shallow depths from nearly cooled hydrothermal solutions—that is, deposits formed a long distance from the igneous source, above or beyond the epithermal zone. Similarly, Buddington (1935) introduced the *xenothermal* zone to include deposits formed at high temperatures and shallow depths.

In recent years, proponents of the theory of granitization and of the formation of ore deposits during regional metamorphism have advanced ideas to explain the origin of various deposits. These geologists reason that during metamorphism, the more mobile constituents, including many of the metallic elements, are "sweated out" of the country rock and migrate along fissures and channels into areas of low pressure and temperature, where they are deposited. Even though metamorphism is generally thought of as a process of dispersion rather than a process of concentration, the mobile constituents are believed to leave the rock and become concentrated along channelways away from the centers of metamorphism. Thus mobilized, the mineral-bearing metamorphic fluids are believed to act the same as fluids of magmatic origin.

Possibly more agreement exists among geologists concerning the origin of sedimentary and residual ores than exists concerning the origin of ores of igneous and metamorphic affiliation. Because sedimentary and residual ores formed near and on the surface, where conditions of transportation and deposition may be observed, they are better understood. Many bedded sulfide deposits are considered by some geologists to be of igneous replacement origin and by other geologists to be of sedimentary origin, possibly contributed to the sea through submarine volcanic vents or even by normal weathering processes.

The view that predominates among economic geologists in the United States is that ore deposits of igneous affiliation are differentiated at depth, and that ore constituents are transported in the uncrystallized fraction. This fluid fraction, commonly mixed with connate or meteoric waters, moves into areas of lower pressure and lower temperature, where structural and environmental conditions are favorable for deposition. Some ores are deposited within the magma during differentiation (magmatic segregation deposits) or migrate as magma fractions and vapors. Still other deposits, generally of small extent, are associated with lavas and related eruptive materials.

It is perhaps significant to this brief review of the development of ore deposit theory that many of the world's largest and most thoroughly studied mines still provide subjects for controversy. Although geology grew up around ore deposits, many of the most fundamental problems relating to the transportation and deposition of ore materials remain unsettled. It is more common to find that two or more hypotheses on the origin of a given ore body are being entertained than that its genesis has been satisfactorily unraveled. The most famous gold deposit in the world, in the Witwatersrand area of South Africa, is still debated as being either placer or hydrothermal in origin. Many lead-zinc deposits, such as those of Mount Isa, Australia, or the Tri-State district in the Mississippi Valley, may be hydrothermal deposits, as some geologists think, or they may be sedimentary beds composed of chemical precipitates. Some massive sulfide deposits and some oxide deposits have been described both as direct products of magmatic differentiation and as replacement ores introduced either in dilute solutions or as gases. Clearly, then, many fascinating problems remain to be solved.

General References

Adams, F. D., 1934, Origin and nature of ore deposits, an historical study: Geol. Soc. America Bull., v. 45, p. 375–424.

————, 1938, The birth and development of the geological sciences: Baltimore, The Williams and Wilkins Co., p. 277–328.

Crook, Thomas, 1933, History of the theory of ore deposits, with a chapter on the rise of petrology: London, Thomas Murby and Co.

Emmons, S. F., 1904, Theories of ore deposition historically considered: Geol. Soc. America Bull., v. 15, p. 1–28.

Geikie, Sir Archibald, 1897, The founders of geology: London, Macmillan and Co., Ltd.

Graton, L. C., 1941, Ore deposits in geology: Geol. Soc. America (50th anniv. volume), p. 473–509.

Zittel, K. A. von, 1889, Geschichte der Geologie und Paleontologie: München und Leipzig.

References Cited

Agricola, Georgius, 1556, De Re Metallica (English translation by H. C. Hoover and L. H. Hoover, 1912): New York, Dover Publications, Inc., 1950.

Anderson, Charles, 1809, New theory of the formation of veins, by Abraham Gottlob Werner, Edinburgh.

Breislak, Scipione, 1811, Introduzione alla Geologia: Milan, Stamperia Reale.

Brunner, Joseph, 1801, Neue Hypothese von Entstehung der Gänge: Leipzig.

Buddington, A. F., 1935, High-temperature mineral associations at shallow to moderate depths: Econ. Geology, v. 30, p. 205–222.

Charpentier, J. F. W., 1778, Mineralogische Geographie der Chursächischen Lande: Leipzig.

————, 1799, Beobachtung über die Lagerstätte der Erze, hauptsächlich aus den sächsischen Gebirgen: Leipzig.

Delius, C. T., 1770, Abhandlung von dem Ursprunge der Gebirge und der darinne befindlichen Erzadern: Leipzig.

————, 1773, Anleitungen zur der Bergbaukunst nach ihrer Theorie und Ausübung: Vienna.

Gardner, Martin, 1957, Fads and fallacies in the name of science: New York, Dover Publications, Inc.

Gerhard, C. A., 1781, Versuch einer Geschichte des Mineral-Reichs: Berlin.

Graton, L. C., 1933, The depth-zones in ore deposition: Econ. Geology, v. 28, p. 513–555.

Hawkes, H. E., and Webb, J. S., 1962, Geochemistry in mineral exploration: New York and Evanston, Harper and Row.

Henkel, J. F., 1725, Pyritologia oder Kieshistorie: Leipzig.

————, 1727, Mediorum chymicorum non ultimum conjunctionis primum appropriatio, etc.: Dresden and Leipzig.

Hutton, James, 1788, Theory of the earth: Roy. Soc. Edinburgh Trans., v. 1, p. 209–304.

————, 1795, Theory of the earth, with proofs and illustrations: Edinburgh.

Lindgren, Waldemar, 1907, The relation of ore deposition to physical conditions: Econ. Geology, v. 2, p. 105–127.

————, 1913, Mineral deposits: New York, McGraw-Hill Book Co., Inc., p. 178–188.

————, 1922. A suggestion for the terminology of certain mineral deposits: Econ. Geology, v. 17, p. 292–294.

————, 1933, Mineral deposits (4th ed.): New York, McGraw-Hill Book Co., Inc.

Oppel, F. W. von, 1749, Anleitungen zur Markscheidekunst nach ihren Anfangsgründen und Ausübung kürzlich entworfen: Dresden.

Playfair, John, 1802, Illustrations of the Huttonian theory of the earth: Edinburgh.

Rickard, T. A., editor, 1903, Ore deposits, a discussion: New York and London, Eng. Mining Jour.

Sandberger, Fridolin, 1882, Untersuchungen über Erzgänge: Wiesbaden.

Spurr, J. E., 1923, The ore magmas: New York, McGraw-Hill Book Co., Inc.

Steno, N. S., 1669, De solido intra solidum naturaliter contento: Florence.

Werner, A. G., 1791, Neue Theorie von der Entstehung der Gänge, mit Anwendung auf den Bergbau besonders den freibergischen: Freiberg.

de Wet, J. P. (editor-in-chief), 1957, Methods and case histories in mining geophysics: Canadian Inst. Mining Metallurgy, 6th Commonwealth Mining and Metallurgical Congress.

Zimmerman, C. F., 1746, Unteradischen Beschreibung der Meissnischen Erzgebirges: Dresden and Leipzig, Obersächsische Bergakademie.

CHAPTER 2 **The Ore-bearing Fluids**

To understand the localization of ore deposits, it is necessary to understand the nature of the transporting media, which in all cases are liquids or gases. Whether the ores are directly related to magmas, are associated with metamorphic processes, or are related to ground waters and sedimentary processes, they are all intimately associated with the movement of fluids. Hydrothermal solutions can be studied near the surface of the earth, but here they are likely to be contaminated with admixed meteoric waters and to have changed their characteristics through extensive reaction with the wall rocks along their passageways. Little is known of the deeper ore-bearing fluids; their nature must be inferred—with attention to sound geochemical principles—either from observations of thermal springs, volcanic gases, and other emanations that are the end products of ore-forming processes or from studies of the ores and their accompanying gangue minerals.

For the purpose of investigating the ore-bearing fluids more closely, they are considered in three categories:

1. magmatic fluids;
2. meteoric waters;
3. fluids associated with metamorphic processes.

Any of these fluids may be hot or cold, deep-seated or near-surface. Moreover, if heated and in the liquid state, each would be considered a *hydrothermal solution*, because this term refers to any hot, watery fluid, and is not used in a genetic sense. If the fluid is in a gaseous form, it is classified as *pneumatolytic*. But, under high pressures, the properties of the fluids are similar whether they are hydrothermal or pneumatolytic. Furthermore, for supercritical fluids under high pressures, the distinction between gases and liquids is meaningless. Thus supercritical fluids or high-pressure gases are commonly (and logically) included under the term hydrothermal.

The Magma and Magmatic Fluids

Magma is "naturally occurring mobile rock material, generated within the earth and capable of intrusion and extrusion. . . ." (A. G. I. *Glossary of Geology and Related Sciences*, 1957); or, to define it less formally, magma is a silicate melt or a mush of liquid and crystals. Solidification of magma produces igneous rocks, the great variety of which, in addition to their diversity of field relations, suggests that the processes by which magmas are generated, transported, and solidified are highly complex. Most magmas are probably not homogeneous in composition; parts may be rich in ferromagnesian constituents, in silica, in sodium or potassium compounds, in volatiles, in reactive xenoliths, or in other substances. Furthermore, the compositions of magmas are thought to be constantly changing due to chemical reactions. Magmas are not static, nor are they closed systems in which we should expect constant equilibrium conditions.

As a magma cools, it crystallizes and separates into fractions by the processes of differentiation. Metallic elements are concentrated in certain of these facies and locally may be abundant enough so that the resulting igneous rock constitutes ore. During differentiation the more mafic parts of the magma are enriched in chromium, nickel, platinum, and, in places, phosphorus and other elements. In contrast, concentrations of tin, zirconium, and thorium are found in the silicic facies. Titanium and iron persist throughout the range of composition and are found in all types of igneous rocks.

If a partly crystallized magma is subjected to stresses, the fluid fraction is squeezed off from the residual crystalline mush. This process, known as *filter pressing* (Daly, 1933), is of value in helping to explain the origin of certain ore deposits. Metallic elements may be concentrated in either the crystalline residual mush or in the more fluid molten fraction. If either of these materials is forced into the surrounding rocks, the process is known as *magmatic injection*, and, if ore is present, the product is known as a *magmatic injection deposit*. At Kiruna, Sweden, for example, an injected liquid rich in iron solidified to form one of the largest iron ore bodies in the world (Geijer, 1931).

Magmas or magmatic fractions that would solidify as ore are called *ore magmas.* Since ore magmas are melts, and not aqueous solutions, they behave like magmas. This is the concept supported during the nineteenth century by Fournet and more recently, in the early twentieth century, by Spurr (1923) and other geologists (Farmin, 1941). Unfortunately, as a result of overzealous and indiscriminate application of the theory to all types of ore deposits, this idea was largely discarded. Lately, after decades of disfavor, the theory has again been called upon to explain the emplacement of certain types of ore deposits; for example, Sales (1954) proposed that an ore magma formed the copper sulfide deposits of the Colorada pipe at Cananea, Mexico. Figure 2-1 shows a most spectacular and conclusive example of an ore magma that was discovered recently in northern Chile; it is a shallow intrusive and "lava flow" of almost pure magnetite-hematite with minor amounts of apatite (Park, 1961). Thus the idea of ore magmas appears to be well established in the science of ore deposits, and there is no theoretical or practical reason why metallic facies of magmas should not exist. The only controversies remaining involve the extent of deposits formed by ore magmas. In short, how important are ore magmas, and do they include sulfide melts and silica melts as well as oxide melts?

FIGURE 2-1. *Vertical section in the Laco Sur magnetite-hematite deposit, Chile. The upper surface of the "flow" is about three feet above the hammer. (From Park, 1961, figure 7.)*

The process of crystallization, including differentiation and crystal settling, gradually increases the concentration of the more volatile and fugitive constituents in a magma, provided no means of escape is open to such substances. The lighter, volatile fractions, plus the compounds that crystallize at lower temperatures than the bulk of the magma, accumulate near the top of the magma chamber. These volatiles and materials of low freezing point are the mother liquors of pegmatites and the hydrothermal or pneumatolytic fluids of magmatic affiliation. They contain the elements known as mineralizers, which are present in small but essential amounts in all magmas.

Mineralizers play an all-important role in the transportation of metals. In general, they are elements of low atomic weight and small ionic radius, though there are some notable exceptions. These elements decrease the viscosity of magmas, lower the freezing points of minerals, and make possible the development of compounds that would not form in a dry melt. They possess great penetrating powers—a factor of considerable significance within the earth's interior. The character of the mineralizers and the role they play in the ore-transporting fluids can be inferred only from the study of ores and the altered rocks associated with ores, from the igneous rocks themselves, and from a few scattered observations in areas of volcanic and hydrothermal activity.

Water—as a fluid phase—is quantitatively the principal mineralizer in all magmas, and it plays a leading part in the transportation of many ores. Estimates of the amounts of water in magmas range from 1 to 8 percent. These estimates have been reached by considering volcanic and metamorphic phenomena as well as by analyzing the water content of volcanic glasses. They emphasize the great difficulties and the many variables encountered in any study of magmas (Daly, 1933; Gilluly, 1937; Morey, 1938). Other important mineralizers are sulfur, chlorine, fluorine, boron, phosphorus, carbon dioxide, and arsenic. Micas, clay minerals, zeolites, and amphiboles contain small amounts of chemically bonded water; tourmaline and axinite contain boron; scapolites contain chlorine; and many other common minerals, such as fluorite, apatite, and topaz, furnish evidence for the presence of a wide range of readily volatile constituents. Many ores and gangue minerals contain microscopic vacuoles and inclusions of liquids and gases, some of which were apparently primary in origin and consequently preserve the mineralizers and volatiles for our observation.

In a series of experiments of particular interest to economic geologists, Goranson (1931) showed that the concentration of the volatile fractions increases as differentiation of granitic magmas proceeds. He concluded that these fractions, rich in water, have definite solubility limitations under specific conditions of temperature and pressure, beyond which they will constitute a separate phase of the magma. Smith (1948) continued the same type of experimentation by slowly cooling an artificial granitic magma that contained an initial 2 percent of water. At one point on the cooling curve, the magma separated into two immiscible liquids, one of which was dominantly water.

Certain of the mineralizers, such as chlorine, are most abundant, though not exclusively, in the mafic differentiates, whereas boron and fluorine are most abundant in the silicic fractions. Sulfur is one of the most dominant and widespread constituents of ore bodies of igneous affiliation, and elemental sulfur is a common product of volcanic emanations. Sulfur is ordinarily said to be most abundant in the mafic rocks, though large amounts are found in rocks of both intermediate and silicic composition. In spite of its abundance, the role played by sulfur—and related elements such as arsenic—in the transportation and precipitation of the metals is but little understood. In many places, the sulfide ion concentration is thought to be of fundamental importance in determining the mineral composition of the ores. It may well prove also to be one of the controlling factors in both the migration and precipitation of ores. Some geologists consider that ores migrate as metallic chlorides, because the chloride complexes are quite soluble, though as Barnes and Romberger (1962) point out, chloride complexes are unstable in the presence of even minor concentrations of sulfide ion. Chlorine is abundant in many volcanic emanations and in liquid inclusions of probable primary origin found in ore minerals.

As crystals grow they may trap some of the gases or liquids contained in the magma from which they crystallize. If the crystal develops at a high temperature within a fluid medium, subsequent cooling will permit the fluids to condense and remain trapped in the crystals as gas inclusions or as two-phase liquid-gas inclusions. If the mineral develops below the boiling point of the fluids, the vacuole will be full (or nearly full) of liquid. The assumption is made that the contents of these vacuoles were deposited from the original ore-bearing fluid, hence they give a clue as to the composition and physical state of the ore solutions. By heating the mineral until the liquid expands to fill the vacuole or until a single phase is formed (see Chapter 7), the minimum temperature of the original fluid can be estimated. In order to determine the composition of the ore-bearing fluids, the minute vacuoles are opened and direct tests made on the liquid contents. Newhouse (1932) found that sodium and chlorine are the most abundant dissolved substances in liquid inclusions and concluded that they are important mineralizers in sulfide ore deposits. If the materials in vacuoles and inclusions actually represent the ore-bearing fluids, then halides possibly play a much larger role than is ordinarily attributed to them.

Smith (1954) also studied the composition of liquid inclusions and concluded that they indicate two classes of mineralizing solutions, one being a hydrous silicate melt and the other being a watery solution containing abundant dissolved salts or dissolved carbon dioxide. The dissolved salts, which amounted to as much as 30 percent of the liquids by weight, were primarily chlorides, sulfates, and carbonates of sodium, potassium, and calcium. Smith further concluded that whether the mineralizing solutions were above or below the critical temperature, they must have had the effective densities and solvent properties of liquids, because after condensation they nearly fill the vacuoles with liquid. Conversely, some inclusions are all gas, and have no liquid phase. An all-liquid inclusion would be formed in a hydrothermal medium, and an all-gas inclusion would be formed in a pneumatolitic medium. Since both types of inclusion are found, as well as all intermediate combinations of gas and liquid, it is reasonable to conclude that the gangue and ore-bearing fluids range from strictly gaseous to strictly liquid (Yermakov, 1957).

Many geologists and geochemists have attempted to estimate the concentrations of dissolved metals in hydrothermal fluids, with widely varying results. Direct measurements of metals contained in fluid inclusions have generally indicated that the ore-forming solutions contained low concentrations of dissolved metals, but recent analyses—based upon a neutron activation technique—have detected concentrations of copper, manganese, and zinc that exceed 100 parts per million (ppm) in liquid inclusions from samples of quartz and fluorite (Czamanske et al., 1963). Such modern techniques of analysis may vastly modify existing fluid-inclusion data.

Calculations on the amounts of water or steam required to transport the metals in individual ore deposits indicate that conveyance as simple dissolved solids would require impossible volumes of fluids. The solubility of HgS is an extreme example of this fact. The true solubility of HgS at high temperatures is unknown, but between room temperature and 200°C, it varies from about 10^{-15} to 10^{-23} moles/liter, depending upon the pH of the solution (Czamanske, 1959). The solubility increases with increased temperature and with increased acidity—that is, the highest figure given, 10^{-15} moles/liter, refers to a solution at 200°C and a pH of 4 to 5. Most cinnabar deposits form below 200°C, therefore this temperature should be reasonable for solubility calculations. If mercuric sulfide were carried in true solution, at 200°C and *p*H 4, one million times the volume of water flowing from the Hudson River per year would be required to deposit a single ton of cinnabar, provided all the dissolved material could be removed from solution at the site of deposition. At a still lower *p*H or at a higher temperature, or both, the amount of HgS carried in solution would increase by many orders of magnitude, but would never reach realistic proportions. The mercury must, of course, exist in some form other than a simple solution of HgS in water. For mercury, transportation as a volatile chloride, a soluble sulfide complex, or a metal vapor will explain the concentrations found in nature, but these mechanisms cannot be called upon to explain occurrences of all metals.

The formation of complex ions—charged particles consisting of several atoms—increases the solubilities of some metals by many orders of magnitude (Barton, 1959). Simple solubilities are measured for the number of single ions or common radicals that go into solution in a given amount of water, but in the presence of other atoms with which the ion can coordinate, the amount of metal that can enter the solution may well surpass its simple solubility limit—that is, the complex ions may be many times more soluble than the simple ions. Thus mercury may remain in solution as HgS_2^{-2}, or perhaps as $HgS_2(H_2O)_n^{-2}$, $HHgS_2^{-}$, and so forth; in any one of these forms, the mercury would be in sufficient concentration to account for its transportation in ore-forming solutions of reasonable volumes. Many metals combine as comparatively stable complex ions in the form of sulfides, polysulfides, hydrosulfides, halides, carbonates, hydroxides, oxides, sulfates, and others. The mineral species deposited will depend upon the temperature, pressure, and ratios of ions rather than on the complex by which the metal was transported, hence there is no need to suggest a special complex for each mineral formed. Accordingly, a simple sulfide may be deposited from a solution containing multiatomic complex ions. Studies of complex ions have been encouraging and may explain a number of problems concerning ore-bearing fluids, but such ions cannot be considered the panacea for all enigmas on ore genesis; at best, they provide only some of the answers. Nevertheless, the presence of metals as complex ions in solution is especially attractive in light of the general sequence of mineral deposition for most sulfide ores, which is in strong accordance with the relative stabilities of complex ions, but is essentially the reverse of that predicted from simple solubilities (see Chapter 6).

Many geochemists argue that the primitive ore-bearing fluids, rich in mineralizers, are initially above the critical temperature for water (Niggli, 1929; Fenner, 1933; Bowen, 1933). Under these conditions, the ions are closely packed, and, in terms of density, the gases behave like liquids; thus they carry considerable amounts of the metallic elements. Krauskopf (1957, 1959) demonstrated the general inadequacy of gas transport in explaining all metal deposits, but he also showed that many common metals are present in magmatic vapors—especially as chlorides—in sufficient quantities to account for the formation of certain ore deposits. His data leave unsolved the question of how important volatility is in relation to solubility in little-known supercritical solutions. In addition to simple transport as a gas, it seems likely that solubility effects must be significant (Morey, 1957), especially in light of the common-ion effect and the probable importance of complex ions.

Even for deposits that have an obvious relationship to igneous activity, there is some question as to the ultimate or immediate source of the metals. In part, the problem is related to the old enigma: where and how do magmas originate? Deep in the earth's mantle? Just below the Moho? Within melted sediments? But this seemingly intangible question bearing on the ultimate source of magmas, or the supply of metals in magmas, has a counterpart of a more practical nature—that is, are the metals in late magmatic fluids actually concentrated by simple fractionation processes, or might they be selectively leached from the country rocks or previously solidified igneous rocks through which the ascending fluids must pass? Some geologists have suggested that deuteric alteration of ferromagnesian minerals may release metallic ions in sufficient quantities to form the ore deposits found along igneous contacts. The evidence for such a mechanism is especially convincing in the Iron Springs district of southwestern Utah (see Chapter 11), where there are replacement ore bodies of magnetite and hematite in limestones that border quartz monzonite porphyry laccoliths (Mackin, 1954; Mackin and Ingerson, 1960). The iron was originally incorporated in hornblende and biotite that crystallized at depth. After intrusion of the magma, the outermost shells of the laccoliths solidified rapidly, undergoing no deuteric alteration, but the interiors of the plutons contained concentrations of volatiles that leached iron from the nearly rigid crystal mush of ferromagnesian minerals and migrated outward along tension cracks through the peripheral shells. These tension joints are encrusted with magnetite and bordered by iron-deficient quartz monzonite. Continuous evidence is exposed from the deep interior of the laccoliths, through the zone where iron minerals were altered, along magnetite-filled fractures that cut the unaltered border zone of the laccoliths, and into the replacement ore bodies at the contacts. The replacement deposits are adjacent to the laccoliths only where there are leached joints. This "deuteric release" hypothesis for the origin of metals is merely a special type of lateral secretion, the theory proposed by Charpentier during the eighteenth century.

The recognition of leaching by deuteric solutions as a mechanism for supplying metals to hydrothermal solutions introduces a further question that may prove fundamental to regional exploration. The question is this: should we expect the igneous rock associated with ore deposits to be enriched, normal, or deficient in the metals? If the ores are associated with special magmas that happen to be enriched in the ore metals, we should expect a slight concentration of these ions in the rock minerals—that is, the associated pluton should give anomalously high assays of the metals. If deuteric alteration has leached the metals from the igneous rock, or if favorable magmatic differentiation has selectively concentrated metals in the latest fluid fraction, we should expect the rock to be anomalously low in these components (Ingerson, 1954). Future geochemical studies may ultimately resolve this problem, but at present the evidence is conflicting, and can be found in support of both hypotheses; indeed, both mechanisms are probably operative. Perhaps the processes involved depend upon the depth of intrusion rather than the original composition of the magma. If this were true, injections to shallow depths would favor deuteric activities.

The pH of ore-bearing fluids is a further point of contention among geologists. Below pH 7 (neutral), fluids are acidic; above pH 7, they are alkaline, or basic. Unfortunately, geologists have used the terms acidic, basic, and alkaline for many years in other ways; as a result, geological literature contains a confusion of terminology whereby the terms acidic, basic, and alkaline refer to categories defined by the classification of igneous rocks and by hypothetical reactions (that may not take place) as well as by pH. Many field geologists still categorize materials containing fluorite or barite as "acid," and define hot springs as "alkaline" (which actually may be acidic in terms of pH) on the basis of a high calcium or sodium content. Moreover, silicic igneous rocks have been termed "acidic" on the erroneous premise that the silica will react with water to form silicic acid, H_4SiO_4, and produce a solution of low pH. Some of these same "acidic" rocks are called "calc-alkaline" because of the presence of lime, potash, and soda. As a result of this confused chemistry, we have a whole category of igneous rocks with the distinction of being both "acidic" and "alkaline" (or, "calc-alkaline"). The use of this terminology is incorrect, and although it must be understood when reading older literature, there is no excuse for continuing it. Geologists should conform to the general chemical definition of acids and bases whereby an acid is a substance that gives free hydrogen (or hydronium) ions when dissolved in water, and a base is a substance that gives free hydroxyl ions when dissolved in water. Alkaline is essentially synonymous with basic.

It is now known that the *p*H of a fluid may be varied by changes in temperature, pressure, and dissolved solids (Barton, 1959), because the *p*H is a function of the dissociation constant for water, and the acidity of a solution will vary as this constant varies. The dissociation constant increases slightly under pressure, causing the *p*H of a neutral solution to drop to slightly less than 7 (Owen and Brinkley, 1941); conversely, the addition of a dissolved salt will bring about a slight decrease in the dissociation constant. These effects are minor, amounting to a few tenths of a *p*H unit at most, but changes in temperature may be highly significant. A *p*H of 7 is neutral only at about 24°C; at 200°C, neutral *p*H is at about 5.6 (Noyes et al., 1907; Ackermann, 1958). Owing to the difficulty in predicting the effect of temperature changes on complex solutions, the *p*H of fluids at depth is largely conjectural. The best evidence from field and laboratory observations seems to indicate that the ore-bearing fluids are nearly neutral and that either strong acids or strong bases are exceptional, though they do exist under special circumstances.

Most crustal rocks are composed either of silicate or carbonate minerals, both of which will react with acidic solutions to form bases (in striking contradistinction to the older terminology which refers to the silica-rich tectosilicates as "acid" minerals and siliceous rocks as "acidic"). Owing to hydrolysis, any solution in contact with silicate or carbonate minerals will eventually become alkaline. Thus, it is logical to assume that ore-bearing fluids are nearly neutral or basic—at least at pressures close to one atmosphere—otherwise they would react immediately with the wall rocks. Such is the case with ordinary ground waters, which are commonly acidic at the surface and become neutral or alkaline at depth. Yet ore deposition might be due to just such a chemical change. The ore-bearing fluids may be acidic at first, and if the metals are soluble in an acid but not in a base, deposition should occur when the solutions are neutralized.

The *p*H of ore-forming fluids can be calculated from thermodynamic considerations if the equilibrium assemblage of minerals is well established. Such calculations have recently become popular and should develop a sound theory of ore-fluid chemistry. Preliminary studies of some common mineral assemblages support the thesis that the fluids were neutral or slightly alkaline when the ores were being deposited (Barnes and Kullerud, 1961).

In spite of the abundance of alkaline waters, fumaroles and hot springs may yield acidic, neutral, or alkaline solutions (Zies, 1929; Allen and Zies, 1923; Brannock et al., 1948; White, 1955). In general, the chemical character of these fluids at the surface cannot be relied upon as an indicator of that at depth, because there is a chance of contamination by surface water and wall rocks, and because changes may occur as a result of decreases in temperature and pressure—specifically, any sulfur present may be oxidized near the surface, forming sulfuric acid and lowering the pH.

Liquid-inclusion data suggest that the ore solutions are generally neutral or nearly neutral (Gushkin and Prikhid'ko, 1952; Newhouse, 1932; Barton, 1959), though these fluids reflect the nature of the ore solutions only after the ores were deposited, and not during transportation.

Attempts have been made to explain the presence of acidic fluids that have traveled long distances through siliceous or calcareous rocks, which should raise the pH to neutrality or above. The suggestion has been made that, as the fluids migrate, they react with the wall rocks to form minerals that are stable in an acidic environment. These minerals thus constitute an insulating layer along the channels, and later fluids are protected from the unaltered wall rocks by a zone of stable minerals. Accordingly, the solutions can travel long distances with a minimum of reaction. A common explanation for the presence of sulfuric acid, which is found in some hydrothermal fluids, is that the acidic solutions are generated by the oxidizing reaction of water on sulfur and sulfides, either carried in the original fluid or present in the rocks through which the fluid moves. The oxidation of sulfur and sulfide minerals, with the production of sulfuric acid, is a widely recognized phenomenon in near-surface environments—especially in the presence of oxygen and water.

Certain minerals are thought to form in acidic environments, there being another polymorph for less acidic or alkaline conditions. For example, as a result of laboratory experiments, the presence of marcasite has been interpreted to indicate deposition from acidic solutions (Allen et al., 1914; Noble, 1950). This supposition has been substantiated by field observation of marcasite developing in natural springs of very low pH.

Meteoric Waters

Water derived from the atmosphere is called meteoric water. Where this water sinks into the earth, it assumes the temperature of the enclosing rocks, and as a result the water temperature generally increases with depth of circulation. Although there are numerous exceptions, the content of dissolved mineral substances generally increases as the water temperature increases. Descending waters gradually change and assume compositions that are in equilibrium with the enclosing rocks. Ascending waters and vapors also tend to reach equilibria with their environments. Hence under given conditions the compositions of descending and ascending waters approach each other, and in the upper parts of the crust, where these waters can be studied, they are difficult or impossible to distinguish. The possibility that the two types of fluids may be mixed also complicates their study. The origin of heated meteoric waters containing minor amounts of magmatic fluids would be difficult to determine—they would probably be called meteoric, and the magmatic fraction would not be recognized.

Meteoric waters are believed to contain the dominant crustal elements, such as sodium, calcium, magnesium, and the sulfate and carbonate radicals. The more fugitive elements, such as boron and fluorine, are characteristic of juvenile waters (Clarke, 1924). The suggestion has been made (Ault, 1959; Ingerson, 1954; Rankama, 1954; White, 1957b; Clayton and Epstein, 1961) that magmatic waters contain higher percentages of the heavy isotopes of sulfur and oxygen than do meteoric waters, but to date this has not been conclusively demonstrated.

Water trapped in sediments at the time they were deposited is known as connate water, a term first applied to the brines flowing into the deeper levels of the Michigan copper mines (Lane, 1908). Connate waters are actually fossil waters. They are widely recognized at present, and a great deal of study has been devoted to them, especially in oil field exploration (these are the salty edgewaters of many oil accumulations). Most connate waters are abnormally rich in sodium and chlorine, but they also contain considerable amounts of calcium, magnesium, and bicarbonate, and may contain strontium, barium, and nitrogen compounds (White, 1957b).

MINE WATERS

No comprehensive study of mine waters has been made in recent years, but valuable information has been obtained from individual mines. Although pore moisture remains, ground water gradually decreases in amount at depth; many deep mines are dry in their lower levels. Most studies made on mine waters have dealt mainly with corrosive waters and their effects on pumps and pipes. Most mine waters are obviously meteoric and are thought to have no relation to the fluids that deposited the ore. Exceptions to this statement are found in areas of recent volcanism; for example, the hot waters in the lower levels of the Comstock Lode, Nevada, may have been, in part, of volcanic origin, although largely diluted by surficial waters. Samples of water from the Comstock Lode were described by Bastin in 1922. These waters apparently were contaminated by sulfuric acid that descended from the zone of weathering. Many mine openings at depths of 2700 feet and less had large flows of water with temperatures up to 70°C. Two analyses of these hot waters, as given by Bastin, are reproduced in Table 2-I. From these analyses it is readily seen that the waters are dominated by sodium and calcium sulfates.

TABLE 2-I

Analyses of Hot Waters from the Comstock Lode, Nevada (in parts per million)

Constituent	Union Consolidated mine, 2650-foot level	C. and C. shaft, 2250-foot level
Na	145.0	131.0
K	8.4	53.4
Ca	204.0	100.3
Mg	4.0	5.9
Al	—	1.3
Fe	0.0	6.4
SO_4	752.0	542.6
Cl	12.0	19.0
CO_3	9.3	20.5
HCO_3	0.0	—
OH	7.5	—
SiO_2	61.0	133.4
TOTALS	1203.2	1013.8

SOURCE: After Bastin (1922).

The presence of sodium carbonate waters is commonly reported from deep mines in areas of recent volcanic activity (Lindgren, 1933, p. 53), and many geologists consider such waters to have direct connection with magmatic sources. A sodium carbonate water of this type, from the Homestake gold mine in South Dakota (which is not a region of recent volcanic activity), was described by Noble (1950). The water was taken from a crevice penetrated by a diamond drill hole at a depth of 2300 feet. Considering the great depth of the crevice and the unique proportions of dissolved constituents, Noble reasoned that the water could not have been contaminated appreciably by surface waters. Although sodium was abundant in the water, it was practically absent from the country rocks and from ordinary ground waters in the mine. Noble concluded that the water and its dissolved constituents were probably the end products of hydrothermal mineralization. Table 2-II presents Noble's analysis of the water. Noble's findings suggest

TABLE 2-II

Analysis of Water from the Homestake Mine, South Dakota (in parts per million)

Constituent	ppm
Na	428
K	60
Ca	13
Mg	11
SiO_2	11
Al_2O_3 and Fe_2O_3	4
CO_2	392
SO_4	351
S_2O_3	20
H_2S	15
Cl	4
TOTAL	1309

SOURCE: After Noble (1950).

that a comprehensive study of deep mine waters by modern methods would probably provide valuable information concerning the origin and composition of ore-bearing fluids.

THERMAL SPRINGS

Thermal springs, solfataras, and fumaroles have been studied intensively by many geologists, resulting in a considerable store of information applicable to the problem of ore solutions. Among the most recent studies of these phenomena are those by White (1957a, 1957b), who applied modern geochemical principles and techniques to the study of Steamboat Springs, Nevada, and other areas of thermal activity in the western United States. On the basis of isotope analyses, whereby the waters of various thermal springs were compared to surface waters of the surrounding areas, White concluded that the contribution of direct magmatic material is insignificant.

Water found in regions of recent volcanic activities is commonly characterized by an abundance of sodium chloride. The sodium chloride waters apparently grade into acidic sulfate-chloride waters that are also found in regions of active volcanism. Other types of water found in volcanic areas contain sodium bicarbonate, acid sulfate, and calcium bicarbonate or mixed sodium and calcium bicarbonate. White considers the sodium chloride waters to be the most closely related to magmatic emanations, the other types of thermal waters being secondary products resulting from reactions with wall rocks and changes in the physical environment. Analyses of sodium chloride waters, reproduced from White, are given in Table 2-III.

According to White, the volcanic sodium chloride waters are distinguished from either connate waters or ocean waters by their relatively high content of lithium, fluorine, silica, boron, sulfur, and carbon dioxide compared to calcium and magnesium. Nonvolatile compounds are slightly to highly soluble in steam at high pressure, high density steam having solvent properties similar to those of liquid water. In the volcanic sodium chloride waters, a high ratio of lithium to sodium and potassium indicates differentiation in a magma and suggests that the alkalies were transported as alkali halides dissolved in liquid or dense vapor. White believes the juvenile fluid is greatly diluted by deeply circulating meteoric water, mixing at a depth of approximately two miles. Where circulation of meteoric water is shallow, the halide-bearing vapors reach low-pressure regions, expand, and precipitate the nonvolatile substances; such a mechanism would remove much of the sodium chloride from the vapor system and produce one of the modified calcium bicarbonate or acid sulfate waters.

The Valley of Ten Thousand Smokes, an area of fumarolic activity that became active in 1912, has provided further evidence on the nature of hydrothermal fluids (Zies, 1929). The fumaroles formed at the surface of a thick accumulation of hot, rhyolitic pyroclastics. Although such a deposit is not the same as a magma crystallizing at depth, the gases—largely from pumice fragments—represent primary constituents of the magma. It is assumed that most of the fumarolic waters were of meteoric origin, but the elements that are not common to rain water were probably derived from the cooling mass of pyroclastic debris. The exhalations were more than 99 percent steam, at temperatures up to 650°C. Enough HCl, HF, and H_2S were dissolved in the steam to make the exhalations acidic at the surface. Different mineral assemblages formed around the vents as the temperature

TABLE 2-III

Analyses of Sodium Chloride Hot Spring Waters (in parts per million)

	Steamboat Springs, Nevada	Morgan Springs, Tehama County, California	Norris Basin, Yellowstone Park, Wyoming	Upper Basin, Yellowstone Park, Wyoming	Wairakei, New Zealand
Temp. °C	89.2	95.4	84	94.5	>100
pH	7.9	7.83	7.45	8.69	8.6
SiO_2	293	233	529	321	386
Fe	—	—	—	Trace	—
Al	—	—	—	0	—
Ca	5.0	79	5.8	4	26
Mg	0.8	0.8	0.2	Trace	<0.1
Sr	1	10	—	—	—
Na	653	1398	439	453	1130
K	71	196	74	17	146
Li	7.6	9.2	8.4	—	12.2
NH_4	<1	<1	0.1	0	0.9
As	2.7	2.2	3.1	—	—
Sb	0.4	0.0	0.1	—	—
CO_3	0	0	0	66	—
HCO_3	305	52	27	466	35
SO_4	100	79	38	15	35
Cl	865	2437	744	307	1927
F	1.8	1.5	4.9	21.5	6.2
Br	0.2	0.8	0.1	—	—
I	0.1	<0.1	<0.1	—	—
B	49	88	11.5	3.7	26
S_2O_3	—	—	—	2	—
H_2S	4.7	0.7	0	0	1.1
CO_2	—	—	—	—	11
TOTALS	2360	4578	1885	1676	3742

SOURCE: After White (1957a).

dropped, the early phase being characterized by magnetite; the later phase, by galena and sphalerite. The incrustations contained iron, lead, zinc, molybdenum, copper, arsenic, antimony, tin, silver, nickel, cobalt, thallium, and bismuth; these metals were combined with sulfur, oxygen, fluorine, chlorine, selenium, and tellurium. Zies pointed out that each of these elements would form a volatile compound and that each was transported in the gaseous state.

Recent unpublished work by Hewett (personal communication, 1960) indicates that many hot spring sinters, thought to be at least partly volcanic in origin, contain minute but detectable amounts of tungsten and other elements, such as boron, strontium, and fluorine.

Fluids Associated with Metamorphic Processes

Under favorable circumstances, connate and meteoric waters enclosed in rocks buried below the surface of the earth may be set in motion and made chemically reactive by heat and pressure accompanying magmatic intrusion or regional metamorphism (Shand, 1943). These are the so-called metamorphic waters that many geologists believe are active ore carriers.

Regional metamorphism is ordinarily and widely regarded as a process whereby metallic and volatile constituents are dispersed rather than concentrated (Taupitz, 1954). In support of this contention, Eskola showed that the palingenetic granites—granites formed by the reconstitution of other rocks—are notably free of metallic constituents. Eskola (1932) proposed that they be distinguished from magmatic granites by their general lack of ore deposits. Owing to such reasoning, mining geologists in general have been slow to accept the idea that ore deposits are produced as a result of regional metamorphic processes. Nevertheless, it is true that none of the phenomena usually taken to denote a magmatic origin are completely incompatible with the concept of a metamorphic origin. A growing number of geologists attach significance to metamorphic processes, and especially to the action of waters set in motion from buried sediments either by the heat from a cooling magma or by regional metamorphism. An example of the stimulating type of discussion now being carried on about ore-bearing fluids involves the Rhodesian copper belt in Africa. Garlick (1953) and Davis (1954) believe the ore-bearing fluids that formed these deposits were the same as those from which the enclosing sediments were deposited; that is, they consider the ores to be syngenetic. In contrast, Gray (1959) argues that connate or meteoric waters were activated during regional metamorphism, leaching the ores from the surrounding rocks and concentrating them in areas of reduced pressure or temperature or in areas of reactive wall rock. Sales (1960) disagrees with both of these ideas, and has advanced evidence that the ore-bearing fluids are directly related to igneous magmas.

Granitization is the process by which nongranitic rocks are converted to rocks of granitic character without passing through a magmatic or liquid stage (Guimarães, 1947; Read, 1948, 1954). During granitization and its associated processes, the volatile and mobile constituents are "activated." They are forced out of the rock and migrate toward cooler and, in general, less deformed regions. These volatile and mobile elements include most of the metallic constituents, but water constitutes most of the fluid. The metal-bearing metamorphic water would be the same whether activated by nearby magma or by regional metamorphism. Trace-element studies on minerals from different metamorphic facies indicate that certain metals are selectively released during regional metamorphism (DeVore, 1955). Accompanying tectonic processes may provide avenues along which the metals and metamorphic fluids travel, producing a hydrothermal system. The water and its metallic content are visualized as moving down the metamorphic gradient, in advance of either the regional metamorphism or the intruding magma.

Granitization, as the term is used by economic geologists, should be susceptible of proof in the field, though the evidence to date is inconclusive. Geochemical studies have not solved the problem; they merely indicate that the original compositions of the sedimentary rocks are highly variable in their content of metals. Shaw (1954) studied the metal content of several fine-grained rocks in New Hampshire and concluded that during regional metamorphism, nickel and copper showed a poorly defined tendency to decrease, whereas elements such as lithium, strontium, and lead increased. Much more careful work is needed before a valid generalization can be drawn. Currently, most of the evidence advanced in support of a relation between granitization and ore genesis is equally applicable to magmatic solutions.

The process of granitization cannot be used to give a convincing explanation of the origin of magmatic segregation deposits, nor can it be used to explain the introduction of ores into igneous masses after these bodies consolidated, as in some of the disseminated copper deposits. A migration of water and of the mobile elements in a rock would, however, be expected during either regional metamorphism or intrusion. Possibly the lack of high-grade metamorphic deposits of the sulfides can be interpreted to mean that during metamorphism the metallic elements migrated out of the system.

One attractive contention holds that both igneous and metamorphic processes play significant roles in the activation of volatile constituents in the rocks. Connate waters and ground waters commonly contain large amounts of soluble salts. Where heated and set in motion, they would be unusually strong solvents and would tend to remove metals from the rocks. In support of this is the fact that inclusions in ore minerals generally contain chlorides, indicating that chlorine was present in many of the ore-bearing fluids. These activated waters might also have combined with magmatic fluids and mineralizers released from a magma.

Goodspeed (1952) supported the thesis that the mineral-bearing fluids might be derived from the breakdown of hydrous minerals during granitization. He pointed out that clay minerals, which are abundant in geosynclinal prisms, contain about 14 percent water, and that a change into feldspars must release this water, providing a potential source of hydrothermal mineralizing solutions.

Guimarães (1947) emphasized the part played by igneous intrusions in activating waters, rather than that played by metamorphic processes. He argued that the mobile elements would move ahead of a slowly advancing intrusive mass, where conditions of temperature and pressure were favorable. Movement of the mobile elements would persist as long as the intrusive continued to advance or until it solidified and partly cooled.

As a result of many laboratory experiments and studies with blast furnace slags, Sosman (1950) concluded that an intruding magma, if undersaturated with respect to water, would establish a gradient of both water pressure and water concentration in the surrounding rocks, such that the direction of decreasing pressure and concentration would be toward the intrusive, and not away from it, as has been commonly assumed. This gradient is reinforced by the phenomenon of thermal transpiration, whereby a gas under constant pressure, in a medium having small pores, travels toward the region of higher temperature. The ground water in sedimentary rocks intruded by a water-deficient magma should therefore travel toward the intrusive, rising in temperature as it approaches the intrusive. This process would result in the incorporation of activated ground waters into the mineral-bearing fluids associated with the magma. Although this scheme seems plausible, field relationships and paragenetic studies indicate that at least the late-stage pneumatolytic and hydrothermal fluids migrate away from intrusives rather than toward them.

Several geologists in Africa have strongly supported the theory that metamorphic waters are the active ore carriers. Macgregor (1951), after many years of study in the gold deposits of Southern Rhodesia, suggested that gold and other minerals were released as a result of "migmatitic extraction" from the rocks engulfed by magmatic stoping. The waters are thought to have been of igneous or magmatic origin; the metals, however, were derived from the country rock. After solution of the metals, the waters migrated upwards and formed epigenetic deposits—that is, deposits of later origin than the enclosing rocks.

Geologists conclude that hydrothermal ore-bearing fluids may be composed largely of ground water or connate water, activated by means of igneous intrusion or metamorphism. Metamorphic waters activated by an intrusion may combine with vapors emitted from the magma. The metals may come either from the magma or from the country rock, but ordinary epigenetic deposits probably originate largely within the magma. Perhaps several of the problems concerning ore-bearing fluids will be solved by the study of samples collected from deep wells penetrating active hydrothermal systems. The possibility of generating power from wells drilled in thermal spring areas has promoted interest in several districts. For example, a 5232-foot well recently drilled for geothermal power near the Salton Sea in California tapped hot brines that may represent diluted magmatic waters from an underlying igneous source (White et al., 1963). These waters contain anomalous concentrations of heavy metals and have no counterparts among known connate and meteoric waters. The temperature exceeds 270°C (as limited by the measuring device) and may be as high as 370°C. The waters and their residues contain abnormal amounts of copper, silver, potassium, lithium, antimony, lead, arsenic, boron, beryllium, bismuth, gallium, and gold. A dark, siliceous deposit that accumulated in the discharge pipe contained about 20 percent copper and 2 percent silver; an estimated 5–8 tons of precipitate formed in the pipe within 3 months. The country rocks appear to be undergoing metamorphism, as evidenced by a mineral assemblage characteristic of the greenschist facies. Ground waters that originally occupied the pore spaces were displaced by the heavier ore-bearing fluids.

References Cited

Ackermann, Th., 1958, The self-dissociation of water from measurements of molar heats of dissolved electrolytes: Zeitschr. Electrochemie, v. 62, p. 411–419.

Allen, E. T., Crenshaw, J. L., and Merwin, H. E., 1914, Effect of temperature and acidity in the formation of marcasite and wurtzite; a contribution to the genesis of unstable forms: Am. Jour. Sci., v. 38, p. 393–431.

Allen, E. T., and Zies, E. G., 1923, A chemical study of fumaroles of the Katmai Region: Natl. Geog. Soc., Contrib. Tech. Papers, Katmai ser., no. 2.

American Geological Institute, 1957, Glossary of geology and related sciences: Washington, D.C., Am. Geol. Inst.

Ault, W. U., 1959, Isotopic fractionation of sulfur in geochemical processes, *in* Abelson, P. H. (ed.), Researches in geochemistry: New York, John Wiley & Sons, Inc., p. 241–259.

Barnes, H. L., and Kullerud, Gunnar, 1961, Equilibria in sulfur-containing aqueous solutions, in the system Fe-S-O, and their correlation during ore deposition: Econ. Geology, v. 56, p. 648–688.

Barnes, H. L., and Romberger, S. B., Ore transport: effects of chloride on sphalerite solubility: Geol. Soc. America Abs., Nov., 1962.

Barton, P. B., Jr., 1959, The chemical environment of ore deposition and the problem of low-temperature ore transport, in Abelson, P. H. (ed.), Researches in geochemistry: New York, John Wiley & Sons, Inc., p. 279–300.

Bastin, E. S., 1922, Bonanza ores of the Comstock Lode, Nevada: U.S. Geol. Survey Bull. 735, p. 57–63.

Bowen, N. L., 1933, The broader story of magmatic segregation, briefly told, in Ore deposits of the Western States (Lindgren volume): New York, Am. Inst. Mining Metall. Engineers, p. 106–128.

Brannock, W. W., Fix, P. F., Gianella, V. P., and White, D. E., 1948, Preliminary geo-chemical results at Steamboat Springs, Nevada: Am. Geophys. Union Trans., v. 29, p. 211–226.

Clarke, F. W., 1924, The data of geochemistry: U.S. Geol. Survey Bull. 779, p. 63–121.

Clayton, R. N., and Epstein, Samuel, 1961, The use of oxygen isotopes in high-temperature geological thermometry: Jour. Geology, v. 69, p. 447–452.

Czamanske, G. K., 1959, Sulfide solubility in aqueous solutions: Econ. Geology, v. 54, p. 57–63.

———, Roedder, Edwin, and Burns, F. C., 1963, Neutron activation analysis of inclusions for copper, manganese, and zinc: Science, v. 140, no. 3565, p. 401–403.

Daly, R. A., 1933, Igneous rocks and the depths of the earth: New York, McGraw-Hill Book Co., Inc.

Davis, G. R., 1954, The origin of the Roan Antelope copper deposit of North-ern Rhodesia: Econ. Geology, v. 49, p. 575–615.

DeVore, G. W., 1955, The role of adsorption in the fractionation and distribution of elements: Jour. Geology, v. 63, p. 159–190.

Eskola, Pentii, 1932, On the origin of granitic magmas: Min. Petrog. Mitt., v. 42, p. 478.

Farmin, Rollin, 1941, Host-rock inflation by veins and dikes at Grass Valley, California: Econ. Geology, v. 36, p. 143–174.

Fenner, C. N., 1933, Pneumatolytic processes in the formation of minerals and ores, in Ore deposits of the Western States (Lindgren Volume): New York, Am. Inst. Mining Metall. Engineers, p. 58–106.

Garlick, W. G., 1953, Reflections on prospecting and ore genesis in Northern Rhodesia: Inst. Mining Metallurgy (London) Trans., v. 63, p. 9–20, 94–106.

Geijer, Per, 1931, The iron ores of the Kiruna type: Geol. Survey Sweden Ann. Rept., ser. C, no. 367.

Gilluly, James, 1937, The water content of magmas: Am. Jour. Sci., v. 233 (5th ser., v. 33), p. 430–441.

Goodspeed, G. E., 1952, Mineralization related to granitization: Econ. Geology, v. 47, p. 146–168.

Goranson, R. W., 1931, The solubility of water in granite magmas: Am. Jour. Sci., v. 222 (5th ser., v. 22), p. 481–502.

Gray, Anton, 1959, The future of mineral exploration: Inst. Mining and Metallurgy (London) Trans., v. 68, pt. 2, p. 23–34.

Guimarães, Djalma, 1947, Mineral deposits of magmatic origin: Econ. Geology, v. 42, p. 721–736.

Gushkin, G. G., and Prikhid'ko, P. L., 1952, Chemical composition, concentration, and pH of liquid inclusions in fluorite: Zapiski Vsesoyuz. Mineral. Obshchestuva, v. 81, p. 120–126. (Chemical Abstracts, 1952, v. 46, col. 10055.)

Ingerson, Earl, 1954, Nature of the ore-forming fluids at various stages—a suggested approach: Econ. Geology, v. 49, p. 727–733.

Krauskopf, K. B., 1957, The heavy metal content of magmatic vapor at 600°C: Econ. Geology, v. 52, p. 786–807.

———, 1959, The use of equilibrium calculations in finding the composition of a magmatic gas phase, *in* Abelson, P. H. (ed.), Researches in geochemistry: New York, John Wiley & Sons, Inc., p. 260–278.

Lane, A. C., 1908, Mine waters and their field assay: Geol. Soc. America Bull., v. 19, p. 501–512.

Lindgren, Waldemar, 1933, Mineral deposits (4th edition): New York, McGraw-Hill Book Co., Inc.

Macgregor, A. M., 1951, The primary source of gold: South African Jour. Sci., v. 47, p. 157–161.

Mackin, J. H., 1954, Geology and iron ore deposits of the Granite Mountain area, Iron County, Utah: U.S. Geol. Survey, Mineral Inv. Field Studies Map, MF 14.

———, and Ingerson, Earl, 1960, An hypothesis for the origin of ore-forming fluid: U.S. Geol. Survey Prof. Paper 400-B, p. B1–B2.

Morey, G. W., 1938, Water in geological processes: Carnegie Inst. Wash. Pub. 501, p. 49–59.

———, 1957, The solubility of solids in gases: Econ. Geology, v. 52, p. 225–251.

Newhouse, W. H., 1932, The composition of vein solutions as shown by liquid inclusions in minerals: Econ. Geology, v. 27, p. 419–436.

Niggli, Paul, 1929, Ore deposits of magmatic origin (translated by H. C. Boydell): London, Thomas Murby and Co.

Noble, J. A., 1950, Ore mineralization in the Homestake gold mine, Lead, South Dakota: Geol. Soc. America Bull., v. 61, p. 221–252.

Noyes, A. A., Kato, Yogoro, and Sosman, R. B., 1907, Hydrolysis of ammonium acetate and ionization of water at 100°, 156°, 218°, and 306°: Carnegie Inst. Wash. Pub. 63, p. 153–235.

Owen, B. B., and Brinkley, S. R., Jr., 1941, Calculation of the effect of pressure upon ionic equilibria in pure water and in salt solutions: Chem. Reviews, v. 29, p. 461–474.

Park, C. F., Jr., 1961, A magnetite "flow" in northern Chile: Econ. Geology, v. 56, p. 431–436.

Rankama, Kalervo, 1954, Isotope geology: New York, McGraw-Hill Book Co., Inc.

Read, H. H., 1948, Granites and granites, *in* Origin of granites: Geol. Soc. America Mem. 28, p. 1–19.

———, 1954, Granitization and mineral deposits: Geologie en Mijnbouw, v. 16, p. 95–99.

Sales, R. H., 1954, Genetic relations between granites, porphyries, and associated copper deposits: Am. Inst. Mining Engineers Trans., v. 199, p. 499–505.

———, 1960, Critical remarks on the genesis of ore as applied to future mineral exploration: Econ. Geology, v. 55, p. 805–817.

Shand, S. J., 1943, Eruptive rocks, their genesis, composition, and classification, with a chapter on meteorites: New York, John Wiley & Sons, Inc.

Shaw, D. M., 1954, Trace elements in pelitic rocks: Geol. Soc. America Bull., v. 65, p. 1151–1182.

Smith, F. G., 1948, Transport and deposition of the non-sulphide vein minerals; III, phase relations at the pegmatitic stage: Econ. Geology, v. 43, p. 535–546.

———, 1954, Composition of vein-forming fluids from inclusion data: Econ. Geology, v. 49, p. 205–210.

Sosman, R. B., 1950, Centripetal genesis of magmatic ore deposits: Geol. Soc. America Bull., v. 61, p. 1505.

Spurr, J. E., 1923, The ore magmas: New York, McGraw-Hill Book Co., Inc.

Taupitz, Karl-Christoph, 1954, Über Sedimentation, Diagenese, Metamorphose, Magmatismus und die Entstehung der Erzlagerstätten: Chemie der Erde, v. 17, p. 104–164.

White, D. E., 1955, Thermal springs and epithermal ore deposits (50th Anniv. volume): Econ. Geology, p. 99–154.

———, 1957a, Thermal waters of volcanic origin: Geol. Soc. America Bull., v. 68, p. 1637–1657.

———, 1957b, Magmatic, connate, and metamorphic waters: Geol. Soc. America Bull., v. 68, p. 1659–1682.

———, Anderson, E. T., and Grubbs, D. K., 1963, Geothermal brine well: mile-deep drill hole may tap ore-bearing magmatic water and rocks undergoing metamorphism: Science, v. 139, no. 3558, p. 919–922.

Yermakov, N. P., 1957, Importance of inclusions in minerals to the theory of ore genesis and study of the mineral forming medium, *in* Internat. Geol. Rev., v. 3, no. 7, 1961, translated by E. A. Alexandrov, p. 575–585.

Zies, E. G., 1929, The Valley of Ten Thousand Smokes: Natl. Geog. Soc. Contr. Tech. Papers, Katmai ser., v. 1, no. 4.

CHAPTER 3 **Migration of the**

Ore-bearing Fluids

ANY HYPOTHESIS concerning the genesis of ores must explain the migration of large amounts of ore-bearing fluids, either as magmas, aqueous solutions, or gases. The movement of fluids underground is as significant in ore genesis as it is in the concentration of oil and gas or in the emplacement of dikes and other intrusive masses. In general, migration is controlled by structure, which determines the avenues of permeability; but in detail, ore solutions may completely permeate the rocks, going around and through the mineral grains. Knowledge of the paths traveled by the ore solution and the mode of ore emplacement is fundamental to the understanding of an ore deposit.

Migration of Magma

The manner in which ordinary magmas move through the rocks has been the subject of much discussion in petrology; the reasons for their movement are controversial, but they do move, and they generally move upward toward areas of lower pressure. Magmas contain gases under pressure, and any release in this pressure will allow the magma to expand. Both the process of expansion and the resultant decrease in their specific gravity will cause magmas to move upward. Furthermore, tectonic stresses may squeeze the magma into overlying or adjacent rocks, starting a movement that will be propagated by gas expansion in the areas of reduced pressure. Many geologists believe that magma may be injected mechanically into the overlying rocks, forcing its way between the rock layers or actually breaking the rocks apart; in fact, it is difficult to envisage any other mechanism of emplacement for most sills and dikes. Some magmas are considered to move by means of stoping—a process whereby the magma works its way upward by engulfing blocks of overlying country rock. Presumably, the stoped blocks sink into the magma chamber and are assimilated at depth. Other magmas are pictured as moving by a sort of migration of heat and mineralizers, whereby the rocks around the upper part of the chamber are slowly melted to form part of the magma. As is true of many geologic phenomena, no single theory will explain the emplacement of all intrusive masses. In certain individual plutons the combined effects of forceful intrusion, stoping, and assimilation are evident (Compton, 1955, 1960).

In ore magmas, where the resultant product is relatively pure ore (such as magnetite), the molten materials cannot have assimilated much of the wall rocks; consequently, the fluids cannot have migrated by dissolving or stoping their way along. It seems likely that most ore magmas move after differentiation at depth and that subsequent directed pressures cause them to be injected into the adjacent or overlying rocks. Tectonic activity or pressures due to the load of overlying rocks may supply the driving force. Since ore magmas are heavy, they cannot move up as a result of density differences; this may be one of the reasons why they are not more abundant near the surface of the earth. But ore magmas are apparently intruded late in the magmatic history of a pluton, and are normally accompanied by gases. Hence where pressure is released, these gases will expand, forcing the magma to rise even higher in the crust.

Migration of Fluids at Great Depths

Ordinarily, permeability and porosity decrease with depth of burial, owing to the pressure of overlying rocks and the cementing action of mineral-laden waters. The lower limit of freely circulating ground waters varies considerably, and may lie anywhere from a few feet to several thousand feet below the surface, depending upon the nature of the rock. Many deep mines extend below this limit and, as a result, are dry and dusty in their lower levels; in fact, it is commonly necessary to pipe water down for drilling purposes. Because of the lack of permeability at depth, some geologists doubt the ability of ascending waters or watery ore-bearing fluids to penetrate these dense, compact rocks for significant distances. Nevertheless, the preponderance of evidence indicates that solutions in large amounts do move through massive rocks at depth. These fluids transport metallic constituents, and where they are concentrated in traps or modified by chemical reaction, they have a tendency to deposit their loads and form ore deposits.

Certainly in crystalline limestones and dolomites, such as shown in Fig. 3-1, the ore-bearing fluids migrated through the rock and replaced parts of it. The mineralizing fluids are generally visualized as penetrating the borders of mineral grains, which they corrode and alter, enabling subsequent solutions to pass more readily.

The idea that fluids under pressure are able to fracture and work their way through rocks has long been attractive. This method of introduction might be likened to the intrusion of dikes, though it is possibly more complex, because the ore fluids are probably less viscous and more mobile than magmas. Since the beginning of the twentieth century, field geologists have been suggesting that the ore-bearing fluids can act with sufficient force to keep fissures open, allowing the fluids to circulate freely and permitting time for reaction and deposition (Graton, 1906, p. 60; Spurr, 1906, 1923; Wandke, 1930). Recently, mathematical analyses and model studies have been applied to the problem, with the conclusion that fluid pressures underground must reach significant magnitudes; these studies support the contention that the fluids are able to fracture rocks and pass through them to areas of lower pressure (Hubbert and Willis, 1957; Hubbert and Rubey, 1959). Such a theory would help to explain the quartz zones commonly found in supposedly impermeable shales and slates—for example, some of the gold-bearing quartz in the Southern Piedmont region of the United States (Fig. 3-2).

Field observations of the relative impermeability of many rocks (such as plutonic masses and shales), combined with evidence from experimental

FIGURE 3-1. *Limestone from Eagle Mountains, California. Note the disseminated magnetite. Natural size.*

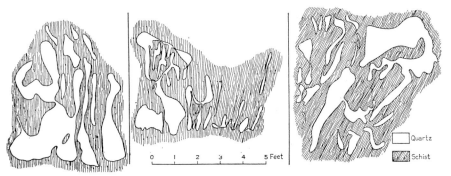

FIGURE 3-2. *Zone of gold-bearing quartz. Laird prospect, Virginia. (After Park, 1936, figure 3.)*

studies of impermeability, suggest that superimposed permeability due to faults and other secondary structures is probably of more significance in the study of ore transportation and deposition than the original permeability of the rock (Rove, 1947). Yet in spite of the obvious importance of superimposed permeability, ore-bearing fluids have, in many instances, apparently moved through rocks that now show no premineralization avenues of permeability.

Anyone who has had an opportunity to examine a large thermal spring area, such as that at Big Geysers near Healdsburg, California (Fig. 3-3), cannot fail to be impressed by the movement of large amounts of hot fluids through relatively impermeable rocks. At Big Geysers, massive and dense graywackes and argillites are thoroughly altered over an area that exceeds 3000 acres. The rocks are softened and saturated with steam and hot water. The altered rock is warm at the surface or within inches of the surface, and shallow drill holes release superheated steam under very high pressures; in fact, the area has recently been exploited as a source of power. The thermal zone at Big Geysers follows the footwall of a large fault. Possibly at depth the permeability along this fault has localized the path of steam migration, but in the exposed area the hot fluids have certainly spread for considerable distances away from the fault and into the footwall. The conclusion seems to be inescapable that ore-bearing fluids are able to move through the densest rocks by working around individual grain boundaries or by other means.

The relative impermeability of massive carbonate rocks has been emphasized by many geologists, and it is effectively demonstrated in the Balmat-Edwards district of New York State. In this mine area, a drift was driven below and within a few feet of an abandoned, flooded winze. In spite of

FIGURE 3-3. *Big Geysers area near Healdsburg, California. The rock was originally Franciscan graywacke and argillite. It has been thoroughly altered to
carbonates, chalcedony, and clay minerals.*

the pressure exerted by a nearly 100-foot head of water, the drift remained
dry. Similarly, drill holes with 600 feet of hydrostatic head (260 pounds per
square inch, or about 17 atmospheres) were plugged where intersected by
mine openings, and no water passed through the limestone around the
plugs (Brown, 1948, p. 38). From this evidence Brown concluded that
limestones are essentially impermeable to cold watery solutions, even where
these solutions are under considerable pressure. Brown (1941, 1947) suggested that ores in limestone migrated through the heated rocks in a gaseous state. He attributes only a minor role to near-surface water, emphasizing that many deep mines are dry in their lower levels, that the rocks at
depth are highly impervious, and that watery fluids would have great difficulty in traversing such material. At Balmat-Edwards, the ore shoots extend
for more than 3000 feet without any great change in character, indicating
that the ore-bearing fluids operated over long distances with surprising
uniformity. The fluids were supposedly guided by openings of microscopic
size, probably near the lower capillary limits. According to Brown, the
process of ore emplacement reduced these openings, rather than enlarged
them.

Many ideas have been advanced and many interesting experiments attempted in efforts to explain the mechanism by which fluids travel through dense rocks at depth. Maxwell and Verrall (1953) heated specimens of marble, limestone, and travertine under high confining pressures, a treatment that apparently developed permanent expansion and increased permeability. It was suggested that possibly this method of expansion will help to explain the permeability to ore-bearing fluids of rocks under high temperature and pressure.

Brown's suggestion that such minerals as the metallic sulfides are volatilized directly from the magma and that neither water vapor nor liquid is required for their transportation has not been widely accepted. Recent work by Krauskopf (1957) has shown that a theory based strictly upon volatility also fails to explain the entire problem of ore transport. Fluids under high temperatures and pressures may transport metallic ions and operate through very minute openings; under these conditions the physical states of liquids and gases are essentially the same. Klinkenberg (1941) determined from experiments that the flow rates of gases are slightly higher than those for liquids; the flow rate of a gas through rock is not inversely proportional to the viscosity as it is in a liquid. For unconsolidated sediments, the error obtained by extrapolating the determinations of permeability made on gases to those expected for liquids is small, but where the medium is a dense carbonate rock, as it is in many ore deposits, the error may be large (Ohle, 1951). Klinkenberg's permeability determinations, in which he used gas, are based upon the theory of "slip." Where gas is flowing along a solid wall, the layer of gas next to the surface is in motion with respect to that surface; that is, it slips. Hence the volume of gas flowing through a medium is greater than if no slip occurred. The less dense the gas, the greater the slippage; conversely, the more pressure upon a gas, or the denser the gas, the more nearly it approaches the behavior of a liquid. In the deeper parts of the earth's crust, gases probably behave essentially the same as liquids.

Ohle (1951) separated the permeability values of the rocks in the east Tennessee zinc district into three main groups, corresponding to dolomite, limestone, and "recrystalline"—dolomitic marble, an alteration product of the limestone near mineralization. As a presulfide phase of the mineralization process, some limestone beds were recrystallized and dolomitized, with a resultant and significant increase in permeability. The original dolomite and the "recrystalline" are virtually the same in composition, but the replacement ore bodies are concentrated in the "recrystalline." Ohle suggests that the localization of ore was controlled by permeability, and that the ability of the limestone to recrystallize made it more favorable than the original dolomite—therefore the replacement ore bodies were practically restricted to zones of "recrystalline" within the limestone. Since his calculations from test results showed that under favorable geologic conditions large volumes of aqueous solutions could pass through the dolomitized marble, Ohle concluded that the amount of dilute solution that could permeate these rocks would be sufficient to account for the ore deposits found in them.

As Ohle pointed out, it is customary to accentuate the relative inefficiency of intergranular flow as compared to flow through open channelways; consequently most geologists have an inaccurate conception of the volume of fluid that will pass through solid rock. Once the permeability of a rock type has been measured, it is possible to calculate with reasonable accuracy the quantitiy of a given fluid that will move through that rock under given conditions. Ohle's conclusion that the quantity is adequate to produce large ore bodies seems to contradict the conclusions of others, who emphasize the impermeable nature of carbonate rocks, especially to the passage of watery solutions at depth. These contradictory conclusions are probably a reflection of the different opinions held concerning the depths at which ore-bearing fluids entered the country rocks.

Because of the difficulties in explaining the migration of ore-bearing fluids at depth, geologists continually return to the attractive ideas of diffusion. Economic geologists define diffusion as a spontaneous movement of particles of molecular or ionic size that causes one substance to become uniformly intermingled with another. Diffusion may take place in the solid, liquid, or gas phase. Thus water moving through the pores of a rock is not included under the definition, whereas the spread of copper ions throughout water is. Experimental and geochemical evidence currently available offers little support of diffusion. Even though a number of experiments indicate that diffusion is unimportant, many field geologists find in this process an appealing and simple answer to problems of ore transport.

Diffusion of ions or molecules through a liquid phase—for example, through saturated, porous rocks—is not difficult to envisage. It is an especially convenient mechanism of transport in replacement processes, because it allows for the movement of ions both toward and away from the replacement front. The ions will diffuse toward the regions of lesser concentration (that is, they will move down their own concentration gradients), and as a result, the replacing ions will migrate toward the country rock while the replaced ions move away from it. As the metal ions are deposited at the replacement front, their concentration is automatically lowered, and more ions move in to take their places. Thus the replacement front grows steadily at the expense of the host until the supply of replacing ions is expended (Holser, 1947).

Diffusion through rocks and solid crystals is less readily accepted as a mechanism of transport, because the rates of diffusion are much slower than for diffusion through liquids. Aside from movement around grain boundaries, the migration of ions diffusing through a solid is controlled largely by imperfections in the crystal structure. Indeed, a perfect crystal, maintaining ideal order under all circumstances, would not permit ionic diffusion except at slow rates (Barrer, 1951, p. 247), or would permit only very small ions to diffuse. Imperfections may be the result of foreign ions existing interstitially within the normal structure, thus distorting this structure, or they may be the result of vacancies in the lattice. Diffusion takes place from one structural imperfection to another, or, in the case of vacant lattice positions, by the migration of holes, whereby an adjacent ion moves into the vacancy and leaves a hole behind. Thus diffusion may involve an advancing ion or a retreating vacancy working its way through the crystal structure, and in the case of the migrating vacancy, each ion in the row will move one lattice position ahead. The rate of diffusion will, of course, be strongly dependent upon the radius of the particle moving through the crystal. It will also be a function of the temperature, because near its melting point, a mineral's crystal structure is disordered and expanded. Within one or two hundred degrees of its melting point, the diffusion through a crystal may be increased by many orders of magnitude (Holser, 1947; Barrer, 1951).

Diffusion can be measured for various fluids or ions through different media. The rate of diffusion is always proportional to the concentration gradient (that is, the change in concentration with distance) and to a diffusion coefficient, which is a constant for each host material. The concentration gradient is partly dependent upon the solubility of the diffusing substance in the solvent, and the rate of diffusion is accordingly a function of the fluid or ion undergoing diffusion and of the medium through which diffusion takes place; the larger the solubility product, the greater the rate of diffusion (Barrer, 1951). Replacement reactions may maintain a two-way concentration gradient, with the host material diffusing away from the replacement front and the replacing mineral diffusing toward it; deposition of the ore will necessarily reduce the concentration in solution at that point (Duffell, 1937). Indeed, any other mechanism of transfer to and from a replacement front is difficult to imagine.

Field evidence in support of diffusion is afforded by the trace-element halos in the wall rocks near veins. According to diffusion theory, the metal content of wall rocks should incease logarithmically toward the ore deposit (Hawkes and Webb, 1962). Studies of wall-rock aureoles have demonstrated this logarithmic pattern in several areas. For example, Morris (1952) found a logarithmic dispersion of copper, lead, and zinc outward from basemetal veins in dolomite and quartz monzonite of the Tintic district, Utah; dispersion through dolomite was confined to 10 feet or less from ore, but trace amounts of the heavy metals had moved several times this distance through quartz monzonite. Where fractures permitted fluid flow to modify the diffusion pattern, trace-element aureoles are irregular.

From calculations of the rate of diffusion through various media, Garrels et al. (1949) concluded that the ore-bearing fluids must be brought into an area along small, closely-spaced fractures, but that diffusion along both sides of each crack will easily account for any massive ore deposits in a reasonable length of geologic time. Even under near-surface conditions—for which many geologists are reluctant to acknowledge a diffusion effect—it can be shown that ions will diffuse significant distances through solid rocks. In fact, Garrels and Dreyer (1952) calculated that diffusion of galena through limestone will be at least 300 times more effective than forced flow, even if the diffusion is assumed to take place at only 100°C and the forced flow is given a pressure gradient well beyond that for a reasonable geologic environment.

The process of diffusion is perhaps best illustrated by the well-known phenomenon of exsolution, or unmixing, in ore minerals. For example, Fig. 3-4 shows tiny exsolution blebs of chalcopyrite scattered through a specimen of sphalerite. If the specimen is heated to a temperature of 400°C, the chalcopyrite blebs will disappear, and the sphalerite will appear to be homogeneous. At elevated temperatures, the bonds of a crystal are opened, or loosened, permitting the entrance of foreign materials, and near 400°C chalcopyrite will diffuse, dispersing itself throughout the expanded structure of sphalerite. Upon slow cooling, the bonds tighten again, and the chalcopyrite is forced out of the sphalerite structure. As cooling proceeds, the chalcopyrite is arranged in accordance with the atomic structure of the sphalerite, or where a great excess of chalcopyrite has been exsolved, it may

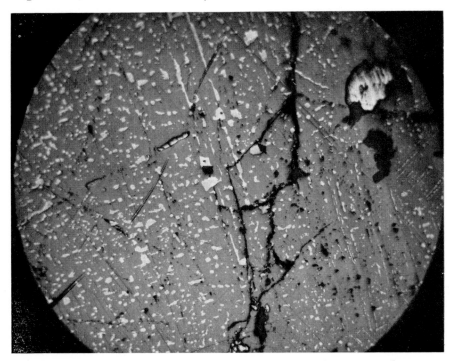

FIGURE 3-4. *Chalcopyrite blebs in sphalerite, Darwin, California. Exsolution texture developed by the separation of chalcopyrite from the sphalerite lattice during slow cooling. ×80.*

actually form mineral grains along the boundaries of the sphalerite (Edwards, 1954).

Another common example of diffusion where considerable migration may be indicated is furnished by the movement of carbonaceous material during the marmorization (marbleization) of limestone. As recrystallization takes place, the grains of calcite become bleached (in fact, most crystalline limestones are white), and the small particles of carbon to which the limestone generally owes its dark bluish or grayish color are forced out of the calcite structures. In places, the process can be seen to have stopped before completion, and the carbon is concentrated as anthracite or graphite buttons within halos of white marble (Fig. 3-5). Where recrystallization has been carried to completion, the carbon is entirely dispersed. If carbon migrates in this manner, it is reasonable to suppose that sulfides behave similarly under favorable conditions of temperature and pressure. The process would probably be greatly aided by the presence of water in the rock pores, which

FIGURE 3-5. *Button of carbon ("anthracite") in partly crystallized dolomite. Wolf Creek prospect, Metaline Falls, Washington. ×2.*

would facilitate crystal growth and help dissolve and transport soluble extraneous materials.

Niggli proposed a mechanism involving the diffusion of a gas phase, whereby considerable amounts of material may be transferred from a cooling magma into the wall rocks. The area overlying a magma chamber should be saturated with vapors evolved from the magma, and if these wall rocks are capable of replacement reactions with the vapors, they may act as an absorption apparatus, continually removing the gases and allowing for more "evaporation" from the magma (Niggli, 1929, p. 8–9).

Regarding the efficacy of diffusion in ore genesis, Edwards (1952) emphasized the small scale of the migration involved in exsolution. Even though ore minerals provide the most favorable structures for solid diffusion—far more so than the more rigid silicate structures—and even though the sulfides form under conditions likely to promote a maximum of diffusion (that is, high temperatures), the linear movement of a given ion during exsolution rarely exceeds a few millimeters, and is generally measurable only in microns. But the fact that the exsolved mineral has a larger volume than the host is compensated for by a corresponding reduction in volume of the residual host mineral, so that although there is separation, there is no migration away from the place of deposition.

The important factor shown by the process of exsolution, however, is the rate at which diffusion takes place in sulfides, rather than the ultimate magnitude of diffusion. Concerning the former problem, Gill (1960) produced significant diffusion through copper sulfides; in fact, he demonstrated that metal ions, such as ferrous iron, diffuse through sulfides at an appreciable rate (on the order of 1–3 millimeters per day) without the aid of hydrothermal solutions and within the temperature range in which many ores have formed. The best results were obtained using CuS, and similar, though less striking, results were observed with FeS, PbS, and ZnS.

In contrast to the results obtained by Gill, experimental work has shown that diffusion in silica and the silicates takes place very slowly and over extremely small distances. For example, Verhoogen (1952) attempted to diffuse potassium ions into a quartz crystal and found that, even at a temperature of 500°C, and under the influence of a concentration gradient, the ions would travel at the rate of only 110 centimeters per million years.

The migration of fluids through rocks is greatly facilitated if the rocks are in a state of stress, and during mountain-building episodes—when many ores are emplaced—stress is the normal condition. Under a triaxial stress system, fluids tend to migrate along the planes of tension—that is, normal to the axis of minimum principal stress. Fractures, cleavage planes, and crystal boundaries provide the channelways. Edwards (1954, p. 142) pointed out that if quicksilver is spread on unstrained brass it forms only a thin coating, but when the brass is bent, the mercury works through it—largely along grain boundaries—and the brass eventually breaks.

Thus the importance of diffusion to ore transport remains unresolved, but in light of the field evidence and the laboratory results that support this mechanism, diffusion in the solid state must be acknowledged as a reasonable possibility under favorable circumstances. The importance of relatively open channelways provided by fault and joint systems cannot be overemphasized; long-distance migrations of ore-bearing fluids are undoubtedly controlled by these fissures. But on the local scale—especially within the vicinity of ore deposition, where free circulation may be impeded—diffusion of metal ions through both liquid and solid media probably makes a significant contribution to the movement of materials and to the final configuration of ore deposits.

Migration of Fluids at Shallow Depths

Near the surface of the earth, within the range of drill holes and mine openings, the behavior of fluids underground has been carefully studied, but even at these shallow depths our knowledge is incomplete (Scheidegger,

1960; Hubbert, 1940, 1953; Muscat, 1937; Meinzer, 1923; Clough, 1936).
The factors to be considered in the movement of fluids at shallow depths
include: the character of the fluid, especially its viscosity and density; the
nature of the medium being traversed, especially its porosity and permeability; and the hydraulic head, or liquid pressure. It is readily seen that the
study can be extremely complex, depending upon the amount of material
in solution, the presence or absence of gases, the character and heterogeneity
of the rocks invaded, the geologic structure, and the temperature and pressure of the fluids. Many problems related to the migration of fluids at depth
are also encountered in the study of near-surface fluids. Thus the role of
gases versus liquids is debatable, as is the importance of diffusion.

Probably the simplest and most fundamental law that describes the movement of fluids underground is Darcy's law. This law relates the amount of
fluid that can pass through a porous medium to the velocity of fluid movement, the permeability of the fluid-bearing materials, and the hydraulic
gradient of the system (Darcy, 1856). Since 1856, when Darcy made the
original statement of his law, the subject has received concentrated study,
and many modifications covering special conditions have been stated, though
Darcy's fundamental contribution has proven to be a reasonably correct
approximation. The law may be expressed in its simplest form as

$$V = \frac{kh}{l},$$

where V = the velocity of the moving liquid,
   h = the difference in head at the two ends of the column of ma-
      terial through which the fluid moves,
   l = the length of the column, or distance traversed, and
   k = a constant that depends upon the nature of the fluid and the
      material being traversed

Quantitatively, Darcy's law may be expressed as

$$Q = \frac{K(P_1 - P_2)A}{\mu l},$$

where Q = the quantity of fluid measured,
   K = a constant dependent upon the nature of the medium (co-
      efficient of permeability),
   $P_1 - P_2$ = the difference in fluid pressure (head),
   A = the cross-sectional area under consideration,
   μ = the viscosity of the fluid, and
   l = the length of the column, or distance traversed.

This formula, or a modification of it, is used extensively in determining the laminar flow of water or other liquids through homogeneous, permeable media. Darcy's law, as written, does not apply if the flow is turbulent— that is, rapid enough to cause eddying. In all probability, turbulent flow takes place only in openings of unusually large size, and is of little significance in the passage of ore-bearing solutions.

Hubbert (1953) has demonstrated that during the migration of fluids containing oil, gas, and water, the three components separate and will migrate at different rates and in different directions. These findings would apply not only to oil, gas, and water, but to all fluids at shallow depths. In an oil-gas-water system, the interfaces will not be horizontal, provided at least one of each pair of fluids is in motion in a nonvertical direction; nor will the migration paths of gas or oil droplets in moving water be the same. That is, the impelling forces for oil and gas will not be parallel, and the two fluids will migrate in divergent directions to different traps or to different parts of the same trap. Since ore-bearing fluids in many environments are thought to contain both liquids and gases, and since their behavior should be similar to that of oil, gas, and water, they tend to separate during migration. Liquids of different densities also will follow divergent paths during migration, provided they are separate fluids. This phenomenon has been demonstrated for salt-water/fresh-water interfaces (Hubbert, 1953). The migration of hydrothermal solutions along the top of a ground water aquifer and the concentration of these solutions off-center from the crests of structures should be expected from the relationships determined by Hubbert. Thompson (1954)—applying hydrodynamics in his reasoning— proposed just such a migration path for the mercury-bearing fluids that deposited the ores of the Terlingua district, Texas. Reasoning of this kind may show, for example, that separation of liquid and gas phases is responsible for zoning of ores around a source (see Chapter 6). Similarly, such reasoning may explain the presence of monomineralic deposits such as those of mercury, in which other sulfide minerals are commonly absent or are present only in minor amounts.

Whereas diffusion through comparatively dry rocks under near-surface conditions is thought by many geologists to be ineffective in the transportation of ores, diffusion through solutions in saturated rocks is generally considered to be important. For example, ores are commonly concentrated in permeable layers beneath shales or other relatively impermeable rocks, but in a few places, ores thought to have been deposited from ascending waters are found in receptive rocks *above* the impermeable layers. Such an

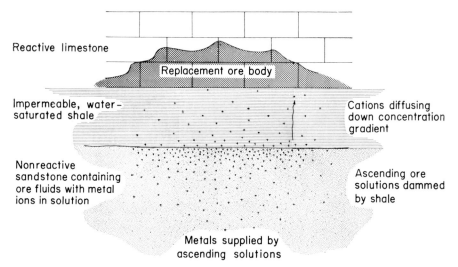

Reactive limestone

Replacement ore body

Impermeable, water-saturated shale

Cations diffusing down concentration gradient

Nonreactive sandstone containing ore fluids with metal ions in solution

Ascending ore solutions dammed by shale

Metals supplied by ascending solutions

FIGURE 3-6. *Schematic cross section, showing the diffusion of metal ions through an impermeable shale. Anions, such as sulfur, would migrate with the metal ions. The ascending ions move down the concentration gradient. Any radical change in chemistry of the country rock, such as the change from shale to limestone, could affect the ore solutions, and as a result metals would be deposited immediately after the solution emerged from the shale.*

apparently anomalous situation may result from the diffusion of ions through water-saturated rocks (Fig. 3-6). If a soluble salt is introduced from below into a sequence of saturated, alternately permeable and impermeable layers, the salt—owing to the concentration gradient—tends to diffuse through the rocks, even though the pore water is not circulating. Since the pore fluids cannot circulate through the strata, the fluid in each layer will attain its own equilibrium composition with the host rock, and the presence of a chemically receptive stratum directly above the impermeable layer will cause the immediate precipitation of the metals as they emerge from the diffusion zone. Similarly, the replaced materials should diffuse back through the impermeable stratum.

The force of growing crystals has been considered by some geologists as being effective in forcing open the walls of fissures and enabling fluids to pass through. Growing crystals undoubtedly exert a considerable force, as is shown by the fact that ice will split rocks or rupture an automobile crankcase. The force of growing crystals is limited, however, by the internal strength of the crystals; if this limit is exceeded, the crystals will collapse or cease to develop. Thus it is difficult to believe that the force of growing crystals would be sufficient to force apart rocks in the depths of the earth.

Yet under light loads, this force may be significant (Taber, 1916, 1926; Boydell, 1926, 1928).

Migration of Metals in the Colloidal State

The possibility that colloids may be present in the ore-bearing fluids has been considered by many geologists, but has not been widely accepted, perhaps because the behavior of colloids at elevated temperatures and pressures is one of the least understood phases of physical chemistry (Barton, 1959; Williams et al., 1951; McBain, 1950; Lindgren, 1933; Boydell, 1925, 1927; Lasky, 1930; Liesegang, 1913).

A colloidal system consists of two phases, one of which (the dispersed phase) is diffused in the other (the dispersion medium). Colloidal particles range in size between those in true solution and those in coarse suspension, the general limits being 10^{-7} and 10^{-3} centimeter (Williams et al., 1951, p. 511). The colloidal material may be solid, liquid, or gas, and may be dispersed in any of these same phases, but in the study of ore transport we are concerned essentially with solids dispersed in liquid, or possibly gaseous, media. A colloidal system consisting of solid particles dispersed in a liquid is called a sol.

Colloidal particles have large surface areas per unit volume, and as a result, ions adsorbed on the surface are able to control the behavior of the particles themselves. A given kind of colloidal particle may adsorb cations and behave as a positively charged body, or it may adsorb anions and become negatively charged. Since the particles of a sol all have the same charge, they repel each other and prevent coagulation. Accordingly, if an electrolyte is added to the sol, the colloidal particles become neutralized, which allows them to flocculate. The dispersed phase is generally made up of molecular clusters, which may be in the form of sulfides, oxides, hydroxides, or other chemical compounds. Most sulfide sols and organic sols are negative, whereas most oxide and hydroxide sols are positive; but there are some serious exceptions to these generalizations (for example, colloidal silica carries a negative charge). Some sols have particles with a definite electrical charge that is not easily changed; others may be positive, negative, or neutral, depending upon the pH of the dispersion medium. Considering these properties, it is easy to imagine how various theories could be proposed to explain both the transportation and deposition of ore minerals in colloidal systems.

The possibility that colloidal metals are transported in hydrothermal systems depends upon whether the sols are stable at high temperatures and pressures, but such stability relationships have not received adequate study. Colloids are most stable in cool, dilute solutions and may be much more stable in the presence of a second (protective) colloid. Frondel (1938) studied the stability of colloidal gold under simulated hydrothermal conditions and concluded that silica acts as a protective colloid, stabilizing the colloidal gold against electrolytes and against coagulation due to an increase in temperature. Unprotected sols (gold) containing no added electrolyte coagulated spontaneously at 150–250°C, but protected sols (gold and silica) were stable at 350°C.

The pros and cons of the hypothesis that metals migrate in the colloidal state have been debated from both chemical and geological viewpoints. In support, laboratory studies have established that colloids of metals can exist at moderate temperatures and pressures. Further, certain minerals and mineraloids are found in forms that suggest flocculation from a sol (see p. 125).

One of the most difficult problems related to the migration of ore-bearing fluids at depth consists in explaining how these fluids are able to pass through dense and relatively impermeable materials. As regards colloids, the problem would seem to be intensified (Boydell, 1925, 1927), because colloidal particles are larger than ions, atoms, and molecules. Nevertheless, there are geologists who argue that some deep-seated ores were emplaced as colloids, and there are others who suggest that the ore fluids change from solutions at depth to colloidal sols in near-surface environments (Herzenberg, 1936).

References Cited

Barrer, R. M., 1951, Diffusion in and through solids: London, Cambridge Univ. Press.

Barton, P. B., Jr., 1959, The chemical environment of ore deposition and the problem of low-temperature ore transport, *in* Abelson, P. H. (ed.), Researches in geochemistry: New York, John Wiley & Sons, Inc., p. 279–300.

Boydell, H. C., 1925, Role of colloidal solutions in the formation of mineral deposits: Inst. Mining Metallurgy (London) Trans., v. 34, p. 145–337.

———, 1926, A discussion on metasomatism and the linear "force of growing crystals": Econ. Geology, v. 21, p. 1–55.

———, 1927, Operative causes in ore deposition: Inst. Mining Metallurgy (London) Bull., no. 227, p. 1–85.

———, 1928, Metasomatism and the pressure of growing crystals; a discussion: Econ. Geology, v. 23, p. 214–218.

Brown, J. S., 1941, Factors of composition and porosity in lead-zinc replacements of metamorphosed limestone: Am. Inst. Mining Engineers Trans., v. 144, p. 250–263.

———, 1947, Porosity and ore deposition at Edwards and Balmat, New York:

Geol. Soc. America Bull., v. 58, p. 505–545.

———, 1948, Ore genesis: New Jersey, Hopewell Press.

Clough, K. H., 1936, Study of permeability measurements and their application to the oil industry: Oil Weekly, v. 83, p. 27–34.

Compton, R. R., 1955, Trondhjemite batholith near Bidwell Bar, California: Geol. Soc. America Bull., v. 66, p. 9–44.

———, 1960, Contact metamorphism in Santa Rosa Range, Nevada: Geol. Soc. America Bull., v. 71, p. 1383–1416.

Darcy, Henry, 1856, Les fontaines publiques de la ville de Dijon: Paris, Victor Dalmont.

Duffell, Stanley, 1937, Diffusion and its relation to ore deposition: Econ. Geology, v. 32, p. 494–510.

Edwards, A. B., 1952, The ore minerals and their textures: Clark Memorial Lecture, Roy. Soc. New South Wales Jour. and Proc., v. 85, p. 26–45.

———, 1954, Textures of the ore minerals and their significance: Melbourne, Australasian Inst. Mining Metallurgy.

Frondel, Clifford, 1938, Stability of colloidal gold under hydrothermal conditions: Econ. Geology, v. 33, p. 1–20.

Garrels, R. M., and Dreyer, R. M., 1952, Mechanism of limestone replacement at low temperatures and pressures: Geol. Soc. America Bull., v. 63, p. 325–379.

———, and Howland, A. L., 1949, Diffusion of ions through intergranular spaces in water-saturated rocks: Geol. Soc. America Bull., v. 60, p. 1809–1828.

Gill, J. E., 1960, Solid diffusion of sulphides and ore formation: 21st Internat. Geol. Cong., pt. 16, p. 209–217.

Graton, L. C., 1906, Reconnaissance of some gold and tin deposits of the southern Appalachians: U.S. Geol. Survey Bull. 293.

Hawkes, H. E., and Webb, J. S., 1962, Geochemistry in mineral exploration: New York and Evanston, Harper and Row.

Herzenberg, Robert, 1936, Colloidal tin ore deposits: Econ. Geology, v. 31, p. 761–766.

Holser, W. T., 1947, Metasomatic processes: Econ. Geology, v. 42, p. 384–395.

Hubbert, M. K., 1940, The theory of ground water motion: Jour. Geology, v. 48, p. 785–944.

———, 1953, Entrapment of petroleum under hydrodynamic conditions: Am. Assoc. Petroleum Geologists Bull., v. 37, p. 1954–2026.

———, and Rubey, W. W., 1959, Role of fluid pressure in mechanics of overthrust faulting; part I: Geol. Soc. America Bull., v. 70, p. 115–166.

Hubbert, M. K., and Willis, D. G., 1957, Mechanics of hydraulic fracturing: Jour. Petroleum Technology, v. 9, no. 6, p. 158–168.

Klinkenberg, L. J., 1941, The permeability of porous media to liquids and gases, in Drilling and production practice: Am. Petroleum Inst., p. 200–211.

Krauskopf, K. B., 1957, The heavy metal content of magmatic vapors at 600°C: Econ. Geology, v. 52, p. 786–807.

Lasky, S. G., 1930, A colloidal origin of some of the Kennecott ore minerals: Econ. Geology, v. 25, p. 737–757.

Liesegang, R. E., 1913, Geologische diffusionen: Dresden and Leipzig, Theodor Steinkopff.

Lindgren, Waldemar, 1933, Mineral deposits (4th ed.): New York, McGraw-Hill Book Co., Inc.

Maxwell, J. C., and Verrall, Peter, 1953, Expansion and increase in permeability of carbonate rocks on heating: Am. Geophys. Union Trans., v. 34, p. 101–106.

McBain, J. W., 1950, Colloid science: Boston, D. C. Heath & Co.

Meinzer, O. E., 1923, The occurrence of ground water in the United States: U.S. Geol. Survey Water-Supply Paper 489.

Morris, H. T., 1952, Primary dispersion patterns of heavy metals in carbonate and quartz monzonite wall rocks; Part

II, *in* Morris, H. T., and Lovering, T. S., 1952, Supergene and hydrothermal dispersion of heavy metals in wall rocks near ore bodies, Tintic district, Utah: Econ. Geology, v. 47, p. 698–716.

Muscat, Morris, 1937, The flow of homogeneous fluids through porous media: New York, McGraw-Hill Book Co., Inc. (Internat. Ser. in Physics).

Niggli, Paul, 1929, Ore deposits of magmatic origin (translated by H. C. Boydell): London, Thomas Murby and Co.

Ohle, E. L., 1951, The influence of permeability on ore distribution in limestone and dolomite: Econ. Geology, v. 46, p. 667–706, 871–908.

Park, C. F., Jr., 1936, Preliminary report on gold deposits of the Virginia Piedmont: Virginia Geol. Survey Bull. 44.

———, and Cannon, R. S., Jr., 1943, Geology and ore deposits of the Metaline quadrangle, Washington: U.S. Geol. Survey Prof. Paper 202.

Rove, O. N., 1947, Some physical characteristics of certain favorable and unfavorable ore horizons: Econ. Geology, v. 42, p. 57–77, 161–193.

Scheidegger, A. E., 1960, The physics of flow through porous media: New York, The Macmillan Co.

Spurr, J. E., 1906, Ore deposits of the Silver Peak quadrangle, Nevada: U.S. Geol. Survey Prof. Paper 55, p. 112–128.

———, 1923, The ore magmas: New York, McGraw-Hill Book Co., Inc.

Taber, Stephen, 1916, The growth of crystals under external pressure: Am. Jour. Sci., 4th ser., v. 41, p. 532–556.

———, 1926, Metasomatism and the pressure of growing crystals; a discussion: Econ. Geology, v. 21, p. 717–727.

Thompson, G. A., 1954, Transportation and deposition of quicksilver ores in the Terlingua district, Texas: Econ. Geology, v. 49, p. 175–197.

Verhoogen, Jean, 1952, Ionic diffusion and electrical conductivity in quartz: Am. Mineralogist, v. 37, p. 637–655.

Wandke, Alfred, 1930, Ore deposition in open fissures formed by solution pressure: Am. Inst. Mining Engineers Tech. Pub. 342; Trans., v. 96, p. 291–304, 1931.

Williams, J. W., Alberty, R. A., and Kraemer, E. O., 1951, The colloidal state and surface chemistry, *in* Taylor, H. S., and Glasstone, Samuel (eds.), A treatise on physical chemistry (v. 2): New York, D. Van Nostrand Co., Inc., p. 509–692.

CHAPTER 4 **Deposition of**

the Ores

KNOWLEDGE OF THE CAUSES BEHIND ORE DEPOSITION is essential in exploration. Without this knowledge, most prospecting is left to blind chance; but the careful field observer who has a thorough understanding as to why an ore deposit was localized in a given environment has a definite advantage in the search for other deposits in similar environments.

Whether an ore deposit is a product of igneous, sedimentary, or metamorphic processes, its localization is generally the result of many factors. One factor, or series of factors, may account for the ore constituent; another may cause the material to be deposited; and another is usually necessary to restrict the depositional area so that the concentration is of economic grade. The ore metals may be supplied by a differentiating magma or by the weathering of rocks at the earth's surface, but whatever the source, a reason for deposition and a place for concentration are essential conditions in the development of an ore deposit. Some ores are deposited by gravity; thus an early formed chromite crystal will settle out of a residual magma, and a fragment of gold will settle to the bottom of a layer of agitated sediments. Other ores are deposited because of chemical changes in the system, such as a change in pH due to reactions between the ore-bearing solutions and the host rocks. A drop in temperature, pressure, or velocity of the transporting medium, or the admixture of a second solution, would also bring about chemical reactions that might cause ore deposition. Localized deposition may in turn depend upon the permeability, structure, brittleness, or chemistry of the rocks. In fact, the reasons for deposition and the causes of localization are often the same.

Ground Preparation

Many epigenetic deposits—ores formed later than the host rock—are restricted to areas that have undergone a favorable premetallization change. Such a change may make the country rock more receptive or more reactive to the ore-bearing solutions; accordingly the process is known as *ground preparation*. Syngenetic deposits—ores formed at the same time as the host rock—are unrelated to this process, because they are not emplaced in a pre-existing rock.

Ground preparation takes place in several ways. Any premetallization process that increases the permeability, causes a favorable chemical change, or induces brittleness in the rocks may develop an area that will localize deposition from the ore-bearing fluids. Hence the type of ground preparation will depend upon both the country rock and the preparing agent, which may be heat, fluids, tectonics, or a combination of these. Silification, dolomitization, and recrystallization are all common examples of ground preparation.

Epigenetic deposits are typically, though not necessarily, introduced during periods of tectonic activity; in fact, many are late-phase products of associated igneous intrusions. Under these circumstances, ground preparation would be related to the same activity; for example, dolomitization and ore emplacement may occur sequentially in the country rock around a cooling pluton. Dolomitization tends to make the rocks brittle, and subsequent movements in the magma chamber shatter the dolomitized rock, producing a clean, permeable breccia. Since the ore-bearing fluids are typically emitted during the late history of the cooling igneous mass, the ground will already have been dolomitized and shattered, serving as a porous receptacle for ore deposition.

Much ground preparation is chemical. Among the several modes of chemical ground preparation, perhaps the most common is the addition of silica, either as a form of SiO_2 or as silicates. One important type of silicification is the formation of jasperoid—a cryptocrystalline silica deposited by replacement, generally from hydrothermal solutions (Lovering, 1962). Jasperoid is abundant at Leadville, Colorado, at Metaline Falls, Washington, and in many other mining districts, where it forms conspicuous and resistant masses, knobs, and hills along shear zones or faults. Jasperoid is most common in limestones and dolomites, and in some districts ore is restricted to the silicified rock. In some jasperized districts, the rocks were first hardened by the addition of fine-grained silica, and were later shattered by faulting. Brecciation of silicified rocks thus develops a favorable location for the circulation of fluids, due to increased permeability along relatively continuous zones. (Not all jasperoid rocks that are hosts to ore bodies have been brecciated, however, hence it may be that silicified ground is chemically favorable to ore deposition rather than being just a zone of greater permeability.) Gunning (1948) noted that the ore minerals of the Privateer mine, Vancouver Island, Canada, were concentrated in fissures, the development of which was favored by pre-ore silicification of limy and argillaceous country rocks. The hardness of the silicified materials resulted in clean faulting, with a minimum of powdering. These rocks were also relatively inert to the ore-forming fluids and therefore were not softened by hydrothermal action. The net effect was essentially continuous fissuring, unobstructed by gouge (rock powder or paste) and altered wall rock. In contrast, where the veins cut quartz diorite, they narrow strikingly, because the diorite was powdered during faulting and was subsequently hydrothermally altered; both the gouge and the alteration effectively reduced the permeability.

In some districts the ground was prepared by simple crystallization of the country rock, which increased its permeability and brittleness. Recrystallization is common adjacent to intrusive masses. The pluton may also heat the country rocks prior to the introduction of ore-bearing fluids, permitting the entry and passage of hydrothermal solutions that otherwise might have reacted and precipitated earlier.

The development of skarn is another type of ground preparation. *Skarn* is a rock composed of lime-bearing silicates produced by metasomatism; specifically, by the introduction of silicon, aluminum, iron, and magnesium into carbonates. Many skarn zones contain ore bodies, the ore in each having been introduced contemporaneously with, or shortly after, the skarn. Moreover, the skarn is generally replaced in preference to the unaltered country rock, which suggests that the silicified material has greater permeability or more favorable chemical properties. It is commonly thought that the skarn is preferentially replaced because it is readily brecciated and rendered permeable to ore-bearing solutions. But this is not necessarily the answer; some skarn zones that have not been brecciated are selectively replaced by ore, and in other deposits the skarn and the ore were formed contemporaneously. Accordingly, the common association of ore within skarn zones may not be related to the mechanical influence of ground preparation; instead, it may be a product of physicochemical factors (Titley, 1961).

Deposition of Magmatic Segregation Deposits

Magmatic segregation deposits form as a direct result of igneous differentiation. Some are early differentiates that settled through the magma in response to gravity; others are late products of fractionation. Magmatic products of this type migrate and solidify in the same manner as dikes and minor intrusives of ordinary igneous rocks. In fact, they are merely igneous rocks of special economic value. Accordingly, the ores show a wide range of physical and chemical features. Some consist of strongly layered ore zones; in others the metals are disseminated through massive igneous rocks; and in still others, the ore itself is a massive igneous rock.

Parallel bands of igneous differentiates are known as compositional layers. Magmatic segregation deposits of this type are well developed in the Bushveld igneous complex of South Africa and in the Stillwater complex of Montana. Compositional layering is especially abundant in mafic or intermediate igneous rocks containing ilmenite, magnetite, or chromite. It may result from any of several different processes active during differentiation. One widely accepted process is crystal settling, such as Bowen (1928) proposed. As the temperature and pressure of a magma are lowered, crystals begin to form. The composition of these crystals depends, of course, upon the composition of the melt with which they are in equilibrium. In general, the ferromagnesian minerals—including the spinel family—crystallize first. Since these early minerals are more dense than the residual magma, they settle and collect near the base of the igneous chamber. As crystallization proceeds, crystals of progressively different composition develop, producing a layered rock. Another hypothesis concerning the origin of compositional layering is that it may be a product of liquid immiscibilities in the magma (Fenner, 1948). Compounds that are mutually soluble under certain conditions of temperature and pressure may become immiscible under other conditions. The heavier liquid would settle through the lighter one, thereby producing compositional layering of the liquids. Upon solidification, the igneous mass would contain magmatic segregation layers of a different, though perhaps indistinguishable, type from those formed by crystal settling. Still another suggestion is that the layers may be formed by successive injections of magma into a rock, each intrusion having a different composition from the others. During the differentiation of a magma, the rest melt, which constantly changes in composition as the solid phases develop, may be intermittently injected into the country rock; if the injections are controlled by bedding or structure, they may become parallel layers of different composition within a progressively growing intrusive mass. It is even conceivable, though not probable, that compositional layering could be produced by a single intrusive that employed all three of these mechanisms. In such a case, crystals would sink; immiscible liquids would develop within the magma chamber; and some of the liquid fraction would be squeezed off into the surrounding country rock.

The concentration of ore minerals in a massive igneous rock may be great or small, depending upon the kind of mineral and the degree of differentiation. Moreover, the economic situation may determine whether an igneous differentiate constitutes ore. Thus the presence of either monazite, cassiterite, or ilmenite disseminated throughout an igneous rock as an accessory mineral may be enough to establish that rock as ore, whereas a relatively rich but inaccessible iron ore deposit may have to contain more than 65 percent of iron to be profitable. For example, the titanium ore of the Tahawus district, New York, contains ilmenite as one of the minor rock constituents, but the Kiruna iron ore of Sweden consists of practically pure, massive magnetite. It might be pointed out for emphasis that the Tahawus ore was originally prospected for iron, which is much more abundant in the rock than titanium, but the titanium impurity made smelting costs prohibitive; now that titanium is a valuable commodity, the ores are worked mainly for the subordinate ilmenite, and the iron is a by-product (Killinger, 1942).

Massive ore deposits of direct magmatic affiliation are widespread. The deposits of massive ore are associated with both mafic and silicic rocks, and they may contain monazite, tin, titanium, iron, or other economic constituents. Again, the massive ore may be either an early differentiate or a late liquid fraction. If the ore mineral settles during differentiation, the residual melt may be squeezed off to leave nothing but the crystal mush, in which case what started out to be a layered deposit would instead end up as a relatively homogeneous mass of just the solid phase. Similarly, the liquid phase may form either a layered or a massive ore body upon solidification, depending upon the way it is injected into the country rocks.

In general, it is thought that massive sulfides form directly from the magma, but some geologists have argued for both an immiscible sulfide liquid phase and a sulfide ore magma. Sales (1954) proposed that the copper ore body of the Colorada pipe, Cananea, Mexico, was formed by the crystallization of an ore magma which had been injected into the top of a porphyry breccia pipe. Similar hypotheses have been advanced for other massive sulfide deposits.

In summary, the mechanism of ore deposition in magmatic segregation deposits is straightforward; it is either a matter of crystal settling or the simple crystallization of an ore-grade fluid phase. The ore may crystallize in place or it may be squeezed into the surrounding rocks as a separate magma. Nevertheless, distinguishing among the types of magmatic segregation deposits offers problems; moreover, some massive replacement deposits resemble deposits formed by magmatic segregation. Consequently, just because the theoretical processes of magmatic segregation are not complex does not mean that the interpretation of a deposit will be simple.

Physical Controls of Ore Deposition

Detailed studies of structural geology are greatly emphasized in exploration. These studies have unquestionably led to the discovery of more ore than has any other directed effort, because the movement of fluids underground is controlled by permeability, which in turn is a function of the original character of the rock plus the elements of superimposed structure. The function of permeability and structure is readily understood by petroleum geologists. Oil and gas are commonly channeled to the crest of a dome or to an area of overlap, causing these fluids to be ponded against an impermeable layer. The laws that govern the migration of oil and gas apply to all fluids underground, including the ore-bearing gases and liquids. Faults or other permeable features, either primary or superimposed, tap a supply of mineral-bearing fluid and allow it to migrate into a "trap" where it cools and precipitates the mineral content or, more commonly, where it has sufficient time to react with and replace receptive country rocks.

Serious efforts have been made to classify ore deposits according to their structural control. In general, these efforts have not produced an acceptable classification, largely because *any* structural or sedimentary feature that permits passage of ore-bearing fluids may contain areas favorable for the precipitation of ore; for this reason, a particular ore deposit is likely to be mineralized along more than one structure. Nevertheless, there are many districts where the ore concentrations follow definite patterns; where the deposition is not haphazard but is associated with predominately one type of structure.

The structures and textures that control ore deposition can best be described as primary or superimposed (secondary), according to whether they were formed at the same time as the rock mass or were formed later. In certain types of ore deposits, the primary controls are dominant; in others, superimposed features, such as faults, are the only basic controls of ore deposition. Establishing a physical control and differentiating between the two types are fundamental problems in the exploitation of any mineralized district.

PRIMARY FEATURES

Primary structures and textures of both igneous and sedimentary rocks commonly control the distribution of ore-bearing fluids, and hence the localization of the ores. Any textural or structural feature that influences the porosity and permeability of a rock may control the deposition of ores, and as a result, the variety of primary controls is practically unlimited. A few of the most obvious primary structural controls are:

1. permeable (clastic) limestone or dolomite, especially where it is dammed by impermeable cap rocks;
2. well-sorted conglomerates that permit easy circulation of ore-bearing fluids;
3. broken and permeable tops of lava flows, which also permit ready circulation of ore-bearing fluids;
4. permeable sandstones, especially channel sands and beach deposits.

Ohle and Brown (1954) described a sedimentary arch structure of depositional origin that controlled the ore trends in the southeastern Missouri lead district. The arch structures apparently were built up by currents that formed ridges or bars of limy sediments parallel to their direction of movement. Much of the sediment making up the ridges was clastic shell material, an exceptionally permeable rock compared to the limy muds in adjacent troughs. Ascending aqueous solutions were directed along these permeable arches and restricted from further movement by an overlying bed of impermeable limestone. In this same district, other ore bodies are controlled by buried knobs and ridges of Precambrian granite, against which Cambrian and younger sediments were deposited. The sediments have initial dips in all directions away from the granite highs. Ascending ore solutions migrated along a basal sandstone that pinches out against the Precambrian granites. Upon reaching the up-dip termination of the sandstone, the ore-bearing fluids entered the overlying carbonate sediments and deposited their ore minerals (James, 1949; Ohle and Brown, 1954). Brecciation produced by slumping during deposition and compaction of the overlying sediments has been described as yet another control of ore deposition in this district. Differential compaction over the clastic shell ridges led to oversteepening of slopes and to consequent slumping into the basin regions. These submarine landslides produced huge breccia zones that were especially favorable for the subsequent ingress of ore-bearing solutions. Individual ore bodies in the slides range up to more than 6000 feet in length, and contain several million tons of ore (Snyder and Odell, 1958). Secondary superimposed fracture zones have exerted a strong influence on the distribution of ores in southeast Missouri, but much new ore has been discovered by mapping and following such sedimentary features as buried ridges.

Dolomites and dolomitic limestones are ordinarily somewhat more permeable and porous than pure limestones, and for this reason dolomites permit mineralizing solutions to circulate more readily than do limestones. Hence many geologists believe that dolomite is more likely to be a host for ore (Hayward and Triplett, 1931). In such districts as the Sierra Mojada, Nuevo León, Mexico, and in many other areas, ores are concentrated in dolomitic rocks, and the purer limestones are barren or low-grade. This is not universally true, however, for in the Metaline district of northeastern Washington, the ores are in limestones beneath an impermeable black shale, and the underlying dolomites are either barren or only weakly mineralized. Evidently, factors other than permeability must be considered for many deposits.

The copper ores of the Keweenaw peninsula in northern Michigan furnish excellent examples of hydrothermal deposits that have been channeled into their present positions through permeable conglomerates and broken tops of lava flows (Butler and Burbank, 1929). Concentrations of ore are found in conglomerate beds between the lava flows and in the fragmental, vesicular surface layers of individual flows. These regions have been favorable for ore deposition because of their extremely high permeabilities.

Permeable zones formed by channel deposits and sands interbedded with siltstones have been mineralized in the Gas Hills uranium district of central Wyoming. The ore deposits are restricted to the coarse-grained facies and are especially concentrated along the valleys of a buried land surface. Apparently, the ore-bearing solutions mixed with ground waters and moved laterally along permeable zones until they were dammed by facies changes or by impermeable shales across the basal unconformity (Zeller, 1957).

SUPERIMPOSED, OR SECONDARY, FEATURES

In most epigenetic ore deposits, structures superimposed on the rocks have exerted a great influence upon the path of circulation followed by the ore-bearing fluids. Faults and folds are probably the most common secondary structures, though breccia zones, pipes, and other features are locally of great significance.

Faulting is found nearly everywhere, and many ore deposits are related directly to the resulting structures. Because fault surfaces are uneven, movement along a fault will produce breccia and gouge. A zone of fine-grained gouge will frequently hinder the circulation of fluids, either along or across a fault. On the other hand, coarse, clean breccia, containing a minimum of powdered rock material, results in a considerable increase in permeability, especially in brittle rocks that are fractured under light loads (Lovering, 1942). Accordingly, faults of minor displacement may be much better hosts for ore solutions than faults of large magnitude, which are more likely to develop gouge. As a general rule, then, tight fractures filled with gouge are less favorable places for ore deposition than the more open fractures. As is usual in geology, there are exceptions to this generalization. For example, the Santa Rosa mine in the Huantajaya district of northern Chile is said to have contained silver ore in clay along the side of what seems to be a more permeable quartz vein (Hector Flores, 1958, personal communication).

Veins are tabular bodies, long in two dimensions and short in the third. They form along cracks or fissure zones in the earth's crust, and fault planes are especially favorable loci. They are either the simple filling of open fissures or the replaced country rock along a narrow but permeable fracture. Veins are classified as simple (Fig. 4-1), complex (Fig. 4-2), irregular, and anastomosing (Fig. 4-3), depending respectively upon whether they are sheets of a single injection, composite lodes made up of multiple injections along the same fracture, veins of variable thickness, or braided or mutually interlacing mineral zones. Vein patterns are further described by qualifying terms such as conjugate (two sets of veins that have the same strike but dip in opposite directions) and coordinate (two sets of veins that strike at 90 degrees to each other). Seldom is an entire vein filled with ore; the valuable constituents are usually concentrated in restricted zones, called ore shoots. Where many small veinlets are distributed along a tabular zone, the deposit is called a lead, a lode, or a fissure zone.

Small movements along curved faults cause pinching and swelling, separat-

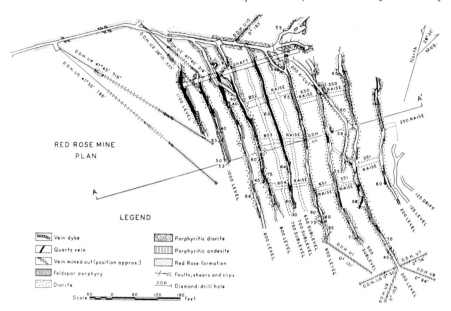

RED ROSE MINE
PLAN

LEGEND

Vein dyke   Porphyritic diorite

Quartz vein   Porphyritic andesite

Vein mined out (position approx.)   Red Rose formation

Feldspar porphyry   Faults, shears and slips

Diorite   Diamond-drill hole

Scale 60   0   60   120   180   Feet

ing the footwall from the hangingwall in places (Fig. 4-4). Ore-bearing
fluids migrate along the more open parts of the fissures (the "swells") and
are deflected around the tighter zones (the "pinches"). As a result, rolls or
changes in attitude of either the strike or dip of a vein commonly mark the
beginning or end of an ore shoot, and such irregularities along veins have
long been recognized as features of great significance in mineral exploration.

Contour maps based upon assay values, and dilation maps showing the
thickness of a vein, are of considerable interest and use in exploration, provided sufficient information about a vein is available. The contour map is
constructed by plotting assay values on a longitudinal section drawn through
the vein. The assay data usually represent the entire width of a vein, though
they may portray only the richer parts, such as a footwall or a hangingwall
streak. Contours are then drawn through points of equal value, the thickness
of the vein being ignored. A contour map of this type, when used alone, has
limited value, as it shows only the unit value of the material in the vein. A
similar type of contour map that is used in places is based upon the total
metal content in the vein.

Where sufficient information is available—which, unfortunately, is seldom
the case—dilation maps may be constructed; such maps may be of great
value both in exploration and in the study of ore genesis. These maps are
constructed by passing a reference plane below and roughly parallel to the

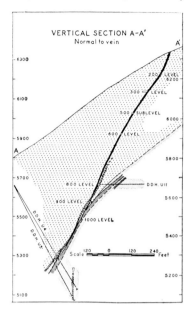

FIGURE 4-1. *Simple vein. Red Rose tungsten mine, Canada. Plan (facing page) and section. (After Brown, 1957.)*

footwall of a vein. Distances from this plane to the footwall are plotted, and contours are drawn through points at equal distances from the footwall. A similar map is then constructed, on which distances from the same plane to the hangingwall are plotted. Each map will show "hills" and "valleys" where irregularities are present in either wall. If the vein is a simple fissure filling, the two contour maps can be adjusted until the contours of one agree closely with the contours of the other. From this, the amount and direction of movement along the fissure may be ascertained. Contours based upon the thickness of the vein—or the amount of dilation—may be drawn from an overlay of the hangingwall and footwall maps. If the amount and direction of movement along a vein, plus the amount of dilation, are known, the locations of the widest and most favorable parts of the vein may be projected into undeveloped ground. An interesting and economically rewarding study of this type was made by Roscoe (1951) in the Rambler mine of the Slocan district, British Columbia (Fig. 4-5).

Pipes or chimneys, as the names imply, are bodies relatively short in two dimensions and long in the third. The two names are used interchangeably, though efforts have been made to restrict one term or the other to rod-shaped deposits having a specifically defined plunge. For example, many geologists restrict the term pipe to steeply dipping rod-shaped bodies, and use the word *manto* (Spanish; mantle, or cloak) for flat-lying rod-shaped

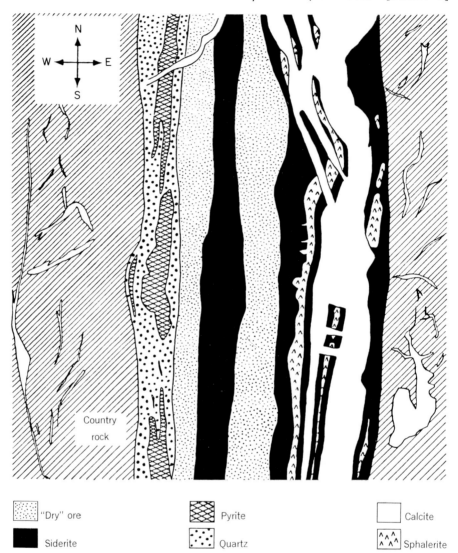

FIGURE 4-2. *Complex vein, Příbram, Czechoslovakia. (After Kutina, 1955.)*

bodies. However, *manto* is more correctly used to describe beds or flat, bedded, and sheet-like deposits (Prescott, 1915). Pipes are known to change their attitudes from nearly vertical to nearly horizontal, therefore it is desirable to use the term without regard to plunge or dip. Most pipes contain broken rock material and are accordingly known as breccia pipes.

Many large and valuable ore bodies have been mined from pipes dis-

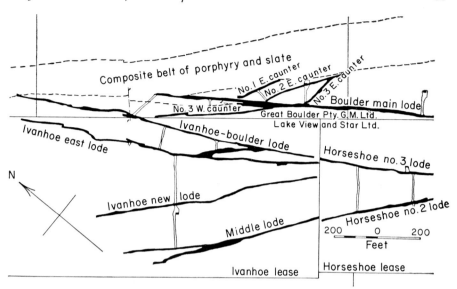

FIGURE 4-3. *Branching vein, West of Boulder Dyke, Kalgoorlie district, Western Australia. (After Finucane, 1948.)*

tributed widely throughout the world. The pipes are generally brecciated country rock and either pre-date ore deposition or are formed by the mineralizing processes. The origin of pipes is one of the most fascinating problems in the field of ore geology; it can also be one of the most rewarding. Ore pipes are found in many different environments, and result from various combinations of processes. Although the genesis of many pipes is unknown, some are readily interpreted. Pipes commonly form at the intersection of any two tabular features, such as faults, fissures, dikes, bedding, lava flows, or joints. Where the tabular features are faults, brecciation is likely to be most extensive if the fractures intersect at small angles (Fig. 4-6). Pipes also form at the crests of folds, especially where the rocks are highly fractured and where permeability has been increased by strata sliding over each other, leaving areas of re-

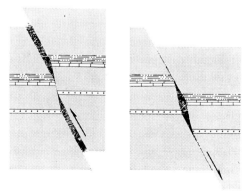

FIGURE 4-4. *Openings caused by normal and reverse movements along veins.*

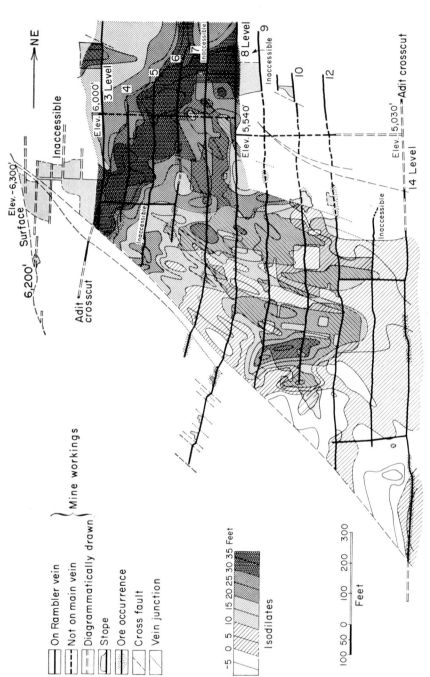

FIGURE 4-5. *Dilation map of the Rambler vein, Slocan district, British Columbia. (After Roscoe, 1951.)*

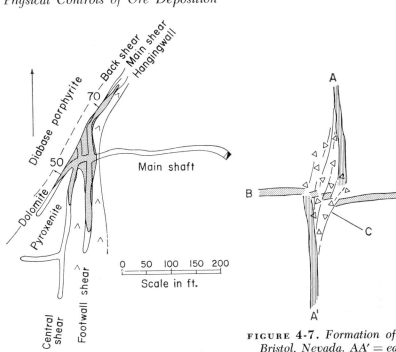

FIGURE 4-6. *Plan of the Magnet orebody, Tasmania, at about the 14th level. Shows concentration of ore at the intersection of fissures at flat angles. (After Edwards, 1960.)*

FIGURE 4-7. *Formation of pipe at Bristol, Nevada. AA′ = early fracture, BB′ = later fracture offsetting AA′. The breccia pipe, C, was caused by renewed movement along AA′. (Paul Gemmill, personal communication.)*

duced pressure at the crests. Ore pipes have developed against igneous contacts, either where solutions were channeled along irregularities or where differential movements caused brecciation. They form in the throats of old volcanoes, in diatremes, solution channels through carbonate rocks, in shoestring sands, along rolls or changes in dip or strike of a vein, and within small cupolas or other igneous bodies (Bryner, 1961; Perry, 1961; Blanchard, 1947; Kuhn, 1941; Emmons, 1938; Butler, 1913; Ransome, 1911; Wagner, 1927). Paul Gemmill (1959, personal communication) studied the ore-bearing pipes in the Bristol mine of eastern Nevada and concluded that some of them resulted from renewed movement along the earlier of two intersecting fractures (Fig. 4-7). Other pipes at Bristol are aligned along single faults and could not have been formed in this manner (MacDiarmid, 1960). Figure 4-8 shows a pair of these pipes thought to have developed in the open zones of pinch-and-swell structures along an irregular fault.

Locke (1926) suggested that mineralization stoping was active in form-

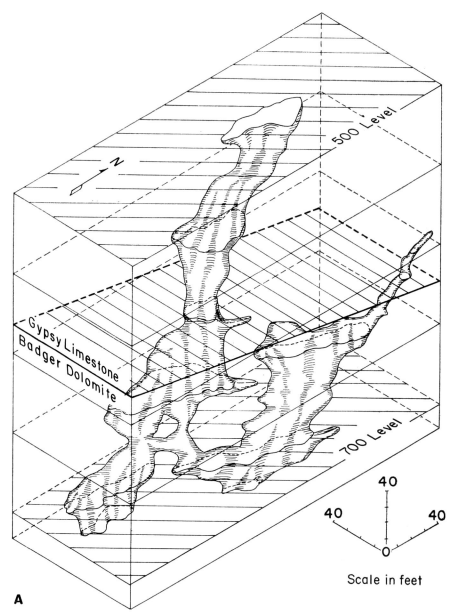

A

FIGURE 4-8 (A) *Isometric drawing of an ore pipe, Bristol mine, Nevada.*
(B) *Facing page. Probable development of breccia pipes. (a) Irregular fault surface before displacement. (b) After vertical displacement, showing development of swells. (c) Pipes along which collapse breccias would form.*

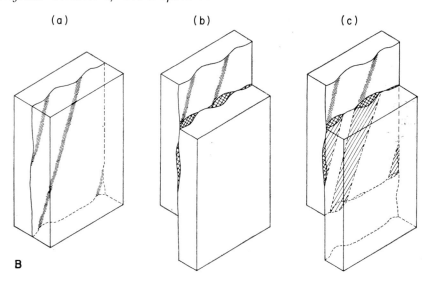

ing ore pipes. This process involves the ascent of ore-bearing fluids through the crust of the earth by stoping their way upward. The undermined and partly dissolved blocks break loose from the roof and settle into the solution cavern, forming a pipe of collapse breccia. The ore and gangue are then deposited in the brecciated mass. Mineralization stoping may well be active under special conditions, but many pipes show little or no alteration near their tops, which should be manifest where the rocks were partly dissolved.

Diatremes, or volcanic explosion vents, form where gas-charged magmas vesiculate at an explosive rate, causing the gas and magma to rush upwards violently. The process is probably similar to the two-phase water-steam action in the throats of active geysers, and it may take place where ascending magmas suddenly encounter a porous, water-saturated clastic sediment (Williams, 1936). Numerous, well-defined diatreme breccia pipes have been described from northeastern Arizona; they are funnel-shaped, with diameters that range in thickness from 4000 feet near the top to 500 feet at depth (Hack, 1942). Since the diatremes form in areas of igneous activity, and represent highly porous avenues for the escape of hydrothermal fluids, they stand a reasonable chance of becoming loci of pipe-shaped ore deposits.

Actually, this two-step process (that is, development of a diatreme with subsequent hydrothermal activity) is not essential for all "volcanic" ore pipes. The explosive escape of gases from confined magmas and superheated meteoric waters may cause brecciation along a pipe-like course, with ore deposition taking place during the waning stages; thus both the breccia pipe and the metallization are attributed to a single agent. This mechanism of brecciation is analogous to the rapid vesiculation of magma that forms diatremes. Under high-velocity gas flowage, the sediments tend to expand, shatter, and rotate or become agitated. Continued acceleration of the gas will form streams or avenues of relatively high-velocity gas, which transport the rock fragments upwards. Such a process, known as *fluidization,* has been utilized in large-scale industrial operations for the intimate mixing of fine-grained aggregates (Reynolds, 1954).

A well-defined example of a breccia pipe in Arizona has been attributed to explosive penetration of superheated steam (Barrington and Kerr, 1961). The pipe, circular in cross section and about 100 feet in diameter, supports a local, 300-foot high, cone-shaped hill known as Black Peak, and extends vertically through the Navajo Sandstone and underlying sediments. Its shape and diameter seem to persist with depth. Surrounding the brecciated axis is a 10-foot vesiculated collar of indurated sandstone and a more extensive, somewhat irregularly shaped zone of hydrothermal alteration. The alteration aureole is elongated parallel to a north-south fracture system, which also controls the orientation of small monchiquite dikes. The pipe breccia consists of subangular to rounded fragments of sandstone, mudstone, shale, and altered monchiquite in a friable sandstone matrix. These breccia fragments range from one to several inches in diameter, though sporadic blocks measure 2 feet across. Alteration of Navajo Sandstone around the pipe grades from bleaching, argillization, cementation, and partial recrystallization near the vesicular collar, to the development of illite from kaolinite in marginal or lower-grade zones. Silica, carbonates, alunite, and minor amounts of iron, manganese, gold, and silver are associated with the pipe.

Striking evidence for a pressurized, pneumatolytic origin of the pipe lies in the presence of vesiculation and in the fact that the sand grains are encircled radially with acicular quartz crystals (rather than cryptocrystalline quartz in concentric layers); moreover, a liquid-solid (as opposed to a gas-solid) process should cause grading and only minor rounding of the breccia particles (Reynolds, 1954). Barrington and Kerr (1961) concluded that the breccia pipe was produced by the turbulent penetration of steam along a joint or joint intersection. They suggested that the brecciation and mixing resulted from a gas-solid fluidization system and that the lack of uranium and copper may be attributed to their solubilities rather than their absence from the gas. Theoretically, metallization would be expected to have occurred somewhere beyond (that is, above) the section of pipe exposed

FIGURE 4-9. *Tightly folded Metaline Limestone adjacent to a strong fault. Note the thickening of layers at the crest of the fold and the presence of fractures parallel to the axial plane. Natural size. (From Park and Cannon, 1943.)*

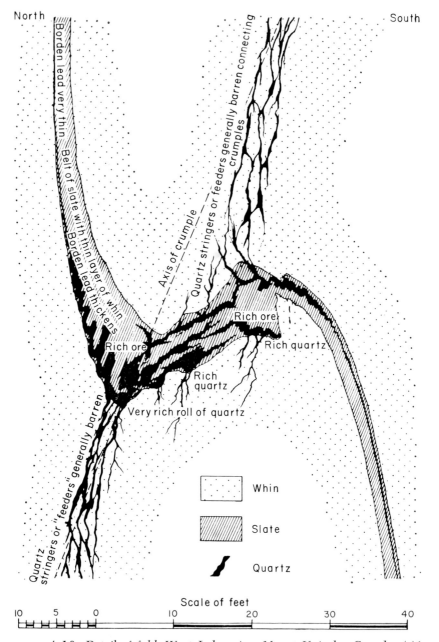

North

South

Borden lead very thin

Quartz stringers or feeders generally barren connecting crumples

Belt of slate with thin layer of whin

Axis of crumple

Quartz stringers of feeders generally barren

Borden lead thickens

Rich ore

Rich ore

Rich quartz

Rich quartz

Very rich roll of quartz

Quartz stringers or "feeders" generally barren

Whin

Slate

Quartz

Scale of feet

10   5   0   10   20   30   40

FIGURE 4-10. *Detail of fold, West Lake mine, Mount Uniacke, Canada. (After Faribault as quoted by Malcolm, 1912, figure 2.)*

at Black Peak. A single underlying body of cooling magma would account for the early monchiquite dikes and the later pipe-forming steam jet.

When a sequence of beds is folded, the beds tend to slide over one another, undergoing compression on the flanks and dilation along the crests, which represent regions of relative pressure release. Fractures develop parallel to the axial planes of the folds and are especially prominent in competent rocks along the crests of anticlines, though they are present to a lesser extent along the troughs of synclines (Fig. 4-9). The result of folding and its concomitant fracturing is the development of openings, or an increase in permeability, within the thickened beds at the crests of folds. As mineralizing fluids move along the permeable crests, they fill the openings and replace favorable rocks nearby. The resultant ore bodies are pipe-shaped, and where situated above one another, are called saddle reefs (Fig. 4-10). Excellent examples of saddle reefs are the well-known Bendigo gold field, Victoria, Australia (Fig. 4-11) and the gold measures of Nova Scotia (Fig. 4-12).

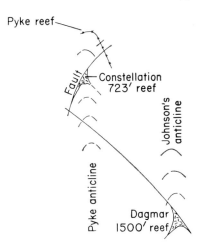

FIGURE 4-11. *Sketch of relation between two faults and the Pyke, Constellation, and Dagmar reefs, Bendigo goldfield, Australia. (After Stillwell, 1919, figure 6.)*

In the Piedmont region of the southeastern United States, many iron and gold deposits are rod-shaped bodies, the long axes of which range in attitude from nearly horizontal to nearly vertical. Some of the rods are as much as 100 feet in cross section and have been mined down the dip of their long axes for more than 1000 feet. Many, however, are small, especially in the gold-bearing areas. They may be no more than a few inches thick, but at Dahlonega, Georgia, they were so close together that the entire rock could be mined at the surface. These ore bodies are replacement saddle reefs formed at or near the crests of small, tight folds in schist (Fig. 4-13). Much money and effort have been expended in an attempt to find continuations of the individual rods at depth, owing to the erroneous assumption that these structures are veins.

Pipe-like ore bodies that resemble saddle reefs sometimes form where a fracture intersects a steeply dipping bed. The ore-bearing fluids migrate

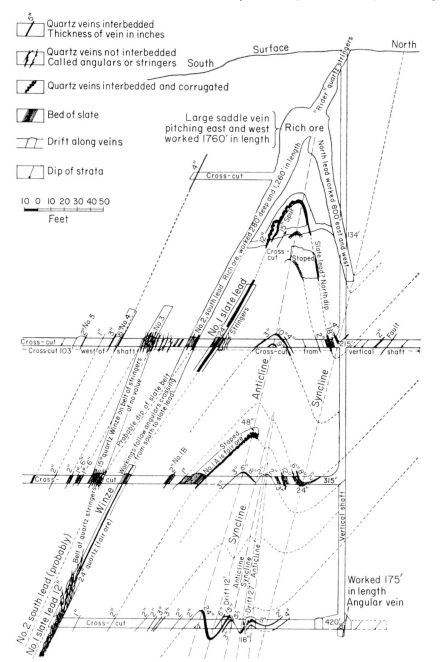

FIGURE 4-12. *Saddle reefs in the Dufferin mine, Salmon River gold district, Nova Scotia. (After Faribault as quoted by Malcolm, 1912, figure 9.)*

up the fault or up the bedding, or both, and the ore localizes along the footwall of the fault in permeable breccias or beneath impermeable strata. The shape of the deposits may suggest a folded structure, and for this reason they are known as *false saddle reefs* (Fig. 4-14).

Small amounts of ore are recovered from *ladder veins*, which, as their name implies, are veins arranged in step-like or ladder-like form. They are ordinarily confined to dikes or competent strata that lie within shales or other incompetent rocks (Grout, 1923). Movement within the shales is taken up by flowage or cumulative displacements along foliation planes, whereas the competent rock tends to fracture (Fig. 4-15). Moreover, ladder veins have been known to form where mineralizing solutions have invaded shrinkage joints in dikes, sills, and lava flows. As the igneous rock cools, it contracts, and cracks develop normal to the planar direction. The Morning Star gold mine at Wood's Point, Victoria, Australia, is a classic example of a ladder vein deposit (Threadgold, 1958). Gold-quartz veins fill a conjugate set of reverse faults developed across a 250-foot dike (Fig. 4-16).

Carbonate rocks below shales are favorable places to find ore, especially if faulting has taken place along the contact. Where a sequence of shales and carbonate rocks has been faulted or folded, the bedding slip is commonly taken up in the more mobile, fissile shales. The movement and drag are partly reflected in the limestones or dolomites, especially near the shale contact, increasing the permeability and permitting easier access of solutions.

EXAMPLES OF STRUCTURAL CONTROL

Structurally controlled ore deposits abound; examples are legion. Rather than superficially describe a group of such deposits, we prefer to give a relatively detailed treatment of three spectacular examples: the Trepça mine in Yugoslavia, the Tsumeb mine in South-West Africa, and the Rambler vein in the Slocan district of Canada.

Trepça Mine, Yugoslavia

The Trepça, or Stari Trg (for "Old Market Place"), lead-zinc deposit is in southern Serbia, Yugoslavia, slightly over 200 kilometers south of Belgrade (Fig. 4-17). The mine area has been studied by Forgan (1948), Schumacher (1950, 1954), and other geologists (Christie, 1950; Brammall, 1930).

Geologic formations consist of the Stari Trg Series, possibly of Ordovi-

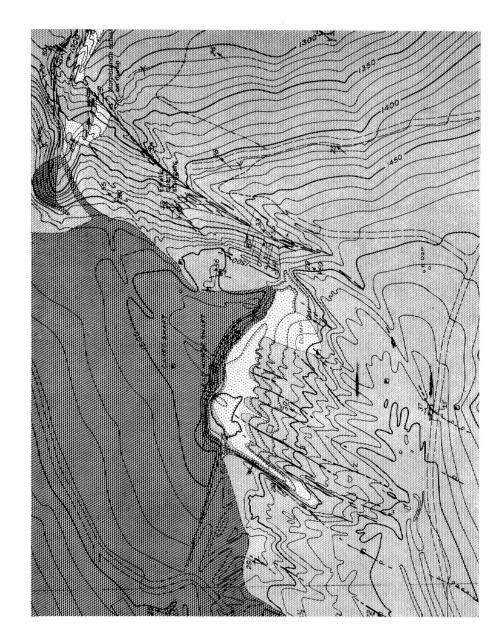

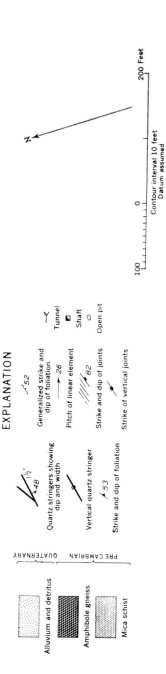

FIGURE 4-13. *Gold-quartz rods formed at the crests of small folds in schist, near Dahlonega, Georgia. (After Pardee and Park, 1948, plate 48.)*

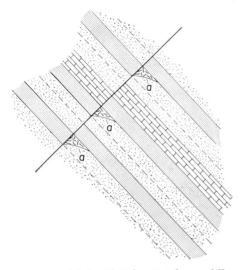

FIGURE 4-14. *Sketch of false saddle reefs.* (*a = ore.*)

cian-Silurian age, which forms a complex of schist, phyllite, quartzite, and marmorized limestone. Within this series is one fairly thick bed of pure, recrystallized limestone, called the Mazic Limestone, the principal mineralized stratum in the district. The Stari Trg Series is unconformably overlain and partly obscured by andesite flows and tuffs of Miocene(?) age and is also intruded by associated igneous rocks ranging from monzonite porphyry to hornblende andesite.

The older rocks of the region are sharply folded. An anticlinal structure, along which the mine is developed, plunges about 40°NW (Forgan, 1949). A nearly circular dacite and breccia pipe transects the Stari Trg-Mazic Limestone contact along the crest of the anticline. This pipe is a volcanic plug. At the surface and in the upper parts of the mine, the pipe contains a core of dacite surrounded by a mantle of breccia. The dacite decreases in amount with depth, and is absent in the lower levels of the mine. The breccia in the upper levels is composed of subangular fragments of the country rock and rounded fragments of dacite. In the deeper levels, even the groundmass of the breccia is composed of crushed sedimentary materials.

Ore distribution was controlled both by the structure, which directed the fluid flow, and by the character of the country rock, part of which was reactive to the ore-bearing solutions. The ores are concentrated in the Mazic Limestone around the breccia pipe and along the limestone-schist contact; away from the pipe, the ore gradually thins. The intrusion and the breccia pipe modified the limestone-schist contact, so that in plan the upper contact of the limestone, against the schist and breccia, is M-shaped, with the pipe representing the upper re-entrant of the letter (Fig. 4-18). The two top points of the M are the most favorable loci for ore, though mineralization does spread laterally in the limestone just below. Within the points of the M, the limestone is completely replaced by ore, from pipe to schist. The ore bodies themselves are pipe-shaped and plunge northwest, following the breccia pipe (Fig. 4-19).

All significant deformation took place before the ore was deposited, as shown by the relationships between the ore bodies and the breccia pipe, and by the mineralization of the drag folds along the limestone-schist contact. The dacite was intruded along a zone of pressure relief, and the jacket of breccia was apparently formed by subsequent explosive activity; thus it is a diatreme breccia. Ore deposition followed consolidation of the pipe, as a late phase of the same igneous activity; hence mineralization took place in the favorable structures defined by the breccia and the schist-limestone contact (Forgan, 1948). The limestone reacted with the ore-bearing solutions and consequently was replaced in preference to the schist, breccia, and dacite.

The ore is a massive, coarse-grained sulfide mixture of silver-bearing galena, high-iron sphalerite (12–13% Fe), pyrite, and pyrrhotite, with minor amounts of arsenopyrite, jamesonite ($Pb_4FeSb_6S_{14}$), boulangerite ($Pb_5Sb_4S_{11}$), bournonite ($PbCuSbS_3$), and chalcopyrite. The galena contains recoverable bismuth in addition to the silver. Gangue minerals are minor in most of the ore body; they consist of quartz and the carbonates—calcite, rhodochrosite, siderite, manganosiderite, and dolomite. A skarn type of mineralization is found in parts of the mine, and appears to increase with depth. The minerals of the skarn are principally actinolite, hedenbergite, ilvaite [$CaFe_2(FeOH)(SiO_4)_2$], garnet, and magnetite. Gypsum and a little vivianite are found in cavities along with jamesonite.

According to both Forgan (1948) and

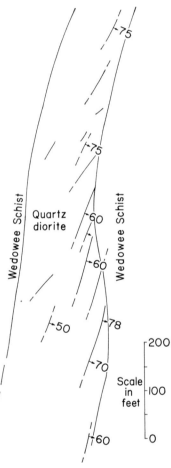

FIGURE 4-15. *Ladder veins in dike. Dutch Bend mine, Alabama. (After Pardee and Park, 1948.)*

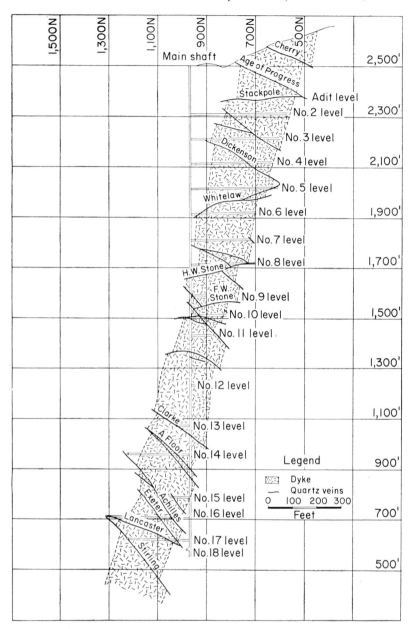

FIGURE 4-16. *Cross section through the main shaft, Morning Star dike, Australia. Fissures are mineralized. (After Clappison, 1953. figure 3.)*

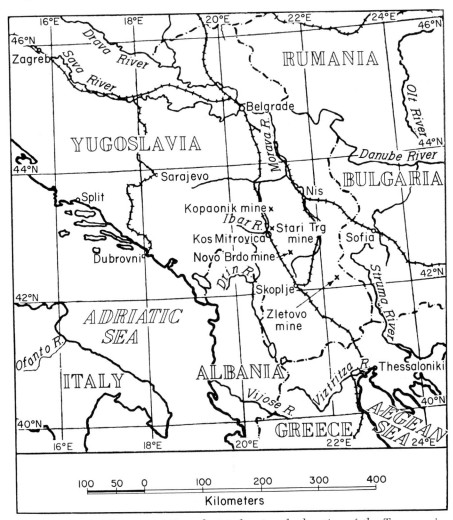

FIGURE 4-17. *Index map of Yugoslavia, showing the location of the Trepça mining district.*

Schumacher (1950, 1954), the mineralization changes with depth. Galena remains fairly constant, but sphalerite is relatively more abundant in the upper levels than in the deeper workings, and becomes progressively more abundant away from the breccia pipe. Both silver and bismuth show a steady increase with depth. Pyrite and pyrrhotite are present in nearly equal proportions in the upper levels, but at depth the pyrrhotite predominates, especially near the borders of the pipe. Jamesonite is largely confined to the upper levels. Rhodochrosite also decreases in depth, but quartz increases.

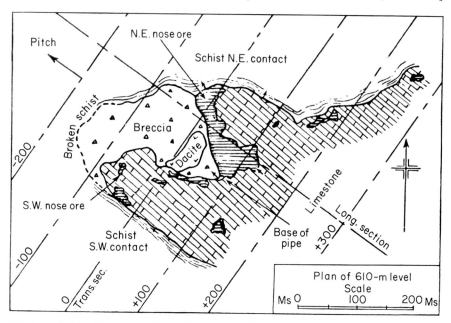

FIGURE 4-18. *Trepça, or Stari Trg, mine, Yugoslavia. Plan of 610-meter level.* (*After Forgan, 1950.*)

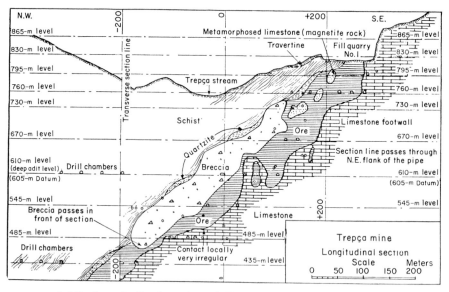

FIGURE 4-19. *Longitudinal section of Trepça, or Stari Trg, mine, Yugoslavia.* (*After Forgan, 1950.*)

Skarn is restricted in the upper workings to the contact between limestone and dacite or breccia, but lower in the mine, it is intimately mixed with the ore. The textures are coarse in the upper levels and finer-grained below. Along the flanks of the structure, however, the ore at depth is not greatly different from the ore in the upper levels.

These changes in mineralization, following a pattern symmetrical to the breccia pipe, are significant to the history of ore deposition. The mineralizing solutions evidently ascended along the breccia pipe, gradually changing in composition with time and with distance away from the pipe. The deep, near-pipe minerals, such as pyrrhotite and quartz, were deposited early, before the ascending solutions reached the upper levels; the later, or relatively spent, solutions produced sphalerite, jamesonite, and rhodochrosite. The different mineral assemblages probably reflect changing conditions, from availability of metal ions in time to a drop in temperature and pressure, a change in pH, or a relative increase in the partial pressure of sulfur. Such progressions in ore deposition are common, but Trepça is of special interest because some of the changes are unusual. In most lead-zinc deposits the Zn:Pb ratio increases with depth; at Trepça it decreases, yet the pyrrhotite-pyrite relationship is normal. Probably the most anomalous feature is the restriction of dacite to the upper parts of the breccia pipe; igneous intrusives are normally thought to originate at depth, but there is no sign of dacite low in the Trepça pipe.

Mining at Trepça is difficult, because the limestone is highly fractured and contains much water. Ore is approached through inclines in the comparatively impermeable schist. All development in the water-saturated rocks is done behind the protection of isolating concrete dams. According to Christie (1950), the lower levels are intensely hot and uncomfortable. Visible ore reserves in 1950 were said to aggregate between 3 and 4 million tons, with a grade of about 6.9 percent lead, 4.2 percent zinc, and 3.8 ounces of silver per ton. Possible reserves amounted to about 10 million tons.

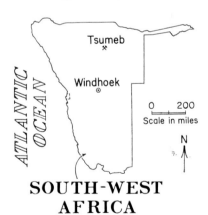

SOUTH-WEST AFRICA

Tsumeb Mine, South-West Africa

Another classic example of an ore pipe

FIGURE 4-20. *Index map of South-West Africa, showing the location of the Tsumeb mine.*

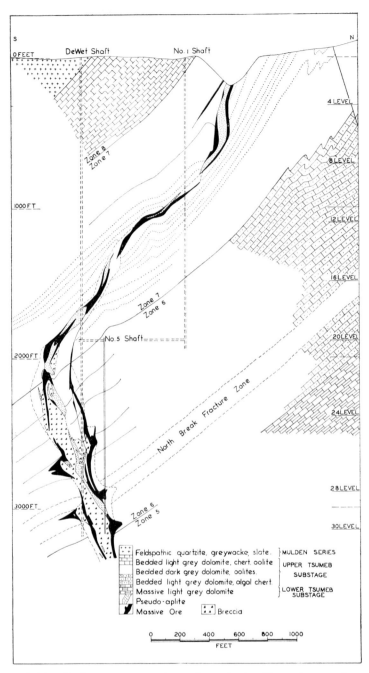

FIGURE 4-21. *Geologic cross sections through the Tsumeb ore pipe. Above: North-South. Right: East-west. (After Tsumeb Corporation Staff, 1961, figures 3 and 4.)*

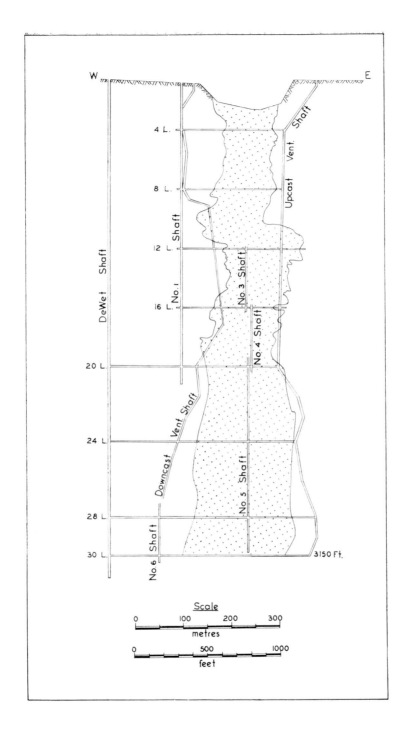

W   E

4 L.

8 L.

12 L.

16 L.

20 L.

24 L.

28 L.

30 L.

DeWet Shaft

No. 1 L. Shaft

Vent. Shaft

Upcast Vent. Shaft

No. 3 Shaft

No. 4 Shaft

No. 5 Shaft

Downcast Vent Shaft

No. 6 Shaft

3150 Ft.

Scale

0   100   200   300

metres

0   500   1000

feet

is the Tsumeb deposit, recently described by Söhnge (1963) and the staff
of the Tsumeb Corporation (1961). The Tsumeb mine is in northern South-
West Africa, 235 miles north of Windhoek, the capital (Fig. 4-20). Precambrian sediments of the Otavi Highland overlie older metamorphic and
igneous rocks in the Tsumeb area. Mineralization is confined to a dolomite
sequence known as the Tsumeb Stage of the Otavi Formation. This Upper
Precambrian dolomite is a fine-grained, compact rock containing shale lenses,
chert nodules, stromatolites, limestone beds, and oölitic zones. The sediments
were folded into open synclines and anticlines and subsequently intruded
by dikes, sills, and pipes of diabase, kersantite, and a rock known locally as
pseudoaplite. Both the kersantite and the diabase are post-ore intrusives,

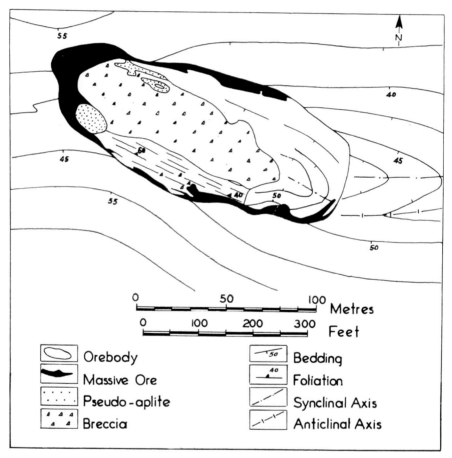

FIGURE 4-22. *Geologic plan of the Tsumeb pipe, 26th level.* (*From Tsumeb
Corporation Staff, 1961, figure 5.*)

but the pseudoaplite was emplaced before the ore-bearing fluids ascended along the pipe (Schneiderhöhn, 1929, 1931, 1941; Söhnge, 1952, 1963).

The mine is developed along a pseudoaplite pipe that cuts the north limb of a syncline. Petrographically, the pseudoaplite resembles a feldspathic quartzite, because it consists of rounded and crushed grains of quartz, microcline, and sodic plagioclase. There is no thermal metamorphism associated with the pseudoaplite, but it is definitely intrusive (Söhnge, 1952, 1963).

Tsumeb produces lead, zinc, and copper, with accessory germanium, silver, and cadmium, from ore containing such primary minerals as galena, sphalerite, tennantite, chalcocite, bornite, digenite, and enargite, plus subordinate pyrite, chalcopyrite, germanite [$Cu_3(Fe,Ge,Zn,Ga)(S,As)_4$], reniérite [$(Cu,Fe)_3(Fe,Ge,Zn,Sn)(S,As)_4$], molybdenite, wurtzite, luzonite (Cu_3AsS_4), greenockite (CdS), and stromeyerite. Numerous products of oxidation are also found in the mine, including many rare mineral species (Sclar and Geier, 1957; Moritz, 1933).

Figures 4-21, 4-22, and 4-23 show the configuration of the ore pipe. It is an elliptical structure that pinches and swells irregularly and is continuous from the surface to a depth of at least 4000 feet. Along constrictions it consists of a sparse network of thin veins, but it widens abruptly into plan sections of over 10,000 square feet. At its widest section, on the 2390-foot level, the major and minor axes measure 600 feet and 250 feet, respectively (Söhnge, 1952).

The pipe was developed by fracturing, brecciation, and intrusion of pseudoaplite. Brecciation was restricted to the deeper levels, especially where the pipe cuts the axis of a fold. Reverse faulting along the bedding planes, which dip about 45° to the south, caused drag folding, local thrusts across bedding, and brecciation. The pipe is nearly vertical above the 700-foot level and below 2000 feet, but the intervening section follows a zone of concentrated bedding-plane faults, forming a relatively constricted pipe that plunges about 50° south. The sausage-like intrusive of pseudoaplite was injected after the folding, faulting, and brecciation had taken place. It is centrally located in the upper portion of the pipe, but branches and lenses irregularly through the breccia (Tsumeb Corporation Staff, 1961).

The origin of pseudoaplite and its associated ore minerals has been a long-standing enigma. Söhnge (1963) points out that it is neither a simple igneous dike nor a simple clastic dike—it seems to be a blend of the two. One possibility is that the materials were mobilized by deep-seated palingenesis and the escape of volatiles along a previously formed fracture zone.

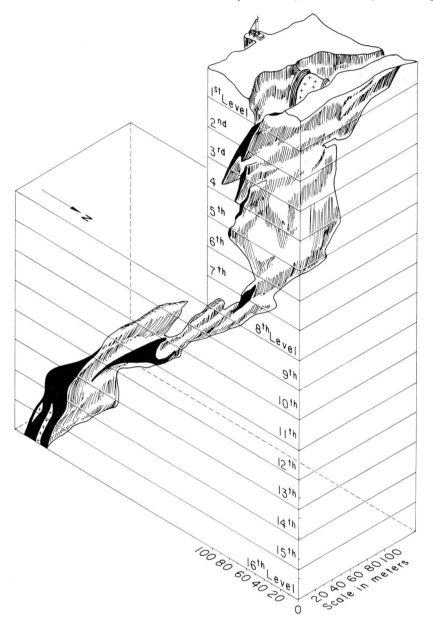

FIGURE 4-23. *Isometric drawing of the Tsumeb ore body. (After Schneiderhöhn, 1929, figure 9.)*

Thus clastic grains from lower formations would be partly dissolved and partly lifted (fluidized) from their original positions. A second hypothesis attributes the pseudoaplite and ores to the intrusion of a highly volatile magmatic fraction of the Karroo intrusives—cogenetic with carbonatites reported in the region, and carrying clastic fragments of quartzite derived from below.

Metallization follows the periphery of the pipe, at places forming rich pods and vein-like masses as well as large tonnages of disseminated, low-grade ore. The main ore pipe is a horseshoe-shaped complex of veins with massive ore and intervening low-grade disseminations. High-grade mantos were developed where the pipe intersects breccia zones along bedding slippages; these mantos project as much as 300 feet both north and south of the pipe. The pipe is widest where it crosses the bedding; narrowest where it parallels the bedding (see Fig. 4-21).

Individual masses or shoots of ore vary in their ratios of lead, copper, and zinc, but in general, lead is the most abundant metal. Massive sulfide bodies contain up to 60 percent in metals. One large sulfide mass contained 26.7 percent lead, 12.4 percent zinc, and 3.6 percent copper; and high-grade copper ores have produced as much as 23 percent copper. The disseminated ores occur as stockworks (networks of fissures) in dolomite and breccia and as interstitial specks and veinlets in the pseudoaplite. All rock containing over 3.5 percent metals is considered ore by the Tsumeb Corporation.

Gangue minerals and wall-rock alteration products are not widespread. Where gangue is found, it consists of quartz, calcite, and dolomite. The wall rock is partially bleached and altered to calcite within the ore pipe, and the pseudoaplite is sericitized.

In spite of the fact that minor amounts of sulfides occur even at the surface, oxidation has affected the Tsumeb ores to great depths. Supergene minerals predominate above about 1200 feet. Between about 1200 and 2500 feet below the surface, the oxidation products diminish strikingly, but the lowest portions of the pipe are thoroughly oxidized. This deep-seated oxidation zone is located along a permeable horizon in the Tsumeb dolomites, where ground waters migrating along bedding planes and brecciated strata attacked the sulfides even more efficiently than the near-surface waters. Supergene enrichment increased the copper values along upper portions of the pipe, though zinc was concomitantly leached and removed.

Since the first shipments in 1907, Tsumeb has produced over 2 million tons of metal, half or more being lead. These metals were recovered from some 7 million tons of ore, averaging 15.1 percent lead, 7.0 percent zinc,

FIGURE 4-24. *Index map of British Columbia, showing the location of the Slocan district.*

and 5.9 percent copper. In other words, the ore thus far produced has averaged 28 percent in metals, or eight times the established cut-off percentage—an enviable margin of profit.

Rambler Mine, British Columbia

Structural control of ore deposition along a fault is well exemplified by the Rambler vein in the Slocan district of southeastern British Columbia (Fig. 4-24). The many ore deposits in the Slocan district are nearly all structurally controlled (Cairnes, 1934, 1935, 1948; Ambrose, 1957). The ore-bearing structures include fissures through competent rocks, directional changes along faults, brecciation against dike contacts, and intersections of fissures; but for the sake of simplicity, only the Rambler vein—a combination of the first two types—will be described.

The Rambler ore bodies are shoots in a complex vein that was emplaced along a normal, oblique-slip fault with 40–100 feet of displacement (Roscoe, 1951). Argillaceous sedimentary rocks of the Slocan Series and granodiorite porphyry sills and dikes are the only rock units near the Rambler mine. The Slocan Series is thought to be Triassic; the granodiorite was intruded during the Late Cretaceous (Cairnes, 1934). Ore-bearing solutions probably ascended from the Nelson batholith, which is exposed to the south and presumably underlies the mineralized areas.

The Rambler fault cuts the sediments and intrusives at a large angle. It varies in strike and dip, and where it swings to the east, or steepens, it has formed openings. The vein is thickest along these changes in attitude and narrowest where the fault turns westward, or flattens.

The Rambler ore bodies are composite veins of massive sulfides, small sulfide veinlets, and disseminated sulfides in altered wall rock within the fault zone. The veins, which consist of galena, sphalerite, and pyrite in a subordinate gangue of quartz and siderite, range in thickness from a few inches to several feet. The most dilatant zones reach 20 feet in thickness along major shoots. Argentiferous tetrahedrite and pyrargyrite accompany the galena in significant amounts, and recoverable quantities of silver are found in some of the sphalerite and pyrite; thus silver is a major product of the mine.

Roscoe (1951) studied the details of ore distribution along the Rambler fault. He was able to show that the fault plane was refracted where it crossed contacts between sediments and granodiorite. Wherever the attitude of the granodiorite-Slocan Series contact was favorably oriented with respect to the attitude of the fault, an opening (or low pressure area) formed along the fault surface. It was along such openings that mineralization took place. This interpretation is strongly supported by the fact that ore bodies are restricted to a region of dike swarms and are not found where the fault passes through massive granodiorite or thick, uniform sediments; moreover, the fault is planar except where it passes through the dike swarm.

By constructing dilation maps of the vein, Roscoe demonstrated that as the fault displacement increased, there was a progressive widening along the central portion of the ore shoots. Furthermore, the mineralization was contemporaneous with faulting and spread outward from the central part of dilatant zones. Recurrent displacements of small magnitude along the Rambler fault were accompanied by deposition of pyrite, sphalerite, and galena, in successive stages. Pyrite was the first mineral to be deposited. As dilation along the ore shoot continued, sphalerite moved into the central zone, replacing the pyrite, which was forced to migrate to the fringes. Subsequent movements allowed the galena and silver minerals to take over the central portion while both pyrite and sphalerite were forced to spread outward. The structural and paragenetic sequences are clear; the ore shoots grew in size and developed progressive zones of mineralization as faulting created an expanding area of pressure release. As a result, the ore shoots are disk-shaped bodies of composite veins located where the Rambler fault is favorably deflected across contacts between competent and incompetent rocks (Fig. 4-25). The outside, tapered edge of each disk is predominantly pyrite, and the central portion is chiefly sphalerite and galena. Where a dilatant area opened rapidly during the initial stages of faulting and then developed only slight widening during later movements, the shoot is predominantly pyrite with a little sphalerite in the core. Conversely, shoots that dilated during the late stages of faulting contain a high ratio of galena to sphalerite and pyrite. Thus the configuration and mineral composition of Rambler ore bodies are strictly dependent upon structural events and are not functions of the wall-rock chemistry.

The Rambler mine has been productive since 1895, though it was shut

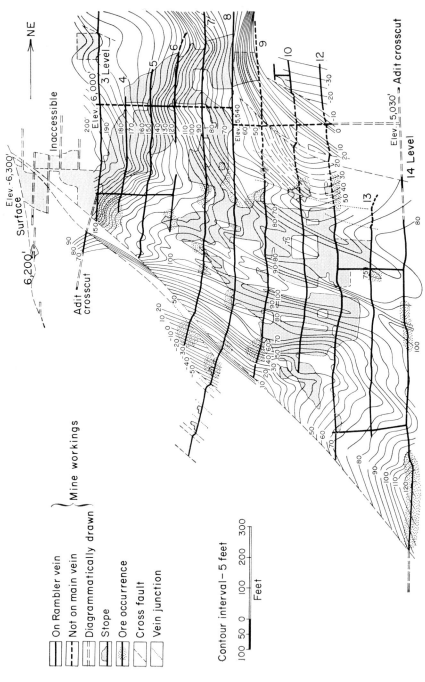

FIGURE 4-25. *Ore shoot along the Rambler fault, Slocan district, British Columbia. (After Roscoe, 1951.)*

down between 1926 and 1947. Roscoe states that the average metal content of the ore mined has been about 25 ounces of silver per ton, $7\frac{1}{2}$ percent lead, and $5\frac{1}{2}$ percent zinc.

Chemical Controls of Ore Deposition

The simple existence of a favorable structural environment, and even the presence in this structure of the ore-bearing fluids, does not necessarily mean that ore will be deposited. Ore-bearing fluids react continuously with the wall rocks, and they are constantly changing in character as well as changing the character of the material they traverse. Moreover, factors such as reductions in temperature and pressure may bring about chemical reactions or decrease solubilities and contribute to the deposition of ore minerals. In many places geologists are unable to explain why certain beds are mineralized and other beds, both above and below the ore horizon, are barren. These barren beds may have compositions and physical characteristics identical with the mineralized strata. Even though we do not understand everything about chemical controls, we can often demonstrate the existence of such controls. For example, Fig. 4-26 shows a polished slab of diabase cut by a veinlet of calcite and native silver. The silver in the veinlet is restricted almost entirely to the area occupied by a large feldspar crystal, but calcite fills the veinlet where it passes through diabase. Note that the width of the veinlet is about constant across the specimen. The silver is thought to have been deposited as a result of chemical reaction between the silver-bearing fluid and the large feldspar crystal, rather than from physical differences between the feldspar and the diabase. Here the fracture served as a permeable channel that permitted introduction of the fluid to the proper environment, and deposition resulted only along the chemically receptive portion of the vein.

Much of the ground preparation that takes place prior to the introduction and deposition of ores is really chemical. Silicification, dolomitization, and recrystallization are all chemical processes, and even much of the brecciated ground was made brittle by chemical reaction with earlier solutions.

One explanation advanced for the common localization of ores in carbonate rocks beneath relatively impermeable covers is that ascending ore-bearing fluids are impounded and forced to move laterally in the more permeable carbonate rocks. Since carbonates are permeable and are chemically favorable host rocks, the additional migration through them that results from forced lateral movement allows ample contact for chemical reaction

A

FIGURE 4-26(A) *Specimen of native silver in a veinlet of calcite from Cobalt, Ontario, Canada. The silver is restricted to a large feldspar crystal, and the calcite is in diabase. Note that the width of the veinlet is nearly constant across the specimen.*

(B) *Facing page. Sketch of the specimen shown in (A).*

to take place, which results in the precipitation of ore minerals. Carbonates are termed chemically reactive rocks because they break down readily in the presence of acids and because they are relatively soluble in water. Just as limestones are preferentially dissolved in humid climates, so they are selectively replaced by mineralizing solutions.

The effects of temperature and pressure are important in the deposition of ores. The solubilities of many substances increase in direct proportion to the temperature of the solution. As a result, cooling solutions will precipitate any materials whose saturation values have been exceeded, and it is very probable that some ore-bearing fluids travel away from the source and de-

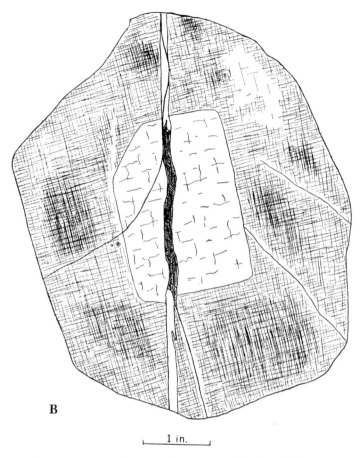

B

1 in.

posit the metals as soon as they reach a zone of reduced temperature, regardless of the type of host rock. A reduction in pressure may have a similar
effect. An ore-bearing fluid that is flushed into a brecciated zone may deposit its load as a result of the room for expansion and resultant loss in
pressure. Pressure losses would be especially effective in a supercritical
fluid, because the dissolving power of this phase is directly proportional to
the molecular density, which in turn is a function of pressure; as the pressure drops, the molecules become less densely packed, and any dissolved
matter previously at the saturation point will be precipitated. It has even
been suggested that ore deposition may take place along constrictions in
channelways, because where the fissures narrow down, the velocity of passing solutions will increase, and consequently the pressure will decrease, in
accordance with the Bernoulli principle (Bain, 1936). Furthermore, the

solubility of an ore mineral may be dependent upon the concentration of dissolved volatiles, such as H_2S or CO_2; hence a reduction in pressure will allow these gases to leave the solution, causing a concomitant precipitation of the ore minerals. The importance of such a mechanism is debatable, but it is probably operative in open-fissure deposits. Solutions ascending through veins will naturally undergo a drop in pressure, and the deposition of ores may be dependent upon such a factor.

The stability of a solution may be determined by the conditions of pH and the oxidation potential of the environment, changes in which could cause precipitation of the dissolved materials. The oxidation potential is a measure of the energy involved in the addition or removal of electrons during the change of elements to various valence states. The ability of an environment to supply or accept electrons will determine the valence state of any ions present, and the valence state may in turn determine whether the ion can remain in solution. For example, iron in simple solution is quite soluble in the ferrous state and nearly insoluble (except at low pH) when oxidized to the ferric state. Accordingly, the oxidation potential of the environment might determine whether iron will go into solution or be deposited in a given area. The energy required to oxidize or reduce an element is modified by the pH, thus both the oxidation potential and the pH determine whether an ion will remain in solution, and a change in either may cause precipitation. The significance of these factors to hydrothermal solutions is presently unknown, but calculations and laboratory experiments suggest that they are important. However, the control of oxidation potential and pH over the deposition of sedimentary ores or the modification of mineral deposits by weathering processes may be predicted with confidence. Such predictions have tremendous economic value because they allow us to establish the most favorable environments of deposition for certain metals, such as iron and manganese.

Sales and Meyer (1949) pointed out a significant relationship concerning the concentration of sulfur in a mineral vein. They found that the composition of the ore at Butte, Montana, is directly related to the ratio between sulfur and sulfide-forming metal ions in the original fluids. Apparently, a high sulfur ratio favored the stability of simple copper and iron sulfides (chalcocite, covellite, and pyrite), whereas lower ratios favored the combined copper-iron sulfides (bornite and chalcopyrite). Sulfur combined with wall-rock iron to form pyrite, hence the ratio of sulfur to sulfide-forming metal ions in the vein solutions gradually decreased as the solutions moved away from the source of supply. Yet at any single reference point along a vein, the sulfur ratio increased with time, because the entire system of ore solutions was expanding outward. That is, the outermost minerals to form at any given time would be the copper-iron sulfides, because of the low sulfur ratio, but subsequent sulfides deposited at the same location might be the simple sulfides, because the zone high in sulfur would be expanding outward from the source area. Certainly in many sulfide deposits the abundance of sulfur in the ore-bearing fluids is a principal factor in controlling the character of mineralization.

Mineral solubilities and the affinities of metallic elements for sulfur are of considerable interest in the study of ore deposition (Kolthoff and Sandell, 1952). Considerable experimental work has been done on metal-sulfur complexes in an attempt to help explain both transportation and deposition of the metallic minerals (see Chapter 2). Experimental evidence so far obtained indicates that such complexes play a leading part in ore genesis (Barnes, 1962; Hemley, 1953; Treadwell and Hepenstrick, 1949; Treadwell and Schaufelberger, 1946). One aspect favoring the theory that ores are transported in the form of complexes is that the mineral composition of a given deposit will be independent of the complex in solution; thus more than one mineral can be deposited from a single complex. Moreover, the solubilities of heavy metals will change markedly in response to relatively small changes in composition of the solutions, hence a solution that passes through a fissure may deposit the metals along a restricted portion of the vein where contamination by wall rocks has modified the solutions significantly, and the gangue minerals will tend to persist beyond these limits (Barton, 1959).

It is impossible to consider the very large, massive pyrite-chalcopyrite deposits at Ducktown, Tennessee, at Yanahara, Japan, or at Rio Tinto, Spain, without attributing a significant role in their formation to the presence of large amounts of sulfur. Many volcanic areas contain abundant sulfur, which (at least near the surface) is thought to have been transported in the gaseous state and to have been deposited either directly as a sublimate or through reaction with wall rocks. An example of sulfur that was probably deposited by solfataric activity is the Matsuo deposit in central Honshu, Japan, where a bleached, gypsiferous tuff within a large crater is estimated to contain a minimum of 160 million tons of ore with an average content of about 35 percent sulfur (Fig. 4-27). An estimate of 50 million tons of native sulfur is reasonable; this is in addition to large amounts of sulfur tied up in the tremendous quantities of gypsum and in finely divided pyrite, plus small amounts of arsenic, bismuth, and antimony sulfides that are

FIGURE 4-27. *Gypsiferous tuff, Matsuo mine, Japan. (Courtesy of the Matsuo Company.)*

widely distributed in the ore. The ratio of pyrite to native sulfur is approximately 1:2. If the original tuff at Matsuo had been rich in iron, large bodies of massive pyrite would probably have been formed in place of the native sulfur (Fujita, 1954).

At another Japanese locality, the Siretoko-Iosan volcano in Hokkaido, direct observations were made on the deposition of native sulfur by volcanic or solfataric activity (Watanabe, 1940). Molten sulfur was ejected intermittently from a small geyser-steam vent. The sulfur flowed down a valley for nearly a mile, reaching thicknesses of more than 16 feet and widths of 65–85 feet (Fig. 4-28). The associated water was very acidic, owing to the presence of sulfuric acid. Much of the water, however, was meteoric, and probably leached the sulfur from previously deposited materials in the underlying volcanic agglomerate. That is, the original magmatic fluids may have supplied sulfur in the form of H_2S, the eruptions of native sulfur being second-cycle products after remobilization. A seasonal and hourly periodicity, reflecting recharge of water, supports this hypothesis.

Certain ore deposits of near-surface or sedimentary origin have been attributed to the action of anaerobic bacteria or other organic processes. Some bacteria reduce the sulfur in sulfates, producing H_2S, which in turn may combine with any metals present in the solution to form metal sulfides. Other bacteria actually store sulfur granules within their cells, possibly forming native sulfur deposits or combining with metal ions upon decomposition of the organisms. Oxides or hydroxides of the metals—especially iron and manganese—may be deposited directly as a result of the life processes of certain bacteria, the oxidation of these metals supplying energy to the organism for the assimilation of food; other bacteria release oxidized metals from organic compounds used for food or simply accumulate the metals mechanically against their mucilaginous sheaths. The importance of these processes to the genesis of ore deposits is extremely debatable, and has been a topic of controversy in the literature (Harder, 1919; Schouten, 1946; Schneiderhöhn, 1923). Many large and important ore deposits have been considered products of bacterial activities, but for most of these a hydrothermal origin cannot be disproved. If the metals were deposited by bacteria at the bottom of stagnant seas—similar to the present Black Sea—they should have been precipitated as simple minerals in an intimately mixed or rhythmic sequence; no such sulfide deposits are known (Edwards, 1956). Nevertheless, the ability of bacteria to precipitate metal compounds cannot be denied; this mechanism is certainly operative under special con-

FIGURE 4-28. *Valley filled with native sulfur from the Siretoko-Iosan volcano, Hokkaido, Japan. (From Watanabe, 1940.)*

ditions, such as those that obtain in bog iron environments. Recently, Jensen (1958) suggested that sandstone-type uranium ores owe their precipitation to the reducing action of H_2S generated earlier from sulfates by anaerobic bacteria. Long after the H_2S was produced, according to this hypothesis, uranium-bearing solutions migrating through the sediments encountered the gas, which reduced the uranium from the soluble hexavalent form (UO_4^{-2}) to the relatively insoluble, tetravalent UO_2. Accompanying iron and copper ions were deposited as sulfides.

Decaying organic matter in general has been known to precipitate certain metals in concentrations of economic value. Petrified logs and dinosaur bones with extremely high uranium contents are occasionally found, and coal or carbonaceous material concentrates such elements as uranium, vanadium, molybdenum, germanium, nickel, titanium, gold, silver, lead, and zinc. Lignites or black shales may contain anomalous concentrations of any of these metals. Some organic matter acts as a reducing agent or supplies sulfide ions, causing the metals to become insoluble. Living organisms also concentrate certain metals, which are essential requirements of some plants and animals but are merely incidental requirements of others. For most life forms, the mechanism of enrichment remains a mystery (Krauskopf, 1955).

A simple control that may be significant in the deposition of ores at shallow depths is the precipitation of solids from hydrothermal solutions where they encounter connate waters or ground waters. Such interstitial waters are generally brackish and may contain large quantities of sulfate ions. Upon merging with these solutions, metal ions might be precipitated as sulfides or sulfates, depending upon the prevailing conditions of pH and oxidation potential. Ransome (1909) suggested that the bonanza gold ores at Goldfield, Nevada, were deposited where ascending ore-bearing solutions encountered descending sulfate waters, and he emphasized the widespread development of alunite with the ores as evidence for this mechanism. Similarly, any colloid could be forced to flocculate by the ground waters, which may contain strong electrolytes.

AN EXAMPLE OF CHEMICAL CONTROL

The limestone replacement deposits of lead-zinc in the Pioche district, Lincoln County, Nevada (Fig. 4-29), offer a good example of a chemically controlled zone of deposition. Since operation began in 1869 (Westgate and Knopf, 1932), the district has produced about $100 million worth of ore. The principal ore deposits are in the Pioche Hills, a northwesterly strik-

ing range, but related ore has
been recovered from small mines
scattered along the length of the
Highland-Bristol Range to the
west, which extends for 15–20
miles in a north-south direction.
Lower and Middle Cambrian
rocks make up the bulk of the
stratigraphic section within the
mountain ranges, though Tertiary lava flows and tuffs cover
large areas on all sides of the
district. The Cambrian sequence
grades from clastics at the bottom to carbonates at the top. A
quartz monzonite stock of probable Tertiary age intrudes the
Highland-Bristol Range along its
west-central edge, and numerous
granite porphyry and diabase
dikes are found near the mining
areas.

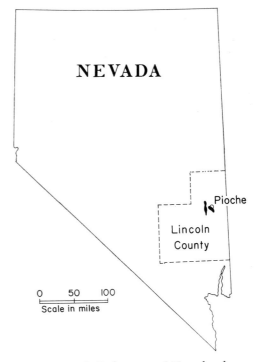

FIGURE 4-29. *Index map of Nevada, showing the location of the Pioche district.*

The mountain ranges are typi-
cal basin-range structures and are thoroughly broken by normal faulting
(see Fig. 4-30). The ore-bearing solutions ascended along these faults; in
fact most of the high-grade ore mined in the early days came from structurally controlled fissure veins in Lower Cambrian quartzites. Where the mineralizing fluids passed through the quartzites and into the overlying
carbonate rocks, deposition was by replacement, generally in the first limestone intersected. Nearly all production since 1924 has come from deposits
in these limestone beds.

The principal ore-bearing beds in the district are within the Pioche Shale,
of Lower to Middle Cambrian age. This formation contains several thin
limestone beds that have undergone selective replacement by ore minerals.
Carbonate formations overlying the Pioche Shale were also mineralized, but
the limestone beds within the shale were the first carbonates met by ascending solutions and were accordingly the most highly mineralized.

The importance of reactive limestone to ore-bearing solutions is strikingly
shown by the concentration of ores within the Pioche Shale. The lowermost
bed of limestone, known locally as the Combined Metals, or C.M., Lime-

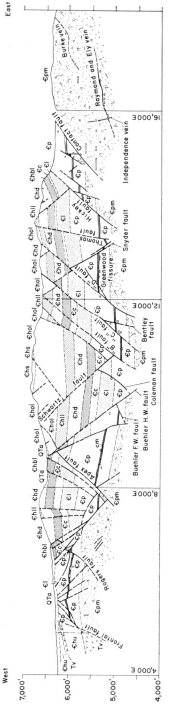

FIGURE 4-30. *East-west cross section through the Pioche Hills, Nevada. €pm = Prospect Mountain Quartzite; €p = Pioche Shale, which includes the C. M. Limestone member (cm), €l = Lyndon Limestone; €c = Chisholm shale; €hbl, €hd, €hll, €hol, and €hs are oldest to youngest members of Highland Peak Limestone (€hu) mapped in this section; Tv = Tertiary volcanic rocks; QTa = Tertiary and Quarternary clastics. (After Park, Gemmill, and Tschanz, 1958.)*

stone, has produced more than 90 percent of the replacement ores in the Pioche Hills and is also an important ore producer elsewhere. This limestone stratum is as much as 50 feet thick; the lower half contains most of the ore, but in places the whole bed is replaced by sulfides. Numerous replacement ore bodies are localized along fractures that acted as channels for the ore-bearing solutions. Elongate, "bedded" ore bodies, which reach widths of 400 feet, persist along single fractures as much as 2 miles long, though the C.M. bed (and hence the ore zone) is offset at many places along this distance by pre-ore cross-faults (Young, 1948).

The "bedded" ore bodies, or mantos, consist of an intimate mixture of pyrite, argentiferous galena, and sphalerite. Near the edges of the ore bodies manganosiderite is abundantly developed, suggesting that manganese traveled farther from the source before being deposited; similarly, manganese concentrations have been mined from some of the zones above the Pioche Shale.

At the Bristol mine, 14 miles northwest of Pioche, most of the ore bodies are in limestones and dolomites above the Pioche Shale; nevertheless, drilling has shown that the C.M. Limestone is mineralized with lead and zinc at depth, emphasizing the fact that this bed is exceptionally receptive to ore deposition wherever it is cut by the fissures that supplied metal-bearing fluids. In fact, the limestone beds within the Pioche Shale contain replacement deposits of lead-zinc in other Nevada mining districts, such as the Groom district, located nearly 100 miles southwest of Pioche (Humphrey, 1945). The fluorite-tungsten-beryllium deposits in the Snake Range, about 75 miles to the north, are also in the same lithologic and stratigraphic position (Whitebread and Lee, 1961).

Where the ore-bearing solutions were confined to quartzite, they deposited their metals in veins. But where these fluids were able to ascend beyond the quartzite without depositing their metals, they encountered beds of limestone in the overlying Pioche Shale and younger formations. The carbonates were more porous than the shale, allowing the solutions to move laterally; and even more important, they were reactive to the ore fluids, causing them to deposit their contained metals. If the localization of ore were primarily a direct function of the high permeability in limestone, mineralization would ordinarily be concentrated along the upper half of the C.M. bed, rather than along its lower half. But the influence of structure should not be minimized; the ore-bearing fluids ascended along structures, forming the ore bodies where these structures intersect the limestone beds. The recognition of this origin is naturally of great economic value, because any mineralized fissures found in rocks above the Pioche Shale are strong evidence for the possibility of replacement deposits along the same structures where they intersect the C.M. Limestone at depth.

Depositional Textures

Ore deposits are formed with various textures, depending upon the nature of the mineralizing fluids, the physical and chemical characteristics of the host rocks, and the mode of emplacement. In syngenetic deposits—a category including sedimentary, magmatic segregation, and some pegmatite ores—the textures will reflect the proximity to a source or the rates of crystallization. Furthermore, resorption of early-formed crystals may produce peculiar textures in magmatic segregation ores (Figs. 4-31 and 4-32), and diagenetic changes may modify the texture of sedimentary deposits. The textures of hydrothermal ores, however, tend to be much more diversified;

in fact, the manner of ore deposition is often clearly shown by the textures produced.

In spite of the great amount of work that has been done in the interpretation of mineral textures and structures, such interpretation is extremely difficult and at times problematical. The causes of many textures are poorly understood, and the same textures are subject to several interpretations. For example, the type of texture shown in Fig. 3-4 has been attributed to exsolution (Schwartz, 1931), replacement (Loughlin and Koschmann, 1942), or, as for chalcopyrite and bornite, the removal of part of the iron from chalcopyrite by hot water or steam (Park, 1931). Formerly, it was thought that textures of this type would result from crystallization of the minerals in eutectic proportions, though this idea is no longer seriously held. Excellent treatises on the textures of ore minerals are available and should be studied by serious students of ore deposits (Edwards, 1952, 1954; Van der Veen, 1925; Ramdohr, 1955; Bastin, 1950; Schneiderhöhn and Ramdohr, 1931; Schouten, 1934).

Ores may be deposited either by open-space filling or replacement. Ores deposited in openings are likely to have followed textural or structural

FIGURE 4-31. *Chromite grains in plagioclase. The concavities were produced by partial resorption of early formed chromite. From Bushveld igneous complex, South Africa.* ×20. (*Photo by C. M. Taylor.*)

FIGURE 4-32. *Orbicular chromite in altered peridotite. From Greece. Three-fourths natural size. (Photo by C. M. Taylor.)*

controls; conversely, those that replaced pre-existing rocks were probably chemically controlled. Accordingly, it is of fundamental importance for the understanding and development of an ore deposit to ascertain whether the minerals are of replacement or open-space origin, though a deposit formed by either mechanism alone would be an exception, because open-space filling is likely to be accompanied by some replacement, and vice versa. Moreover, the textures developed may indicate whether the metals were carried in solution or as colloids. The three so-called types of textures—replacement, open-space filling, and colloidal—will be discussed separately.

REPLACEMENT

As defined by Lindgren (1933, p. 91), replacement—or metasomatism—is ". . . the process of practically simultaneous capillary solution and deposition by which a new mineral of partly or wholly differing chemical composition may grow in the body of an old mineral or mineral aggregate.' Replacement ordinarily implies little or no change in the volume of the replaced rock, although in some rocks considerable shrinkage or expansion takes place. The process of metasomatism is of great significance in the emplacement of epigenetic ore deposits; many ores are deposited almost entirely in this manner, and nearly all ores show some evidence of replace-

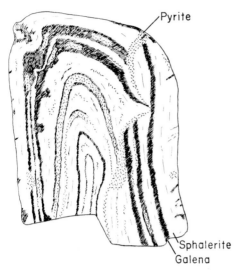

Pyrite

Sphalerite

Galena

FIGURE 4-33. *Sketch of a specimen of ore from the Sullivan mine, British Columbia, showing replacement and preservation of folded layers. One-half natural size.*

ment. The process is especially characteristic of those deposits formed at high temperatures and under high pressures where open spaces are scarce and where communication with the surface is impeded.

The efficacy of replacement is often astounding. The intimate preservation of plant cells or growth rings in petrified wood is well known, and people have come to accept the fact that wood—a fibrous substance composed of carbon, hydrogen, oxygen, nitrogen, and minor elements—has been replaced by silica, even though there is no apparent similarity between the two substances. The replacement of one mineral by another may be equally as striking and indisputable; fossils, sedimentary textures, and folded structures are also commonly preserved in faithful detail (Fig. 4-33). A compilation of the minerals that can replace one another will indicate that there is practically no limit to the direction of metasomatism; as a bold generalization, it might be stated that, given the proper conditions, any mineral can replace any other mineral, though natural processes usually make for unilateral reactions. The important factor seems to be the chemical difference between the mineral or rock being replaced and the medium—liquid, gas, or wave of diffusing ions—causing the metasomatism. Hence, merely because quartz is stable at the earth's surface, we cannot conclude that quartz will resist metasomatism; in fact, quartz and the silicates very commonly undergo replacement. In contrast, a fluid that reacts with and replaces limestone may be inert to quartz, or vice versa, and as a result, selective replacement may be of the most detailed character. Bastin et al. (1931) proposed, as general rules for replacement, that sulfides, arsenides, tellurides, and sulfosalts replace all rock, gangue, and ore minerals; gangue minerals replace rock and other gangue minerals but do not commonly replace sulfides, arsenides, tellurides, and sulfosalts; high-temperature oxides replace all rock and gangue minerals but are only rarely replaced by gangue minerals; and oxides rarely replace sulfides, arsenides, tellurides, and sulfo-salts.

Although replacement has been generally recognized and described for many years, the means by which the actual transfer of materials takes place has been the subject of much debate. One fundamental question is how the tremendous volumes of replaced materials are removed by the same solution that deposits the minerals. Presumably the removed materials are simply transported from the replacement front by the spent ore solutions or by diffusion. The fact that replacement takes place roughly volume for volume raises another major problem: how to write chemical equations representing electrically and molecularly balanced reactions with equal volumes of solid materials on each side.

Ridge (1949, 1961) attempted to demonstrate replacement by writing equations that would balance molecularly, volumetrically, and electrically. His work helps to explain the replacement of one sulfide by another and also sheds light on the difficult problem of substituting the sulfur in sulfides for the oxygen in oxides, a process that must take place but seems illogical because of the large sizes of these ions. Ridge found that he could write equations acknowledging the known facts of chemistry and geology under near-surface conditions, but could develop only rough approximations for deep-seated reactions. As an example of the problem to be faced by geologists, Ridge described the replacement of covellite by argentite, a process likely to take place where surface outcrops are being leached and where deposition is taking place below the water table. For an aqueous, sulfate environment (without regard to the volumes), this reaction may be expressed as

$$(1) \quad 2Ag^+ + CuS \longrightarrow Ag_2S + Cu^{+2}$$

According to Ridge, there would be a gain of nearly 70 percent in volume of the solid phases during this reaction. Such a volume change does not, of course, take place in nature. If we assume the oxidation of some sulfur, from cupric sulfide to cupric sulfate, and the concomitant reduction of some iron, from ferric to ferrous, a reasonable reaction may be written:

$$(2) \quad 17CuS \, (582.08\text{Å}^3) + 20Ag^+ + 10SO_4^{-2} + 56Fe^{+3} + 168Cl^- + 28H_2O$$
$$\longrightarrow 10Ag_2S \, (581.10\text{Å}^3) + 17Cu^{+2} + 17SO_4^{-2} + 56Fe^{+2} + 112Cl^-$$
$$+ 56H^+ + 56Cl^-$$

if the iron is in solution as a chloride; or

(3) $17CuS + 20Ag^+ + 10SO_4^{-2} + 56Fe^{+3} + 84SO_4^{-2} + 28H_2O \longrightarrow$
$\qquad 10Ag_2S + 17Cu^{+2} + 17SO_4^{-2} + 56Fe^{+2} + 56SO_4^{-2}$
$\qquad\qquad\qquad\qquad\qquad\qquad\qquad\qquad + 56H^+ + 28SO_4^{-2}$

if the iron is in solution as a sulfate. The volumes, shown in angstrom units, are the same whether the iron is considered to be a sulfate or a chloride. Since either form of iron is likely under the conditions chosen, it is reasonable to assume that both reactions take place simultaneously. Similarly, in the weathering of a sulfide vein it is not unreasonable to expect fairly acidic conditions, which would be necessary to keep the ferric iron in solution. As written, the volume change in either reaction is only 0.17 percent. The same reaction can be expressed in terms of fewer molecules if a volume change of 1 or 2 percent is considered acceptable. Ridge illustrated such a reaction by the equation

(4) $5CuS (171.20 \text{ Å}^3) + 6Ag^+ + 3SO_4^{-2} + 16Fe^{+3} + 24SO_4^{-2} + 8H_2O \longrightarrow$
$\qquad 3Ag_2S (174.33 \text{ Å}^3) + 5Cu^{+2} + 5SO_4^{-2} + 16Fe^{+2}$
$\qquad\qquad\qquad\qquad\qquad\qquad\qquad + 16SO_4^{-2} + 16H^+ + 8SO_4^{-2}$

for which there is a volume increase of 1.80 percent.

It will be noticed that equations (2), (3), and (4) introduce components on both sides of the equation, which, while taking part in the reaction, leave no solid evidence behind. In nature, there would be no trace of such materials.

The replacement of carbonates by sulfides, of silicates by oxides, and so forth, can be expressed in a similar manner. In some replacement reactions, there is even less of a problem, because the reactants may not have any ions in common; that is, there will be no chemical reaction that needs balancing. Ridge offers the replacement of limestone by sphalerite as an example; the simple, unbalanced expression is

(5) $Zn^{+2} + S^{-2} + CaCO_3 \longrightarrow ZnS + Ca^{+2} + CO_3^{-2}$

The equation can be balanced by simple ratios based on the difference between the unit cell volumes of sphalerite and calcite. The resulting hypothetical equation,

(6) $31Zn^{+2} + 31S^{-2} + 20CaCO_3 (1220.60 \text{ Å}^3) \longrightarrow$
$\qquad\qquad\qquad 31ZnS (1220.47 \text{ Å}^3) + 20Ca^{+2} + 20CO_2^{-2}$

shows a volume difference of only 0.01 percent. The only problem for such a replacement is the physical transfer of materials, which pertains for any type of metasomatism and may be a matter of diffusion or practically simultaneous solution and redeposition.

Buerger (1948) pointed out that when the temperature of a mineral is raised, a point is reached at which the atomic structure is disordered but loosely tied together, allowing ions to diffuse through the crystal with ease. The process occurs most readily in sulfides, because the tetrahedral coordination of sulfur ions makes for a relatively open crystal structure. Even at moderate temperatures, sulfides will take up ions from the surrounding solutions, and as the ions are passed along, a wave of replacement will move away from the source of supply. The reasoning behind this explanation is like that of Fairbairn (1943), who suggested that minerals having a high packing index (high ratio of ion volume to unit cell volume) should be more slowly replaced than loosely packed minerals. We would logically expect replacement to take place more readily in calcite (packing index = 4.0) than in quartz (packing index = 5.2), grossularite (packing index = 6.4), wollastonite (packing index = 5.2), or similar closely packed sili-cates. Such a relation is shown in tactite ores, in which interstitial calcite is generally selectively replaced before the silicates are attacked.

Limestone replacement under low temperature and pressure was studied by Garrels and Dreyer (1952), who were able to produce replacement textures similar to natural replacement textures under controlled laboratory conditions. Many variables were examined, but the major control of replacement was thought to depend upon the pH of the mineralizing fluid, which in turn controls the solubility of the carbonate host rock. Garrels and Dreyer suggested that the dissolved limestone produces a change in the ore-bearing solutions, causing the ores to be precipitated. Accordingly, they consider the solubility of the host to be the key factor in metasomatism. It has also been proposed that the principal factor is the solubility of the replacement product in a given solution relative to the solubility of the host rock in the same solution, rather than merely the solubility of the host (Ames, 1961). In any case, the importance of simultaneous dissolving action and precipitation from solution seems fairly well established.

Garrels and Dreyer also found that ideal conditions for replacement exist where there are numerous small, closely spaced openings creating a somewhat higher secondary permeability. They concluded that the mineralizing solutions are brought into an area along these zones of secondary permeability, but that movement from the channels to the replacement front takes place mainly by diffusion, rather than by forced flow.

The amount of replacement that can take place depends upon the amount of time the ore-bearing fluids are in contact with the host; that is, the distance through which ionic diffusion occurs is a function of time. Accordingly, metasomatism is likely to be the most thorough at great depths where open-space circulation is very limited.

Much has been written about the criteria by which replacement may be recognized. A few of the criteria, such as pseudomorphs and relict textures, are considered to be diagnostic, but most others are only indicative and are also formed in ways other than by replacement. With the exception of the few diagnostic criteria, it is unwise to base conclusions upon single indications; the confidence of any determination is directly proportional to the number of criteria available. A list of twenty of the more reliable criteria is given below; most are illustrated in Fig. 4-34. The scale of the illustrations is microscopic, though most of them might be used in the field (Bastin et al., 1931; Schouten, 1934).

1. *Pseudomorphs.* If the form of a pre-existing mineral is preserved, especially if the internal structure is also discernible, a replacement origin is essentially indisputable.

2. *Widening of a fracture filling to an irregular mass where the fracture crosses certain chemically reactive mineral grains or rock layers.* If a veinlet widens across only one type of mineral, it suggests that this mineral was favorably receptive to replacement. A mineral vein widening into massive manto deposits along limestone beds would be a large-scale example of this criterion.

3. *Formation of vermicular intergrowths at wide places along cracks and at boundaries of areas that are not related to crystallographic directions.* The vermicular intergrowths may represent an advance wave of replacement, not yet completed. Replacement is not the only mechanism by which vermicular intergrowths are formed, however; they also develop during crystal growth in a eutectic mixture and by exsolution during the slow cooling of some solid solutions. Such primary vermicular intergrowths are typically related to crystallographic directions, and as a result, only the nonoriented intergrowths should be used as a criterion of replacement.

4. *Islands of unreplaced host mineral or wall rock.* For example, chalcopyrite may replace pyrite, but if the process is arrested before it goes to completion, remnants of pyrite will be found within the chalcopyrite.

5. *Surfaces concave into the host.* The diffusion of ions at the replacement front may take place at different rates, causing some parts of the front to advance faster than other parts. Consequently, the replacement develops concave re-entrants, as if the replacing mineral bit into the host.

6. *Unmatching borders or walls of a fracture.* If the replacement is working outward from a central fissure, the opposite fronts of replacement should not match in detail, and may differ radically.

7. *Rims penetrating the crystallographic directions of the host mineral.* Replacement may work outward from any small fissures, including cleavages. For example, galena may be replaced by covellite along a network of directions that are obviously parallel to the cleavages.

8. *Oriented unsupported fragments.* If a piece of the host is completely surrounded by the secondary (replacement) mineral and still maintains its orientation with respect to the host material on the outside, it is practically diagnostic of replacement. (The difficulty lies in proving that the fragment is unsupported.) The fragment may be any size, and the orientation may be proved by crystallographic directions, cleavage, bedding, or foliation.

9. *Selective association.* Since the chemistry is an important factor, some minerals or strata may be selectively replaced while others are left barren. For example, chalcocite may be found with chalcopyrite in preference to pyrite.

10. *Physicochemical incompatibility between metacrysts and minerals of the host.* If the metacrysts normally do not form by the same processes as the host material, a replacement origin is suggested. Similarly, the presence of chemically unrelated substances suggests that metacrysts and host are of different origins, and as regards the metacrysts, replacement, rather than open-space filling, is the only logical explanation. For example, pyrite crystals within calcite are anomalous because these minerals have no ions in common.

11. *Metacrysts transecting original structures.* The presence of a crystal that cuts across planes of bedding or foliation suggests that the structure developed before the metacryst was formed. If the crystal had grown by any process other than replacement, it would have pushed the structure aside.

12. *Metacrysts deposited in obvious relation to fractures, cleavage planes, or crystal boundaries.* Since the ore-bearing fluids are introduced along small fractures, the development of crystals by replacement should take place in the wall rock adjacent to these passageways.

13. *Disparity in size of the metacrysts and the minerals of the host.* Large crystals in a fine-grained groundmass, and vice versa, may indicate that the metacrysts grew independently of the host rock.

14. *Metacrysts deposited along what was clearly an advancing zone of alteration.* If deposition took place by open-space filling, the ore minerals should stop abruptly against the host. Conversely, the replacement may have taken

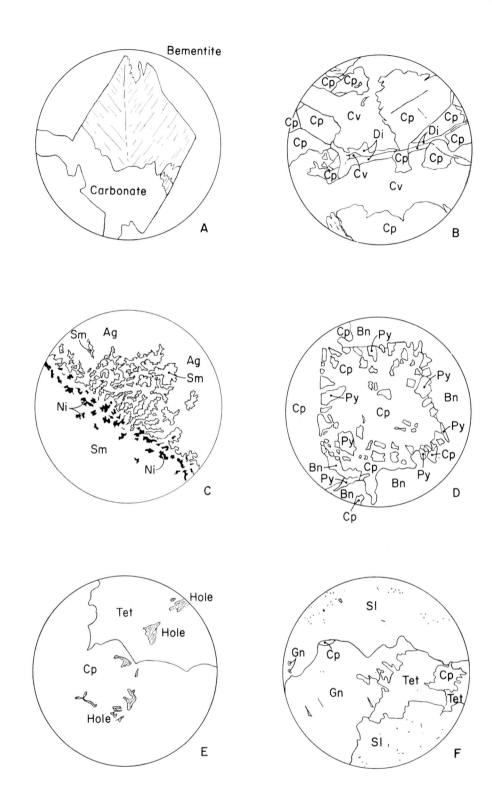

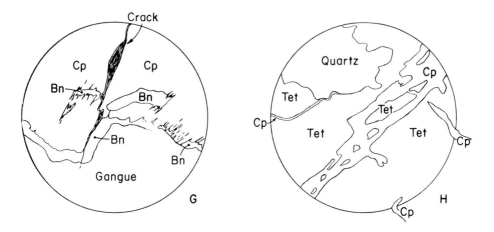

FIGURE 4-34. *Illustrations of criteria indicative of replacement.*

(A) *Pseudomorph. Bementite (hatchured) replacing calcite crystal. Olympic Peninsula, Washington. ×60.*

(B) *Widening of a fracture-filling to an irregular mass, where the fracture crosses certain chemically reactive mineral grains on rock layers. Veinlet of digenite (Di) and covellite (Cv) in chalcopyrite (Cp). Note how the digenite veinlet pinches out where the fracture crosses chalcopyrite. Cananea, Mexico. ×37.5.*

(C) *Formation of vermicular intergrowths at wide places along cracks and at boundaries of areas that are not related to crystallographic directions. Preferential replacement of niccolite (Ni) by native silver (Ag) in intimate admixture of niccolite in smaltite-chloanthite (Sm). Cobalt, Ontario, Canada. ×30. (Unpublished photo by D. E. Eberlein.)*

(D) *Islands of unreplaced host mineral or wall rock. Pyrite (Py) cube largely replaced by chalcopyrite (Cp). Bornite (Bn) borders part of the grain. Bisbee, Arizona. ×37.5.*

(E) *Concave surfaces into the host. Chalcopyrite (Cp) replacing tetrahedrite (Tet). Coeur d'Alene, Idaho. ×45.*

(F) *Unmatching walls or borders of a fracture. Galena (Gn), tetrahedrite (Tet), and chalcopyrite (Cp) cutting sphalerite (Sl). Cananea, Mexico. ×30.*

(G) *Rims penetrating the crystallographic directions of the host mineral. Bornite (Bn) in chalcopyrite (Cp). Cananea, Mexico. ×40.*

(H) *Oriented unsupported fragments. Tetrahedrite (Tet) in chalcopyrite. Coeur d'Alene, Idaho. ×45.*

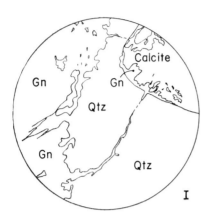

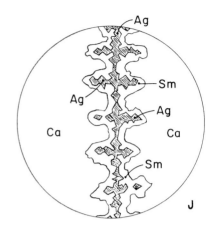

I

J

K

L

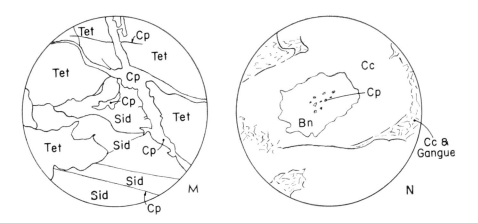

FIGURE 4-34. (I) *Selective association. Galena (Gn) replacing calcite in preference to quartz. Darwin, California. ×45.*

(J) *Physicochemical incompatibility between metacrysts and minerals of
the host. Silver (Ag) and smaltite (Sm) in calcite (Ca). Cobalt, Ontario, Canada. ×30. (Photo by K. Bhatt.)*

(K) *Metacrysts deposited in obvious relation to fractures, cleavage planes,
or crystal boundaries. Quartz replacing siderite. Příbram, Czechoslovakia. ×160. (From Kutina, 1963.)*

(L) *Doubly terminated quartz crystal from stibnite vein, Wolf Creek, Fair-
banks district, Alaska. Shows included stibnite crystals. Crystal is said
to be a replacement of gangue minerals in vein. ×18. (Collected by
P. O. Sandvik. Photo by W. J. Crook.)*

(M) *Intersecting fractures having no offset at the intersection. Tetrahedrite
(Tet), chalcopyrite (Cp), and siderite (Sid). Coeur d'Alene, Idaho.
×30.*

(N) *Depositional sequence in which minerals become progressively richer in
one constituent. Bornite (Bn) with blebs of chalcopyrite (Cp) in the
center, surrounded by chalcocite (Cc) and gangue. Tsumeb, South-West
Africa. ×45.*

(O) *Metacrysts of pyrite cutting foliation. Mother Lode, California. About
nine-tenths natural size.*

place by the gradual enlargement and merging of metacrysts along the replacement front. Such an advancing zone should be evident from the progressive increase in size of metacrysts and from the completeness of replacement from the wall rock into the ore.

15. Zonal sequence in which minerals become progressively richer in one constituent. For example, if polybasite ($Ag_{16}Sb_2S_{11}$) was acted upon by silver-rich solutions, the replaced material should show a progressive enrichment in silver. A crystal or fragment of polybasite may grade first to argentite (Ag_2S) and finally to native silver, reflecting the gradual replacement of antimony and sulfur. An intermediate-stage specimen might have a core of polybasite, rimmed in sequence by argentite and native silver.

16. Preservation of original structures and textures. Certain features of sedimentary, igneous, or metamorphic rocks, as well as organic remains, may be preserved pseudomorphically. For example, folded structures or oölites may be of obvious pre-ore development, in which case their presence in ore is just as conclusive of replacement as is any other pseudomorph.

17. Doubly terminated crystals. If a crystal grows within an open cavity, it will attach itself to one wall and develop crystal faces only at the free end. This restriction does not affect crystals growing by replacement, and as a result, the presence of doubly terminated crystals may indicate a replacement origin. Naturally, this criterion is limited, because doubly terminated crystals may also develop within magmas and by other processes.

18. Gradational boundaries. Replacement processes may produce either abrupt or gradational contacts between the host rock and the ore body, but —at least on a microscopic scale—open-cavity filling should form abrupt contacts. Thus a gradational boundary is an indication of advancing replacement.

19. Residual resistant minerals. Some minerals will be stable in the mineralizing solutions and may be left after the surrounding minerals have been replaced. For example, zircon or corundum crystals, known to be present in a nearby schist, may be found in the same proportions within the ore body; such an occurrence would support the argument that the ore had replaced some of the same schist. The resistant minerals may also be considered as special types of islands or unreplaced fragments of host rock (criterion 4).

20. No offset along the intersections of fractures. The spreading of a fissure by open-space filling will cause an offset along any planar or linear feature that transects the fissure obliquely. Conversely, replacement along the fissure will cause no offset of an intersecting fracture. Both fractures may be replaced and trend across one another without any change in course, but it would take a coincidence of displacement to rematch intersecting veins that were spread apart and filled.

OPEN-SPACE FILLING

Open-space filling is common in the shallow zones of the earth's crust, where rocks yield by breaking rather than by flowing. The openings tend to remain open and are not closed by rock pressures. At shallow depths, the ore-bearing fluids are thought to have relatively free circulation and connection with the surface, with the result that deposition is brought about by fairly rapid pressure and temperature changes rather than by prolonged contact with rocks that will slowly undergo chemical changes. Ores deposited in vugs and open cavities have a characteristic appearance that is readily distinguished from that of ores formed by replacement processes. A list of the common criteria by which open-space filling may be recognized is given below. The criteria are illustrated in Fig. 4-35.

1. Many vugs and cavities. Some veins or ore bodies contain vugs and cavities, which may be interpreted as spaces left due to the incomplete filling of a larger open space. For example, an open fissure may be filled with ore and gangue minerals, which will grow inward from the sides, but inward growth will stop when opposite walls meet one another along the center. Of course, opposite sides will not reach the center simultaneously all along the fissure, and eventually the circulation will be impeded, leaving pockets that have not completed their growth. Hence there are likely to be many open cavities along the vein after mineralization has ceased.

2. Fine-grained minerals on the walls of a cavity and coarser minerals in the center. The first crystals to form along the sides of a vein are usually fine-grained due to loss of heat to the wall rocks and consequent rapid crystallization. Conversely, the crystals forming in the center have more time to develop, and probably form from a more dilute solution, which will be less viscous and allow the ions to move about freely.

3. Crustification. As ore-bearing solutions change in composition, they deposite different minerals along the walls of a vein or cavity. Early-formed crystals will be succeeded by, or encrusted with, later minerals. The occurrence of small, euhedral dolomite crystals on top of large, euhedral fluorite crystals is a common example. Some veins have a banded appearance due to crustification.

4. Comb structure. Along the junction of crystals that have grown inward

A

1 in

FIGURE 4-35. *Illustrations of criteria by which open-space filling is recognized.*
    (A) *Vein-filling (quartz). Note the presence of many vugs. Locality unknown.*
    (B) *Facing page. Vug showing fine-grained quartz grading into coarser crystals. Locality unknown.*

from opposite walls of a fissure, there is generally an interdigitated, vuggy zone due to the meeting of pointed crystal ends. This jagged zone of juncture resembles the outline of a rooster's comb and is accordingly known as comb structure. Its presence indicates inward growth from vein walls—that is, open-space filling.

5. *Symmetrical banding.* Crystals deposited along the sides of a cavity or fissure should grow symmetrically toward the center. Thus the orientation and composition of crystals on opposite sides of a vein should be mirror images of one another. As the ore fluid changes in composition, the minerals deposited will differ in composition, forming crustification in a symmetrical pattern that grows inward from the vein walls. Such symmetrical banding may involve many mineralogical and color changes, producing a spectacularly banded vein.

6. *Matching walls.* Where a fissure has opened to allow filling, the opposite walls should match in outline. That is, if the vein material were removed, the wall rocks on opposite sides should fit together like mated pieces of a jig-saw puzzle. The fit across many veins is readily apparent.

7. *Cockade structure.* Mineralization within the open spaces of a breccia (or any other fragmental rock) will commonly produce a special pattern of symmetrical banding or crustification known as cockade structure. In this structure, each opening will be a center for sequential deposition, and the

B

1 in

C

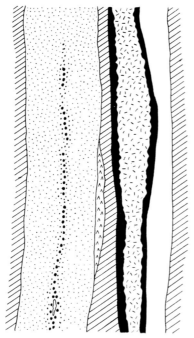

D

| 1in |

FIGURE 4-35. (C) *Veinlet of aragonite through limestone and shale. Shows crustification, comb structure, and open spaces. Locality unknown.*
    (D) *Matkobozska vein, Příbram, Czechoslovakia. An illustration of reopening and symmetrical deposition. (After Kutina, 1957.)*
    (E) *Facing page. Cockade structure, quartz in breccia. Locality unknown.*

:::: Gangue   ▓ Siderite

:::: Quartz   ⬡ Ankerite

⋀⋀ Sphalerite   ☐ Calcite

E

1 in

overall rock will present a random pattern of host-rock fragments and angular, concentric rings of mineralization.

8. *Offset oblique structures.* Where a pre-existing planar or linear feature intersects a vein obliquely, it will be offset at right angles to the vein walls because it was spread apart as the fissure opened. A replacement vein would cause no offset along such a pre-existing structure.

DEPOSITION OF COLLOIDS

Amorphous minerals, such as opal, neotocite, wood tin, and garnierite, are thought to have been deposited from colloidal solutions. Moreover, many of the cryptocrystalline minerals—chalcedony, some manganese oxides, pyrite, marcasite, pitchblende, and the oxidation products of copper, lead, and zinc (malachite, azurite, chrysocolla, anglesite, cerussite, and smithsonite)—are often considered to have been carried and deposited as colloids that were crystallized shortly after deposition. Some geologists think that gold, especially in the shallow bonanza deposits, traveled in the colloidal state. Conversely, many geochemists consider the existence of colloids in hydrothermal systems as highly unlikely.

The criteria by which colloidal deposition is recognized are not well established; most of them may be interpreted in other ways and should be considered only as indicative. The best criteria are listed below and illustrated in Fig. 4-36.

A

FIGURE 4-36. *Criteria that suggest col-*
loidal deposition.

(A) *Colloform texture. Globular sphal-*
erite with concentric banding.
Considered to be of colloidal ori-
gin. Orzel Bialy mine, Katowice,
Poland. Natural size. (After Ku-
tina, 1953.)

(B) *Shrinkage cracks. Ore from La-*
rap, Philippine Islands. ×87.
(Photo by J. E. Frost.)

(C) *Facing page. Diffusion banding*
as illustrated by an agate. Note
also the pattern of filling in the
central vug. Locality unknown.
×1.7. (Photo by W. J. Crook.)

B

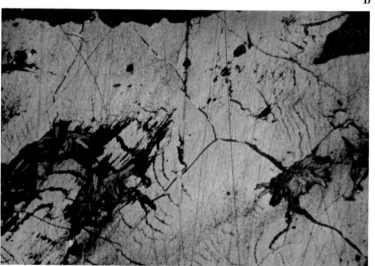

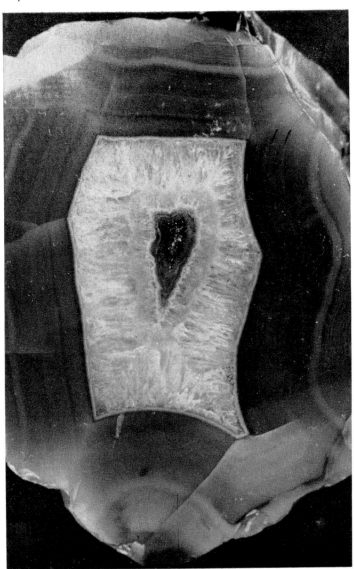

C

1. Colloform textures. Artificial colloids and natural materials thought to be of colloidal origin typically develop colloform structures where they extend into open spaces. Hence the presence of colloform textures is strong evidence in favor of colloidal deposition, especially if the botryoids approach sphericity—the shape created by surface-tension phenomena. Care must be taken to distinguish between the truly spheroidal colloform structures and other colloform deposits that develop from precipitation around corners of rock fragments.

2. Shrinkage cracks. Laboratory gels develop shrinkage cracks due to dehydration, hence similar cracks should be expected in natural colloidal deposits. Their presence is evidence in favor of colloidal deposition, but most so-called colloids show no signs of shrinkage.

3. Diffusion banding or Liesegang rings. Colored bands may form in a gel if an electrolyte is allowed to diffuse into it. Liesegang rings are readily produced in laboratory gels, and the presence of similar banding in amorphous or microcrystalline rocks, such as agates, is generally interpreted to indicate a colloidal origin.

4. Absorption of foreign materials causing a variable composition. Colloids act as sponges for many ions, due to their electrical charge, and they may remove constituents from any surrounding fluids that would otherwise remain in solution indefinitely. The presence of rare metals in psilomelane or wad may be due to this phenomenon.

5. Chaotic, noncrystalline structure. Amorphous minerals or mineraloids are thought to originate as colloids. Since colloidal gels are unstable, however, they tend to crystallize, therefore the amorphous state would not be expected to last indefinitely. Thus a colloidal precipitate may or may not be amorphous.

6. Columnar crystals extending in crystallographic continuity through more than one color or compositional zone without interruption. Colloidal masses that take on colloform shapes generally crystallize into clusters of radiating crystals trending normal to the periphery of the botryoids. Diffusion bands or color variations may also be present in these colloidal masses. Radiating, columnar crystals are able to extend through the diffusion bands, because the process of crystallization occurs later than, and independent of, the formation of Liesegang rings.

7. Spheroids. Some masses of chert, of probable colloidal origin, contain distinct spherulitic structures, similar to pisolites. The round structures are a result of surface tension, which should exist in any liquid of low viscosity. If these spheroids were formed during crystallization of a gel, as some geologist maintain (Lindgren, 1925; Lindgren and Loughlin, 1919; Gilluly, 1932; Bastin, 1950), the presence of such textures should suggest colloidal deposition, though similar forms may develop in other ways.

A further criterion used in the past is the presence of framboidal textures. Clusters of tiny crystals or mineral grains grouped into a spheroidal mass are known as framboidal spherules (after *framboise*, the French word for raspberry, which the spherules resemble). The clusters range from about 4–50 microns in diameter, and the individual crystals are less than one-tenth the size of the spherule. Pyrite, chalcopyrite, bornite, and chalcocite mineral grains have been reported in spherules. Because framboidal textures have been found in ores thought to be of colloidal origin, they have been considered to be indicative of colloidal deposition (Rust, 1935; Bastin, 1950). The framboidal masses were thought to be composite concretions or crystallized globules of gel in which crystallization started simultaneously from many centers. Recent studies have shown, however, that framboidal textures are related to bacterial forms, the sulfide crystals having filled chambers or cells in the organic structures (Love, 1962). The sulfides are probably precipitated out of solution—rather than from colloidal gels—owing to the reducing action of H_2S produced by the bacteria (Jensen and Dechow, 1962). Hence framboidal textures can no longer be considered as evidence of colloidal processes.

Silica gel produced in the laboratory changes first to opal and then to a chalcedony-like material as it "ages" or dries and becomes compact. It undergoes a progressive volume reduction caused by the loss of water and develops characteristic shrinkage cracks. Similar gels in nature should also form shrinkage cracks, but since such cracks are seldom detected, many doubt the existence of natural colloids. Nevertheless, cracks attributed to the shrinkage of hardening colloids have been described from several districts (Gilluly, 1932; Roy, 1959; Kutina, 1952). The absence of these dehydration cracks in most deposits of supposed colloidal origin may be due to a gradual accumulation of colloidal material, whereby individual, shell-like layers precipitate and solidify before the subsequent layer is deposited. Such a mechanism is known as the Wiegner effect (Liesegang, 1931; Park and Cannon, 1943); it takes place by means of the coagulation of small colloidal particles around nuclei of larger particles, and may bring about deposition from dilute colloidal systems. The Wiegner effect is significant for deposition or replacement along very small openings, because it requires only thin layers of gel at any one time. Accordingly, a large mass of gel may never be able to undergo shrinkage from dehydration, but a sizable volume of solidified colloid with no visible shrinkage cracks may be built up gradually.

Even though the part played by colloids in the processes of ore deposition is poorly understood, it seems likely that under near-surface conditions and in watery solutions at comparatively low temperatures, the role may be appreciable. Many deposits have been described for which a colloidal origin is probable or in which colloids have played a supporting role. Among the best examples are the lead-zinc deposits of Upper Silesia (see Chapter 15, p. 337–343) and the Kuroko ores of Japan. In order to illustrate the lines of evidence and types of problems involved in attributing a colloidal origin to a mineral deposit, we describe the Japanese Kuroko ores below.

The Japanese Kuromono or Kuroko ore, which is a peculiar, fine-grained aggregate of sulfides, has been attributed to colloidal processes by many workers (Kinoshita, 1924, 1929, 1931; Collins, 1950; Griggs, 1947; Kurushima, 1956). Unfortunately, most of the descriptions of the Kuroko ores are written in Japanese. The deposits are most abundant on the island of Honshu, though they are also found on Hokkaido. As far as is known, such ores are unique to Japan and have not been described elsewhere. The ores are thought to be of shallow origin—probably the epithermal zone of Lindgren's classification. They are in altered and brecciated Tertiary sediments and volcanics, most of which are tuffs and tuff breccias. Genetically, the ores are considered to be related to rhyolitic and andesitic volcanic rocks, with which the mineralized zones are commonly associated.

Three types of ore are distinguished on the basis of composition; these formed in successive stages of mineralization and are known as siliceous ore, yellow ore, and black ore, respectively. The siliceous ore consists of sulfide minerals disseminated throughout siliceous rock; the yellow ore is primarily pyrite, but contains minor chalcopyrite and quartz; and the black ore is an intimate mixture of sphalerite, galena, barite, and minor pyrite and chalcopyrite. Wurtzite, enargite, tetrahedrite, and marcasite occur sporadically. Veins and large masses of gypsum are found as related but separate deposits.

The Kuroko ore bodies range in size from small nodules to large irregular masses as much as 2400 feet long by 1000 feet wide by 300 feet thick. All the ore is extremely fine-grained, and a concentric banded structure is common in the nodules of black ore. The ore bodies are almost everywhere enclosed in envelopes of clay, the composition of which has been determined as montmorillonite, iron-montmorillonite, sericite, and chlorite (Sudo, 1954).

Kinoshita, a geologist thoroughly acquainted with the Kuroko ores, conducted extensive laboratory experiments and concluded that the ore-bearing fluids were colloids of hydrothermal origin. Textures are considered to indicate that the colloids somehow replaced the country rocks, rather than merely filled open spaces in the pyroclastics. The hydrothermal solutions were probably siliceous fluids that contained abundant colloidal particles of the metals as well as sodium, potassium, and calcium sulfides. Such fluids would precipitate the siliceous ores and yellow ores if they were forced to mix with ascending CO_2 and SO_2. The black ores would be deposited from the resulting carbonate-sulfate sols, which would be alkaline in character. Kinoshita demonstrated in the laboratory that colloidal solutions of the ore are stable in caustic potassium solutions through which H_2S is passed and that precipitation takes place when most of the H_2S has been expelled.

Pieces of typical wall rock placed in colloidal baths had different effects on the system. Tuff and shale fragments caused a relatively rapid coagulation of the colloid, whereas volcanic rocks caused a much slower reaction. This experiment implies that the tuff and shale should be the most effective precipitants for ascending or circulating colloidal fluids, and that if the Kuroko ores were actually deposited as colloids, they should show a relative preference for the tuff and shale strata. That this preference is well established in the mines supports the colloidal theory of origin (Kinoshita, 1924, 1929; Collins, 1950).

Several textural features of the Kuroko ores also indicate that they were deposited from colloidal systems. The ore is an intimate mixture of very fine-grained minerals, suggesting that slight recrystallization followed deposition. Some of the ores are highly porous and have a microscopic honeycomb structure that may reflect shrinkage due to dehydration of a sol. Tiny shrinkage(?) cracks have also been found. Colloform textures are common and involve pyrite, marcasite, sphalerite, wurtzite, galena, and opal. The sulfide minerals are somewhat softer and less dense than their holotypes, just as colloidal silica (opal) is softer and less dense than quartz. Banding is also found in some of the ores, and although it could possibly be the result of rhythmic deposition from solution, it is more readily explained as a product of Liesegang diffusion (Kinoshita, 1929).

The colloidal theory is not accepted by all workers. Nearly every possibility from syngenetic to epigenetic, magmatic to hydrothermal, and hot to cold has been proposed. But the colloidal theory explains more features and poses fewer problems than any other, and as a consequence it is strongly favored by most of Japan's geologists.

References to Selected Districts Showing Structural Control of Ore Deposits

Balmat-Edwards District, New York

Brown, J. S., 1936, Structure and primary mineralization of the zinc mine at Balmat, New York: Econ. Geology, v. 31, p. 233–258.

————, 1936, Supergene sphalerite, galena, and willemite at Balmat, New York: Econ. Geology, v. 31, p. 331–354.

————, 1941, Factors of composition and porosity in lead zinc replacements of metamorphosed limestone: Am. Inst. Mining Engineers Trans., v. 144, p. 250–263.

————, 1942, Edwards-Balmat zinc district, New York, *in* Newhouse, W. H. (ed.), Ore deposits as related to structural features: New Jersey, Princeton Univ. Press, p. 171–174.

————, 1947, Porosity and ore deposition at Edwards and Balmat, New York: Geol. Soc. America Bull., v. 58, p. 505–545.

Cushing, H. P., and Newland, D. H., 1925, Geology of the Gouverneur quadrangle: New York State Museum Bull. 259.

Newland, D. H., 1916, The new zinc mining district near Edwards, N.Y.: Econ. Geology, v. 11, p. 623–644.

————, 1917, Zinc-pyrite deposits of the Edwards district, New York: New York State Defense Council Bull. 2.

Smyth, C. H., Jr., 1918, Genesis of the zinc ores of the Edwards district, St. Lawrence County, N.Y.: New York State Museum Bull. 201.

San Juan Mountains, Colorado

Bastin, E. S., 1923, Silver enrichment in the San Juan Mountains, Colorado: U.S. Geol. Survey Bull. 735-D, p. 65–129.

Burbank, W. S., 1930, Revision of geologic structure and stratigraphy in the Ouray district of Colorado, and its bearing on ore deposition: Colorado Scientific Soc. Proc., v. 12, no. 6, p. 151–232.

————, 1933, The western San Juan Mountains: 16th Internat. Geol. Cong. Guidebook 19, p. 34–63.

————, 1933, Vein systems of the Arrastre Basin and regional geologic structure in the Silverton and Telluride quadrangles, Colorado: Colorado Scientific Soc. Proc., v. 13, no. 5, p. 135–214.

————, 1940, Structural control of ore deposition in the Uncompahgre district, Ouray County, Colorado: U.S. Geol. Survey Bull. 906-E, p. 189–265.

————, 1941, Structural control of ore deposition in the Red Mountain, Sneffels, and Telluride districts of the San Juan Mountains, Colorado: Colorado Scientific Soc. Proc., v. 14, no. 5, p. 141–261.

————, 1951, The Sunnyside, Ross Basin, and Bonita fault systems and their associated ore deposits, San Juan County, Colorado: Colorado Scientific Soc. Proc., v. 15, no. 7, p. 285–304.

————, Eckel, E. B., and Varnes, D. J., 1947, The San Juan region, *in* Vanderwilt, J. W. (ed.), Mineral resources of Colorado: State of Colorado Mineral Resources Board, p. 396–446.

Collins, G. E., 1931, Localization of ore bodies at Rico and Red Mountain, Colorado, as conditioned by geologic structure and history: Colorado Scientific Soc. Proc., v. 12, no. 12, p. 407–424.

Cross, Whitman, and Larsen, E. S., 1935, A brief review of the geology of the San Juan region of southwestern Colorado: U.S. Geol. Survey Bull. 843.

Larsen, E. S., Jr., and Cross, Whitman, 1956, Geology and petrology of the San Juan region, southwestern Colorado: U.S. Geol. Survey Prof. Paper 258.

Moehlman, R. S., 1936, Ore deposits south of Ouray, Colorado: Econ. Geology, v. 31, p. 377–397, 488–504.

Purington, C. W., 1905, Ore horizons in the San Juan Mountains: Econ. Geology, v. 1, p. 129–133.

Ransome, F. L., 1901, Economic geology of the Silverton quadrangle: U.S. Geol. Survey Bull. 182.

Bawdwin, Burma

Brown, J. C., 1917, Geology and ore deposits of the Bawdwin mines, Burma: Geol. Survey of India Rec., v. 48, p. 121–178.

Clegg, E. L. G., 1941, A note on the Bawdwin mines, Burma: Geol. Survey of India Rec., v. 75, no. 13.

Dunn, J. A., 1937, A microscopic study of the Bawdwin ores, Burma: Geol. Survey of India Rec., v. 72, p. 333–369.

Loveman, M. H., 1917, The geology of the Bawdwin mines, Burma, Asia: Am. Inst. Mining Engineers Trans., v. 56, p. 170–194.

References Cited

Ambrose, J. W., 1957, Violamac mine, Slocan district, B.C., *in* Structural geology of Canadian ore deposits (vol. II): Canadian Inst. Mining Metallurgy, p. 88–95.

Ames, L. L., Jr., 1961, The metasomatic replacement of limestones by alkaline, fluoride-bearing solutions: Econ. Geology, v. 56, p. 730–739.

Bain, G. W., 1936, Mechanics of metasomatism: Econ. Geology, v. 31, p. 505–526.

Barnes, H. L., 1962, Mechanisms of mineral zoning: Econ. Geology, v. 57, p. 30–37.

Barrington, Jonathan, and Kerr, P. F., 1961, Breccia pipe near Cameron, Arizona: Geol. Soc. America Bull., v. 72, p. 1661–1674.

Barton, P. B., Jr., 1959, The chemical environment of ore deposition and the problem of low-temperature ore transport, *in* Abelson, P. H. (ed.), Researches in geochemistry: New York, John Wiley & Sons, Inc., p. 279–300.

Bastin, E. S., 1950, Interpretation of ore textures: Geol. Soc. America Mem. 45.

———, Graton, L. C., Lindgren, Waldemar, Newhouse, W. H., Schwartz, G. M., and Short, M. N., 1931, Criteria of age relations of minerals, with special reference to polished sections of ores: Econ. Geology, v. 26, p. 561–610.

Blanchard, Roland, 1947, Some pipe deposits of Eastern Australia: Econ. Geology, v. 42, p. 265–304.

Bowen, N. L., 1928, The evolution of the igneous rocks: New Jersey, Princeton Univ. Press.

Brammall, A., 1930, The Stantrg lead-zinc mine, Yugoslavia: Mining Mag., v. 42, p. 9–15.

Brown, A. S., 1957, Red rose tungsten mine: *in* Structural geology of Canadian ore deposits (v. II): Canadian Inst. Mining Metallurgy, p. 17–20.

Bryner, Leonid, 1961, Breccia and pebble columns associated with epigenetic ore deposits: Econ. Geology, v. 56, p. 488–508.

Buerger, M. J., 1948, The role of temperature in mineralogy: Am. Mineralogist, v. 33, p. 101–121.

Butler, B. S., 1913, Geology and ore deposits of the San Francisco region, Utah: U.S. Geol. Survey Prof. Paper 80, p. 172–178.

———, and Burbank, W. S., 1929, The copper deposits of Michigan: U.S. Geol. Survey Prof. Paper 144.

Cairnes, C. E., 1934, Slocan mining camp, British Columbia: Canadian Geol. Survey Mem. 173.

———, 1935, Descriptions of properties, Slocan mining camp, British Columbia: Canadian Geol. Survey Mem. 184.

———, 1948, Slocan mining camp, *in* Structural geology of Canadian ore deposits: Canadian Inst. Mining Metallurgy, p. 200–205.

Christie, J. J., 1950, Inside Yugoslavia— II, The Trepča mine's great possibilities: Eng. Mining Jour., June 1950, p. 77–79.

Clappison, R. J. S., 1953, The Morning Star mine, Wood's Point, *in* Edwards, A. B. (ed.), Geology of Australian ore deposits: Melbourne, Australasian Inst. Mining Metallurgy, p. 1077–1081.

Collins, J. J., 1950, Summary of Kinoshita's Kuroko deposits of Japan: Econ. Geology, v. 45, p. 363–376.

Edwards, A. B., 1952, The ore minerals and their textures: Clarke Memorial Lecture, Roy. Soc. New South Wales Jour. and Proc., v. 85, p. 26–45.

———, 1954, Textures of the ore minerals and their significance: Melbourne, Australasian Inst. Mining Metallurgy.

———, 1956, The present state of knowledge and theories of ore genesis: Melbourne, Australasian Inst. Mining Metallurgy Proc., no. 177, p. 69–116.

———, 1960, Contrasting textures in the silver-lead-zinc ores of the Magnet mine, Tasmania: Neues Jahr. für Min. Petrog. Abhand., v. 94, p. 298–318.

Emmons, W. H., 1938, Diatremes and certain ore-bearing pipes: Am. Inst. Mining Engineers Tech. Pub. 891.

Fairbairn, H. W., 1943, Packing in ionic minerals: Geol. Soc. America Bull., v. 54, p. 1305–1374.

Fenner, C. N., 1948, Immiscibility of igneous magmas: Am. Jour. Sci., v. 246, p. 465–502.

Finucane, K. J., 1948, Ore distribution and lode structures in the Kalgoorlie Goldfield: Melbourne, Australasian Inst. Mining Metallurgy Proc., no. 148–149, p. 111–129.

Forgan, C. B., 1948, Ore deposits at the Stantrg lead-zinc mine: 18th Internat. Geol. Congress, Symposium on the geology, paragenesis, and reserves of the ores of lead and zinc, p. 162–176.

Fujita, Yoshizo, 1954, Three-way geophysical method points up huge pyrite deposit: Eng. Mining Jour., December, 1954, p. 84–88.

Garrels, R. M., and Dreyer, R. M., 1952, Mechanism of limestone replacement at low temperatures and pressures: Geol. Soc. America Bull., v. 63, p. 325–379.

Gilluly, James, 1932, Geology and ore deposits of the Stockton and Fairfield quadrangles, Utah: U.S. Geol. Survey, Prof. Paper 173.

Griggs, A. B., 1947, Zinc-lead resources of Japan: Supr. Comm. for the Allied Powers, Nat. Resources Sec., Rept. no. 65, p. 23–26.

Grout, F. F., 1923, Occurrence of ladder veins in Minnesota: Econ. Geology, v. 18, p. 494–505.

Gunning, H. C., 1948, Privateer mine, *in* Structural geology of Canadian ore deposits: Canadian Inst. Mining Metallurgy, p. 86–88.

Hack, J. T., 1942, Sedimentation and volcanism in the Hopi Buttes, Arizona: Geol. Soc. America Bull., v. 53, p. 335–372.

Harder, E. C., 1919, Iron depositing bacteria and their geologic relations: U.S. Geol. Survey Prof. Paper 113.

Hayward, M. W., and Triplett, W. H., 1931, Occurrence of lead-zinc ores in dolomitic limestones in northern Mexico: Am. Inst. Mining Engineers Tech. Pub. 38, class I.

Hemley, J. J., 1953, A study of lead sulfide solubility and its relation to ore deposition: Econ. Geology, v. 48, p. 113–138.

Humphrey, F. L., 1945, Geology of the Groom district, Lincoln County, Nevada: Univ. of Nevada Bull., v. 39, no. 5.

James, J. A., 1949, Geologic relationships of the ore deposits in the Fredericktown area, Missouri: Missouri Geol. Survey and Water Resources Rept. of Inv., no. 8.

Jensen, M. L., 1958, Sulfur isotopes and the origin of sandstone-type uranium deposits: Econ. Geology, v. 53, p. 598–616.

———, and Dechow, E., 1962, The bearing of sulphur isotopes on the origin of the Rhodesian copper deposits: Geol. Soc. South Africa Trans., v. 65, pt. 1, p. 1–17.

Killinger, P. E., 1942, Report on the titanium mine at Tahawus, New York, *in* Rocks and Minerals, v. 17, p. 409.

Kinoshita, Kameki, 1924, Colloidal solutions as the mineralizing solutions of the "Kuromono" deposits: Tohoku Imperial Univ. Science Repts., 3rd ser., v. 2, p. 23–30.

———, 1929, On the genesis of the "Kuromono" deposits: 15th Internat. Geol. Congress, Comptes Rendus, v. 2, p. 454–474.

———, 1931, On the "Kuroko" (black ore) deposit: Japanese Jour. Geology and Geography, v. 8, p. 281–352.

Kolthoff, I. M., and Sandell, E. B., 1952, Textbook of quantitative analysis: New York, The Macmillan Co., p. 67–68.

Krauskopf, K. B., 1955, Sedimentary deposits of rare metals: Econ. Geology (50th Anniv. Volume), p. 411–463.

Kuhn, T. H., 1941, Pipe deposits of the Copper Creek area, Arizona: Econ. Geology, v. 36, p. 512–538.

Kurushima, Hidesaburo, 1956, Study on the industrial method of perfect utilization of mineral resources: Japan, Dowa Mining Co.

Kutina, Jan, 1952, Mikroskopischer und spektrographischer Beitrag zur Frage der Entstehung einiger Kolloidalstrukturen von Zinkblende und Wurtzite: Geologie, v. 1, p. 436–452.

———, 1955, Genetische Diskussion der Makrotexturen bei der geochemischen Untersuchung des Adalbert Hauptganges in Pribram: Chemie der Erde, Zeits. für chemische Mineral. Petrog. Bodenkunde und Geochem., v. 17, p. 241–323.

———, 1957, A contribution to the classification of zoning in ore veins: Universitas Carolina, Geologica, v. 3, no. 3, p. 197–225.

Liesegang, R. E., 1931, Colloid chemistry and geology: in Jerome, Alexander (ed.), Colloid chemistry (v. 3): New York, Chemical Catalog Co., Inc., p. 251–260.

Lindgren, Waldemar, 1925, Metasomatism: Geol. Soc. America Bull., v. 36, p. 247–261.

———, 1933, Mineral deposits (4th ed.): New York, McGraw-Hill Book Co., Inc.

———, and Loughlin, G. F., 1919, Geology and ore deposits of the Tintic mining district, Utah: U.S. Geol. Survey Prof. Paper 107.

Locke, Augustus, 1926, The formation of certain ore bodies by mineralization stoping: Econ. Geology, v. 21, p. 431–453.

Loughlin, G. F., and Koschmann, A. H., 1942, Geology and ore deposits of the Magdalena mining district, New Mexico: U.S. Geol. Survey Prof. Paper 200.

Love, L. G., 1962, Biogenic primary sulfide of the Permian Kupferschiefer and Marl Slate: Econ. Geol., v. 57, p. 350–366.

Lovering, T. G., 1962, The origin of jasperoid in limestone: Econ. Geology, v. 57, p. 861–889.

Lovering, T. S., 1942, Physical factors in the localization of ore, in Newhouse, W. H. (ed.), Ore deposits as related to structural features: New Jersey, Princeton Univ. Press, p. 5–9.

MacDiarmid, R. A., 1959, Geology and ore deposits of the Bristol Silver mine, Pioche, Nevada: Ph.D. thesis on file at Stanford University, California.

———, 1960, Controls on ore deposition at the Bristol Silver mine, Pioche, Nevada: Geol. Soc. America Bull., v. 71, p. 1921.

Malcolm, Wyatt, 1912, Gold fields of Nova Scotia: Canadian Geol. Survey Mem. 20-E.

Moritz, H., 1933, Die sulfidischen Erze der Tsumeb-Mine vom Ausgehenden bis zur XVI. Sohle (−460 m): Neues Jahr. für Min., Geol. und Paläon., supp. v. 67, sec. A, p. 118–154.

Ohle, E. L., and Brown, J. S. (ed.), 1954, Geologic problems in the southeast Missouri lead district: Geol. Soc. America Bull., v. 65, p. 201–222.

Pardee, J. T., and Park, C. F., Jr., 1948, Gold deposits of the Southern Piedmont: U.S. Geol. Survey Prof. Paper 213.

Park, C. F., Jr., 1931, Hydrothermal experiments with copper compounds: Econ. Geology, v. 26, p. 857–883.

———, and Cannon, R. S., Jr., 1943, Geology and ore deposits of the Metaline quadrangle, Washington: U.S. Geol. Survey Prof. Paper 202.

Park, C. F., Jr., Gemmill, Paul, and Tschanz, C. M., 1958, Geologic map and sections of the Pioche Hills, Lincoln County, Nevada: U.S. Geol. Survey Min. Invest. Field Studies Map, MF 136.

Perry, V. D., 1961, The significance of mineralized breccia pipes: Mining Eng., v. 13, p. 367–376.

Prescott, Basil, 1915, The main mineral zone of the Santa Eulalia district, Chihuahua; Am. Inst. Mining Engineers Bull. 98, p. 155–198.

Ramdohr, Paul, 1955, Die Erzmineralien und ihre Verwachsungen: Berlin, Akad. Verlag.

Ransome, F. L., 1909, Geology and ore deposits of Goldfield, Nevada: U.S. Geol. Survey Prof. Paper 66.

———, 1911, Geology and ore deposits of the Breckenridge district, Colorado: U.S. Geol. Survey Prof. Paper 75, p. 144–147.

Reynolds, D. L., 1954, Fluidization as a geological process, and its bearing on the problem of intrusive granites: Am. Jour. Sci., v. 252, p. 577–613.

Ridge, J. D., 1949, Replacement and the equating of volume and weight: Jour. Geology, v. 57, p. 522–550.

———, 1961, Gain and loss of material in a series of replacements: Geol. Soc. America, Abstracts for 1961, Spec. Paper, no. 68, p. 252–253.

Roscoe, S. M., 1951, Dilation maps, their application to vein-type ore deposits: Ph.D. thesis on file at Stanford University, California.

Roy, Supriya, 1959, Mineralogy and texture of the manganese ore bodies of Dongari Buzurg, Bhandara district, Bombay State, India, with a note on their genesis: Econ. Geology, v. 54, p. 1556–1574.

Rust, G. W., 1935, Colloidal primary copper ores at Cornwall mines, southeastern Missouri: Jour. Geology, v. 43, p. 398–426.

Sales, R. H., 1954, Genetic relations between granites, porphyries and associated copper deposits: Am. Inst. Mining Engineers Trans., v. 199, p. 499–505.

———, and Meyer, Charles, 1949, Results from preliminary studies of vein formation at Butte, Montana: Econ. Geology, v. 44, p. 465–484.

Schneiderhöhn, Hans, 1923, Chalkographische Untersuchung des Mansfelder Kupferschiefers: Neues Jahr. für Min., Geol. und Paläon., supp. v. 47, p. 1–38.

———, 1929, Das Otavi-Bergland und seine Erslagerstätten: Zeit. prakt. Geol., v. 37, p. 85–116.

———, 1931, Mineralische Bodenschätze im südlichen Afrika: Berlin.

———, 1941, Lehrbuch der Erzlagerstättenkunde: Jena, Gustav Fischer, p. 459–471.

———, and Ramdohr, Paul, 1931, Lehrbuch der Erzmikroskopie: Berlin, Geb. Borntraeger.

Schouten, C., 1934, Structures and textures of synthetic replacements in "open space": Econ. Geology, v. 29, p. 611–658.

———, 1946, The role of sulphur bacteria in the formation of the so-called sedimentary copper ores and pyritic ore bodies: Econ. Geology, v. 41, p. 517–538.

Schumacher, Friedrich, 1950, Die Lagerstätte der Trepça und ihre Umgebung: Belgrade, 1950.

———, 1954, The ore deposits of Yugoslavia and the development of its mining industry: Econ. Geology, v. 49, p. 451–492.

Schwartz, G. M., 1931, Textures due to unmixing of solid solutions: Econ. Geology, v. 26, p. 739–763.

Sclar, C. B., and Geier, B. H., 1957, The paragenetic relationships of germanite and reniérite from Tsumeb, South-West Africa: Econ. Geology, v. 52, p. 612–631.

Snyder, F. G., and Odell, J. W., 1958, Sedimentary breccias in the southeast Missouri lead district: Geol. Soc. America Bull., v. 69, p. 899–925.

Söhnge, P. G., 1952, The Tsumeb story: pipe-like, massive-sulphide ore body appears to fill volcanic pipe in depth: Mining World, v. 14, no. 6, p. 22–24.

——, 1963, The geology of the Tsumeb mine: Geol. Soc. South Africa Trans., in press.

Stillwell, F. L., 1919, The factors influencing gold deposition in the Bendigo goldfield, Australia, pt. III: Adv. Council Sci. and Industry, Bull. 16.

Sudo, Toshio, 1954, Types of clay minerals closely associated with metalliferous ores of the epithermal type: Tokyo Kyoiku Daigaku Science Repts., ser. C, no. 23, p. 186–192.

Threadgold, I. M., 1958, Mineralization at the Morning Star gold mine, Wood's Point, Victoria: Melbourne, Australasian Inst. Mining Metallurgy Proc., no. 185, p. 1–27.

Titley, S. R., 1961, Genesis and control of the Linchburg orebody, Socorro County, New Mexico: Econ. Geology, v. 56, p. 695–722.

Treadwell, W. D., and Hepenstrick, H., 1949, Über die Löslichkeit von Silbersulfid: Helv. Chim. Acta, v. 32, p. 1872–1879.

Treadwell, W. D., and Schaufelberger, F., 1946, Zur Kenntnis der Löslichkeit des Quecksilbersulfids: Helv. Chim. Acta, v. 29, p. 1936–1946.

Tsumeb Corporation Staff, 1961, Geology, mining methods and metallurgical practice at Tsumeb: Trans. 7th Commonwealth Mining Metallurgical Cong. Papers and Discussions, v. 1, South African Inst. Mining Metallurgy, p. 159–179.

Van der Veen, R. W., 1925, Mineragraphy and ore deposition: The Hague, B. Naeff.

Wagner, P. A., 1927, The pipe form of ore deposit: Econ. Geology, v. 22, p. 740–741.

Watanabe, Takeo, 1940, Eruptions of molten sulphur from the Siretoko-Iôsan volcano, Hokkaidô, Japan: Japan. Jour. Geology and Geography, v. 17, p. 289–310.

Westgate, L. G., and Knopf, Adolph, 1932, Geology and ore deposits of the Pioche district, Nevada: U.S. Geol. Survey Prof. Paper 171.

Whitebread, D. H., and Lee, D. E., 1961, Geology of the Mount Wheeler mine area, White Pine County, Nevada: U.S. Geol. Survey Prof. Paper 424-C, p. 120–122.

Williams, Howel, 1936, Pliocene volcanoes of the Navajo-Hopi Country: Geol. Soc. American Bull., v. 47, p. 111–171.

Young, E. B., 1948, The Pioche district: 18th Internat. Geol. Cong., Symposium on the geology, paragenesis, and reserves of the ores of lead and zinc, p. 98–106.

Zeller, H. D., 1957, The Gas Hills uranium district and some probable controls for ore deposition: Wyoming Geol. Assoc., 12th Ann. Field Conference, Guidebook to Southwest Wind River Basin, p. 156–160.

CHAPTER 5 **Alteration and Gangue**

THE COUNTRY ROCKS bordering ore deposits of hydrothermal origin are generally altered by the hot fluids that have passed through them and with which the ores are associated. The alteration is considered to be due as much to the mineralizing processes as the ore itself; indeed, replacement ores are merely products of wall-rock alteration that have a commercial value. The nature of the alteration products depends upon (1) the character of the original rock, (2) the character of the invading fluid, and (3) the temperature and pressure at which the reactions took place. Wall-rock alteration has been recognized for many years as a valuable tool in exploration, because the alteration halos around many deposits are widespread and much easier to locate than the ore bodies. Alteration effects may have reached the surface, or they may be blind and found only in underground workings or in drill holes. Within recent times, equipment for rapid and precise determination of the mineralogy has become available, and a great deal of work has been done in an attempt to determine the exact relationships between ores and alteration minerals. The main problems involve such questions as: What types of alteration products are associated with ores deposited at depth? How do they differ from near-surface alterations? What changes are to be expected in the country rocks at various distances from the ore bodies? Where in the alteration halos are the ores most likely to be found?

The gangue minerals in hydrothermal deposits are also direct products of the ore-forming processes. In disseminated copper deposits and in some contact metamorphic ores, gangue and altered wall rock are the same materials; in some veins, the gangue has been derived from the wall rock by alteration processes; and in magmatic segregation deposits the gangue and the wall rock may be similar petrologic units, differing only in the percentage of ore mineral present. Gangue minerals may also be used for prospecting. They generally extend beyond the ore shoots and, as a result, may be used to distinguish mineralized veins from barren structures. Similarly, minor changes in the distribution of gangue minerals may indicate which direction along a vein is likely to lead to ore.

Wall-rock Alteration

If the wall rocks are unstable in the presence of early, ground-preparing hydrothermal fluids, or of ore-forming solutions, they will undergo physical and chemical changes to reach equilibrium under the prevailing conditions. The resulting alteration may be very subtle, such as the incipient hydration of selected ferromagnesian minerals; or it may be very complete, as in the silicification of limestone. The alteration may range from simple recrystallization to the addition, removal, or rearrangement of chemical components.

The physical products of wall-rock alteration include recrystallization, changes in permeability, and changes in color. Carbonate rocks are characteristically recrystallized along the borders of a vein or near an igneous contact. The recrystallized area is generally more permeable than the unaltered rocks, suggesting that some ores owe their localization to increased permeability caused by an advanced wave of recrystallization. Conversely, argillization may reduce the permeability of a rock, leaving the ore body enclosed within a relatively impermeable shell. Color changes include bleaching, darkening, and aureoles of various colors. Pastel colors are especially prominent around some ore deposits, and may form conspicuous leads to ore at the earth's surface. Clay minerals are generally white or light shades of green, brown, and gray, hence argillization may produce a noticeable bleaching effect; even a black basalt may be altered to a white or light-green product of clays and other hydrous minerals. Similarly, the addition of chlorite or epidote, which are common in certain alteration zones, will produce a green color.

Since iron is one of the most abundant metals in the earth's crust, pyrite is a standard alteration product around sulfide ore bodies. Normally, pyrite will form wherever sulfur is added to a host rock containing iron or ferromagnesian minerals. Even if pyrite is finely disseminated, it may cause a striking color change. For example, the pyritization of a red sandstone or shale containing iron-oxide pigment will produce a bleached zone due to the reduction of iron. Conversely, any pyritized rock is likely to be made

conspicuous at the earth's surface by oxidation of the iron, which will produce a red or red-brown weathered zone. Most of the physical effects
produced by wall-rock alteration are brought about by chemical reactions.
Thus hydration or reduction may result in bleaching. Studies of wall rocks
at progressively greater distances from veins have shown that the average
altered rock has undergone a complex process of ion exchange, whereby
some constituents are removed, others are added, and still others are merely
redistributed. Silicification, carbonatization, argillization, and hydration are
typical examples of the processes that may take place in alteration zones—
and they may all operate simultaneously. Generalizations are hazardous,
because the possibilities are too diverse; but in specific environments, certain reactions can be expected. For example, water is usually added to the
alteration zone, except where the rocks are completely replaced by anhy-
drous silica; and carbon dioxide is generally removed from carbonate host
rocks. Furthermore, certain minerals are to be expected in alteration zones.
Sericite, quartz, chlorite, pyrite, epidote, zoisite, carbonates, and clay minerals are probably the most common (Schwartz, 1959), but many others
have been formed by hydrothermal alteration.

At various distances from a vein, the conditions of temperature and
chemistry are usually different, and as a result, different types of alteration
are likely to be produced simultaneously (Hemley, 1959; Burnham, 1962).
In the outer fringes of the alteration zone, the ferromagnesians may have
been slightly hydrated while the interior zone was being silicified or sericitized, and the intermediate zone argillized. The natural product of this
system is a zoning of different alteration products arranged symmetrically
about the central vein. In some deposits this zoning is conspicuous and may
be an excellent guide to ore. At Casapalca, Peru, for example, the veins that
traverse grayish-green porphyry intrusives are outlined by white, pink, green,
and purplish alteration zones in a sequential pattern from the veins outward
(McKinstry and Noble, 1932).

It should be emphasized that any hydrothermal solution passing through
rock pores or along a fissure is likely to alter the country rocks. This is true
whether the vein contains ore minerals or not. Thus not all alteration zones
will be guides to ore deposits, and any mineralized region that has undergone a complex history of hydrothermal activity will be complicated by
transgressing and sequential zones of alteration associated with both metalliferous and barren phases. On the other hand, the chemistry of each hydrothermal solution may be reflected in details of the wall-rock alteration,

slight differences in which can be used to indicate the proximity of metal-bearing shoots.

Different kinds of ore deposits are typified by certain alteration minerals and different degrees of alteration. Owing to their depth of burial, the wall rocks around deep-seated ores are relatively impermeable and usually almost as hot as the ore-bearing fluids; therefore, unless there is a strong chemical contrast between the ore fluids and the country rock, the alteration zone is likely to be thin and inconspicuous. Conversely, hot solutions that invade cool, shallow, permeable rocks typically produce prominent, widespread alteration halos, because the country rocks are far out of equilibrium with the fluids. On the following pages, we describe the general products of alteration for each type of ore deposit, beginning with magmatic segregations and extending to the shallowest zone.

Wall-rock alteration around magmatic segregation and magmatic injection deposits is generally inconspicuous and nondiagnostic. The contact zones commonly have assay walls; that is, the valuable constituents gradually decrease in amount, and the gangue minerals increase to a ratio at which the material is below ore grade. In some deposits, however, the contacts between ore and gangue are sharply defined; this is especially true for injection-type deposits that were differentiated at depth, prior to emplacement. Wall-rock alteration around injection deposits is likely to be very thin or absent, unless the injection was accompanied or followed by hydrothermal activity. A thin reaction zone may be present in some deposits that have been concentrated by gravity settling, due to a reaction between the ore minerals and the rest melt.

Contact zones around pegmatites may be either narrow and sharply defined or wide and gradational. Some pegmatites contain rare minerals, and the contact zone around these igneous masses may have been invaded by ions of the rare earths, boron, fluorine, beryllium, lithium, and other pegmatitic constituents, producing a varied and unique mineralogy of alteration products. Among the alteration minerals found near pegmatites are beryl, monazite, sphene, tantalite-columbite, lithium micas, topaz, zircon, fluorite, allanite, and so forth, but the most widespread products of wall-rock alteration are disseminations of feldspars, micas, garnets, and tourmaline (Jahns, 1955). Many pegmatitic fluids are rich in potassium, which may be introduced into the wall rocks in conspicuous amounts; the conversion of wall-rock amphiboles to biotite is common evidence of this process.

Jahns (1946) recorded the development of fine-grained muscovite, plagioclase, potash feldspars, and quartz in the poorly delimited border zones of pegmatites in the Petaca district of New Mexico. Wall rocks that permitted soaking by the pegmatitic fluids were most conspicuously altered; a slabby micaceous quartzite formation showed characteristic alteration for a few feet or even many tens of feet from the pegmatite. The most extensive alteration projects as tongues along bedding or joint planes in the quartzite. Around some pegmatite bodies the zone between true pegmatite and unaltered quartzite consists of a hybrid rock, making it difficult to define a contact between igneous rock and wall rock.

Metacrysts of black tourmaline and garnet are said to be present in the wall rocks of nearly all mica and beryl pegmatites of the Avon district, Idaho. The host-rock mica schists and gneisses were altered to a light-colored aggregate of plagioclase, quartz, muscovite, and schorl, which was formed by the recrystallization of original constituents and accompanying metasomatism by pegmatitic materials. Relict bedding and schistosity are recognized in most places. In general, the alteration zone is less than 1 foot wide, but at the Muscovite mine it extends about 20 feet from the pegmatite (Stoll, 1950).

The Etta spodumene mine near Keystone, South Dakota, is noteworthy in having a pronounced contact zone around the pegmatite. The alteration halo is sharply defined and consists of a friable, fine-grained, sugary rock produced by recrystallization and metasomatism of a fine-grained mica schist. The biotite and muscovite of the schist were altered to a granoblastic and poikilitic assemblage of plagioclase, orthoclase, and microcline. Apatite and tourmaline also were formed in the contact aureole, which has an average width of 7–8 feet and a maximum width of 15 feet (Schwartz and Leonard, 1927).

Pegmatites commonly occur within the parent igneous mass, where the physical and chemical conditions are not amenable to the development of a conspicuous alteration zone. In such cases the contact between pegmatite and host rock is likely to be a gradational change in texture rather than a noticeable change in mineralogy or rock type. Conversely, some pegmatites may represent a gradual and simple change in mineralogy, with or without an increase in grain size over that of the host pluton. For example, in the Kaniksu batholith of northeastern Washington, large, irregular or oval-shaped bodies of muscovite-quartz-feldspar rock crop out in the normal biotitic intrusive mass. These bleached products are usually of the same grain size as the main intrusive mass, though locally—along fractures and in the centers of the bodies—the grain size is coarser and grades into characteristically pegmatitic materials. The most notable feature of these pegmatites is the bleaching and removal of iron minerals from their borders. Biotite is changed to muscovite, and much of the rock shows well-developed myrmekitic intergrowths (Park and Cannon, 1943).

In general, the alteration zones around pegmatites are thin and of little or no value in prospecting. Even the conspicuous halos, which are rare, extend only a few feet from the pegmatite. At a few places, for example in the African pegmatites, studies of the minor elements in barren zones indicate the presence of ores (Hornung, 1962).

Wall-rock alteration products associated with igneous-metamorphic deposits around intrusive masses are in many places extensive, and contain conspicuous, diagnostic minerals—garnets (especially grossularite, andradite, and almandite), wollastonite, epidote, the pyroxenes (such as hedenbergite, salite, and diopside), the amphiboles (principally tremolite and actinolite), ilvaite, idocrase, minerals of the humite group, serpentine, spinels, scapolite, and many others. The character of the alteration products depends in large part upon the nature of the invaded materials; for example, the introduction of a siliceous fluid into limestone will ordinarily result in such alteration products as wollastonite and idocrase, which are high in calcium, whereas the invasion of the same fluid into dolomites will result in the formation of magnesium-rich minerals, such as serpentine and diopside.

Shales in igneous metamorphic zones tend to develop the characteristic sugary texture of a hornfels; locally, knots of chlorite, andalusite, garnet, or cordierite form; and epidote may be abundant. Volcanic rocks may undergo comparable alteration. For example, zones within the abundant andesites and andesitic tuffs of central and northern Chile contain conspicuous epidote near intrusive masses. Carbonate rocks adjacent to intrusives are apt to be thoroughly metasomatized to skarn, consisting of various silicate and oxide minerals. In some igneous-metamorphic deposits the limestones and dolomites are merely recrystallized. The rocks contain no new constituents, but have been changed to coarsely crystalline marbles. There is a tendency during recrystallization for the carbonate rocks to expel impurities, such as carbon, thus the resulting rocks are generally whiter than their unaltered equivalents.

The alteration effects around contacts between igneous and sedimentary rocks range in width from a few feet to a mile or more. In general, the more extensive the metamorphic zone, the more favorable the area is for the discovery of ore, because the development of metamorphic minerals indicates that heat and hydrothermal fluids have penetrated the rocks, reworking the original constituents and in many places adding new materials to the contact aureole. Contact zones that are simply recrystallized and show no other metamorphic effects are said to be "dry." They are seldom favorable areas to prospect for ore deposits.

Silicification is abundant around igneous metamorphic deposits. The silica may be introduced by hydrothermal fluids, or it may represent a recrystallization of silica already present in the rock. Shales, which are ordinarily impermeable and not overly receptive to the introduction of ore-bearing fluids, may be rendered hard and brittle by silicification. Silicified shales are typically aphanitic, but small, doubly terminated quartz crystals can be distinguished in some of them. This process of silicification is one form of ground preparation, whereby soft, impermeable, and unfavorable rocks are made more competent and more receptive to the introduction of fluids and the deposition of ores.

The deepest hydrothermal veins grade into both pegmatites and igneous metamorphic deposits at their lower limits, and into the intermediate-vein zone above. Accordingly, the alteration products associated with the deeper hypothermal ores may be similar to either pegmatitic alterations or igneous metamorphic alterations, and the upper hypothermal alteration products may grade into the mineral suites that are characteristic of mesothermal deposits. Some deep-seated veins are mineralogically similar to pegmatites. For example, at the Passagem mine, Brazil, the gangue, and in places the wall rock, contains abundant quartz plus garnets, tourmaline, muscovite, mariposite, phlogopite, biotite, orthoclase, plagioclase, kyanite, and ankerite; Hussak (1898) has described the deposit as a pegmatite. Minerals closely akin to those developed around pegmatites are found in the Southern Piedmont region of the United States. Near Dahlonega, Georgia, these same minerals are found both in gangue and in country rock. Within the ore bodies the minerals are coarse-grained, decreasing in size laterally into the schists, where it is impossible to pick the precise limit of mineralization (Pardee and Park, 1948, p. 47). Alteration of this type, apparently related to pegmatitic fluids, is seldom identifiable more than a few feet away from ore; it is of little value in exploring for new deposits.

A second type of alteration associated with the deeper hydrothermal deposits is that shown by the ores of the Homestake gold mine, South Dakota, and by the Morro Velho gold mine of Brazil. This type grades into the extensive alteration zones characteristic of the mesothermal, or middle-vein, zone. Ankerite is a common alteration product, though other carbonates may also be present. The country rocks are commonly silicified, and generally contain either sericite or chlorite, or both, but seldom in large amounts. Where both are developed, the sericite is typically closer to the ore deposit than is the chlorite. Pyrite, arsenopyrite, and pyrrhotite are widely distributed and locally abundant.

Alteration products are most conspicuous and most useful around ore deposits of intermediate and shallow depths, although all such deposits do not necessarily show alteration halos. Sericite is the most persistent and abundant alteration mineral in mesothermal deposits. Carbonates are also common—especially calcite and dolomite, though siderite, rhodochrosite, and ankerite are conspicuous in places. Chlorite, most characteristic of epithermal deposits, may also form around mesothermal veins; it commonly develops next to sericite, but on the cooler side, away from the ore. Silica is generally present and in many places abundant. A prevalent feature is jasperoid, the fine-grained silica of hydrothermal origin. Pyrite is another widespread and conspicuous alteration product, and may form euhedral crystals associated with the sericite or, less commonly, with the chlorite. In places, the wall rocks around veins of the intermediate depth-temperature zone are altered to a fine-grained aggregate of silica, sericite, pyrite, and to a lesser extent feldspars and clay minerals.

The Mother Lode district of California furnishes an excellent example of the alteration products developed in the deeper parts of the mesothermal zone (Knopf, 1929, p. 41–45). In these deposits ankerite—the dominant alteration mineral—has been extensively formed in all types of wall rocks. Sericite is probably second in importance—except in serpentine, where mariposite, the chromium mica, is common. The chief characteristic of the alteration zone is the addition of large amounts of carbon dioxide, the quantity apparently depending upon the abundance of iron, magnesium, and calcium in the original rock. Other added elements are potassium, sulfur, sodium, and arsenic, represented by sericite, pyrite, and arsenopyrite. Large volumes of silica were removed from silicates; the amount is more than enough to account for all silica in the veins, hence it is unnecessary to attribute this compound to the magma. In places the alteration extends laterally for 10 feet or more from the edges of the veins, forming a valuable guide to the associated vein.

The extensive alteration zones within and around disseminated copper deposits, which probably form at intermediate depths and temperatures, are conspicuous and well studied. Within recent years, unaltered orthoclase has been widely recognized in the altered igneous host rock, and is easily confused with original constituents. Alteration feldspars have been described by Gilluly (1946), Schwartz (1947), and Anderson (1950), and are recognized in such districts as Bingham Canyon, Utah; Ely, Nevada; and Bagdad, Arizona, among others. Argillic alteration has been described in the disseminated copper deposit at Castle Dome, Arizona (Peterson et al., 1946), and was recognized by Schwartz at Morenci and San Manuel, Arizona, and at Santa Rita, New Mexico. Sericitic alteration is common to all disseminated deposits, and silica is abundant in places. In many of these deposits the mafic minerals are altered to biotite.

Probably one of the most abundant minerals in the wall rocks around epithermal deposits is chlorite, and in deposits such as the Comstock Lode, Nevada, the enclosing rocks are highly chloritized to a propylite. Sericite is commonly present, though in smaller amounts than in mesothermal deposits. Other alteration minerals are alunite, zeolites, chalcedony, opal, and calcite, plus other carbonates. Argillization may be especially widespread; among the numerous clay minerals involved are nacrite, dickite, kaolinite, beidellite, illite, and montmorillonite. The alteration products in shallow deposits are ordinarily fine-grained, and many are difficult to separate for identification. Probably the most diagnostic minerals are the clays and chlorite. The country rock may be thoroughly altered for several hundred feet from an ore body, making it a problem in these extensive zones to locate the ore within the alteration aureole.

The alteration products formed in telethermal deposits, such as those of the Mississippi Valley lead-zinc district, are few and inconspicuous. Telethermal deposits are thought to have been formed by warm waters, probably of magmatic origin, at great distances from any igneous source. They are characterized by calcite, dolomite, marcasite, and cryptocrystalline silica, but these materials are seldom helpful in exploration.

It is logical to assume that the physical and chemical characteristics of the ore-bearing fluids will vary outward from the vein into the cooler wall rock. It is also logical to assume that the solutions passing through the vein will change in both temperature and composition during the history of hydrothermal activity. Such changes are in fact recorded in the different zones of alteration parallel to the contact. A good example is the common association of chlorite—a typical epithermal mineral—outside the sericite zone of a mesothermal vein. Alteration zones ordinarily grade into lower-temperature types wherever ores have been deposited in country rocks that were appreciably cooler than the ore-bearing fluids. Wall-rock alteration associated with xenothermal deposits—ores formed in shallow zones but at high temperatures—is a good example; these ores are characterized by a mixture of alteration minerals typical of the entire hydrothermal range, from hypothermal to epithermal.

Studies of wall-rock alteration have shown that the old theory of lateral secretion was not entirely fantasy. In most cases the metals cannot have originated in the adjacent wall rocks, but the silica may conceivably have been removed from the wall rocks during alteration by hydrothermal solutions. Schmitt (1954) pointed out that the altered wall rock in many mineral deposits contains less silica than the unaltered rock. He thought, as do many field geologists, that the silica was simply rearranged and concentrated locally. It possibly traveled short distances along the vein, but there is no necessity to suggest a magmatic source; local supplies of silica are generally more than adequate. Thus the quartz host in the Mother Lode gold veins has been attributed to lateral secretion from the alteration zone (Knopf, 1929); similarly, Boyle (1955) has suggested that the quartz in the Canadian Yellowknife veins was secreted from the walls and did not originate in the magma.

The mineralogy of hydrothermal alteration is not only dependent upon the composition and temperature of the ore-bearing fluids; it is partly controlled by the composition of the wall rocks. As Schwartz (1950) pointed out, the ore solutions at Butte, Montana, and Bisbee, Arizona, both contained manganese, but only the Bisbee wall rocks were affected by this metal. No manganese minerals were formed in the alteration zone at Butte, where the wall rock is quartz monzonite, though as much as 12 percent manganese (as manganocalcite) was added to the limestone wall rocks at Bisbee. Rhodochrosite and rhodonite are abundant in the Butte gangue, proving that the ore solutions contained an appreciable amount of manganese. As a corollary to the fact that the type of alteration may be dependent upon the nature of the wall rock, it should be emphasized that the absence of an element in the alteration zone does not indicate its absence in the ore-bearing fluid.

The relationship of alteration to ore deposits may be obvious, or it may be obscure or nonexistent. Areas subjected to a complex history of hydrothermal activity will retain a complex record of alteration, of which ore deposits may or may not be a part. One fundamental problem that has evolved from the study of deposits showing more than one type of alteration is whether the different types are produced by a single, continuous hydrothermal phase or by a series of separate injections. If the alteration is produced by multiple stages of hydrothermal activity passing along different avenues, the use of alteration zones as prospecting guides is seriously complicated.

A thorough and remarkably clear study by Sales and Meyer (1948, 1949, 1950) of the Butte, Montana, veins demonstrated that the alteration products there are an integral part of the mineralization: the alteration minerals were deposited at essentially the same time and by the same fluids as the ore. Successive zones of sericitized and argillized quartz monzonite lie adjacent to every ore-bearing fissure, regardless of its size, attitude, ore mineralogy, or relative age. Except where overlap of the alteration effects between adjacent fissures has eliminated the lower grade zone, the two types of alteration always occupy the same relative positions: sericite adjacent to the vein; and clay minerals between the sericitized rock and fresh quartz monzonite. Nowhere does the sericite zone grade directly into fresh wall rock. In detail, the sequence of alteration is even more striking. The argillic zone is made up of a kaolinitic phase close to the vein and a montmorillonite-rich phase close to the unaltered wall rock. Moreover, the relative proportions of chemical components vary systematically from the vein outward, presenting a graphic picture of the hydrothermal alteration process. As shown by Fig. 5-1, the lime, soda, and silica contents diminish rapidly toward the vein, and the H_2O content increases; a similar but less striking decrease is also shown by iron and magnesium. These changes reflect the fact that plagioclase was readily hydrolyzed, releasing silica, calcium, and sodium, and that the ferromagnesians were altered to chlorite. Continued alteration leached iron and magnesium from the montmorillonite to form kaolinite. Further leaching finally broke down the orthoclase, supplying potassium for the production of biotite and sericite. The iron and sulfur contents show a marked increase near the vein, because iron leached from the early destruction of ferromagnesians combined with hydrothermal sulfur to form pyrite. Silica released from feldspars was deposited as quartz near the vein. Thus there was a two-way transfer of ions by diffusion, some ions moving into the wall rock and others moving toward the vein. As long as active circulation continued along the vein, each zone migrated away from the fissures; that is, it grew at its outer edge and simultaneously receded at its veinward edge because of encroachment by the next innermost zone. Sales and Meyer concluded that a hydrothermal solution, at a given distance from its magmatic source, would cause a specific type of alteration in a reactive wall rock, whereas at a different distance from the source, the same fluid in the same country rock would cause a different type of alteration. The

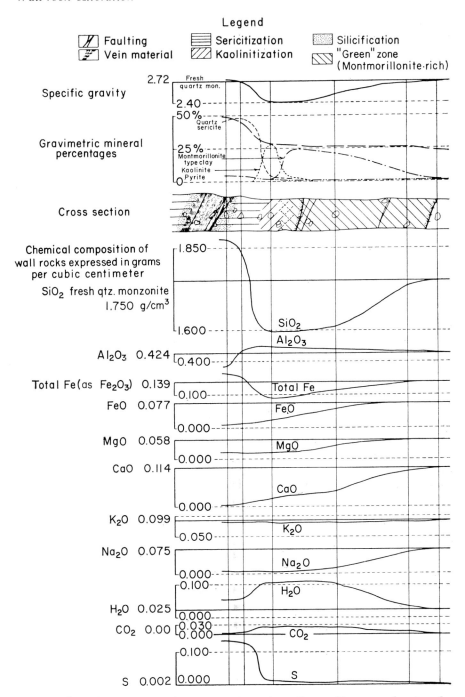

FIGURE 5-1. *Cross section of a copper-zinc vein at Butte, Montana, showing the physical, chemical, and mineralogical changes throughout the zone of alteration. (After Sales and Meyer, 1948, figure 7.)*

various mineralogical and chemical responses to the attack by ore-bearing fluids depend upon continuous changes in the physicochemical environment within the wall rock, and not upon a complete change in composition of the hydrothermal fluid.

Bundy (1958) came to a similar conclusion after making a detailed study of the clay minerals formed by wall-rock alteration in the Cochiti mining district of New Mexico. He distinguished four zones, represented from the vein outward by (1) dickite, (2) illite-kaolinite, (3) vermiculite-halloysite, and (4) chlorite-montmorillonite. Each mineral was formed during a continuous process of alteration in the order chlorite, montmorillonite, vermiculite, halloysite, illite, kaolinite, and dickite—a paragenesis that records the outward growth of the alteration zones very convincingly. Bundy suggested that the intensity of alteration is a function of time and *p*H, rather than temperature and pressure or changes in the composition of vein solutions.

Lovering (1949) reached a different conclusion regarding the alteration at Tintic, Utah. He described five stages of hydrothermal alteration, which he considered mutually independent. The five stages are (1) an early barren stage, during which limestones were dolomitized and volcanics were chloritized; (2) a mid-barren stage, characterized by argillization; (3) a late barren stage closely associated with the ore shoots and characterized by jasperoid, barite, pyrite, and minor chlorite in the sediments (carbonates, quartzites, and shales) plus allophane, quartz, barite, pyrite, calcite, and minor delessite (iron-rich chlorite) in the volcanics; (4) an early productive stage closely associated with ore bodies but consisting of only an inconspicuous zone of sericite-hydromica (representing the introduction of potassium), plus minor quartz and pyrite; and (5) the productive stage, during which the ore was deposited. According to Lovering's interpretation, each of these stages represents a period of hydrothermal activity separated from the others by appreciable time intervals, and the close association of ore with more than one of these stages reflects the common source of solutions rather than any contemporaneity in genesis.

Each of these two conflicting views was reached after a great deal of careful work, and neither can be regarded as a completely demonstrated generality. It does seem, however, that a fluid capable of transporting large amounts of ore minerals and of reacting with country rocks sufficiently to cause the deposition of these minerals would also have other effects—in places profound—upon the nonmetallic wall-rock constituents. Similarly, it is difficult to believe that the ore-bearing fluids are active only within the narrow confines of their channels; the fluids must permeate the walls and must surely react with some of the mineral constituents. It is possible, however, that the mineral-bearing fluids are injected in surges, each successive surge being of a somewhat different composition, temperature, and pressure. If Lovering is correct and much of the alteration is independent of the ore, then it follows that the chances of finding ore as a result of alteration studies are greatly reduced. [Nevertheless, recognition of the chronologic order of alteration phases can well be applied to prospecting, as it has by Lovering and others—with impressive success—in the Tintic district (Bush et al., 1960).] Alteration products and ore would be related only where the fluids used the same paths of migration. Likewise, the spatial and mineralogical relationships between alteration and ore should not be constant. For example, why should ore bodies be surrounded by envelopes of silica, sericite, and chlorite in successive zones away from the ore? Some geologists believe that in most mining districts the solutions that deposited the ores were at the same time reacting with the wall rocks and producing the alteration minerals. The injection of hydrothermal fluids in surges is considered exceptional.

It is generally concluded that alteration products in the walls of ore deposits are of great potential aid in the discovery of new ore bodies, especially in deposits formed at shallow to intermediate depths and in deposits formed along igneous contacts. Alteration products deserve much more careful attention than has been given them in the past. The identification of fine-grained minerals, such as the clays, is difficult and time-consuming, but with modern techniques—including differential thermal analysis, spectrographic studies, and x-ray equipment—it is now possible to identify the materials with confidence. More precise information, similar to that obtained by Sales and Meyer, Lovering, and Bundy, is needed about the distribution and relationships of these fine-grained minerals.

In many outcrops the alteration products are easily recognized and are of wide extent. Elsewhere the surface expression of alteration is small and inconspicuous; possibly only minor amounts of hydrothermal fluids leaked through a capping rock to reach the surface. In still other areas no surface expression of the alteration is found, but indications may be discovered in drill cores or in underground workings. It is, of course, easier to find a large body of alteration products than it is to locate the smaller ore bodies within the envelope of alteration materials. Further study is needed concerning the details of the genetic relationships between the different types of alteration products and the distribution of ores relative to these products. When such relationships are better understood, it is reasonable to assume that the study of alteration zones will help lead to the discovery of new ore bodies.

The Nature of the Gangue

Gangue includes any minerals in an ore deposit that have no economic value. It is a flexible economic term, because a gangue mineral in one deposit may be an ore mineral in another, and a gangue mineral of today may become an ore mineral should future technological advances make it economic. The concentration of a mineral may also be determinative; for example, accessory amounts of fluorite are generally discarded as gangue, but a vein containing large amounts of pure fluorite may be a valuable ore deposit.

The gangue minerals are principally silicates and carbonates, accompanied by subordinate fluorides, sulfates, and oxides. Other compounds, even sulfides, may be gangue minerals, but are not usually classified as such. Some geologists feel that any sulfide or any metallic mineral should be classified as an ore mineral, regardless of its economic status in the deposit. For this reason, a few geologists group pyrite—usually a gangue mineral—among the ore minerals. Similarly, any opaque mineral included in a petrographic description is apt to be categorically classed as an ore mineral. Such modifications of the terms ore and gangue are widely used and easily recognized by informed geologists.

Studies of gangue minerals have widespread scientific and economic potentials. The composition of gangue minerals and the age relationships between the ore and gangue must be considered in any hypothesis regarding the nature of the ore-bearing fluids and the history of ore deposition. The metallic ore minerals generally replace the nonsulfide gangue minerals, since the ores are normally deposited shortly after the gangue; the opposite reaction is always possible, however, given the proper conditions and the required sequence of deposition.

Liquid-inclusion studies are generally easier to perform on the transparent gangue minerals, because most ore minerals are opaque. The temperatures of ore deposition and the composition of the ore-forming fluids may be estimated by considering the gangue, acknowledging, of course, the time-genetic relationship between the ore and the gangue. Moreover, knowledge of a common origin for the ore and gangue minerals may be especially important for prospecting; if the gangue was produced by the same mechanism as the ore, its presence may be used as a guide to ore-bearing structures or potentially favorable environments. Mining engineers, metallurgists, and geologists must be aware of the physical and textural relationships between ore and gangue minerals in a deposit, because the entire milling program—and perhaps the economic criterion dividing ore from sub-grade material—is largely a function of the relative densities, magnetic properties, wetting abilities, and intimacy of mixture between the valuable and waste fractions of the rock.

Certain gangue minerals are unique to hydrothermal environments, an association that may be universal or only local. For example, smoky quartz may indicate the presence of uranium, because the color is generally due to radioactive bombardment. Similarly, a strong association between dark purple fluorite and economic concentrations of uranium minerals has been observed. An association has also been noted between fluorite and beryllium and between fluorescent varieties of calcite and certain ores. Some calcites fluoresce salmon-pink or red under ultraviolet excitation, and it has been suggested that trace amounts of manganese and possibly a second activator (such as lead) are responsible for this phenomenon. Whatever causes the fluorescence, a striking relationship between ore bodies and fluorescent calcite has been recorded at some mines, indicating that the calcite was formed along with the ore (Stone, 1959; MacDiarmid, 1959).

Trace amounts of metal ions can be detected in gangue minerals by spectrographic analyses or chemical assays. Nonmetallic minerals that form in the presence of a metal-bearing fluid can be expected to contain these metals in trace amounts, and the trace-metals will, in turn, act as guides to ore-bearing structures. Some metals, such as gold, may even reach ore grades as "impurities" within seemingly barren gangue minerals. Gold-bearing pyrite, for example, would undoubtedly be discarded if the gold content were not discovered by laboratory analysis.

Certain associations between ore and gangue minerals are well known. Quartz is a common gangue mineral in vein deposits, and it is especially prominent with gold. The bull-quartz of many gold deposits characteristically forms conspicuous ridges across the mining district. Because of the common association between bull-quartz and gold, the early prospectors made a practice of testing all quartz veins for the presence of gold. The need for such a policy becomes obvious when one realizes that a ton of gold ore worth $100 will contain only about three ounces of gold; that is, a block of this bull-quartz more than 12 cubic feet in volume will contain only about one-fourth of a cubic inch of gold dispersed throughout the entire mass of quartz on a volume ratio of about one part gold to 80,000 parts quartz. In most areas, gold ore worth $100 per ton would be considered high-grade material.

Another common ore-gangue association is magnetite with apatite. Iron deposits with this combination have been described from all over the world and include magmatic segregations as well as hydrothermal veins and replacement ores. The veins in any district may range from pure apatite to pure magnetite. In central Chile many small mines have been opened on strong apatite veins, which grade in depth into apatite-bearing magnetite. Fluid immiscibilities in a silica melt, as proposed by Fischer (1950), may explain many magnetite-apatite deposits of magmatic segregation origin, but the hydrothermal replacement and "lateral secretion" (or "deuteric release") ores demand either a modification of this theory or another mechanism.

Well-known but less common associations are: fluorite with lead and zinc deposits; barite with lead, silver, and copper ores; tourmaline and topaz with cassiterite veins; and arsenopyrite with tin, tungsten, and gold.

Almost any mineral can be mined for some use if it occurs pure and in large volume. Many gangue minerals commonly found as waste products in metalliferous deposits are the sole or principal ore minerals in other mines.

Pyrite is a gangue mineral in most ore deposits, but in localities close to industrial centers, pyrite is mined as an iron ore. More commonly, pyrite is recovered from a metal mine for the manufacture of sulfuric acid, as a by-product, or for use in the smelters of the same mine.

Barite and fluorite are widespread gangue minerals in hydrothermal deposits. They form under similar conditions and are frequently associated in a single deposit. Wherever either barite or fluorite is concentrated in large deposits, it is likely to be ore. Barite is found both in veins and in massive replacement ores, deposited possibly as a result of the oxidation of a sulfide solution. Fluorite is mined from fissure veins and replacement deposits in many types of rock, but limestone is the most common. The Kentucky-Illinois area, covering 700 square miles, was once the world's largest source of fluorite; most of the ores fill open fissures along faults that pinch and swell, causing the ore bodies to vary in thickness from 0 to 60 feet within short distances. A substantial portion of the Kentucky-Illinois fluorite was deposited as a replacement of Mississippian limestones (Weller et al., 1952; Gillson, 1960). The principal gangue mineral with both barite and fluorite ores is normally calcite.

Even quartz is sometimes mined as an ore. Silicon is an increasingly important commodity and is produced by driving the oxygen from quartz. Small, pure deposits of vein quartz are mined for silicon, in preference to the relatively impure varieties that occur as gangue in metalliferous veins. Other quartz deposits are of economic value because they contain large quartz crystals of optical quality; Brazil is the world's most noteworthy producer of optical quartz.

The study of ore-gangue relationships is especially important to the engineers and geologists who determine how to concentrate ore minerals. The grain size of both ore and gangue will establish how fine the ore must be ground. Relative wetting abilities, specific gravities, and magnetic properties between the ore and gangue minerals limit the mechanisms by which ore can be separated from the gangue after crushing. In many oxidized ores, such as copper carbonates and silicates, the physical properties between ore minerals and gangue or host rock are so similar that mechanical beneficiation cannot be done successfully, and the ore must be sent directly to the smelter.

References Cited

Anderson, C. A., 1950, Alteration and metallization in the Bagdad porphyry copper deposit, Arizona: Econ. Geology, v. 45, p. 609–628.

Boyle, R. W., 1955, The geochemistry and origin of the gold-bearing quartz veins and lenses of the Yellowknife greenstone belt: Econ. Geology, v. 50, p. 51–66.

Bundy, W. M., 1958, Wall-rock alteration in the Cochiti mining district, New Mexico: New Mexico Bur. Mines and Mineral Resources Bull. 59.

Burnham, C. W., 1962, Facies and types of hydrothermal alteration: Econ. Geology, v. 57, p. 768–784.

Bush, J. B., Cook, D. R., Lovering, T. S., and Morris, H. T., 1960, The Chief Oxide-Burgin area discoveries, East Tintic district, Utah; a case history: Econ. Geology, v. 55, p. 1116–1147, 1507–1540.

Fischer, Reinhard, 1950, Entmischungen in Schmelzen aus Schwermetalloxyden, Silicaten, und Phosphaten: Neues Jahr. für Min., Abh. v. 81, p. 315–364.

Gillson, J. L. (editor-in-chief), 1960, Industrial minerals and rocks (3rd ed.): Am. Inst. Mining Engineers, p. 364–365.

Gilluly, James, 1946, The Ajo mining district, Arizona: U.S. Geol. Survey Prof. Paper 209.

Hemley, J. J., 1959, Some mineralogical equilibria in the system K_2O-Al_2O_3-SiO_2-H_2O: Am. Jour. Sci., v. 257, p. 241–270.

Hornung, G., 1962, Wall rock composition as a guide to pegmatite mineralization: Econ. Geology, v. 57, p. 1127–1130.

Hussak, E., 1898, Der goldführende, kiesige Quarzlagergang von Passagem in Minas Geraes, Brasilien: Zeit. prak. Geol., v. 6, p. 345–357.

Jahns, R. H., 1946, Mica deposits of the Petaca district, Rio Arriba County, New Mexico: New Mexico Bur. Mines and Mineral Resources Bull. 25.

———, 1955, The study of pegmatites: Econ. Geology (50th Anniv. Volume), p. 1067–1070.

Knopf, Adolph, 1929, The Mother Lode system of California: U.S. Geol. Survey Prof. Paper 157.

Lovering, T. S., 1949, Rock alteration as a guide to ore—East Tintic district, Utah: Econ. Geology Mon. 1.

MacDiarmid, R. A., 1959, Geology and ore deposits of the Bristol Silver mine, Pioche, Nevada: Ph.D. thesis on file at Stanford University, California.

McKinstry, H. E., and Noble, J. A., 1932, The veins of Casapalca, Peru: Econ. Geology, v. 27, p. 501–522.

Pardee, J. T., and Park, C. F., Jr., 1948, Gold deposits of the Southern Piedmont: U.S. Geol. Survey Prof. Paper 213.

Park, C. F., Jr., and Cannon, R. S., Jr., 1943, Geology and ore deposits of the Metaline quadrangle, Washington: U.S. Geol. Survey Prof. Paper 202.

Peterson, N. P., Gilbert, C. M., and Quick, G. L., 1946, Hydrothermal alteration in the Castle Dome district, Arizona: Econ. Geology, v. 41, p. 820–840.

Sales, R. H., and Meyer, Charles, 1948, Wall rock alteration at Butte, Montana: Am. Inst. Mining Engineers Trans., v. 178, p. 9–35; and Tech. Pub. 2400.

————, 1949, Results from preliminary studies of vein formation at Butte, Montana: Econ. Geology, v. 44, p. 465–484.

————, 1950, Interpretation of wall-rock alteration at Butte, Montana: Colorado School of Mines Quart., v. 45, no. 1B, p. 261–273.

Schmitt, H. A., 1954, The origin of the silica of the bedrock hypogene ore deposits: Econ. Geology, v. 49, p. 877–890.

Schwartz, G. M., 1947, Hydrothermal alteration of the porphyry copper deposits: Econ. Geology, v. 42, p. 319–352.

————, 1950, Problems in the relation of ore deposits to hydrothermal alteration: Colorado School of Mines Quart., v. 45, no. 1B, p. 197–208.

————, 1959, Hydrothermal alteration: Econ. Geology, v. 54, p. 161–183.

————, and Leonard, R. J., 1927, Contact action of pegmatite on schist: Geol. Soc. America Bull., v. 38, p. 655–664.

Stoll, W. C., 1950, Mica and beryl permatites in Idaho and Montana: U.S. Geol. Survey Prof. Paper 229.

Stone, J. G., 1959, Ore genesis in the Naica district, Chihuahua, Mexico: Econ. Geology, v. 54, p. 1002–1034.

Weller, J. M., Grogan, R. M., and Tippie, F. E., 1952, Geology of the fluorspar deposits of Illinois: Illinois Geol. Survey Bull. 76.

CHAPTER 6 **Paragenesis and Zoning**

AN ORE-BEARING FLUID will gradually change as it migrates away from a magmatic source. It will react with the wall rocks, changing in chemical composition and pH; it will travel into regions of lower pressures; and it will lose heat to the cooler country rocks. As these physical and chemical changes take place, the relative stabilities of any metals being transported will reach critical values and cause a sequential deposition of ore minerals that will be regulated along both time and space coordinates. Each of these depositional dimensions—time and space—will be recorded in the ore deposit, leaving the geologist detailed evidence of the evolutionary trends in an ore-forming solution.

The time sequence of mineral deposition is known as the *paragenesis* of a deposit; the spatial distribution is described as *zoning*. The paragenesis, or chronologic order of minerals, is determined by studies of mineral relationships, with the emphasis on microscopic textural features. Zoning patterns are manifested by mineralogical changes along both vertical and horizontal traverses across mineralized areas. The zones may be defined by differences in mineral species, differences in types of metal, differences in sulfur content, or even subtle differences in the ratios between certain elements. But whatever the relationship used to define a zone, in each case the zoning and the paragenesis will be cogenetic, because they are merely two different aspects of the same phenomenon.

From a thorough study of carefully chosen samples made into thin sections and polished sections, in conjunction with detailed field mapping, the geologist may be able to develop a reasonably complete picture of the ore and wall rocks, including the changes along the three space coordinates and those that took place as the ore was emplaced. Details in the character of mineralization—correlated with the structure, with the character of the wall rocks and their alteration products, with such factors as permeability and porosity of the host rocks, and with the chemical reactions involved—will lead to a better understanding of the processes of ore genesis and hence to sound exploration for new ore deposits.

Paragenesis

Studies of mineral sequences are practically restricted to the microscope, because microtextures and microstructures are used to decide which formed first—though relationships between mineralized veins that cut across one another are also valuable clues to mineral paragenesis. In the study of any single mine or mineralized district, the geologist will record the relative ages of each distinguishable mineral pair. He may find, for example, that chalcopyrite always formed earlier than sphalerite and that sphalerite formed either earlier or at the same time as galena, but that some galena definitely formed later than sphalerite. He may find, further, that pyrite was ubiquitous. Such results would be plotted to show the relative sequence of mineral deposition, and the graph would be a paragenesis diagram similar to the one given in Fig. 6-1.

The work of many geologists, studying countless polished sections throughout the world, has established a general sequence of mineral deposition in ore deposits. This sequence is based upon the mineral stability ranges and is fairly constant for most deposits, regardless of the depth and temperature of formation, and regardless of origin—whether direct magmatic, pegmatitic, hydrothermal, pneumatolytic, or metamorphic. Since the character of an ore-bearing fluid gradually changes as it moves, different minerals will be formed along different parts of the vein; while one mineral is being deposited under certain conditions at one place or level, other minerals will be forming elsewhere, under different conditions. Thus it is likely that the deposition of one mineral will overlap the deposition of other minerals, both in space and in time. Slight changes in temperature, pressure, or chemistry of the transporting fluids may also alter the

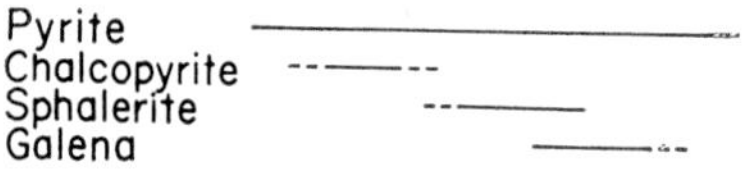

Pyrite   ——————————
Chalcopyrite ---———--
Sphalerite   --————
Galena   ————--

FIGURE 6-1. *Sample diagram of paragenesis, showing the formation of chalcopyrite before sphalerite and galena, with an overlap in the deposition of sphalerite and galena. Pyrite was deposited with all of the ore minerals. Relative time is indicated from left to right.*

normal course of deposition and cause reversals or other interruptions in the process. Furthermore, the paragenesis of each stage in a multiple pulsation system will be a chronologic sequence of its own, hence the order of mineral deposition in any two pulses may not agree exactly. For example, a mineralized fissure may be repeatedly reopened by tectonic activity (a common phenomenon), allowing discontinuous surges of ore-bearing fluids to enter; and since the chemistry of the fluids may change in time, the mineralogy of each surge may be different. The order of deposition is therefore seldom simple, and the true paragenesis can rarely be ascertained from the study of a few samples; it requires an examination of many thin sections and polished sections from samples taken at widely scattered locations within the deposit.

TABLE 6-I

Paragenesis in Hydrothermal Ore Deposits

1. Quartz (continued), chlorite, tourmaline, lime-iron silicates, sericite, albite, adularia, barite, fluorite, siderite, rhodochrosite, ankerite, calcite (continued).

2. Magnetite, specularite (sometimes later), uraninite.

3. Pyrite, arsenopyrite, cobalt and nickel arsenides.

4. Cassiterite (sometimes preceding pyrite), wolframite (scheelite), molybdenite(?).

5. Pyrrhotite, pentlandite, chalcopyrite, stannite, bismuthinite(?).

6. Sphalerite, enargite, tennantite, tetrahedrite, chalcopyrite, bornite, galena, chalcocite, stromeyerite, argentite, ruby silver, polybasite, chalcopyrite, lead-silver sulfantimonides, native silver, native bismuth, electrum, tellurides, native gold.

7. Stibnite, cinnabar.

SOURCE: After Lindgren (1937).

The established mineral sequence, as determined first by Lindgren and later by Edwards is given in Tables 6-I and 6-II. The minerals within each group are listed in the order of their deposition, the earliest-formed minerals being listed first. It must be emphasized that although the mineral sequence holds in general, there are many exceptions, reversals, and examples of overlapping deposition.

The agreement between Lindgren's and Edwards' paragenetic models suggests that we can formulate some generalized statements about the sequence of ore deposition. Thus we note that the oxides are deposited early; sulfides and arsenides of iron, nickel, cobalt, tin, and molybdenum are generally contemporaneous with or slightly later than the oxides; zinc, lead,

TABLE 6-II

Paragenesis in Hydrothermal Ore Deposits

ORE MINERALS
1. Magnetite, ilmenite, chromite, hematite.
2. Cassiterite, tantalite, wolframite, molybdenite.
3. Pyrrhotite, pentlandite, löllingite, arsenopyrite, pyrite, cobalt and nickel arsenides.
4. Chalcopyrite, sphalerite (interchangeable), bornite.
5. Tetrahedrite, galena, lead sulfosalts, silver sulfosalts, native bismuth and bismuthinite, tellurides, stibnite, cinnabar.

GANGUE MINERALS
1. Quartz, tourmaline, topaz.
2. Siderite (often manganiferous), fluorite, calcite, barite, chalcedony.

Source: After Edwards (1947, 1952).

silver, and combined copper-iron sulfides are intermediate in the paragenesis and are mixed with or slightly older than the copper, lead, and silver sulfosalts; native metals and tellurides are typically late; and antimony and mercury sulfides are the latest.

Zoning

The paragenesis of mineral formation in moving ore fluids produces changes in ore mineralogy along the course of deposition. Such changes are described as zoning, and are found in sedimentary deposits as well as in magmatic and metamorphic ores. In the ideal case of a radiating hydrothermal or pneumatolytic fluid, changes in chemistry, temperature, and pressure along the fissures result in the deposition of different minerals in concentric zones at increasing distances from the magmatic source. Syngenetic deposits, however, may be zoned parallel to a contemporaneous shore line or along a stream channel leading away from the source rock. Any detection of a zonal pattern—epigenetic or syngenetic—is important to economic geology, because it helps to predict changes in mineralization as a deposit is developed and mined.

The theory of zoning was probably stated first as a generalization by Spurr (1907), though many workers had previously recognized the phenomenon (de la Beche, 1839; Henwood, 1843; Collins, 1902; Waller, 1904;

de Launay, 1900). At the present time, zoning is widely recognized and is accepted as a working hypothesis. Yet the causes of zoning are still being debated, and it is difficult to explain why certain deposits are zoned and others are not (Czechoslovak Acad. Sci., 1963).

Zoning in ore deposits is conveniently divided into three intergradational classes, based upon size but independent of the origin. These classes are: (1) *regional zoning*—zoning on a very large scale, as exemplified by the Southern Piedmont region of the southeastern United States and by ore deposits associated with the Sierra Nevada batholith (Park, 1955); (2) *district zoning*—the zoning shown by closely grouped mines, a category which includes the well-known mining districts of Butte, Montana (Sales and Meyer, 1949), Cornwall, England (Davison, 1927; Lilley, 1932), and Bingham, Utah (Peacock, 1948); and (3) *ore-body zoning* changes in the character of mineralization within a single ore body or a single ore shoot (Riley, 1936): many vein deposits in the volcanic rocks of Japan, as well as many single ore bodies within zoned districts, are in this category. Because of the great disparity in size between mineralized regions and individual ore bodies, confusion often arises in the discussion of zoning. This confusion led Sampson (1936) to suggest that the term zoning be limited to districts. But restricting the term in this way further confuses the usage. The addition of adjectives to indicate the relative scale—regional, district, and ore-body —is preferable. This dimensional classification of zoning is not universally accepted by European geologists, some of whom feel that ore deposits usu-ally result from discontinuous surges or pulsations of mineralizing solutions, resulting in a complicated overlapping of zones; they suggest that zoning should be classified according to whether the deposits were developed by a single pulsation or by many, and whether they are in normal or reversed sequence (Kutina, 1957).

For zoned deposits of all scales, field observation has shown that groups of minerals were formed in more or less constant sequence from the source of ore fluids outward. By gradually piecing together the field data on rela-tive zoning in individual regions, districts, and ore bodies, geologists have been able to construct a theoretical vein system against which any single deposit may be compared. Early observers noted that tin minerals charac-teristically lie deeper or closer to the magma chamber than copper minerals, and that copper minerals, in turn, occur inside the silver zone. Expansion of these observations led to the relatively detailed model vein system repro-duced in Table 6-III. No single example contains all of the mineral groups given in the model, but the vein system is of value in the study and understanding of zoning. Note the similarity between this system and the models of paragenesis given by Lindgren and Edwards.

As would be expected, there are many discrepancies between the ob-

TABLE 6-III

A Reconstructed Vein System, from the Surface Downward

---

1. *Barren:* Chalcedony, quartz, barite, fluorite. Some veins carry small amounts of mercury, antimony, or arsenic.

2. *Mercury:* Cinnabar deposits, commonly bearing chalcedony, marcasite. Barite-fluorite veins.

3. *Antimony:* Stibnite deposits, locally passing downward into galena with antimonates. Some carry gold.

4. *Gold-silver:* Bonanza gold deposits and gold-silver deposits. Argentite with arsenic and antimony minerals common. Tellurides and selenides in places. Relatively small amounts of galena, adularia, alunite, with calcite, rhodochrosite, and other carbonates.

5. *Barren:* Most nearly consistent barren zone; represents bottom of many Tertiary precious-metal veins. Quartz, carbonates, and small amounts of pyrite, chalcopyrite, sphalerite, and galena.

6. *Silver:* Argentite veins, complex silver minerals with antimony and arsenic, stibnite, some arsenopyrite; quartz gangue, in places with siderite.

7. *Lead:* Galena veins, generally with silver; sphalerite usually present, increasing with depth; some chalcopyrite. Gangue of quartz and carbonates.

8. *Zinc:* Sphalerite deposits; galena and some chalcopyrite generally present. Gangue is quartz and, in some deposits, carbonates of calcium, iron, and manganese.

9. *Copper:* Tetrahedrite, commonly argentiferous; chalcopyrite present. Some pass downward into chalcopyrite. Enargite veins, generally with tetrahedrite.

10. *Copper:* Chalcopyrite veins, most with pyrite, many with pyrrhotite. The gangue is quartz and, in some places, carbonates and feldspar. Orthoclase and sodic plagioclase not rare, but high-calcium plagioclase very rare. Generally carry precious metals. Uranium; probably main horizon of uraninite.

11. *Gold:* Deposits with pyrite, arsenopyrite, quartz, carbonates, and some with feldspar gangue. Tourmaline. Tellurides not uncommon and at places abundant. Some deposits have zones 10 and 11 reversed.

12. *Arsenic:* Arsenopyrite with chalcopyrite.

13. *Bismuth:* Bismuthinite, native bismuth, quartz, and pyrite.

14. *Tungsten:* Veins with tungsten minerals, arsenopyrite, pyrrhotite, pyrite, chalcopyrite. Tungsten occurs in higher zones in fairly large amounts, but this is the main horizon.

15. *Tin:* Cassiterite, with quartz, tourmaline, topaz, feldspar.

16. *Barren:* Quartz, feldspar, pyrite, carbonates, and small amounts of other minerals.

SOURCE: After Emmons (1936).

served and the theoretical vein system. Irregularities and reversals result from rapid deposition and the overlapping of zones, among other factors. Discrepancies and poorly defined zoning are caused by the overlapping of deposits from two or more magmatic centers, by the retreat or advance of magmatic centers during one period of deposition, by repeated periods of mineralization in a single area, and by other causes not understood. Where the minerals of one zone overlap those of another, the deposit is said to be *telescoped*. Near the surface, magmatic fluids are subjected to steep temperature and pressure gradients, causing rapid deposition of the ore minerals and a shortening, or telescoping, of the ore zone. At depth, the temperature and pressure gradients are gentle; under these conditions deposition takes place slowly, and the separation of minerals is well defined. Telescoping is hence restricted largely to deposits formed under shallow conditions, where changes in temperature and pressure are rapid (Borchert, 1951). Where conditions change gradually, as in the high-temperature, high-pressure deposits, zoning is generally minor and is expressed, for example, by variations in the fineness of gold (Pryor, 1923) or in the amounts of minor constituents. Many districts and mines show no recognizable zoning; ore from the lower levels is apparently identical with ore from the upper levels. Probably the best examples of unzoned deposits are some of the deeper gold mines, though any type of metal mine may lack zoning. At Morro Velho, Brazil, for example, the ore in the bottom workings, at a depth of about 8500 feet vertically—or about 13,000 feet down the dip—is, as far as has been determined, identical with ore from the upper workings. The Mother Lode district of California is another example of a high-temperature, high-pressure gold district that shows no zoning, either in the district or in individual ore bodies. Yet when all the mineral deposits (including those in Nevada) associated with the Sierra Nevada batholith are plotted on a map, they show a regional pattern. Deposits of the California copper belt, as well as other base-metal deposits, are farther from the intrusive complex than are the gold deposits. The tungsten ores of Bishop, Kings Canyon, and other areas, also fit into the zonal pattern; they are closer to the intrusive than are the gold deposits. Analogous regional zoning may be present in Brazil near the Morro Velho deposits, but not enough is known of the area to permit definite conclusions.

SOUTHEASTERN PIEDMONT PROVINCE

An example of regional zoning is furnished by the ore deposits of the Southern Appalachian-Piedmont province from Washington, D.C., southward to the Coastal Plain of Alabama (Pardee and Park, 1948). In this region the metalliferous deposits are zoned around the central core of the Piedmont region, where both late Paleozoic and Precambrian intrusives are abundant. The central part of the region contains deposits of pyrite and gold. East of this central gold-pyrite zone, Mesozoic Coastal Plain sediments cover the evidence; regional zoning is well shown only to the west of the core. Closely associated with the gold ores, but slightly to the west, are deposits of pyrrhotite and pyrite, as at the Gossan Lead, Virginia. Farther westward are pyrrhotite-chalcopyrite ores of the type found at Ducktown, Tennessee; west of the copper zone are the lead-zinc deposits at Austinville, Virginia, and in the Mascot-Jefferson City district, Tennessee. The outermost zone is defined by barite, which has been mined from several areas west of the lead-zinc ores. Figure 6-2 shows the zonal arrangement of these deposits in relation to the intrusive masses. It is unknown whether the ores are genetically associated with the plutonic rocks or whether both the ores and the intrusives are products of metamorphism deep within the Appalachian geosyncline.

These studies of regional zoning have considerable economic value. In the Southern Piedmont, for example, generally favorable sites for the discovery of lead-zinc deposits lie in the area between southwestern Virginia and southwestern Tennessee, as well as north and south of the known limits of mineralization. If there are any mineral deposits in the eastern part of this region, they are buried under Coastal Plain sediments; as geophysical methods are developed and refined, additional ores may be found beneath these materials.

CORNWALL-DEVON, ENGLAND

The tin-copper district of Cornwall and Devon Counties, England, has long been recognized as one of the classic examples of district zoning. The mines have been ably described by many geologists since the early comprehensive report of de la Beche (1839), and the literature describing the geology of the district is voluminous. Although there are many excellent descriptions of the deposits, no modern detailed studies have been published discussing the causes of zoning. The accepted hypothesis is that zoning was the result of ore deposition away from an igneous center, and that the control was largely caused by decreases in temperature and pressure.

Much of the Cornwall-Devon area is thought to be underlain by granitic intrusive materials, as evidenced by five stock-like masses and associated satellitic plutons, which are exposed at the surface (Fig. 6-3). The granites intrude a sequence of intricately folded and faulted Paleozoic strata consisting of slates, sandstones, grits, limestones, and greenstones (Davison, 1921, 1926, 1927; Dewey, 1925, 1935). Many minor pegmatite dikes and other small intrusives of quartz porphyry and "trap" are present.

Five principal types of hydrothermal alteration are associated with the intrusives—tourmalinization, greisenization, chloritization, silicification, and kaolinization. The tourmaline is generally black and is abundantly developed at places. Parts of the granite itself are altered almost completely to black tourmaline (schorl rock), and in the lower levels of the tin lodes a rock composed of tourmaline and quartz is common. The equivalent facies in rocks that are rich in alumina and lime is represented by axinite. Greisenization is essentially restricted to the granites, which are changed into rock composed of quartz and sericite, many samples of which show minor amounts of topaz and tourmaline. Chloritization is intense around some high-temperature ores, at places resulting in an alteration product made up entirely of chlorite and quartz. Kaolinization is limited principally to the granitic rocks. In parts of the area, alteration was so thorough that it formed some of the world's largest and most pure kaolin deposits. Silicification accompanied all other types of alteration, some of the quartz being produced as a by-product during the breakdown of wall-rock minerals and some being primary silica (Hosking, 1951).

The metals yielded by the Cornish mines were dominantly tin and copper, though lesser amounts of arsenic, tungsten, lead, zinc, silver, uranium, radium, iron, manganese, bismuth, nickel, and cobalt have been produced. The ores are in lodes along fissures that traverse both the granite and the nearby slates. As a rule, the lodes in slates dip away from the granite, and those which strike east-west, parallel to the sedimentary rocks, are cut by those trending north-south. The ores are genetically associated with the granite, and veins in the slates at some distance from the granite typically contain small amounts of granitic material intruded with them along the same fissures. The presence of topaz and black tourmaline, which form most readily under high temperature and pressure, also indicates a close association between the ores and an intrusive source. Many workers have emphasized the relation between the ores and the igneous rocks. Jones (1931) stated that the granite masses are to some extent stanniferous, and that as far as could be determined, the cassiterite was genetically and intimately

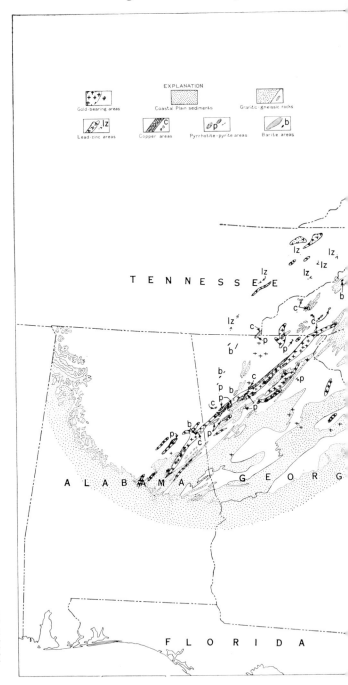

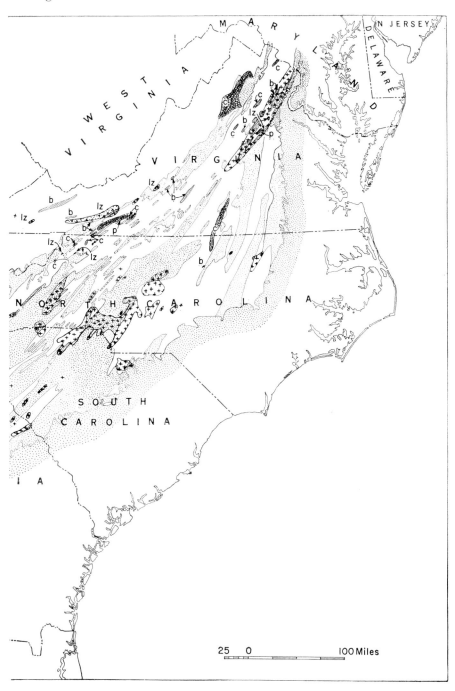

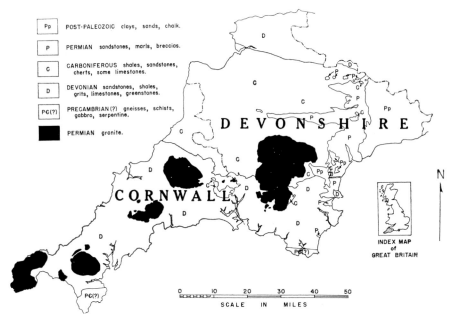

FIGURE 6-3. *Geological map of the Cornwall-Devonshire region, England. (After the geological map of Great Britain, Geological Survey, 1957.)*

related to the granites. Cassiterite also appears to be as much an indication of the common parentage of the different igneous masses as any other mineral common to them.

Most, but not all, of the commercial ore is recovered from veins or lodes. In a few places greisen contains enough metallic constituents—chiefly tin —such that it can be mined. Mineralized greisen consists of many tiny veinlets scattered through the rock; it is a typical stockwork, or net of small veinlets.

According to MacAlister (1908), the intrusions, and the accompanying mineralization, took place in three gradational stages: (1) intrusion of granitic magma with accompanying thermal metamorphism in the rocks near the intrusive masses; (2) intrusion of quartz porphyry dikes along cleavage planes of the metamorphosed sedimentary rocks; and (3) deposition of the ores in both sedimentary and igneous host rocks.

Variations in mineralization (that is, zoning) of the lodes has been known for many years and has been used as a tool for exploration. Changes in mineralization are recognized not only along the strikes of the lodes, but also at depth.

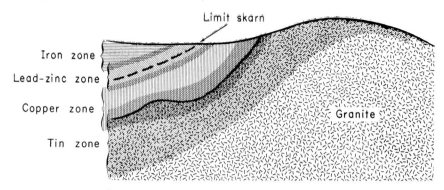

FIGURE 6-4. *Sketch of Cornish mineral zones. (After Davison, 1926.)*

Four zones were recognized by Davison (1926). Iron-manganese ores containing minor amounts of antimony were deposited farthest from the granitic rocks. Next toward the intrusives are the lead-zinc-silver ores, which in turn lie beyond the copper-arsenic-tungsten minerals. Closest to the intrusives—in fact, extending well into them—are the tin ores. A diagram showing these zones is reproduced in Fig. 6-4. As may be seen, many of the zones overlap, and locally copper and tin are mined together. In other mines, copper and tin are separated by as much as several hundred feet of barren rock. Before the separation of minerals into zones was understood, the presence of the thick layer of barren rock led to the abandonment of many mines that produced copper in their upper levels. These mines were later reopened as the barren zone was penetrated and tin ore was encountered at depth.

Field data accumulated subsequent to Davison's work indicate that the mineral zones are not parallel to the granite contact, though there seems to be no objection to Davison's model for the relative sequence of deposition. Deeper mining has shown that the ore zones reflect the granite contacts, but they are less steeply inclined (Fig. 6-5). Consequently, the tin zone is confined to the granite only at

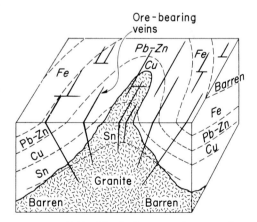

FIGURE 6-5. *Block diagram showing the arrangement of ore zones relative to granite-slate contact, Cornwall, England. (After Hosking, 1951.)*

the peaks of the stocks; on the flanks it may lie entirely within the meta-morphosed sediments (Dines, 1933; Hosking, 1951). Presumably, the zones represent isogeothermal surfaces, which compromise in attitude between the horizontal ground surface and the inclined granite-slate contact.

The iron-manganese ores are mostly oxidation products such as limo-nite, hematite, manganese oxides, and the hypogene carbonates, siderite and rhodochrosite. A small amount of rhodonite has also been identified. Studies of the paragenesis indicate that these minerals were the last of the ores to form. This outer zone is beyond the limits of recognized meta-morphism caused by igneous activity and is of only minor economic value.

The lead-silver ores originated slightly later than the tin and copper-bearing lodes and are slightly older than the iron-manganese lodes. They are not as numerous as the tin and copper ores of the deeper zones. Most of these lead-zinc-silver deposits are found beyond the outside edges of the metamorphic aureoles, but locally they extend into the metamorphosed ground. The minerals present include argentiferous galena, pyrargyrite, jamesonite, sphalerite, stibnite, bournonite, tetrahedrite, argentite, pyrite, quartz, dolomite, fluorite, chalcedony, barite, and minor amounts of ura-nium, nickel, bismuth, and cobalt minerals.

Deposition of the copper-arsenic-tungsten ores took place during and after formation of the deeper tin minerals. The copper-arsenic-tungsten zone itself is differentiated into an upper chalcopyrite-rich region and a lower arsenopyrite-wolframite region. Most of the copper-rich lodes extend from near the borders of the granites into the metamorphic aureoles, but not beyond the limits of thermally metamorphosed slates. Gangue minerals are quartz, chlorite, tourmaline, fluorite, pyrite, muscovite, and jasper. The chlorite is restricted to the upper zones, and tourmaline is found only at depth. Small amounts of cassiterite are recognized in the deepest parts of the copper-arsenic-tungsten lodes.

Tin belongs to the deepest of the recognized zones, and is generally found from depths of about 4000 feet within the granite to a short distance above the granite in the metamorphosed slate. The principal ore mineral is cas-siterite, accompanied by minor amounts of other metallic minerals from the copper-arsenic-tungsten zone. Throughout the district there is a well-defined tendency for the tin content to increase in all lodes at depth. The character of the gangue also changes: chlorite, so common in the inter-mediate zones, disappears at depth, and its place is taken by a fine-grained, dense, blue quartz that is crowded with tiny black tourmaline crystals.

The blue quartz is brecciated in many mines and has been recemented by coarse-grained cassiterite and tourmaline.

Hosking (1951) proposed a more detailed sequence of zones, recognizing seven rather than just four (see Table 6-IV). His outermost zone is defined by the presence of pyrite and the absence of ore minerals. In sequence

TABLE 6-IV

Primary Zones of Cornish Lodes. Vertical Distribution of Mineral Zones at Cornwall, England

Gangue	Zone and ore minerals	Class	Metals
	7. Barren (pyrite)		—
	6. Hematite, Goethite, Jamesonite, Stibnite, Pyrargyrite, Bournonite, Tetrahedrite, Siderite, Pyrite, Marcasite.	MESO/EPITHERMAL Lodes generally at right angles to granite ridges.	Fe Sb Ag
	5. Argentite, Pitchblende, Galena, Niccolite, Sphalerite, Cobaltite, Smaltite, (Bismuth, bismuthinite).		Pb Ag Zn U Co Ni Bi
	4. Chalcopyrite, (sphalerite), Wolframite, Arsenopyrite, Pyrite.		Cu
	3. Chalcopyrite, (Stannite, molybdenite), Wolframite, Arsenopyrite, Cassiterite, wood tin.	HYPOTHERMAL Lodes generally parallel to granite ridges.	W As
	2. Wolframite Arsenopyrite, Cassiterite.		Sn
	1. Cassiterite, Specularite (Earliest).		Fe

Gangue columns (left to right): Quartz; Feldspar, Mica / Tourmaline; Chlorite / Fluorite; Dolomite; Chalcedony / Barite / Calcite.

SOURCE: After Hosking (1951).

toward the deepest zones, Hosking describes an iron-antimony-silver zone; a lead-silver-zinc-uranium-cobalt-nickel-bismuth zone; a copper zone; a tungsten-arsenic zone; a tin zone; and a specularite zone. The upper three zones are considered mesothermal to epithermal; the deepest four, hypothermal. Gangue minerals do not conform directly to the zones as classified, but each is characteristic of a contiguous sequence of zones. In general, the minerals of the deeper zones were deposited first, and they decrease slightly in age away from the intrusives. Moreover, the older, hypothermal veins fill fissures that strike parallel to the sediments and granite ridges, and the lower temperature lodes fill younger, cross-cutting fissures.

Although zoning is clearly recognized in many of the mines and in the district as a whole, there are still complications. Northward-dipping lodes containing sulfides, arsenides, and tungstates are cut locally by later, northward-striking lodes containing tourmaline and cassiterite. Accordingly, it is inferred that the temperatures increased during this period of mineral deposition, since cassiterite and tourmaline are thought to have formed at slightly higher temperatures than the sulfides, arsenides, and tungstates. (However, numerous other hypotheses, based upon physical-chemical reasoning, could be advanced.) Such a reversal of the normal sequence of mineral formation naturally leads to confusion. Another complicating factor is that many of the lodes have been subjected to repeated movements, brecciation, and subsequent infilling, with changes in composition of both the gangue and the metalliferous minerals. In spite of the complications, however, the zoning at Cornwall is well established and has been used successfully as a tool in exploration.

TONOPAH, NEVADA

The Tonopah district in Nevada is a good example of how subtle the effects of zoning may be, even when considered over an entire district. The Tonopah mines are closely spaced and do not encompass as large an area as the Cornwall district, but the zoning is nevertheless defined by the deposits as a whole rather than by single ore bodies.

Silver was discovered in the Tonopah district at the beginning of the twentieth century—late enough so that the U.S. Geological Survey was able to witness its development and record the geologic and mineralogic details with accuracy. Numerous reports were published by some of the foremost geologists in the United States (Spurr, 1905, 1915; Burgess, 1909; Locke, 1912; Bastin and Laney, 1918; Nolan, 1935); from these and later studies, geologists have developed a three-dimensional picture of the mineralization.

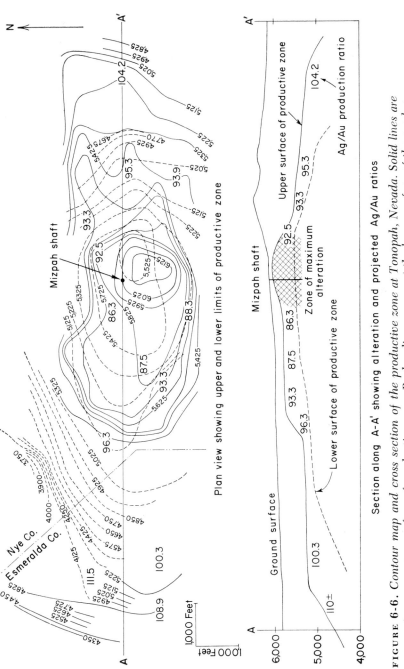

FIGURE 6-6. *Contour map and cross section of the productive zone at Tonopah, Nevada. Solid lines are contours on upper surface of productive zone. Broken lines represent the lower surface of the productive zone. Cross hatching represents the quartz-sericite-adularia alteration zone; elsewhere the dominant alteration is chlorite-carbonate. The bold numbers are ratios of silver to gold recorded for all mines that produced over 100,000 ounces of hypogene silver. (After Nolan, 1935.)*

The ore at Tonopah is mined principally for silver, though gold is also recovered. Faults provided avenues for mineralizing fluids, and the deposits occur mainly as replacement lodes along these fissures. The host rock is a confusing sequence of altered and faulted Tertiary volcanics ranging in composition from rhyolite to trachyte and andesite, and including lava flows, dikes, and pyroclastics. The most common ore minerals are argentite, electrum, polybasite, and pyrargyrite, which occur in a gangue of quartz, barite, and a pinkish carbonate mineral (rhodochrosite or dolomite?). Two principal types of alteration have been defined in the district: a central zone of quartz-sericite-adularia, and a surrounding envelope of chlorite-carbonate alteration, both of which are superimposed upon early, district-wide albitization (Nolan, 1935).

As a result of detailed field studies, Nolan (1935) discovered that the ratio between silver and gold varies in a systematic way, matching the configuration of the ore horizon as well as the pattern of alteration. Nolan contoured the upper and lower limits of mineralization over the district as a whole and found that the productive zone describes a somewhat symmetrically domed shell that persists without interruption across formation contacts and is only locally modified across faults. Furthermore, the higher-temperature alteration, represented by quartz-sericite-adularia, coincides with the central part of this domed shell, and the chlorite-carbonate alteration describes a peripheral zone. A plot of silver-gold ratios over the contour and alteration map (see Fig. 6-6) shows relatively low ratios near the top of the dome, compared to higher silver-gold ratios around the outside; silver tended to travel farther than gold. The symmetrical pattern of Nolan's compilation, along with the zoning of alteration products and the distribution of silver-gold ratios, led him to suggest that the lower and upper surfaces of the productive zone represent the approximate isothermal lines for temperature limits of ore deposition, theoretically reflecting a deeper magmatic source. This hypothesis is supported by the fact that deviations from a truly symmetrical dome correspond to major fault zones, along which the mineralizing fluids could ascend most readily.

RED MOUNTAIN, COLORADO

The best examples of ore-body zoning are among the deposits formed at shallow depths, where temperatures and pressures change rapidly. Many of the deposits are in regions of comparatively recent volcanic activity; they are typically of Tertiary age and, in general, were formed at depths only slightly below their present locations.

The Red Mountain district, in the Silverton volcanic series of the San Juan Mountains, between Ouray and Silverton, contains excellent examples of ore-body zoning. The volcanic rocks of Red Mountain are intruded by many plugs and pipes of breccia, porphyritic latite, and porphyritic rhyolite. Fracturing in and around these pipes is intense, and the area contains many weakly mineralized fissures. Large bodies of the rocks are impregnated with finely divided pyrite and hydrothermal alteration products, especially clay minerals, diaspore, alunite, and quartz.

Active mining in the Red Mountain district was restricted to the last decades of the nineteenth century. Typical ore bodies were vertical chimney-like masses of roughly elliptical outline, bordered by fractures and fault planes. Within the main brecciated and mineralized pipes there were subsidiary chimneys, fissures, and irregular bodies of ore. Most, but not all, of the chimney ore bodies were surrounded by envelopes of silicified country rock, which, in turn, were enclosed within highly argillized zones (Ransome, 1901; Burbank, 1941, 1947).

Ore-body zoning was especially well developed in the Guston and Yankee Girl mines (Ransome, 1901), though it was recognized in many other properties of the Red Mountain district. Just below the weathered outcrop, the main ore body of the Guston mine contained galena and possibly some tetrahedrite, which assayed 50–60 percent lead, 30–40 ounces per ton of silver, and only a trace of gold. This ore continued to a depth of about 115 feet, where high-grade stromeyerite abruptly increased the silver values. Appreciable amounts of galena were found to a depth of about 290 feet, but below this level the lead content gradually diminished. With increasing depth, stromeyerite and ruby silvers, associated with pyrite and chalcopyrite, characterized the rich ore of the mine. The best and most abundant ore was recovered between the fifth and sixth levels (288 and 378 feet below the surface); select carloads assayed up to 15,000 ounces of silver per ton, and the general ore ran 12 percent copper and 1/10–3 ounces of gold per ton. At a depth of about 500 feet the ore body was cut by a fault, below which the content of silver was appreciably lower and the ore was harder and more compact. Mineralization down to the lowest level, at a depth of nearly 1300 feet, consisted largely of silver-bearing pyrite (low-grade) and some bornite, enargite, chalcopyrite, and barite; stromeyerite was not present in quantity. Some of the best ore in this fault block was found on the ninth level, about 680 feet beneath the surface. It consisted of bornite carrying 125 to 450 ounces of silver and $\frac{1}{4}$ to $\frac{1}{2}$ ounce of gold per ton, as well as 25–50 percent copper; chalcopyrite with 15–75 ounces per ton of silver, up to one ounce of gold per ton, and 8–15 percent copper; and massive pyrite that assayed up to 15 ounces of silver per ton. The most striking changes below the fault were a gradual increase in the ratio of pyrite to copper and silver minerals and an increase in the gold content. Ore on the ninth level and below carried up to 29 ounces of free gold per ton; much of the gold was in barite. The deepest levels contained large masses of low-grade pyrite with sporadic nodules of bornite, chalcopyrite, and barite. In general, the zoning pattern was one of gradual and overlapping changes from galena to stromeyerite, to bornite, to chalcopyrite, and finally to pyrite, considering the most prominent mineral in each zone; also, the gold content increased with depth. These zones did not grade smoothly from one to the next, however, and complications were not uncommon. Pyrite had the greatest vertical range; chalcopyrite extended above bornite but was important only within or below the bornite zone; the upper limit of stromeyerite was abrupt rather than gradational; and the highest values of silver and gold were associated with the greatest concentrations of copper. Nevertheless, zoning in the Guston mine was clearly evident when the ore was being extracted. The vertical changes in mineralogy were indisputable; but not all of the zoning was confined to the vertical dimension, as evidenced by horizontal sections of the high-grade ore between the fifth and sixth levels, where the main ore was stromeyerite and galena, enveloped in a low-grade pyrite-chalcopyrite aureole.

Causes of Sequential Deposition

The reasons for a time and space arrangement in mineral deposits constitute one of the most controversial subjects in this branch of geology. Attempts have been made to correlate zoning and mineral paragenesis with the densities of fluids, atomic weights of the metals, mineral hardnesses, free energies of mineral formation, volatilities, metal-sulfur ratios, electrode potentials, and many other properties. Any hypothesis offered must explain the general mineral sequence as given by Lindgren's and Edwards' paragenetic tables and Emmons' zoning model. And, as in most geologic controversies, we must be aware that more than one hypothesis will probably be valid under various circumstances; discrepancies in the theoretical ore sequence may be the result of relative abundance of elements in the ore fluid or of differences in the local geologic conditions.

According to Stôces (1934) and Brown (1948), the latest minerals to form in an ore deposit are those farthest from the igneous source, and the earliest minerals are those formed at depth under high temperatures and pressures. Aside from the fact that the temperature of ore-bearing solutions should decrease with time, however, this observation does not explain the paragenesis of minerals at any one location, nor does it explain zoning. In the past, local zoning was explained mainly in terms of the mineral solubilities—the most insoluble minerals are supposed to have been deposited nearest the source; and the more soluble, farther away. But the observed zoning does not agree with the known mineral solubilities as determined in the laboratories. Although there are notable exceptions, the zonal distribution of minerals is generally the reverse of what would be expected from solubilities, and the younger minerals are typically the least soluble in a paragenetic series. For example, the copper and iron minerals commonly deposited in many central zones are more soluble than the far-removed cinnabar. Similarly, galena is typically younger and farther from the center of control than is the more soluble sphalerite. The manganese-lead relationship would be an exception to this inverse-solubility distribution, because manganese is more soluble than lead, yet the minerals of manganese are generally deposited beyond the galena zone. As an explanation of these relationships, Magnée (1932) suggested that the solubilities reverse at elevated temperatures, but laboratory experiments have discredited this hypothesis (Verhoogen, 1938). Newhouse (1928) has proposed that the chronologic order of deposition reflects the sequence of removal from the watery rest melt within differentiating magmas; the least soluble would be the last to be removed from the magma, and consequently would be the latest to arrive at the mineral deposit. The geochemistry of this process seems a little dubious, but if the metals are supplied by deuteric leaching from a nearly crystallized pluton, perhaps it is the answer to some mineral parageneses. In replacement deposits, deposition may take place in an inverse order of solubilities, the least soluble mineral being deposited at the expense of more soluble minerals (Newhouse, 1928).

Owing to the evidence against simple mineral solubilities as an answer to the paragenesis and zoning of mineral deposits, various alternative hypotheses have been proposed. A popular explanation holds that the sequential deposition may be at least partly related to the mineral volatilities, which match the zoning sequence more closely than the solubilities. This hypothesis is based on the observation that the minerals are formed roughly in the order of decreasing vapor pressure, if we assume that the metals travel mainly as sulfides, oxides, and chlorides. Holland (1959) demonstrated that most mineral assemblages are in equilibrium with

S_2-O_2-CO_2 gas at the time of deposition, without implying that these gases are the transporting agent. Holland's thermochemical considerations indicate that deposition should be controlled by the temperature and fugacity (effective partial pressure) of the gases, and the resulting mineral parageneses would correspond to those generally observed in nature. This concept cannot explain all deposits, however, because abnormally high temperatures would be required to account for the deposition of some minerals (Krauskopf, 1957). Furthermore, it seems difficult to explain the gaseous replacement and removal of nonvolatile host rocks, such as chert and limestone.

Correlations between atomic weights or ion percentages and mineral sequences have been the basis of some plausible hypotheses on zoning and paragenesis. Newhouse (1928) pointed out the relationship between atomic weights of the metals and their chronologic order of deposition—the heavier elements are generally the youngest in any given deposit. A similar correlation can be shown for the oxides, sulfides, arsenides, and antimonides, which seem to form in the order of increasing atomic number of the anion. The implication of this observation is that the lighter elements are more readily expelled from the magma chamber. Brown (1950) prefers to relate zoning and paragenesis to the specific gravity of the ore minerals, rather than to the atomic weight of the elements, and his correlation is even more striking. He suggests that the ore fluids are stratified within the magma chamber according to specific gravity and geochemistry, just as the melt in a blast furnace is layered into slag, matte, and speiss. Escape as volatiles would remove the light silicates and oxides (slag) first and the progressively heavier sulfides and native metals (matte and speiss) later. Similarly, fluids of different densities, and those containing both liquids and gases, might separate into fractions during migration; such separation might produce different types of mineralization around the source and would thus be a possible explanation of zoning. Bandy (1940) suggested that the fundamental control over paragenesis is a progressive change in the weight percent of the anion radical. According to Bandy's hypothesis, each successive oxide mineral has a higher weight percent of the anion radical than the next older mineral. The sequence determined in this manner is essentially the same as that given by both Lindgren and Edwards, with a few minor exceptions. The sulfide relationship may be stated in another way, considering the metal ions rather than the anion radical. Accordingly, the percentage of metal in the sulfide minerals seems to be inversely proportional to their relative ages; late sulfides contain more metal ions than earlier ones.

As a result, the hardness of ore minerals may be shown to follow a paragenetic pattern, the younger, metal-rich sulfides being softer than the older
sulfides.

The order of mineral deposition in zoning has been related to the electrode potentials of the elements (Butler and Burbank, 1929; Butler, 1956).
The electrode potentials are thought to have a direct and controlling influence on oxidation-reduction reactions and thus to have a vital bearing
on ore deposition. Arranged in the order of their electrode potentials, the
elements show a periodicity and a definite and striking relation to their distribution in primary ore minerals.

Zoning on a small scale, especially in replacement ore bodies, may be
due in part to differential diffusion, because the diffusion rate decreases
with increasing ionic radius. The small ions should diffuse farther than the
large ones (Holser, 1947). A comparison of ionic sizes with the apparent
distances of diffusion in replacement ores, however, seems to refute this
hypothesis, because the sequence is more nearly the reverse of what would
be expected. Perhaps metals migrate to the replacment front as hydrated
ions, in which case the effective ionic radius would be inversely proportional to the radius of the metal ions (Edwards, 1956).

Magnée (1932) suggested that precipitation of sulfides is conditioned by
a complex equilibrium between H_2O, H_2S, HCl, HF, CO_2, and the oxides,
sulfides, chlorides, and fluorides of the metals. The sulfides are the least
soluble, and in the presence of excess H_2S, differential precipitation should
be governed by the solubilities of the sulfides in water. According to this
hypothesis, the concentration of sulfides in the magma-derived solution
would be proportional to the relative abundance of the metals. Slight
changes in concentration would be equivalent to large changes of temperature in determining when and where crystallization takes place. Zonal
distribution would result from a single solution in the course of its migration from the magma.

From a study of the Mississippi Valley lead-zinc deposits, in which galena
was deposited beyond sphalerite, Garrels (1941) concluded that concentrated chloride solutions could have been responsible for the zoning. Many
workers think that chloride ion complexes furnish the most reasonable explanation for the nonsolubility order of mineral precipitation. Garrels and
Dreyer (1952) suggested that a common constituent of the ore solution,
such as a complex bisulfide, would make the metal sulfides soluble. In the
presence of these complex ions, simple metal sulfides would be expected to
precipitate in the order of their activity products.

Recently, complex ions have become a favorite subject of hypotheses concerning problems in ore transport, deposition, paragenesis, and zoning. Too frequently, however, their role is suggested merely as a possible answer when flaws are encountered in other hypotheses, because concrete experimental and theoretical data concerning complexes are lacking. But the study of complex ions is beginning to receive concentrated attention, and it is very likely that they will have to be considered in any problem involving the geochemistry of ore fluids. Recent studies by Barnes (1962) have shown that the sequence of mineral deposition as predicted by the stabilities of covalently bonded complexes matches the observed paragenesis and zoning of ores, both in detail and on a large scale. Using thermodynamics we can determine the relative stabilities of complex ions, provided we consider metals of the same valence for a single type of complex. Using this approach, Barnes found that cobalt, iron, nickel, tin, zinc, copper, lead, and mercury should, in that order, be increasingly stable (increasingly soluble as a complex) within any single type of anion complex. Furthermore, his calculations indicate that chalcopyrite and sphalerite should be closely related, and that chalcopyrite should be zoned nearer the center of mineralization. These thermodynamic considerations imply a wide gap between lead and mercury, the latter being more distantly removed from the magmatic source. Since this sequence refers only to the simple sulfides, iron occurs as pyrrhotite (or troilite), and tin, if included, would probably occur as stannite. Comparison of this theoretical sequence with those given by Lindgren, Edwards, and Emmons will show a remarkable match —in fact, as Barnes suggests, too remarkable to be fortuitous. However, any natural sequence of ore minerals will be more complicated than the divalent sulfide series outlined above, because each nondivalent mineral will belong to its own, unrelated paragenetic series.

Sales and Meyer (1949, 1950) noted a relationship at Butte, Montana, that is possibly a product of these complexing sulfide ions. They found that a high sulfur:metal ratio in solution appears to favor deposition of the simple copper and iron sulfides, chalcocite and pyrite, whereas a relatively lower sulfur ratio favors the combined copper-iron sulfides, bornite and chalcopyrite. Covellite and digenite are also more prevalent in the high-sulfur environment, as their compositions would suggest. The sulfur concentration did not determine the actual sulfur content of each mineral; the critical variable was the fugacity, or partial pressure. Thus pyrite accounts for most of the sulfur in the chalcocite-pyrite zone. At Butte, the sulfur:metal ratios decrease outward from the center of mineralization, describing a district zoning with the sulfur-rich minerals in the center and at depth. The sulfur ratio determined the nature of the minerals formed, and was in turn reduced by deposition of the early sulfur-rich ores. Wall-rock alteration reduced the sulfur ratio further, because destruction of ferromagnesian minerals in the quartz monzonite supplied iron that combined with sulfur from the vein fluids to form pyrite.

Sosman (1950) made the novel suggestion that zoning reflects a migration of metals toward an intrusive rather than away from it. He argues that a magma undersaturated with respect to water should imbibe water from the surrounding sediments. Thus a gradient of both water pressure and water concentration would be established toward the intrusive. Moreover, the process of thermal transpiration should contribute to this gradient; that is, a gas under constant pressure, in a medium having small pores, will travel up the temperature gradient (toward the cooling magma) and down a chemical potential gradient. Most field evidence, however, does not support this hypothesis. Paragenetic studies of ore suites from many districts indicate that, with few exceptions, minerals closest to the igneous central zone are deposited before those farther away. In view of this evidence, an explanation which holds that fluids migrate toward the magma is difficult to maintain. Most ore-bearing fluids probably migrate away from the magma rather than toward it.

District zoning is not always described in terms of intrusive igneous rocks. For example, Brown (1936) suggested that the zoning of Austinville, Virginia, is related to faulting rather than to a magmatic center. In the Michigan copper deposits, zoning is expressed as a slight increase in the arsenic content of the lodes at depth (Broderick, 1929); presumably this increase takes place in the direction of the magmatic source, though intrusive rocks are not encountered at depth. Similarly, Pryor (1923) found that the fineness of gold increases with depth in the famous Kolar deposits of India.

The causes of regional zoning are probably similar to the causes of district and ore-body zoning, but the time interval involved in regional zoning is likely to be much longer than in the other types. For example, in a region undergoing tectonic disturbances and the intrusion of a batholith or a complex of nested batholiths, the rate at which the igneous masses are differentiated, intruded, and cooled, is of tremendous significance. The mechanics of intrusion possibly involve long periods of time, during which the overlying rocks are slowly elevated, engulfed, or metamorphosed. Crystallization and differentiation of the magma cause the volatile fraction and rest melt to change radically from the earliest stages until the latest, ore-forming stages. Similarly, fluids entrapped in the country rock may be activated and set into motion. The escape paths of the fluids may be different at successive stages of intrusion or metamorphism. If the batholith pushes its way up slowly, the overlying rocks may be elevated into a slowly rising dome, with the formation of both radial and concentric faults; thus the history of fissuring may depend upon the evolution of a domal structure, and the zoning of ore deposition may, in turn, be patterned according to the progressive order of faulting (Wisser, 1960). The zoning established during one stage of intrusion or metamorphism may be complicated or effectively masked by other ores deposited at a later stage. If the intrusion or metamorphism takes place during more than one geologic period, the zoning may also be of two, or even more, geologic ages. In this case, ores of different periods may have the same source, and they may fit together in a regionally zoned arrangement.

Some regional zoning seems to be independent of igneous activity, in which case it may be related to metamorphic processes active near the bases of eugeosynclines. As metamorphism proceeds in the deeper wedge of the geosyncline, residual fluids are activated that should dissolve the most readily soluble materials. The fluids then migrate upward and outward into locations where the metallic salts are precipitated (Wells, 1956). Under these conditions, the fluids migrate and behave as though they originated in a magma. Metamorphic zoning, based upon the intensity of metamorphism and mineralogic rearrangement of chemical constituents, has been described in many areas and is universally accepted by petrologists. Original metallic components of the highly metamorphosed rocks are generally considered to have been dispersed rather than concentrated during metamorphism, but this is not necessarily always true. Conceivably, conditions near the edges of the most intensely metamorphosed zones could be such that metallic sulfides might be precipitated and preserved.

The lead-zinc ores of the Åmmeberg district in central Sweden have been attributed to metamorphism, and they are zoned (on a district scale) about the center of metamorphic intensity (Magnusson, 1950). In sequence from the highest to the lowest metamorphic facies, the rock types include migmatitic gneisses; a complex unit of banded gray leptite containing lenses of metamorphosed limestone, biotite gneiss, skarn minerals, and ore deposits; and a barren red leptite (Fig. 6-7). The ores and skarn minerals appear to have formed by the same process, and pegmatites found within the ore zones indicate a similar genetic relationship. The sulfide minerals

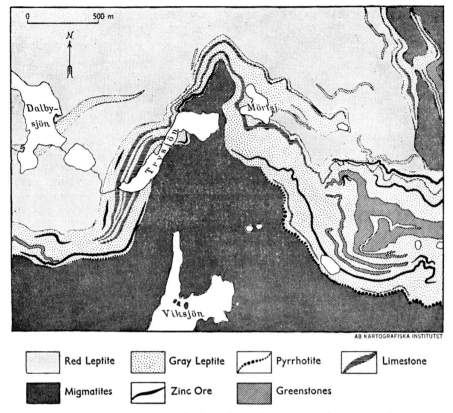

FIGURE 6-7. *Geologic map of the Åmmeberg district, Sweden.* (*After Magnusson and Johansson, 1950, figure 65.*)

include pyrrhotite, sphalerite, and galena, which are zoned in sequence away from the migmatite front. A traverse away from the gneiss would encounter, successively: pyrrhotite, wollastonite-diopside skarn, pyroxene-garnet-hornblende-mica skarn with pyrrhotite, sphalerite-rich ore, and finally galena-rich ore. All of the economic concentrations of lead and zinc are near the migmatite front, and the intensity of sulfide mineralization decreases gradually into the lower-grade metamorphic facies. Magnusson (1950) concludes that the migmatitic gneisses were formed by palingenesis during intense metamorphism, driving the sulfide solutions, skarn-forming solutions, and some pegmatitic solutions ahead of the migmatite front, where they were deposited in receptive rock formations and along favorable structures.

References Cited

Bandy, M. C., 1940, A theory of mineral sequence in hypogene ore deposits: Econ. Geology, v. 35, p. 359–381, 546–570.

Barnes, H. L., 1962, Mechanisms of mineral zoning: Econ. Geology, v. 57, p. 30–37.

Bastin, E. S., and Laney, F. B., 1918, The genesis of the ores at Tonopah, Nevada: U.S. Geol. Survey Prof. Paper 104.

Beche, H. T., de la, 1839, Report on the geology of Cornwall, Devon, and West Somerset: London, p. 283–289.

Borchert, Hermann, 1951, Die Zonengliederung der Mineralparagenesen in der Erdkruste: Geol. Rund., v. 39, no. 1, 81–94.

Broderick, T. M., 1929, Zoning in Michigan copper deposits and its significance: Econ. Geology, v. 24, p. 149–162, 311–326.

Brown, J. S., 1948, Ore genesis: New Jersey, Hopewell Press.

———, 1950, An alternative to the hydrothermal theory of ore genesis: 18th Internat. Geol. Cong. Rept., pt. II, p. 37–44.

Brown, W. H., 1936, A quantitative study of the zoning of ores at the Austinville mine, Wythe County, Virginia: 16th Internat. Geol. Cong. Rept., v. 1, p. 459.

Burbank, W. S., 1941, Structural control of ore deposition in the Red Mountain, Sneffels, and Telluride districts of the San Juan Mountains, Colorado: Colorado Sci. Soc. Proc., v. 14, no. 5, p. 178–209.

———, 1947, Red Mountain district, Ouray County, in Vanderwilt, J. W. (ed.), Mineral resources of Colorado: State of Colorado Mineral Resources Board, p. 428–431.

Burgess, J. A., 1909, The geology of the producing part of the Tonopah mining district: Econ. Geology, v. 4, p. 681–712.

Butler, B. S., 1956, Mineralizing solutions that carry and deposit iron and sulfur: Am. Inst. Mining Engineers Trans., v. 205, p. 1012–1017.

———, and Burbank, W. S., 1929, Relation of electrode potentials of some elements to formation of hypogene ore deposits: Am. Inst. Mining Engineers Trans., Yearbook, p. 341–356.

Collins, J. H., 1902, Notes on the principal lead-bearing lodes of the west of England: Roy. Geol. Soc. Cornwall Trans., v. 12, p. 713.

Czechoslovak Acad. Sci., 1963, Symposium on the problems of postmagmatic ore deposition: Prague, Czechoslovak Acad. Sci.

Davison, E. H., 1921, The primary zoning of Cornish lodes: Geol. Mag., v. 58, p. 505–512.

———, 1926, Handbook of Cornish geology: Roy. Geol. Soc. Cornwall, p. 65–77.

———, 1927, Recent evidence confirming the zonal arrangement of minerals in the Cornish lodes: Econ. Geology, v. 22, p. 475–479.

Dewey, Henry, 1925, The mineral zones of Cornwall: Geol. Assoc. Proc., v. 36, p. 107–135.

———, 1935, Copper ores of Great Britain: 16th Internat. Geol. Congress, Copper resources of the world, v. 2, p. 595–598.

Dines, H. G., 1933, The lateral extent of ore shoots in the primary depth zones of Cornwall: Roy. Geol. Soc. Cornwall Trans., v. 16, p. 279–296.

Edwards, A. B., 1947, Textures of the ore minerals: Melbourne, Australasian Inst. Mining Metallurgy.

———, 1952, The ore minerals and their textures: Clarke Memorial Lecture, Roy. Soc. New South Wales Jour. and Proc., v. 85, p. 26–46.

———, 1956, The present state of knowledge and theories of ore genesis: Melbourne, Australasian Inst. Mining Metallurgy Proc., no. 177, p. 69–116.

Emmons, W. H., 1936, Hypogene zoning in metalliferous lodes: 16th Internat. Geol. Cong. Rept., v. 1, p. 417–432.

Garrels, R. M., 1941, The Mississippi Valley type lead-zinc deposits and the problem of mineral zoning: Econ. Geology, v. 36, p. 729–744.

————, and Dreyer, R. M., 1952, Mechanism of limestone replacement at low temperatures and pressures: Geol. Soc. America Bull., v. 63, p. 325–379.

Henwood, W. J., 1843, The metalliferous deposits of Cornwall and Devon: Roy. Geol. Soc. Cornwall Trans., v. 5, p. 213–224.

Holland, H. D., 1959, Some applications of thermochemical data to problems of ore deposits. I. Stability relations among the oxides, sulfides, sulfates and carbonates of ore and gangue metals: Econ. Geology, v. 54, p. 184–233.

Holser, W. T., 1947, Metasomatic processes: Econ. Geology, v. 42, p. 384–395.

Hosking, K. F. G., 1951, Primary ore deposition in Cornwall: Roy. Geol. Soc. Cornwall Trans., v. 18, p. 309–356.

Jones, W. R., 1931, Discussion on "Genesis of ores in relation to petrographic processes": British Assoc. Adv. Sci., Rept. of the Centenary Meeting, p. 387–389.

Krauskopf, K. B., 1957, The heavy metal content of magmatic vapor at 600°C: Econ. Geology, v. 52, p. 786–807.

Kutina, Jan, 1957, A contribution to the classification of zoning in ore veins: Universitas Carolina, Geologica, v. 3, no. 3, p. 197–225.

Launay, Louis de, 1900, Les variations des filons métallifères en profondeur: Rev. Gen. Sci. Pures et Appl., v. 11, p. 575–588.

Lilley, E. R., 1932, Geology and economics of tin mining in Cornwall, England: Am. Inst. Mining Engineers Tech. Pub., Class I, no. 41, p. 5–10.

Lindgren, Waldemar, 1937, Succession of minerals and temperatures of formation in ore deposits of magmatic affiliation: Am. Inst. Mining Engineers Trans., v. 126, p. 356–376.

Locke, Augustus, 1912, The geology of the Tonopah mining district: Am. Inst. Mining Engineers Trans., v. 43, p. 157–166.

MacAlister, D. A., 1908, Geological aspect of the lodes of Cornwall: Econ. Geology, v. 3, p. 363–380.

Magnée, I., de, 1932, Essai d'explication physico-chimique du phénomène de la répartition zonaire des minerais d'origine magmatique: Soc. Géol. Belgique, Ann. 55, Mem., p. M17–35.

Magnusson, N. H., 1950, Zinc and lead deposits of central Sweden: 18th Internat. Geol. Cong., Symposium on the geology, paragenesis, and reserves of the ores of lead and zinc, p. 371–379.

Newhouse, W. H., 1928, The time sequence of hypogene ore mineral deposition: Econ. Geology, v. 23, p. 647–659.

Nolan, T. B., 1935, The underground geology of the Tonopah mining district, Nevada: Univ. of Nevada Bull., v. 29, no. 5.

Pardee, J. T., and Park, C. F., Jr., 1948, Gold deposits of the Southern Piedmont: U.S. Geol. Survey Prof. Paper 213.

Park, C. F., Jr., 1955, The zonal theory of ore deposits: Econ. Geology (50th Anniv. Volume), p. 226–248.

Peacock, Hollis, 1948, An outline of the geology of the Bingham district: Mining and Metallurgy, v. 29, p. 533–534.

Pryor, T., 1923, The underground geology of the Kolar gold field: Inst. Mining and Metallurgy (London) Trans., v. 33, p. 95–135.

Ransome, F. L., 1901, Economic geology of the Silverton quadrangle, Colorado: U.S. Geol. Survey Bull. 182.

Riley, L. B., 1936, Ore body zoning: Econ. Geology, v. 31, p. 170–184.

Sales, R. H., and Meyer, Charles, 1949, Results from preliminary studies of vein formation at Butte, Montana: Econ. Geology, v. 44, p. 465–484.

————, 1950, Interpretation of wall-rock alteration at Butte, Montana: Colorado School of Mines Quart., v. 45, no. 1B, p. 261–273.

Sampson, Edward, 1936, Zonal distribution of ore deposits: 16th Internat. Geol. Cong. Rept., v. 1, p. 461.

Sosman, R. B., 1950, Centripetal genesis

of magmatic ore deposits: Geol. Soc. America Bull., v. 61, p. 1505.

Spurr, J. E., 1905, Geology of the Tonopah mining district, Nevada: U.S. Geol. Survey Prof. Paper 42.

———, 1907, A theory of ore deposition: Econ. Geology, v. 2, p. 781–795.

———, 1915, Ore deposition at Tonopah, Nevada: Econ. Geology, v. 10, p. 713–769.

Stôces, Bohuslav, 1934, How to determine probable changes in primary mineralization with increasing depth: Econ. Geology, v. 29, p. 93–95.

Verhoogen, Jean, 1938, Thermodynamic calculation of the solubility of some important sulphides, up to 400°C: Econ. Geology, v. 33, p. 34–51, 775–777.

Waller, G. A., 1904, Report on the Zeehan silver-lead mining field: Tasmania Geol. Survey Bull., p. 24.

Wells, F. G., 1956, Relation entre gîtes minéraux et géosynclinaux: Rev. de l'industrie minerale, Numero spécial 1R, Jan., p. 95–107.

Wisser, Edward, 1960, Relation of ore deposition to doming in the North American Cordillera: Geol. Soc. America Mem. 77.

CHAPTER 7 **Geothermometry**

THE TEMPERATURES AND PRESSURES at which ores are deposited range from very high to those of the surface. Placer deposits and other sedimentary ores form under atmospheric conditions. Veins, pegmatites, and magmatic segregation deposits may form at a depth of many miles and at temperatures above 500°C, or sometimes even above 1000°C. Lindgren used these fundamental parameters—temperature and pressure—as a basis for his classification of hydrothermal ores, and if we are to use this classification, we must have certain criteria by which we can ascertain the temperature and pressure at the time of ore deposition. As suggested by charts dealing with classification, paragenesis, and zoning (which are all strikingly similar), the mineral assemblage itself must be a fairly reliable indication of the pressure and temperature during deposition. But, aside from the fact that the mineral assemblage can give only a rough approximation of the conditions, we might ask how Lindgren was able to establish numerical limits for his vein categories. That is, how can we determine absolute— rather than relative—temperatures and pressures of ore deposition?

Much knowledge of the temperatures and pressures during deposition of ore minerals is based upon laboratory studies of the ores and their associated gangue minerals. Several methods of study are in common use (Ingerson, 1955a, 1955b; Seifert, 1930), but all must be applied with great care, because laboratory conditions are of necessity simplified, whereas field conditions are complex. Laboratory data on the temperatures and pressures of ore formation may be misleading if minerals that were contained in the ore-bearing fluid or in a reactive wall rock are not present in the ore sample studied. Accordingly, laboratory results must be considered as orders of magnitude when applied to field systems.

There are practical, as well as academic, reasons for studying the temperatures of ore-mineral deposition. Aside from the fact that we cannot understand the genesis of a mineral deposit until we at least roughly ascertain the temperatures involved, it is important for exploration purposes to know if the mineralizing fluids were cold or hot, and if hot, whether they cooled gradually or rapidly. Thus a deposit that formed at a high temperature would be more likely to persist in depth than one that formed at a low temperature, and if the ascending solutions were cooled slowly, the vertical extent of ore would probably be greater than that in a deposit formed from rapidly cooling solutions. As a logical generalization, we might state that deep, high-pressure thermal gradients will be more gradual than shallow, low-pressure thermal gradients. Consequently, ores deposited under deep-seated, high-temperature conditions will generally show little change over long distances, compared to shallow deposits, which will be affected by significant temperature and pressure differences along the vein.

There are ten methods in common use for the determination of the physical conditions of mineral genesis. The remainder of the chapter is devoted to their description.

Synthesis of Minerals

A great deal of work has been done on the synthesis of minerals, although much of it was conducted with dry components, under conditions that do not approach those in nature. Probably the most complete treatise on this subject is Doelter's *Handbuch der Mineralchemie* (1912–1931). A review of the literature was made by Morey and Ingerson in 1937.

Ordinarily, in geothermometric studies of synthesis, the components of a mineral are mixed in stoichiometric proportions and are heated in a closed container. The lowest temperature at which a mineral will form under constant pressure is the accepted temperature for application to geothermometry; that is, a minimum temperature is established for that mineral at each specified pressure. In many instances the resulting products are similar to the natural minerals, and such synthetic products have been of special use as chemically pure materials for experimental use (Gaudin, 1938; Gaudin and Dicke, 1939). Unfortunately, natural minerals are rarely chemically pure substances; their structures contain small amounts of foreign elements, the presence of which almost certainly must have changed their conditions of formation. Interpreting the results of synthetic studies is further complicated by the fact that the conditions of mineral genesis in nature depend in part upon the presence of fugitive constituents, such as water, and of the fluxes or other mineralizers, which may never appear as components of the minerals. Consequently, most geologists are reluctant to accept experimental work based entirely on synthetic minerals, especially if the minerals were formed in dry systems.

Determination of Melting Points

The temperature and pressure at which a mineral will melt is logically assumed to mark the upper limit of stability for that mineral (Birch et al., 1942). Actually, melting points are helpful in establishing the maximum temperatures of mineral genesis, but they are of little value in determining the actual conditions of formation. When the melting point is low, it is a

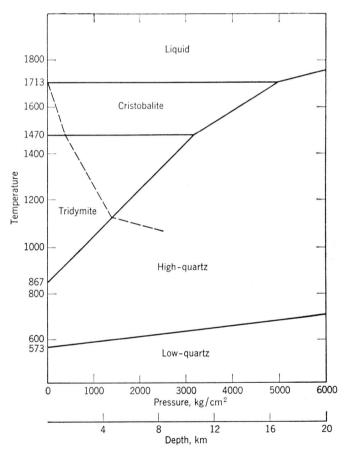

FIGURE 7-1. *Pressure-temperature stability fields of the* SiO_2 *polymorphs. Solid lines are for dry system; broken line is liquidus under water vapor pressure. (After Mason, 1958.)*

meaningful clue to the temperature of formation, but when it is high, it does not even provide an order of magnitude for the temperature. For example, an assemblage of minerals that formed with orpiment (As_2S_3) could not have been deposited above 310°C, whereas a pure corundum deposit could theoretically form at any temperature below 2050°C (Ingerson, 1955a). Again, the presence of small amounts of mineralizers and extraneous materials in crystals may alter the conditions under which synthetic and natural crystals will melt, as exemplified by Fig. 7-1, which demonstrates the profound effect of water on the melting curve of SiO_2.

Determination of Inversion Points and Stability Ranges

Certain minerals undergo internal crystallographic changes at definite temperatures and pressures. Such changes or inversions are commonly recognizable and have been of considerable use in the study of ores (Ramdohr, 1931). The temperature or combination of temperature and pressure that causes the inversion from one polymorph to another should mark, respectively, the minimum or maximum conditions of formation, according to whether the high-temperature polymorph or low-temperature polymorph is being considered. For some polymorphous groups, the inversion temperatures are well established or vary within predictable limits; but the stability ranges for many polymorphs are highly controversial, and may depend upon impurities contained in the crystal structure (Buerger, 1961). Inconsistencies in laboratory results suggest that inversion temperatures in nature may cover wide ranges for some mineral groups. Inversion points also depend upon pressure (Fig. 7-1), since polymorphous inversions always involve density (lattice-volume) changes.

In the Ag_2S system, argentite (isometric) is the stable form at high temperatures, and acanthite (monoclinic) is stable at low temperatures, the inversion temperature being about 180°C (Roy et al., 1959). Here the inversion point seems to be a reliable geothermometer because it does not vary significantly with changes in pressure. The reliability of such a geothermometer may depend upon high purity of minerals and complete stoichiometry; for Ag_2S, the transition temperature between acanthite and argentite is not measurably affected by the likely presence of Pb and Bi as impurities (Van Hook, 1960), or Se (Roy et al., 1959).

In contrast to the acceptance of the argentite-acanthite geothermometer, the validity in geothermometry of the systems Cu-S and Zn-S has been widely debated. Wurtzite has long been recognized as the stable form of

ZnS above 1020°C, sphalerite being the stable polymorph at lower temperatures. Unfortunately, stability is a relative property, hence the "unstable" form may develop under special conditions. In their study of ZnS, Allen et al. (1914) discovered that the hexagonal (wurtzite) crystal will form at low temperatures if the mineralizing solution is acidic. Although the inversion point is always high, it may be significantly lowered by the substitution of iron for zinc in the crystal lattice (Kullerud, 1959; Palache et al., 1944). Thus the presence of wurtzite may indicate either high temperatures or an acidic environment; for this reason its value in geothermometry is extremely limited. The low-temperature form cannot develop, however, above the inversion temperature, thus the presence of sphalerite (as long as it is not a pseudomorph of wurtzite) indicates deposition below 1020°C. The pyrite-marcasite system shows a similar relationship (Allen et al., 1914).

The system Cu-S is one of the most controversial polymorphous systems. According to Posnjak et al. (1915) and Merwin and Lombard (1937), chalcocite occurs in two polymorphs—a high-temperature, isometric form and a low-temperature, orthorhombic form. The inversion temperature was reported by Posnjak et al. to be about 91°C, a low figure that should be of extreme interest to the copper mining industry, because it should serve to differentiate hot (ascending) from cold (descending or meteoric) mineralizers. Relict cleavage remains after chalcocite has passed through the inversion point from the high-temperature to the low-temperature structure, and this cleavage can be recognized under the microscope (Fig. 7-2).

Buerger (1941) questioned the validity of the chalcocite inversion point. He heated powdered mixtures of Cu_2S (chalcocite) and CuS (covellite) and took x-ray diffraction photographs at controlled temperatures during his experiments. The system Cu_2S-CuS was found to contain three compounds at room temperature—chalcocite, digenite

FIGURE 7-2. *Triangular etch pattern in chalcocite. Bn = Bornite. ×405. (After Brummer, 1955.)*

(Cu_9S_5), and covellite. Upon heating, the crystal structures of orthorhombic chalcocite become disordered at 78°C, reaching complete disorder at 105°C. Above 105°C the Cu_2S has a hexagonal structure, rather than the isometric form, as previously thought. The orthorhombic (low-temperature) chalcocite will dissolve up to eight atomic percent of Cu_2S or CuS, and hexagonal (high-temperature) chalcocite will dissolve only about two percent of these compounds. Digenite, which is Cu_9S_5 (or $4Cu_2S \cdot CuS$) at low temperature, was regarded by Buerger as the material that, prior to his work, had been called the high-temperature "isometric" form of chalcocite. Above 78°C digenite is capable of increasing solid solution of Cu_2S and CuS, and on slow cooling, which results in the return to an ordered crystallographic structure, this solution unmixes into either an intergrowth of chalcocite and digenite or an intergrowth of digenite and covellite (Buerger and Buerger, 1944). These complications result from the fact that chalcocite is actually a crystalline solution of the Cu_2S-CuS system (Eitel, 1958). Apparently the orthorhombic polymorph is stable only below the 78–105°C transition temperature, and the hexagonal form is stable above 105°C (Kullerud and Yund, 1960). An isometric form of Cu_2S does exist, but it is stable only above 425°C. This high-temperature polymorph can actually be considered as digenite with extra copper in solid solution, because the amount of Cu admitted by the digenite structure is directly proportional to temperature. At room temperature digenite is roughly Cu_9S_5, but as Cu is taken into solution, the Cu:S ratio gradually increases from 9:5 until it reaches 10:5 ($Cu_{10}S_5$, or Cu_2S) at 425°C (Roseboom, 1960). This discussion suggests that the use of Cu-S minerals as geothermometers is not as straightforward as was previously thought and that the reliability of most past determinations should be questioned. Future studies will have to determine whether the minerals used are truly isometric (digenite), hexagonal (high-temperature chalcocite), or orthorhombic (low-temperature chalcocite), and further, whether they involve exsolution intergrowths.

The nonmetallic minerals are also useful in determining inversion temperatures. Quartz has been studied as much as any gangue mineral. Upon cooling, it changes at 573°C from a high-temperature form to a low-temperature form, maintaining the habit of the original polymorph. The inversion temperature may be strongly modified by the chemical environment (Keith and Tuttle, 1952), but with reservation it can be used to estimate the temperatures at which pegmatites and high-temperature veins are deposited. Furthermore, above 870°C the stable form of silica is tridymite, and above 1470°C it is cristobalite, although there are pressure-controlled modifications of these figures and the presence of water vapor changes the entire configuration (see Fig. 7–1, p. 189).

Determination of Exsolution Points

High temperatures tend to promote disorder in a mineral structure, and under these conditions other elements are readily absorbed and retained. Upon cooling and the development of a more ordered structure, the extraneous materials may be forced out. They tend to accumulate along cleavage surfaces or crystallographically controlled directions, in small blebs and blades. This development of intergrowth structures is called exsolution or unmixing; it is one of the most useful means of determining temperature points on the geologic thermometer as applied to ore deposits. The process has been known for many years in metallurgy and mineralogy, therefore the conditions under which many of the more common examples form are well known (Schwartz, 1942). The usefulness of this method is limited in that it tells us only the point at which order merges into disorder, and it does not necessarily indicate the temperatures at which solidification or replacement takes place. Figure 7-3 shows a common example of this phenomenon. When a specimen of bornite is heated, the chalcopyrite blades eventually disappear, and the bornite assumes a homogeneous appearance. If the temperature is lowered slowly, the blades reappear. Hence we assume the original mineral was formed at temperatures and pressures above those at which unmixing takes place.

Exsolution relationships are common in ore minerals, and they include a wide range of temperatures (Edwards, 1954). Examples include such combinations as blebs of pyrrhotite or chalcopyrite in sphalerite and lamellae or crystallographic intergrowths of ilmenite in hematite (and vice versa); ilmenite or hematite in magnetite; chalcocite or chalcopyrite in bornite; covellite or stromeyerite in chalcocite; and bornite or cubanite in chalcopyrite (Fig. 7-4).

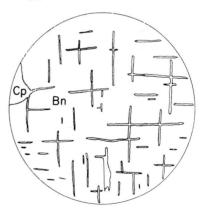

FIGURE 7-3. *Blades of chalcopyrite in bornite. A typical exsolution texture. Brownson mine, Utah.* ×192.

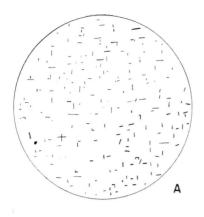

A

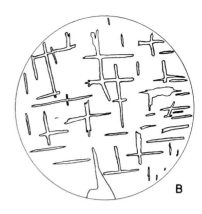

B

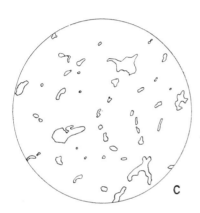

C

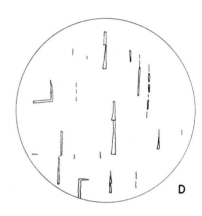

D

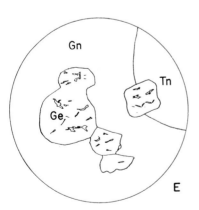

E

FIGURE 7-4. *Examples of exsolution textures.*

(**A**) *Unmixing of ilmenite (tiny laths) in magnetite. Snettisham Peninsula, Alaska.* ×450.

(**B**) *Chalcopyrite blades in bornite. Brownson mine, San Juan County, Utah.* ×192.

(**C**) *Pyrrhotite blebs in sphalerite. Darwin, California.* ×185.

(**D**) *Pyrargyrite blades in galena. La Paz mine, Matehuala district, Mexico.* ×77.

(**E**) *Reniérite blebs in germanite (Ge). Galena (Gn) and tennantite (Tn). Tsumeb, Southwest Africa.* ×520.

Studies of Fluid Inclusions

In recent years, probably more attention has been given to the study of fluid inclusions than to any other method of determining points on the geologic thermometer. The theory behind inclusion thermometry is simple (Newhouse, 1933). It is assumed that the partly filled vacuoles were completely filled with a single fluid phase when the mineral formed. If the inclusion is more than half liquid at room temperature, the ore fluid was hydrothermal; if more than half gas, the ore fluid was pneumatolytic (Yermakov, 1957). The temperature at which the subordinate phase disappears—the homogenization temperature—marks a lower limit for the temperature of mineral genesis. When a specimen is heated, a liquid inclusion will expand until the liquid occupies the entire vacuole (Fig. 7-5), and a gaseous inclusion will simply lose its liquid fraction. Further heating should cause the vacuole to burst. This theory is substantiated by the study of fluid inclusions in artificial crystals formed under controlled conditions.

Two methods are used to study homogenization temperatures of fluid inclusions. If the mineral is transparent, the specimen is heated on a microscope stage, where the homogenization can be observed directly; in fact, if the vacuole has a regular shape, the ratio of liquid to gas can be estimated, allowing the temperature of homogenization to be calculated from thermodynamic considerations. The homogenization temperature should be considered a mini-

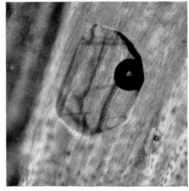

A |0.25mm|

B

FIGURE 7-5. *Fluid inclusion at room temperature (top) and at 130°C (bottom). The bubble within the liquid is much smaller at the higher temperature and would disappear completely above 140°C, the temperature of homogenization in this case. The bubble appears dark due to total reflection along its sides. The specimen shown is fluorite from the Deardorff mine, Cave-in-Rock district, Illinois. (Photos by Bruce M. Harrison.)*

mum temperature of formation for the mineral, provided no leakage exists. Indirectly, the temperature can be studied by heating the specimen until the vacuoles burst, or decrepitate. A curve is obtained by plotting the successive decrepitation points of different vacuoles. Theoretically, the mineral could not have formed at temperatures and pressures above the decrepitation conditions existing at the time of the experiment; hence a maximum temperature of formation is obtained. The decrepitation method is now largely discredited, since the values obtained reflect mineral strength, as well as other variables.

In spite of the wide use of fluid inclusions, the value and reliability of this geothermometer are still debated. Decrepitation temperatures are significantly influenced by rock pressures (Ingerson, 1947); as a result it is necessary to estimate the depth of burial at the time the mineral was formed. Laemmlein (1929) pointed out that some fluid inclusions were introduced into rocks and minerals after the minerals were deposited; hence they may be entirely unrelated to the processes that formed the minerals and may not give an index of the temperature or composition of the mineral-bearing fluid. Kennedy (1950) and Stephenson (1952) expressed further skepticism as to the value of fluid inclusions in geothermometry. They claimed that the contents of the vacuoles may leak out and hence can give no accurate indication of the original constituents or of the original temperatures and pressures. If the fluids do leak out, it is also likely that they may leak in under other circumstances. In support of this contention, Skinner (1953) subjected a slice from a large quartz crystal to changes in temperature and water pressure and concluded that water diffused into and out of the vacuoles. Supporters of fluid inclusion geothermometry acknowledge these criticisms but believe that at least in some of the harder, noncleavable minerals such as beryl, leakage is negligible, and that the liquid or gaseous inclusions furnish a fair sample of the original fluid. They also think that under favorable conditions the presence of leakage can be detected by statistical analyses, because the primary or undisturbed inclusions should give less erratic results than those that have leaked or received additions of fluid (Smith, 1954; Smith and Little, 1953; Smith et al., 1950; Scott, 1948; Ingerson, 1955a; Richter and Ingerson, 1954; Roedder, 1960). The numerous criticisms leveled at the decrepitation method, or even at the use of vacuoles in any way, emphasize the dangers of assuming that all vacuoles contain original ore-bearing fluids. Nevertheless, fluid inclusion studies do give relatively accurate results for artificial minerals; furthermore, the possibility exists that secondary and primary fluid inclusions can be distinguished. These facts suggest that careful determinations may give meaningful results after all. Excellent bibliographies on the subject of vacuoles have been compiled by Smith (1953), Deicha (1955), and Correns (1953).

Studies of Mineral Textures and Habits

Mineral textures and habits have been used by Edwards (1954) to indicate the temperatures of mineral deposition. He likened these textures to similar textures found in smelter products, and pointed out that they disappear upon annealing (or recrystallization). For example, colloform bands, herringbone texture, and columnar crystals in native copper have been interpreted to indicate repeated deposition at low temperatures from solutions of slightly varying composition; at higher temperatures the copper recrystallizes and assumes a texture similar to that obtained by annealing. Edwards also pointed out that textures such as the oölites in hematite are considered to be diagnostic of near-surface conditions, and do not form at high temperatures.

Determination of the Electrical Conductivity of Minerals

Assuming that high-temperature crystals will have fewer structural defects than low-temperature crystals, and that crystallographic imperfections will retard electrical conductivity, Smith (1947) concluded that the electrical properties of conductive minerals should be a measure of their crystallization temperatures. Accordingly, Smith calibrated pyrite as a geothermometer by recording its thermoelectric potentials over the hydrothermal temperature range. Applications of this technique have given inconsistent and conflicting results, however, suggesting that the perfection of crystal growth does not depend upon temperature alone (Smith, 1948; Ingerson, 1955a; Lovering, 1958; Hayase and Otuska, 1952). Perhaps future studies will resolve the discrepancies and establish pyrite (or some other common sulfide) as a reliable geologic thermometer.

Determination of the Conditions Necessary for Ionic Substitutions

High-iron sphalerite, formed in equilibrium with pyrrhotite (thereby indicating an iron-saturated, sulfur-deficient environment in which pyrite will not dominate the iron supply), is generally considered to reflect high-temperature deposition, and the yellow or red "rosin jack" sphalerite is thought to form at low temperatures. Under high-temperature conditions, the sphalerite structure is disordered, thus it will accommodate the substitution of enough Fe^{+2} for Zn^{+2} to impart a dark color to the mineral. Kullerud (1953) studied the equilibrium relationships of the FeS-ZnS system and concluded that the percentage of FeS in sphalerite is a reliable indication of the temperature of formation, provided equilibrium with pyrrhotite and pyrite can be established. In the absence of pyrrhotite, the vapor pressure of sulfur must be established before the temperature of formation can be calculated, because where there is a ready supply of sulfur, the available iron will tend to form pyrite rather than enter the sphalerite structure. That is, the iron content in sphalerite is a measure of the temperature at deposition only if there was an adequate supply of iron and only if this iron was free to enter the sphalerite structure rather than form another mineral (Kullerud, 1953, 1959; Barton and Kullerud, 1957). A few minor refinements have been made in Kullerud's original data (Skinner et al., 1959), but applications of this geothermometer have demonstrated its validity for ores that formed below 600°C (above 600°C the presence of oxidized FeS may affect the temperature determinations). Because sphalerite is a very common ore mineral, whereas sphalerite with pyrrhotite and pyrite is not rare, the sphalerite geothermometer is a definite asset to temperature studies of ore deposits.

Where magnetite forms in the presence of excess titanium—as evidenced by associated ilmenite—the percentage of TiO_2 in the magnetite is largely a function of temperature, though the composition of the hydrothermal or magmatic system is a modifying factor (Buddington et al., 1955). The titaniferous magnetite is of possible use in geothermometry at temperatures between 550°C and 1000°C.

Differential Thermal Analysis

Geologists have attempted several other methods for determining temperatures of deposition. One of these—especially applicable to clay minerals or other fine-grained substances—is differential thermal analysis, a technique that allows the temperature of exothermic or endothermic reactions to be recorded while a mineral is heated at a constant rate. A differential thermal analysis will establish the temperature at which a mineral gives up its chemically bonded water. Theoretically, no mineral is stable under conditions above which its water of crystallization is expelled from the crystal structure.

Determination of Isotope Ratios

Recently, the study of stable isotopes has been extended into temperature ranges that apply to hydrothermal ore deposits. Isotope studies are based on the fact that the mass differences between isotopes should account for relative concentrations of one isotope over another, depending upon the geologic processes involved. In the study of sulfide deposits the most promising phase of isotope geology is the application of $S^{32}:S^{34}$ ratios to problems of genesis and geothermometry. Although this approach is only in the developmental stage, it has begun to produce encouraging results (Ault and Kulp, 1960; Jensen, 1957; Sakai, 1957). Recent studies have shown that oxygen isotope ratios ($O^{18}:O^{16}$) are temperature-dependent and can be used as geothermometers for hydrothermal mineral pairs (Clayton and Epstein, 1961), although they generally pertain to the gangue minerals and cannot be applied directly to the geothermometry of sulfides. The application of both sulfur and oxygen isotope ratios to geologic thermometry is restricted to minerals that formed under chemical and isotope equilibrium —a condition that is very difficult to prove for any given hydrothermal mineral assemblage.

The Application of Geothermometry in Mining Districts

The similarity of results obtained from detailed thermometric studies made in many districts supports not only the science of geothermometry but the general concepts of hydrothermal and pneumatolytic ore deposition. In general, the temperatures determined by use of the various geothermometers are concordant; they define a definite thermal range; and they show that the early minerals formed at the higher temperatures. Moreover, most studies indicate that we cannot rely upon one kind of temperature determination; a thorough investigation must include several techniques as well as many samples from different parts of the deposit. As an example of the modern approach to geothermometry, we describe Lovering's study (1958) of the Gilman district in Colorado.

The ores at Gilman are replacement mantos and pipes of pyrite, sphalerite, chalcopyrite, bornite, and galena, including minor amounts of pyrrhotite, copper-silver sulfosalts, gold-silver tellurides, and native gold. The pipes spread upward into mantos, which are roughly elliptical in cross section. Some are as much as 300 feet wide by 150 feet thick by several hun-

dred feet long. Besides the sulfide minerals, these ore bodies include manganosiderite, barite, dolomite, and quartz. The host rock—the Leadville
Limestone of Mississippian age—was dolomitized prior to the introduction
of sulfide minerals.

Lovering applied several techniques to the problem of geothermometry
at Gilman, and his results generally agreed with the paragenetic relationships. The early minerals typically formed at the highest temperatures;
temperatures recorded for minerals deposited together were comparable;
and wall-rock temperatures were lower than the ore-mineral temperatures.
Temperatures of ore deposition and dolomitization were determined by
studies of mineral assemblages, exsolution textures, the solid solution of
iron in sphalerite, the thermoelectric potentials of pyrite crystals, fluid
inclusions, and even thermoluminescence glow curves.

The mineral assemblages and their paragenesis indicate that the Gilman
ores were formed at an intermediate range of temperatures, corresponding
to Lindgren's mesothermal zone. Thus the range 200–300°C is suggested.
Theoretically, the earliest ore fluids would be the hottest (probably above
300°C), and the final fluids would be as cool as the surrounding wall rocks.
Siliceous limestones and dolomites surrounding the ore bodies would have
developed wollastonite, tremolite, forsterite, or diopside if the temperature
had reached approximately 600°C, hence the absence of these calcium and
magnesium silicates establishes 600°C as a maximum temperature for ore
deposition at Gilman.

Several pairs of ore minerals at Gilman were used to estimate temperatures of deposition, on the basis of the presence or absence of exsolution
textures. Chalcopyrite blebs in the high-iron (high-temperature) sphalerites
indicate a temperature of more than 350°C; some of the low-iron sphalerite
contains no exsolved chalcopyrite, in spite of an apparent availability of
copper and iron, suggesting that the temperatures had dropped below 350°C
before the last of the sphalerite was formed. Lovering applied similar reasoning to other mineral pairs that apparently formed together but failed
to exhibit exsolution textures. Thus the absence of exsolved tetrahedrite in
bornite indicates deposition below 275°C, and the presence of chalcopyrite
without exsolved pyrrhotite indicates deposition below 250°C. The established paragenesis for these mineral pairs is: sphalerite-early chalcopyrite;
tetrahedrite-bornite; late chalcopyrite-pyrrhotite. Exsolution geothermometry accordingly suggests that the ore fluid originally exceeded 350°C and
gradually cooled to less than 250°C. Furthermore, hessite (Ag_2Te) blebs

in galena—the result of either contemporaneous deposition or exsolution—are the low-temperature, anisotropic polymorph, indicating that hessite was deposited (or exsolved) below 150°C; the paragenetic position of hessite supports this interpretation.

Substantiation of the temperature determined with the sphalerite-early chalcopyrite geothermometer was provided by studies of the iron contents in this same sphalerite. Three samples indicated temperatures from about 380°C to 590°C. Since the sphalerite did not form in equilibrium with pyrrhotite, the availability of iron and sulfur could not be established; therefore the temperature determinations represent minimum values. Lovering concluded that the wollastonite-free limestones and the chalcopyrite-free sphalerite indicate that sphalerite began to form at about 590°C and ceased forming just below 350°C.

The application of Smith's pyrite geothermometer to the Gilman district was not entirely successful. Paragenetic studies have established early and late ages of pyrite, and in general the early pyrite indicates a higher temperature of formation than the late pyrite. But the early pyrite, which formed before nearly all of the ore minerals, did not give consistently high values of thermoelectric potential. If deposited before or with the earliest sphalerite, this pyrite should have formed above 500°C; yet most of the early pyrite had lower-temperature electrical conductivities. The younger pyrite, deposited after most of the ore minerals, gave a more reasonable range—generally between 100°C and 200°C. The anomalously low temperatures measured for the early-formed pyrite may be due to its very fine-grained texture and numerous inclusions.

Dolomitization and wall-rock temperatures were estimated by studying liquid inclusions and by testing the thermoluminescence. Homogenization temperatures for two-phase (liquid-gas) inclusions in dolomite suggest that hydrothermal dolomitization took place above 200°C and reached a maximum of slightly more than 300°C.

Thermoluminescence is "frozen-in" phosphorescence, or the ability of a substance to emit light when heated. The light is produced by energy released as electrons escape from high-energy levels to more stable, low-energy levels. Each sample will give a characteristic "glow curve," a graph showing the intensity of luminescence as a function of temperature. Once a sample has been heated, its thermoluminescence is permanently drained, because the electrons remain at the lower energy levels; the sample will not glow when reheated unless it has been re-energized by radioactive bombardment

(Daniels et al., 1953; Ingerson, 1955b). The limestones at Gilman give glow peaks at 235°C and 330°C. Lovering found that the low-temperature peak is generally absent from the dolomitized material, but the 330°C peak is preserved everywhere except near ore. Thus the thermoluminescence data seem to indicate that the wall rocks were heated above 235°C but not above 330°C—figures that agree with the temperatures determined by liquid-inclusion thermometry. Actually, the thermoluminescence of a sample is destroyed if it is heated to a temperature below that at which maximum luminescence is produced. Consequently the absence of the 235°C peak need not imply that the wall rocks were heated above 235°C; this peak could have been removed at temperatures as low as 150°C (MacDiarmid, 1963). Lovering (1958) suggests that these temperatures represent the premetallization phase of dolomitization and do not reflect the wall-rock temperatures attained during ore deposition. Within 40 feet of ore, even the 330°C peak was suppressed, due to heating effects of the post-dolomitization ore fluids.

Two interpretations are possible regarding the hydrothermal history of ore genesis at Gilman. After the preliminary phase of dolomitization, during which the temperature may have exceeded 300°C and then decreased slightly, the metals were deposited either (1) in one continuous sequence, beginning with pyrite and manganosiderite at about 600°C and ending with late pyrite and native gold at about 100°C or (2) in two separate stages, represented by an early, high-temperature (> 300°C) pyrite-sphalerite phase and a late, lower-temperature (100–250°C) phase during which the pyrrhotite, chalcopyrite, tetrahedrite, bornite, galena, hessite, late pyrite, and native gold were deposited. In either interpretation, the paragenesis is the same and is in agreement with a history of waning temperatures.

Comparable results have been obtained from similar studies made in other districts. Besides outlining the general progress of hydrothermal activity or thermal history, perhaps such studies will provide a fruitful approach to the solution of other problems. For example, geothermometry may solve some problems of hydrothermal versus syngenetic origin. Similarly, the metamorphism of a sediment or a low-temperature deposit should produce an assemblage of minerals that all record the peak temperature of metamorphism; such an assemblage could be distinguished from a suite of hydrothermal minerals that formed over a wide paragenetic range of temperatures.

References Cited

Allen, E. T., Crenshaw, J. L., and Merwin, H. E., 1914, Effect of temperature and acidity in the formation of marcasite and wurtzite; a contribution to the genesis of unstable forms: Am. Jour. Sci., v. 38, p. 393–431.

Ault, W. U., and Kulp, J. L., 1960, Sulfur isotopes and ore deposits: Econ. Geology, v. 55, p. 73–100.

Barton, P. B., Jr., and Kullerud, Gunnar, 1957, Preliminary report on the system FeS-ZnS-S and implications regarding the use of the sphalerite geothermometer: Geol. Soc. American Bull., v. 68, p. 1699.

Birch, Francis, Schairer, J. F., and Spicer, H. C., 1942, Handbook of physical constants: Geol. Soc. America Spec. Paper 36.

Brummer, J. J., 1955, The geology of the Roan Antelope ore-body: Inst. Mining Metallurgy (London) Trans., v. 64, pt. 6, p. 257–318.

Buddington, A. F., Fahey, Joseph, and Vlisidis, Angelina, 1955, Thermometric and petrogenetic significance of titaniferous magnetite: Am. Jour. Sci., v. 235, p. 497–532.

Buerger, M. J., 1961, Polymorphism and phase transformations: Fort. Min., v. 39, no. 1, p. 9–24.

————, and Buerger, N. W., 1944, Low-chalcocite and high-chalcocite: Am. Mineralogist, v. 29, p. 55–65.

Buerger, N. W., 1941, The chalcocite problem: Econ. Geology, v. 36, p. 19–44.

Clayton, R. N., and Epstein, Samuel, 1961, The use of oxygen isotopes in high-temperature geological thermometry: Jour. Geology, v. 69, p. 447–452.

Correns, C. W., 1953, Flüssigkeitseinschlüsse mit Gasblasen als geologische Thermometer: Geol. Rund., v. 42, no. 1, p. 19–34.

Daniels, Farrington, Boyd, C. A., and Saunders, D. F., 1953, Thermoluminescence as a research tool: Science, v. 117, no. 3040, p. 343–349.

Deicha, Georges, 1955, Les Lacunes des Cristaux et Leurs Inclusions Fluides: Paris, Masson et Cie.

Doelter, C. A., 1912–1931, Handbuch der mineralchemie (4 vol.): Dresden and Leipzig, T. Steinkopff.

Edwards, A. B., 1954, Textures of the ore minerals and their significance: Melbourne, Australasian Inst. Mining Metallurgy, p. 1–31.

Eitel, Wilhelm, 1958, Structural conversions in crystalline systems and their importance for geological problems: Geol. Soc. America Spec. Paper 66, p. 25–27.

Gaudin, A. M., 1938, Identification of sulfide minerals by selective iridescent filming: Am. Inst. Mining Engineers Tech. Pub. 912.

————, and Dickie, Günther, 1939, The pyrosynthesis, microscopic study and iridescent filming of sulfide compounds of copper with arsenic, antimony and bismuth: Econ. Geology, v. 34, p. 49–81, 214–232.

Hayase, K., and Otuska, R., 1952, Study on pyrite, Part I. On the electrical properties of pyrite: Jour. Geol. Soc. Japan, v. 58, p. 133–143.

Ingerson, Earl, 1947, Liquid inclusions in geologic thermometry: Am. Mineralogist, v. 32, p. 375–388.

————, 1955a, Methods and problems of geologic thermometry: Econ. Geology (50th Anniv. Volume), p. 341–410.

————, 1955b, Geologic thermometry: Geol. Soc. America Spec. Paper 62, p. 465–488.

Jensen, M. L., 1957, Sulfur isotopes and mineral paragenesis: Econ. Geology, v. 52, p. 269–281.

Keith, M. L., and Tuttle, O. F., 1952, Significance of variation in the high-low inversion of quartz: Am. Jour. Sci. (Bowen Volume), p. 203–280.

Kennedy, G. C., 1950, "Pneumatolysis" and the liquid inclusion method of geologic thermometry: Econ. Geology, v. 45, p. 533–547.

Kullerud, Gunnar, 1953, The FeS-ZnS system; a geological thermometer: Norsk Geologisk Tidsskrift, v. 32, p. 61–147.

———, 1959, Sulfide systems as geological thermometers, *in* Abelson, P. H. (ed.), Researches in geochemistry: New York, John Wiley & Sons, Inc., p. 301–335.

———, and Yund, R., 1960, Cu-S system: Geol. Soc. America Bull., v. 71, p. 1911–1912.

Laemmlein, Georg, 1929, Sekundäre Flüssigheitseinschlüsse in Mineralien: Zeit. für Krist., v. 71, p. 237–256.

Lovering, T. G., 1958, Temperature and depth of formation of sulfide ore deposits at Gilman, Colorado: Econ. Geology, v. 53, p. 689–707.

MacDiarmid, R. A., 1963, The application of thermoluminescence to geothermometry: Econ. Geology, v. 58, p. 1218–1228.

Mason, Brian, 1958, Principles of geochemistry (2nd ed.): New York, John Wiley & Sons, Inc.

Merwin, H. E., and Lombard, R. H., 1937, The system Cu-Fe-S: Econ. Geology, v. 32, p. 203–284.

Morey, G. W., and Ingerson, Earl, 1937, The pneumatolytic and hydrothermal alteration and synthesis of silicates: Econ. Geology, v. 32, p. 607–761.

Newhouse, W. H., 1933, The temperature of formation of the Mississippi Valley lead-zinc deposits: Econ. Geology, v. 28, p. 744–750.

Palache, Charles, Berman, Harry, and Frondel, Clifford, 1944, Dana's system of mineralogy (7th ed.), v. 1: New York, John Wiley & Sons, Inc.

Posnjak, Eugen, Allen, E. T., and Merwin, H. E., 1915, The sulphides of copper: Econ. Geology, v. 10, p. 491–535.

Ramdohr, Paul, 1931, Neue Beobachtungen über die Verwendbarkeit opaker Erze als "Geologische Thermometer": Zeit. prakt. Geol., v. 39, p. 65–73, 89–91.

Richter, D. H., and Ingerson, Earl, 1954, Discussion—some considerations regarding liquid inclusions as geologic thermometers: Econ. Geology, v. 49, p. 786–789.

Roedder, Edwin, 1960, Fluid inclusions as examples of the ore-forming fluids: 21st Internat. Geol. Cong., pt. 16, p. 218–229.

Roseboom, E. H., Jr., 1960, High-temperature x-ray studies in the system Cu-S: Geol. Soc. America Bull., v. 71, p. 1959.

Roy, Rustum, Majumdar, A. J., and Hulbe, C. W., 1959, The Ag₂S and Ag₂Se transitions as geologic thermometers: Econ. Geology, v. 54, p. 1278–1280.

Sakai, Hitoshi, 1957, Fractionation of sulfur isotopes in nature: Geochim. et Cosmochim. Acta, v. 12, p. 150–169.

Schwartz, G. M., 1942, Progress in the study of exsolution in ore minerals: Econ. Geology, v. 37, p. 345–364.

Scott, H. S., 1948, The decrepitation method applied to minerals with liquid inclusions: Econ. Geology, v. 43, p. 637–654.

Seifert, H., 1930, Geologische Thermometer: Fort. Min. Krist. Petrog., v. 14, p. 167–291.

Skinner, B. J., 1953, Some considerations regarding liquid inclusions as geologic thermometers: Econ. Geology, v. 48, p. 541–550.

———, Barton, P. B., Jr., and Kullerud, Gunnar, 1959, Effect of FeS on the unit cell edge of sphalerite. A revision: Econ. Geology, v. 54, p. 1040–1046.

Smith, F. G., 1947, The pyrite geo-thermometer: Econ. Geology, v. 42, p. 515–523.

———, 1948, The ore deposition temperature and pressure at the McIntyre mine, Ontario: Econ. Geology, v. 43, p. 627–636.

———, 1953, Historical development of inclusion thermometry: Univ. of Toronto Press.

———, 1954, Discussion—some considerations regarding liquid inclusions as geologic thermometers: Econ. Geology, v. 49, p. 331–332.

———, and Little, W. M., 1953, Sources of error in the decrepitation method of study of liquid inclusions; discussion: Econ. Geology, v. 48, p. 233–238.

Smith, F. G., Peach, P. A., Scott, H. S., Mutch, A. D., Springer, G. D., Boyle, R. W., and Ogden, W. M. M., 1950, "Pneumatolysis" and the liquid inclusion method of geologic thermometry; a reply: Econ. Geology, v. 45, p. 582–587.

Stephenson, T. E., 1952, Sources of error in the decrepitation method of study of liquid inclusions: Econ. Geology, v. 47, p. 743–750.

Van Hook, H. J., 1960, The ternary system Ag_2S-Bi_2S_3-PbS: Econ. Geology, v. 55, p. 759–788.

Yermakov, N. P., 1957, Importance of inclusions in minerals to the theory of ore genesis and study of the mineral forming medium (translated by E. A. Alexandrov), Internat. Geol. Rev., v. 3, no. 7, 1961, p. 575–585.

CHAPTER 8 **The Classification of Ore Deposits**

To CLASSIFY MEANS TO GROUP in classes that have systematic relations, usually founded on common properties or characters. The purpose of classifying ore deposits is thus to group them into a small number of types having certain features in common, in order to facilitate descriptions and, hopefully, to permit generalizations concerning their origin and localization. To be useful, a classification must be as simple as possible; above all, it must be usable in the field. Since Agricola's day, many attempts have been made to classify ore deposits. Most of the resulting classifications have been abandoned, largely because they were too complex; they were conceived in the office, and although theoretically sound, they could not be applied in the field. From observation, we know that the types of deposits grade into each other; thus no classification can be either complete or inflexible.

Past attempts at classification have emphasized form, texture, and the mineral content of ore deposits, whereas modern classifications have been developed around the theories of ore genesis or environments of deposition. It was recognized early that a distinction should be made between sedimentary ores and epigenetic deposits, but further breakdown has been difficult. No universally acceptable classification of epigenetic ores has been proposed, and there are presently three systems in common use. Europeans favor Niggli's volcanic-plutonic classification and Schneiderhöhn's ore-association classification. Most widely accepted in the United States is Lindgren's depth-temperature classification, which is based upon ore genesis and the environment of ore deposition.

Niggli (1929) grouped the epigenetic ores into volcanic, or near-surface, and plutonic, or deep-seated. The plutonic deposits are divided into hydrothermal, pegmatitic-pneumatolytic, and orthomagmatic subgroups, depending upon whether the ores formed from liquids or gases, or as direct crystallization products within the magma. Final classification is based upon chemical and ore-mineral associations.

An outline of Niggli's classification is given in Table 8-I. It can be seen that this system categorizes deposits on the basis of their genesis and mineralogy; for example, it would distinguish between volcanic gold deposits and plutonic gold deposits or between hydrothermal copper ores and pneumatolytic copper ores. Fundamentally, this classification differs little from Lindgren's, and most criticisms applied to Niggli's classification can also be applied to Lindgren's. But since high-pressure fluids above the critical point are neither gases nor liquids, the pneumatolytic-hydrothermal distinction is an artificial one. It is not only questionable in theory; it also defies field application.

TABLE 8-I

Niggli's Classification of Ore Deposits

I. Plutonic or intrusive
  A. Orthomagmatic
    1. Diamond, platinum-chromium
    2. Titanium-iron-nickel-copper
  B. Pneumatolytic to pegmatitic
    1. Heavy metals-alkaline earths-phosphorus-titanium
    2. Silicon-alkali-fluorine-boron-tin-molybdenum-tungsten
    3. Tourmaline-quartz association
  C. Hydrothermal
    1. Iron-copper-gold-arsenic
    2. Lead-zinc-silver
    3. Nickel-cobalt-arsenic-silver
    4. Carbonates-oxides-sulfates-fluorides
II. Volcanic or extrusive
  A. Tin-silver-bismuth
  B. Heavy metals
  C. Gold-silver
  D. Antimony-mercury
  E. Native copper
  F. Subaquatic-volcanic and biochemical deposits

Schneiderhöhn (1941) classified ore deposits according to (1) the nature of the ore fluid; (2) the mineral associations; (3) a distinction between deep-seated and near-surface deposition; and (4) the type of deposition, host, or gangue. The significant category in this classification is the second group—ore associations. Schneiderhöhn proposed a detailed list of typical mineral associations, categorized according to the types of ore, host, and gangue found in each. The principal categories of his classification are reproduced in Table 8-II.

TABLE 8-II

Schneiderhöhn's Classification of Ore Deposits

I. Intrusive and liquid-magmatic deposits

II. Pneumatolytic deposits
    A. Pegmatitic veins
    B. Pneumatolytic veins and impregnations
    C. Contact pneumatolytic replacements

III. Hydrothermal deposits
    A. Gold and silver associations
    B. Pyrite and copper associations
    C. Lead-silver-zinc associations
    D. Silver-cobalt-nickel-bismuth-uranium associations
    E. Tin-silver-tungsten-bismuth associations
    F. Antimony-mercury-arsenic-selenium associations
    G. Nonsulfide associations
    H. Nonmetallic (ore-free) associations

IV. Exhalation deposits

This system of classifying ore deposits is popular in Europe and is also advocated by many Americans. Noble (1955) argues that it is the best genetic classification because ore associations represent metal associations in the ore-forming fluids. Comparison between Schneiderhöhn's and Lindgren's classifications will show that they have fundamental similarities, although they differ in emphasis. Under Schneiderhöhn's system, a deposit that does not fit one of the given ore-mineral associations or its subdivisions is readily categorized merely by formulating a new group or subdivision. The success of this system, however, is inversely proportional to the number of major groups needed to accommodate all ore deposits; that is, each new category needed weakens the classification. As an example of Schneiderhöhn's more complete system of classification, we present the subdivisions of group IIIA.

III. Hydrothermal deposits
    A. Gold and silver associations
        1. Hypabyssal suite (deep-seated)
            a. Katathermal (equivalent to hypothermal) gold-quartz veins
            b. Gold-bearing impregnation deposits in silicate rocks
            c. Gold-bearing replacement deposits in carbonate rocks
            d. Mesothermal gold-lead-selenium deposits
        2. Subvolcanic suite (near-surface)
            a. Epithermal propylitic gold-quartz veins and silver-gold veins
            b. Epithermal gold-telluride veins
            c. Epithermal gold-selenium veins
            d. Alunitic gold deposits
            e. Epithermal silver deposits

The Lindgren classification is strictly independent of the metals deposited and hence can be restricted to a small, permanent number of major categories. Epigenetic deposits are subdivided according to the depth and temperature of ore deposition on the assumption that changes in temperature and pressure are the most significant factors causing the minerals to precipitate. This assumption is supported by thermochemical arguments. Both the solubilities of metal sulfides (Czamanske, 1959) and the fugacities of S_2 and O_2 (Holland, 1957, 1959) in hydrothermal and pneumatolytic systems decrease in direct proportion to temperature. Thus the mineral associations should reflect depth-temperature environments. The advocates of Lindgren's classification feel that the persistence of certain mineral suites to definite depth-temperature zones supports this system. For the field geologist, however, this classification leaves much to be desired, because the pressures and temperatures of ore deposition are never directly observable. (Actually, the deposits are usually categorized by assigning Schneiderhöhn's ore-association classes to their theoretical depth-temperature environments.) Nevertheless, Lindgren's classification seems to be the clearest and best that has been proposed. It has withstood a half-century of use and abuse and still enjoys the leading position in world-wide popularity. This classification (Lindgren, 1913, 1933), somewhat revised and with the addition of the teletethermal (Graton, 1933) and xenothermal (Buddington, 1935) zones, is shown in Table 8-III. It includes not only the ore deposits of magmatic affiliation but also the deposits formed from meteoric waters, whether by chemical or physical processes.

The temperature divisions are meant to be only approximate figures; for example, most of the metallization in mesothermal deposits probably takes place between 300°C and 200°C, but early and late ore deposition may transgress these limits.

TABLE 8-III

Lindgren's Classification of Ore Deposits (modified)

I. Deposits produced by chemical processes of concentration. (Temperatures and pressures vary between wide limits.)

    A. In magmas, by processes of differentiation

        1. Magmatic deposits proper. (Magmatic segregation deposits.) Temperature, 700–1500°C±; pressure, very high.

        2. Pegmatites. Temperature, very high to moderate; pressure, very high.

    B. In bodies of rocks

        1. Concentration effected by introduction of substances foreign to the rock (epigenetic).

            a. Origin dependent upon the eruption of igneous rocks.

                i. By direct igneous emanations

                    a. From effusive bodies. Sublimates, fumaroles. Temperature, 100–600°C; pressure, atmospheric to moderate.

                    b. From intrusive bodies. (Igneous metamorphic deposits.) Temperature, probably 500–800°C±; pressure, very high.

                ii. By hot ascending waters of uncertain origin, but charged with igneous emanations.

                    a. Deposition and concentration at great depth or at high temperature and pressure. (Hypothermal deposits.) Temperature, 300–500°C±; pressure, very high.

                    b. Deposition and concentration at intermediate depths. (Mesothermal deposits.) Temperature, 200°–300°C±; pressure, high.

                    c. Deposition and concentration at slight depth. (Epithermal deposits.) Temperature, 50°–200°C±; pressure, moderate.

                    d. Deposition and concentration from nearly spent solutions. (Teletehermal deposits.) Temperature and pressure low; upper terminus of hydrothermal range.

                    e. Deposition and concentration at shallow depths, but at high temperatures. (Xenothermal deposits.) Temperature, high to low; pressure, moderate to atmospheric.

            b. Origin independent of igneous activity. By circulating meteoric waters at moderate or slight depth. Temperature, up to 100°C±; pressure, moderate.

        2. By concentration of substances contained in the geologic body itself.

            a. Concentration by dynamic and regional metamorphism. Temperature, up to 400°C±; pressure, high.

            b. Concentration by ground water of deeper circulation. Temperature, 0–100°C±; pressure, moderate.

            c. Concentration by rock decay and residual weathering near surface. Temperature, 0–100°C±; pressure, moderate to atmospheric.

    C. In bodies of surface waters

        1. By interaction of solutions. Temperature, 0–70°C±; pressure, moderate.

            a. Inorganic reactions.

            b. Organic reactions.

        2. By evaporation of solvents.

II. Deposits produced by mechanical processes of concentration. Temperature and pressure moderate

The criteria by which mineral deposits are placed in the proper depth-temperature categories are given with the discussion of each zone (Chapters 9–17). None of these criteria are infallible; owing to the complexity and variability of the factors involved, minerals that normally form in one zone also form in other places, at higher or lower temperatures and pressures. Depositional zones are characterized by certain associations of ore and gangue minerals (Schneiderhöhn, 1941; Niggli, 1929), as well as by the presence of certain wall-rock alteration products. Some minerals, such as quartz, feldspar, and pyrite, have wide ranges of stability and persist from the deepest to the shallowest zones. Ore textures may indicate the depth-temperature environment; for example, geologists believe that the fine-grained rhythmic banding of some gold ores develops under near-surface conditions. Oölitic textures and colloidal deposits are also generally attributed to low temperatures and pressures. Although knowledge of geologic thermometry is helpful, it must be used with great caution.

If some ore deposits are shown to be the result of granitization, they will also fit Lindgren's classification, because the *ultimate* origin of the metals is not considered—each category is defined by the environmental conditions at the time and place of final deposition.

Despite the apparent simplicity and universality of Lindgren's classification, numerous criticisms of it have been made. For example, many ore deposits range through two or more of the depth-temperature zones, leaving their classification somewhat arbitrary or misleading. Such complications are in accord, however, with the theory of zoning and may be expected in a continuous vein system; to object to Lindgren's classification on the grounds that it fails to pigeonhole such a deposit would be no more valid than it would be to argue that a given granodiorite batholith cannot be so classified because it includes certain facies of quartz monzonite. As long as the qualification is understood, the classification used is valid and meaningful.

A further criticism of Lindgren's system of classification stems from the fact that temperature and pressure conditions at any given place may change in time. As the magmatic activity wanes, the temperatures should subside and the vapor pressures decrease. Hence the ores in a single ore body—or even in a hand specimen—may represent more than one of Lindgren's categories. This is a serious imperfection in the classification scheme, but again it is inherent in the ore-forming process. Temperatures and pressures within a deep (hypothermal) zone will ordinarily remain high throughout the period of ore deposition, but within shallow zones the possibility that low-temperature minerals will be superimposed on higher-temperature veins is great. Similarly, it is not uncommon to find that a high-temperature mineral assemblage has been fractured and subsequently permeated by a lower-temperature ore fluid. In practice such a deposit is categorized within a particular Lindgren zone according to its most dominant mineral assemblage, leaving the unembodied aspects as parenthetical qualifications; in short, Schneiderhöhn's ore associations are used as a crutch.

In its original form, Lindgren's classification considered pressure and temperature to be fixed variables, but they may in fact vary independently of one another. Buddington (1935) pointed out that there are nine possible categories for depth-temperature zones, representing each combination of high, intermediate, and low values of temperature and pressure. Although it is entirely reasonable to expect high temperatures near the surface (for example, near a cooling pluton intruded to a shallow depth), it is perhaps unreasonable to expect near-surface conditions at great depths. Buddington introduced the term *xenothermal* for high-temperature deposits that form close to the surface. It is not practical to distinguish the nine types in the field, but the term xenothermal is widely used and has been generally accepted.

Lindgren's classification does not take into consideration the chemistry of the wall rocks, which is unquestionably one of the fundamental factors in ore deposition. Theoretically this should make no difference, because depth and temperature are the only parameters used. But a problem is encountered where ores are precipitated prematurely with respect to their normal depth-temperature environment, causing the mineral association to be misleading. Moreover, some igneous metamorphic deposits may, by depth-temperature criteria, be equivalent to Lindgren's hypothermal zone, or even his mesothermal zone (Stone, 1959, p. 1028), the only difference being that the deposit may lie within a carbonate host rather than consist of veins within a less reactive country rock. The aforementioned factors suggest that Schneiderhöhn's classification is favored where ore deposition has been controlled by chemical differences between the hydrothermal fluids and the wall rocks, whereas Lindgren's classification is favored where ore deposition has been controlled by pressure and temperature.

Schmitt (1950a) noted that gradations between deposits of the various zones are not as common as one would expect, especially between the epithermal and mesothermal zones or between pegmatites and deposits of the hypothermal zone. The lack of these gradations is real and has never been adequately explained. Nonetheless, a few examples of such gradations are known, and it is likely that as our knowledge of the physicochemical conditions controlling ore deposition increases, a satisfactory explanation will be advanced. Schmitt (1950b) also proposed a classification chart with the ordinate and abscissa defined by the apparently fundamental, objective factors of depth and temperature. This method, although more precise, requires information that is not readily available in the field.

We have stated that Lindgren's is the system of classification advocated as the standard in the United States. But perhaps it would be more realistic to say that Lindgren's system represents a fundamental standard by which most United States geologists attempt to classify ore deposits. Actually, most deposits are classified also (or further) by metal content, form, replacement versus fissure-filling, and so forth. Thus a disseminated copper deposit is one of many possible types within the mesothermal category; and a lead-zinc ore pipe may be hypothermal, mesothermal, or epithermal, the final decision being considered one of importance for any specific deposit.

The subject of Lindgren's genetic classification of mineral deposits is closely related to zoning and paragenesis. Theoretically, the depth-temperature zones may correspond to actual mineralogic zones, such as those found at Cornwall, England. Similarly, the high-intensity zones should correspond to the earliest paragenetic phase of a district. These three subjects—zoning, paragenesis, and the genetic classification system—are all expressions of the same phenomena and cannot properly be divorced from one another. This fact, in itself, is strong support for the validity of Lindgren's classification.

References Cited

Buddington, A. F., 1935, High-temperature mineral associations at shallow to moderate depths: Econ. Geology, v. 30, p. 205–222.

Czamanske, G. K., 1959, Sulfide solubility in aqueous solutions: Econ. Geology, v. 54, p. 57–63.

Graton, L. C., 1933, The depth-zones in ore deposition: Econ. Geology, v. 28, p. 513–555.

Holland, H. D., 1957, Thermochemical data, mineral associations, and the Lindgren classification of ore deposits: Geol. Soc. America Bull., v. 68, p. 1745.

————, 1959, Some applications of thermochemical data to problems of ore deposits. I. Stability relations among the oxides, sulfides, sulfates and carbonates of ore and gangue metals: Econ. Geology, v. 54, p. 184–233.

Lindgren, Waldemar, 1913, Mineral deposits: New York, McGraw-Hill Book Co., Inc.

————, 1933, Mineral deposits (4th ed.): New York, McGraw-Hill Book Co., Inc.

Niggli, Paul, 1929, Ore deposits of magmatic origin (translated by H. C. Boydell): London, Thomas Murby and Co.

Noble, J. A., 1955, The classification of ore deposits: Econ. Geology (50th Anniv. Volume), p. 155–169.

Schmitt, H. A., 1950a, Uniformitarianism and the ideal vein: Econ. Geology, v. 45, p. 54–61.

———, 1950b, The genetic classification of the bed rock hypogene mineral de-posits: Econ. Geology, v. 45, p. 671–680.

Schneiderhöhn, Hans, 1941, Lehrbuch der Erzlagerstättenkunde: Jena, Gustav Fischer.

Stone, J. G., 1959, Ore genesis in the Naica district, Chihuahua, Mexico: Econ. Geology, v. 54, p. 1002–1034.

CHAPTER 9 Magmatic Segregation Deposits

ORE DEPOSITS FORMED BY MAGMATIC SEGREGATION (concentrated fractions of magmatic differentiates) were recognized and named before Lindgren developed his classification system (Vogt, 1894). The term *magmatic segregation deposit* is now applied to all ore deposits that are direct crystallization products of a magma, exclusive of pegmatites. They usually form in deep-seated intrusive bodies, but deposits have been known to form in sills and even in lava flows. A magmatic segregation deposit may constitute the entire rock mass or a compositional layer, or may be defined by the presence of valuable accessory minerals in an otherwise normal igneous rock. Furthermore, the ore minerals may be early or late fractionation products; they may be concentrated by gravitative settling, immiscibility, or filter pressing; and they may remain in place or be injected as an ore magma into the previously solidified pluton or the surrounding country rock. The possibility that liquid separation is an active process in magmatic segregation ores was advanced by Fischer (1950), who synthesized a magnetite-apatite fluid as an immiscible fraction of a silicate melt.

Certain ore minerals are characteristic of a specific kind of igneous rock, whereas others show no consistent affiliations. The ores commonly found with mafic rocks are chromite, ilmenite, apatite, and platinum; those found with igneous rocks of intermediate composition are magnetite, hematite, and ilmenite; and those associated with siliceous rocks are magnetite, hematite, and such accessories as zircon, monazite, and cassiterite. Many associations are even more restrictive; for example, chromite is closely associated with peridotite and dunite, or with serpentine derived from these ultramafic rocks (Thayer, 1946). This tendency for an ore-host rock association is one of the strongest lines of evidence advanced by the proponents of magmatic segregation as an ore-forming process.

The textures of ore minerals in magmatic segregation deposits are essentially the same as the textures of the including rock (Newhouse, 1936; Ramdohr, 1940; Uytenbogaardt, 1954). Thus chromite in peridotite ordinarily has the same textural characteristics as the rest of the rock, and grains of magnetite in a fine-grained syenite will be smaller than those in a coarser-grained syenite. Conversely, many accessory minerals, such as zircon and monazite, form euhedral crystals, suggesting that they crystallized early in the differentiation process (though this relationship is not everywhere clear, and some euhedral crystals may actually be late products).

Minerals formed early in the history of magmatic differentiation will not be in complete equilibrium with the melt during its later stages. Many of these early-formed minerals will be partly resorbed and will show rounded faces and other effects of late magmatic and deuteric activity (Fig. 9-1). Such corrosive effects may obscure the textures of magmatic segregation deposits, making difficult their distinction from deposits of

FIGURE 9-1. *Thin section of ilmenite-anorthosite from Allard Lake, Canada. Note reaction rim around the ilmenite. Crossed nicols.* ×10.5.

hydrothermal origin. Thus a debate has arisen whether certain deposits were produced by magmatic segregation or by hydrothermal processes. In reality, the two processes probably grade into one another. Singewald (1917) concluded, for example, that many iron ores—especially titaniferous iron ores—are late-stage magmatic differentiates whose concentration is directly related to the action of mineralizers. The process advocated by Singewald had been proposed earlier by de Launay, who suggested that, as crystallization abates, crystal fractionation and hydrothermal activity must overlap and the mineralizers increase in relative proportion. Hence there should be a gradation from the magmatic stage to the hydrothermal stage. If de Launay and Singewald are correct, as is now commonly assumed, then such corrosive effects as those shown in Fig. 4-31 are to be expected in magmatic segregation deposits, and especially in those formed during the later stages of differentiation.

Microscopic studies of magmatic sulfide ores led Tolman and Rogers (1916) to concur that mineralizers play an important role in magmatic segregation. They emphasized that early crystallization requires the concomitant squeezing out or displacement of the residual fluid, a process that is not merely mechanical but due also to gaseous extraction.

The gradation between magmatic segregation and hydrothermal activity is also manifested by wall-rock alteration effects, which are generally absent from early differentiates but may be clearly developed around the products of late fractionation. We should emphasize, however, that wall-rock alteration is not characteristic of magmatic segregation deposits in general. Even the presence of abundant mineralizers—as with the late magmatic products —does not presuppose alteration effects, because in this environment there may be little difference between ore and wall-rock temperatures.

The overlapping zone between magmatic segregation processes and hydrothermal activity becomes most acute in the interpretation of certain sulfide deposits. Large bodies of massive sulfides or arsenides, such as those of the Rio Tinto district, Spain, and the Sudbury district, Ontario, were considered for many years to be direct products of magmatic segregation. With further development of the districts and more detailed studies, this interpretation was gradually changed. As regards Sudbury, the early magmatic segregation hypothesis was discarded in favor of a hydrothermal theory, because the ores did not seem to be simple fractions of magmatic differentiation (Williams, 1942; International Nickel Company, 1946; Yates, 1948). Studies of ore localization indicated that the sulfides invaded the surrounding igneous rock in the same way a hydrothermal deposit would develop, forming ores related to fractures and other structural features. Recently, however, the deposits have, again, come to be considered of magmatic segregation origin (Hawley, 1962). Apparently the controversy arose over the association between hydrothermal replacement effects and magmatic segregation deposits. Clear-cut magmatic ores include unique textures of immiscible silicate-sulfide melts, such as quartz diorite blebs dispersed in a continuous sulfide phase, and vice versa. Injection of the sulfide melt as an ore magma into fracture zones produced cross-cutting deposits. Only minor amounts of hydrothermal alteration and replacement accompanied deposition of the magmatic segregation ores, but subsequent remobilization of sulfides took place during metamorphism and intrusion by post-ore granite and diabase.

Proponents of the magmatic segregation origin for large sulfide masses raise the point that sulfide grains are abundant in many igneous rocks. These grains are generally considered to be original accessory constituents of the rock. Similarly, the association of many nickel sulfarsenide deposits with norite and related mafic rocks indicates a close genetic connection and probably means that the nickel-bearing fluids did not travel far from their magmatic sources.

The case for a magmatic segregation origin for sulfides has not progressed significantly since 1917, when Singewald referred to it as "dubious." He noted that the sulfides are deposited along the peripheries of their asso-ciated igneous masses, and at places, penetrated the wall rock. Moreover, at least some of the sulfides are later than the rock-forming silicates, which they replace without reaction rims (Tolman and Rogers, 1916). Singewald interpreted this relationship to mean that the sulfide-bearing agency also removed the dissolved silicates, indicating the presence of active fluids or mineralizers. Wall-rock alteration around some massive sulfide deposits is further evidence for the presence of mineralizers (Singewald, 1917). The relative mobility of sulfide minerals supports the idea that large masses of sulfides, although related to magmatic processes, nonetheless tend to move with the volatile or fluid fraction away from the crystallizing magma.

Probably the best examples of magmatic segregation ores are found among the chromite deposits, though in places these are thought to be hydrothermal. Wide field experience and the examination of many polished sections of chromite ores led Sampson (1929) to conclude that much chromite crystallizes at a very early magmatic stage, but also that consider-able amounts of the chromite constituents may remain in the residual melt or even pass into a highly aqueous solution capable of considerable migration. Both Fisher (1929) and Sampson (1931) recognized three classes of chromite, including early magmatic, late magmatic, and hydrothermal. These three categories are widely accepted and apply not only to chromite ores but also to other magmatic segregation minerals, such as ilmenite and magnetite.

As implied by Sampson's interpretation, the character of the magma that crystallizes chromite is the same whether the mineral is deposited early by crystal settling or later by hydrothermal fluids. Field evidence corroborates this supposition. For example, at the Lambert mine near Magalia, California, small pods of chromite are associated with similar pods of nearly pure albite in a serpentine-peridotite host. The concentration of these minerals along a zone of shearing suggests that they were deposited by hydrothermal processes, but their confinement to the ultramafic rocks implies a genetic relationship between the ore and the host rock. Apparently the ore-bearing fluids moved only short distances through the ultramafics.

Chromium Deposits

In the Moa district of northeastern Cuba (Fig. 9-2) there are several chromite deposits that are clear-cut products of magmatic segregation. These refractory chromite deposits have been studied in detail by Guild (1947), who described them as sack-like bodies of massive, nearly pure chromite in serpentinized ultramafics (Fig. 9-3). The ore bodies are found within an extensive ultramafic complex, which supports a broadly-domed lateritic slope along the northern range of Oriente Province. There are several chromite-bearing regions along a continuous east-west belt of serpentinized ultramafics in Cuba, but we shall describe only Moa here because it is more thoroughly understood and less complexly deformed than the other districts.

Rapid headward erosion of the short but vigorous streams has cut deep,

Havana

CUBA

Moa district

0   75
Scale in miles

FIGURE **9-2.** *Index map of Cuba, showing the location of the Moa district.*

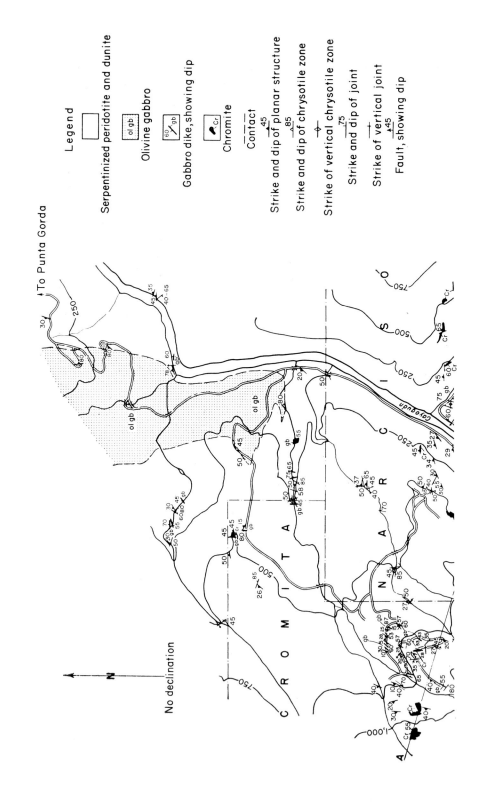

Legend

	Serpentinized peridotite and dunite
ol gb	Olivine gabbro
60 gb	Gabbro dike, showing dip
Cr	Chromite
——	Contact
45	Strike and dip of planar structure
85	Strike and dip of chrysotile zone
75	Strike of vertical chrysotile zone
45	Strike and dip of joint
45	Strike of vertical joint
45	Fault, showing dip

To Punta Gorda

N

No declination

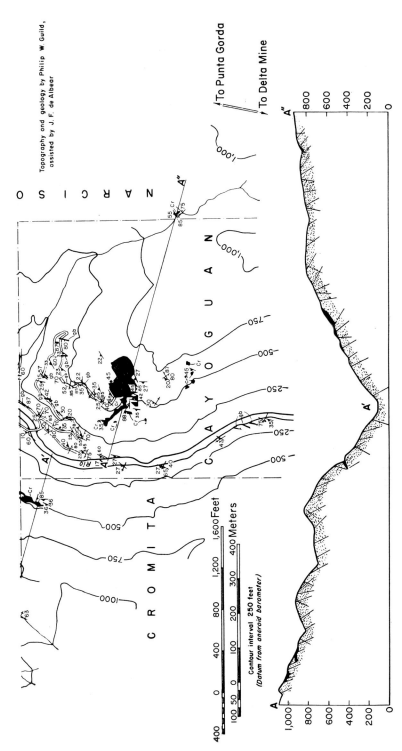

FIGURE 9-3. *Map and section of the Cayoguán group of deposits, Moa district, Cuba. (After Guild, 1947, figure 6.)*

V-shaped valleys, destroying part of the lateritic surface. Between the streams this well-preserved old surface rises at a gradient of three or four degrees from sea level on the north to an altitude of nearly 3000 feet near the crest of the range. The climate is humid, and thick vegetation considerably handicaps geologic mapping. Chromite bodies crop out on the canyon walls at a few places, supplying abundant float to the stream beds. Although the deposits were known since late in the nineteenth century, no exploration work was done until World War I, which motivated a small amount of prospecting. Real development did not begin until 1940, and during the next seven years more than 500,000 tons of refractory chromite were produced, averaging about 33 percent Cr_2O_3 (Guild, 1947).

The chromite deposits of the Moa district are often cited as an example of an injected mush of crystals, interstitial liquid, and chromite blocks. The primary structures are largely preserved; many of these structures probably formed during consolidation of the mass after intrusion, but there is strong evidence that differentiation of the chromite took place at depth (Guild, 1947).

The serpentine massif originally consisted of peridotite with subordinate dunite, chromitite, and pyroxenite. It contains some less mafic facies, such as gabbro, troctolite, and anorthosite, reflecting variable proportions of olivine, pyroxene, plagioclase, and chromite. With the exception of pyroxene and chromite, all combinations and gradations of these minerals are found. The ultramafic rocks are almost completely serpentinized, and the feldspathic rocks are altered to chalky aggregates of hydrous minerals, including antigorite(?), zoisite, edenite, chlorite, and zeolites.

A basement complex made up of chlorite schist, metamorphosed volcanic tuffs and lavas, thin impure marbles, and intrusive diorite, is exposed south of the Moa district and is thought to represent the host into which the ultramafics were intruded. The serpentines show no trace of the intense metamorphism that affected these older rocks, and no diorite has been found in the serpentine. Overlying the ultramafics to the west are Upper Cretaceous conglomerates (which contain cobbles of serpentine) and Tertiary deposits (Fig. 9-4).

The chromite concentration in the ore varies. In some deposits chromite is subordinate to the silicate minerals; but the best deposits contain only a small percentage of gangue minerals, and average ore carries about 5 percent silicates by weight. The most common gangue minerals are serpentinized olivine and alteration products of the feldspars. Low-grade ores contain individual grains of anhedral chromite disseminated in dunite,

FIGURE 9-4. *Map of the Moa chromite district, Oriente Province, Cuba. (After Guild, 1947, figure 2.)*

whereas the high-grade ores, which constitute most of the commercial deposits, appear almost massive and contain only minor amounts of interstitial silicates. Most of the chromite is fine- to medium-grained with a seriate texture, but a few grains are measured in centimeters, and crystals up to 6 inches across have been found.

Weathering has had little effect on the chromite ores, but some high-temperature, deuteric alteration products were formed. In one of the small deposits, a pale green chlorite replaced euhedral chromite, leaving only skeletal crystals of the chromite grains. This chlorite is not chromiferous, suggesting that chromium ions are mobile under certain conditions and capable of diffusing away from the reaction front. The pink, chrome-bearing chlorite, kämmererite, is also encountered in many of the deposits. A more ubiquitous alteration product is uvarovite-grossularite garnet, which fills joints in ore or forms reaction rims between pyroxene and chromite.

Each chromite deposit is surrounded by a dunite jacket ranging in thickness from one foot or less to tens of feet. The chromite-dunite pods occur within peridotite, hence there is a general sequence from chromite to dunite to peridotite in all ore bodies. At any single place, the chromite-dunite contact and the dunite-peridotite contact are essentially parallel. Fault contacts are more common, however, than undisturbed igneous contacts; in fact, the association of chromite with dunite is so well established that faults are plotted where drilling encounters peridotite adjacent to ore (Guild, 1947).

The chromite deposits are tabular to lenticular. They range in size from thin streaks a few feet long to much larger masses, some of which are elongated down the dip and others along the strike. Guild (1947) described one deposit as 700 feet long (down dip), 320 feet wide (along strike), and 90 feet thick. The contacts are sharp in most deposits, but other ore bodies grade outward through alternating parallel layers of variable silicate content in which the proportion of chromite decreases outward from the deposit to the country rock. Still other deposits are composed entirely of layered material and have no central concentration of chromite.

Fortunately, the internal structures of the ultramafic complex have not been obliterated by later deformation, therefore the rock fabric still reflects the processes of crystallization and intrusion. Compositional layering and flat mineral grains give the rocks a planar fabric. The most prominent layering is that of the chromite bodies themselves. Feldspathic lenses and streaks or layers of olivine within the chromite are all parallel to the contacts. Another planar structure is caused by the orientation of flat pyroxene grains within the peridotite. This foliation is generally, but not everywhere, parallel to the compositional layering. It is especially noticeable on weathered outcrops.

The ultramafic complex is intricately jointed and faulted. Joints are encountered every few inches or feet, and all orientations can be found. No systematic pattern of joints can be determined within the massive ore bodies, but the peridotite shows two sets of joints that seem to be related to the planar structures and to the processes of intrusion. The principal joints strike parallel to the foliation and dip at a large angle to this planar fabric. These "cross joints" are thought to define planes normal to the direction of rock flowage. A second set of prominent joints, called *longitudinal joints* (Guild, 1947), dips nearly vertically and strikes normal to the

foliation. Although many joints are simple fractures in otherwise homogeneous rocks, some cross joints have been filled with gabbro, and some of the
longitudinal joints are characterized by chrysotile veins.

Faulting is so complex that it is impossible to reconstruct the original
sizes and shapes of some ore bodies. As a rule, the faults are parallel to the
prominent joint directions. Normal faults predominate, but reverse faults
are also found. The overall picture is one of tension in the dip direction of
the ore deposits. Many of the faults have been filled by gabbro dikes, and
some of the dikes themselves have been slickensided by renewed movement
or offset by cross-cutting faults. Within the chromite masses, these dikes
are more numerous and coarser grained than in the other rocks.

As with most ultramafic complexes, details of differentiation, intrusion,
and solidification of the Moa complex are not completely understood. It is
known, however, that the Moa district did not undergo extreme deformation
subsequent to the emplacement of ultramafics; as a result, many of the
primary features are still preserved as evidence of the processes involved.
Any feasible theory of origin must explain the compositional layering in
the ore, dunite, and peridotite; it must explain why foliation in the peridotite is parallel to the layering in most places but definitely oblique to the
layering in other places; it must relate the joint systems to the planar structures; it must explain why the two principal joint systems are filled with
different materials; and it must acknowledge the predominance of gabbro
dikes in the ore deposits.

Guild (1947) considered the ore a product of early magmatic differentiation, present as discrete lodes before the ultramafics ascended to their
present position. He argued that there could not have been sufficient time
for compositional layering and coarse crystals to develop after intrusion.
Moreover, pyroxene crystals were oriented during growth by the intrusive
forces, and the paragenesis of chromite, olivine, and pyroxene implies that
the ore should have been solid at these temperatures. This point is emphasized by the presence of dunite dikes in the chromitite, which means the
ore bodies were rigid enough to fracture even during the olivine stage. The
presence of plagioclase as a gangue mineral in deposits enclosed within
completely feldspar-free dunite envelopes suggests further that the ore
crystallized at a different temperature than the olivine. The ore bodies are
clustered in a narrow zone within the ultramafic complex, implying
intrusion after solidification. Both the parallelism of the ore bodies and
their layered structures suggest that they were oriented during flow. Two
of the larger ore bodies, the Cayoguán and Narciso-Cromita deposits, have

similar dimensions and almost identical compositions (Table 9-I)—a distinction that cannot be made for any other pair of deposits; this implies that they may be fragments of a single mass that was broken and separated during intrusion.

TABLE 9-I

Composition of Chromite from the Cayoguán, Narciso, and Potosí Deposits, Moa District, Cuba

Component	Cayoguán	Narciso	Potosí
Cr_2O_3	38.03	38.26	39.62
Al_2O_3	30.96	30.30	24.96
Fe_2O_3	2.59	2.55	5.21
FeO	10.36	10.84	14.00
MgO	17.43	17.22	14.60
MnO	0.03	0.09	0.15
CaO	0.02	0.30	0.20
TiO_2	0.06	0.19	0.44
SiO_2	0.24	0.52	0.80
H_2O	0.10	0.12	0.02
P_2O_5	0.06	0.06	—
S	none	trace	—
TOTALS	99.88	100.45	100.06
Ratio Cr/Fe	2.64	2.56	1.86

SOURCE: After Guild (1947).

Guild (1947) concluded that the ultramafic complex probably resulted from the differentiation of a basaltic(?) magma. The mafic fraction, which consisted of olivine, chromite, and interstitial liquid, was subsequently intruded into the overlying rocks during a period of severe downbuckling. Guild divided the entire history into four overlapping stages—magmatic differentiation, intrusion, complete consolidation, and serpentinization. A summary of this sequence, as proposed by Guild, is reproduced in Table 9-II.

Titanium Deposits

The expanded use of titanium in recent years has encouraged a corresponding increase in the development of titaniferous ores. The majority of these ores are titanium-bearing magnetites and hematites or intimate exsolu-

TABLE 9-II

Summary of Proposed Mode of Origin of the Ultramafic Complex

Stage	Processes	Results
Predifferentiation	Homogeneous basaltic(?) magma	
Differentiation and segregation	Crystallization of olivine, anorthite, and chrome-spinel.	—
	Sinking of crystals, increase of Cr_2O_3 content through reaction of spinel with liquid to form olivine and anorthite.	Crystal mush of olivine, chromite, and liquid. Chromite concentrated in one or more layers.
Intrusion	Downbuckling of crust into "tectogene."	—
	Intrusion of crystal mush into rocks of crust.	Layered, sill-like(?) complex of chromite masses in mush of olivine crystals with interstitial pyroxenic and gabbroic liquid.
	Start of crystallization of pyroxene.	Formation of peridotite.
	Laminar flow.	Perfection of layering of peridotite, dunite, and chromitite.
	Fracturing of chromite masses.	—
	Injection of interstitial feldspathic liquid into joints in ore.	Gabbro dikes in ore.
	Reaction of chromite with pyroxenic liquid to form olivine.	Dunite envelopes around ore.
	Local turbulence in flow lines.	Deviations of layering from normal attitude.
Consolidation	Orientation of pyroxene by flow and stresses accompanying consolidation.	Foliation of peridotite.
	Shearing parallel foliation.	Offset of pyroxene layers.
	End of crystallization of pyroxene.	—
	Inward stress from walls of intrusion chamber.	Cross joints.
	Injection of gabbroic liquid into joints.	Gabbro dikes in peridotite.
	Replacement of gabbro in ore by late solutions.	Gabbro pegmatite.
	Replacement of peridotite by feldspathic solutions.	Replacement "dikes" and zones in peridotite.
Serpentinization	Continued stress.	Longitudinal joints.
	Reaction with residual(?) water- and silica-rich solutions.	Alteration of olivine and some pyroxene to serpentine.
	Shrinkage(?), fissure filling by deposition from serpentine solutions.	Chrysotile zones and veinlets.

SOURCE: After Guild (1947).

tion mixtures of these minerals with ilmenite. Most are held to be of magmatic segregation origin.

Several careful studies of the magnetite-ilmenite deposits near Lake Sanford, New York, support the thesis that these ores are differentiates of an anorthosite-gabbro magma (Buddington, 1939; Balsley, 1943; Stephenson, 1948). The ores are thought to have formed from residual segregations of magnetite-ilmenite liquid that was partly trapped within the crystal interstices and partly forced into the still-plastic rock. Material grading from gabbro containing less than 10 percent magnetite-ilmenite to almost pure magnetite-ilmenite rock is found. The magmatic segregation interpretation has been challenged by Gillson (1956), however, who argues that the ores are related to pneumatolytic replacement of the anorthosite-gabbro. He offered convincing evidence that all rock types in the area were produced by alteration of anorthosite along faults and fracture zones, and he considers the metallization to be a late phase of this alteration.

Unusually large ilmenite-hematite deposits have been developed at Allard Lake, about 25 miles north of the village of Havre St. Pierre, Quebec, Canada (Fig. 9-5). The deposits have been interpreted by several geologists as products of magmatic segregation (Dearden, 1958; Hammond, 1951, 1952). They are in a large mass of anorthosite and anorthosite-gabbro that intrudes Precambrian metamorphics and Paleozoic limestones. The anorthosites are in turn intruded by granite. Coarse-grained ilmenite containing exsolved hematite makes up the ore, which forms irregular lenses, narrow dikes, large sill-like masses, and various combinations of these forms. Most

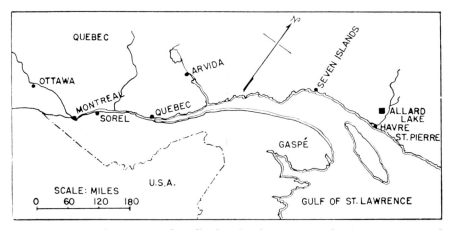

FIGURE 9-5. *Index map of the Allard Lake district, Canada.* (*After Hammond, 1952.*)

of the ore contains 32–35 percent TiO₂. Typical analyses of ore from Allard Lake are given in Table 9-III.

TABLE 9-III

Analyses of Titanium Ore from Allard Lake (in percent)

Constituent	Sample 1	Sample 2	Sample 3
TiO_2	34.8	36.0	34.4
Fe	38.0	42.8	39.1
S	0.36	0.40	0.39
P_2O_5	0.004	0.010	0.012
Cu	0.037	0.12	0.14
V	0.22	0.21	0.21
Mn	0.08	0.08	0.10
Ni	0.03	0.01	0.02
Co	0.014	0.013	0.019

SOURCE: From Hammond (1952).

The titanium ores throughout the region are confined to the light gray, medium- to coarse-grained anorthosites. The Lac Tio deposit, discovered in 1946, is said to be the largest body of titanium ore of its type in the world. This somewhat triangular-shaped ore body has a surface area of 134 acres and contains an estimated 125 million tons or more of ore (Hammond, 1952).

A system of fractures, composed of two steeply dipping sets of joints and faults that trend approximately at right angles to each other, forms a prominent regional pattern throughout much of the anorthosite surrounding the Lac Tio deposit. The more conspicuous set strikes nearly north-south and results in offsets of the normal fault type. The deposits are displaced along the faults, but the ore appears to be independent of these structures.

The Lac Tio ore occurs as crystal aggregates of thick, tabular ilmenite grains up to 10 millimeters across and 2 millimeters thick. Minor amounts (generally about 5 percent) of plagioclase, pyroxene, biotite, pyrite, pyrrhotite, and chalcopyrite make up the interstitial material between ilmenite grains. Microscopic examination reveals an intimate exsolution texture of hematite within the ilmenite, which is remarkable in that there are exsolution lamellae of ilmenite within the hematite lamellae and further exsolutions of hematite within the ilmenite lamellae (progressive cooling). The ilmenite contains up to 25 percent of intergrown hematite, and the ilmenite-hematite mixture is so fine grained that grinding cannot separate the two minerals.

Widespread accessory ilmenite and commercial concentrations of ilmenite in the anorthosite indicate a genetic relationship between the ilmenite and anorthosite. The host rock has been altered only locally, and except for the presence of biotite and the sulfides, no evidence has been found to indicate the presence of the usual mineralizers associated with ores of hydrothermal origin. Dikes and veinlets of ilmenite within anorthosite, as well as inclusions of anorthosite in the ore bodies, testify to the younger age of the ore. Both Hammond (1952) and Dearden (1958) favor the view that the ilmenite and the anorthosite are differentiates of the same parent magma, the large deposits of commercial ore representing a late segregation formed during consolidation of the magma. Gillson (1960) is diametrically opposed to this view; according to his interpretation, the ore is a product of pneumatolytic replacement.

Small amounts of vanadium, generally 0.1–0.2 percent, are found in both the Lake Sanford and Allard Lake deposits. Vanadium is a common constituent in many iron and titanium ores, and it appears to be especially noticeable in ores of magmatic affiliation. At present, vanadium from these ores is seldom recovered, but they form a potential source of large amounts. During World War II, vanadium was recovered from the slag as a by-product of the German iron and steel industry (Fischer, 1946). According to Vaasjoki (1947), vanadium is concentrated with magnetite rather than ilmenite, and he attributes this association to the similarity in ionic size between vanadium and ferric iron. However, Hutton (1945) feels that the differences in ionic size between V^{+3} or Fe^{+3} and Ti^{+4} are not significant enough to cause such a selective concentration of vanadium. He favors the hypothesis that the vanadium becomes concentrated in residual magmatic liquids after the ilmenite crystallizes and is consequently more available during the later growth of magnetite.

Iron Deposits

Probably the best-known and most productive magmatic segregation iron deposit in the world is the high-grade iron ore at Kiruna in northern Sweden (Fig. 9-6). It has been studied intensively over a period of about 50 years, and most geologists who have examined the area agree that the ores are closely associated with magmatic segregation processes (Stutzer, 1907;

Geijer, 1910, 1931a, 1931b, 1960; Geijer and Magnusson, 1952; Schneiderhöhn, 1958).

FIGURE 9-6. *Index map of Sweden, showing location of the Kiruna district.*

The Kiruna district contains several iron deposits, the largest of which is the Kiirunavaara mine. Kiirunavaara is a sill-like ore body between Precambrian syenite porphyry in the footwall and quartz porphyry in the hanging-wall. Overlying the quartz-bearing porphyry is the Lower Hauki complex, consisting of highly altered flows and silicified tuffs(?), and the Vakko Series —or Upper Hauki complex—of sediments. All of these rock units strike north or northeast and dip 50–60° east (Fig. 9-7). The ore body is intrusive between the syenite and quartz-porphyry, extending for over three miles along strike. Except for the narrow northern end of this magnetite sill, which extends for over a half mile out under a lake and is not being mined, the ore averages about 250 feet in thickness. Production began in 1903, and by 1959 production from the Kiirunavaara deposit had totaled 235 million metric tons averaging 62 percent iron—estimated to be about one-eighth of the available ore (Geijer, 1960).

The ore consists of fine-grained magnetite or, more rarely, hematite, and contains variable amounts of fluorapatite. The phosphorus content is generally high (greater than 2 percent), due to the apatite; in fact, the term "Kiruna type ore" is used universally to mean high-phosphorus ores. After apatite, which is common, actinolite and diopside are the most abundant nonmetallic minerals. In places the prisms of apatite exhibit a trachytoidal arrangement, and workers have even observed streaked out or "stratified" alternations of pure apatite and magnetite-apatite laminae.

Contacts between the ore and wall rocks are sharply defined and definitely intrusive in nature. A thin amphibole skarn is found in places, and small veins or apophyses of ore branch out into both the footwall and hanging-

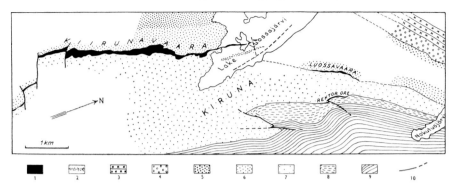

FIGURE 9-7. *Map of the Kiruna district, Sweden. (After Geijer, 1960.) (1) Iron ore. (2) Zone containing ore veins (ore breccia). (3) Kiruna greenstones. (4) Kurravarra conglomerate. (5) Syenite. (6) Syenite porphyry. (7) Quartz-bearing porphyry. (8) Lower Hauki complex. (9) Vakko sedimentary series. (10) Fault.*

wall. Separate systems of ore veins are referred to locally as "ore breccia." Porphyry dikes that are apparently intermediate in composition and texture between the footwall and hangingwall porphyries intrude the footwall and apparently spread out beneath the hangingwall; the dikes are, in turn, broken up and engulfed by the ore, though one such dike definitely intrudes the magnetite. These relations imply that the ore was emplaced after most of the porphyry dikes were intruded but before this igneous activity had abated completely.

The ore is offset by faults with predominately strike-slip movement. Granophyre dikes that seem to be unrelated to the ore deposits and older igneous rocks were intruded during the period of faulting.

Geijer (1931a, 1931b, 1960) concluded that the Kiirunavaara deposit resulted from the intrusion of highly mobile ore magmas, presumably before the country rocks were tilted. The magnetite-apatite fluid became concentrated during magmatic differentiation as an immiscible fraction within the mother magma. Separation of the two immiscible magmatic fractions took place deep within the earth's crust, prior to intrusion. This interpretation is directly supported by Fischer's (1950) experimental and theoretical confirmation that an immiscible magnetite-apatite liquid can exist.

Many lines of evidence support Geijer's hypothesis. The ore bodies are intrusive into the porphyries, and they show striking evidences, such as their trachytoidal texture, of liquid flowage. The contact zones underwent slight metasomatism, indicating the presence of volatiles. These volatile constituents were presumably active in separating the two immiscible magmatic fractions within the mother magma. Furthermore, all minerals in the Kiirunavaara ore body are also found in the associated igneous rocks. Other ore bodies in the district are clearly related in mineralogy, structure, and chronology to the Kiirunavaara deposit, indicating a closely related genesis; all types of ore, from magmatic to hydrothermal, can be seen in these deposits, and it is clear that some formed at lower temperatures than the Kiirunavaara ores. In the entire district, then, there is evidence of closely related magmatic and hydrothermal ore deposition, wherein the early, high-temperature ores were products of direct magmatic segregation and the later ores were influenced by greater concentrations of volatiles.

References to Selected Magmatic Segregation Deposits

Turkish Chromite

Borchert, H., 1958, Die Chrom- und Kupfererzlagerstätten des initialen ophiolithischen Magmatismus in der Türkei: Ankara, Maden Tetkik ve Arama, no. 102.

Ergunalp, Falik, 1944, The chromite deposits of Turkey: Am. Inst. Mining Engineers Mining Technology, v. 8, no. 5, Tech. Paper 1746.

Helke, Adolf, 1955, Beobachtungen an türkischen Minerallagerstätten: Neues Jahr. für Min., Abh., v. 88, p. 55–224.

———, 1961, Beitrag zur Kenntnis der Chromerzlagerstätten des Sori Daği in der Türkei: Neues Jahr. für Min., Abh., v. 96, p. 48–78.

———, 1962, The metallogeny of the chromite deposits of the Guleman district, Turkey: Econ. Geology, v. 57, p. 954–962.

Kovenko, V., 1943, Quelques gîtes de chromite en forme de filons et leur genèse (Turquie): Ankara, Maden Tetkik ve Arama, v. 8, p. 59–90.

———, 1944, Province métallogénique de Guleman-Ergani Maden: Ankara, Tetkik ve Arama, v. 9, p. 29–65.

———, 1945, Gîtes de chromite des régions de Fethive et de Dağardi (Turquie): Ankara, Maden Tetkik ve Arama, v. 10, p. 42–75.

———, 1949, Gîtes de chromite et roches chromifères de l'Asie mineure (Turquie): Soc. Géol. France, Mém. 61, v. 28, pt. 4.

Kromer, Ferid, 1950, Chromite and other mineral occurrences in the Taştepe district of Eskişehir, Turkey: Am. Inst. Mining Engineers Trans., v. 187, p. 108–110.

Wijkerslooth, P. de, 1942, Die Chromerzprovinzen der Türkei und des Balkans und ihr Verhalten zur Grosstektonik dieser Länder: Ankara, Maden Tetkik ve Arama, v. 7, p. 54–75.

Russian Platinum

Betekhtin, A. G., 1935, Character, classification, occurrence, and genesis of platinum mineral deposits of Russia: Acad. Sci. U.S.S.R. (In Russian).

Duparc, L., and Tikonowitch, M., 1920, Le platine et les gîtes platinifères de l'Oural et du monde: Geneva.

Ivanov, A. A., and Lizunov, N. V., 1944, Platinoids in the ultrabasic rocks of the Urals: Acad. Sci. U.S.S.R., B, Sér. Géol. no. 5, p. 76–86 (In Russian).

Padalka, G. L., 1936, The peridotite massif Pai-Er on the Polar Ural: Arctic Inst. Trans., v. 47 (In Russian; English summary, p. 161–174).

Purington, C. W., 1899, The platinum deposits of the Tura River system, Ural Mountains, Russia: Am. Inst.

Mining Engineers Trans., v. 29, p. 3–16.

Zavaritsky, A. N., 1928, Primary plati-num deposits of the Urals: Comm. géol. Matér. géol. livr. 108, Lenin-grad.

References Cited

Balsley, J. R., Jr., 1943, Vanadium-tita-nium-iron ores, Lake Sanford, New York: U.S. Geol. Survey Bull. 940-D.

Buddington, A. F., 1939, Adirondack ig-neous rocks and their metamorphism: Geol. Soc. America Mem. 7, p. 64–67.

Dearden, E. O., 1958, Lac Tio ilmenite deposit: Am. Inst. Mining Engineers Preprint no. 5818A4.

Fischer, Reinhard, 1950, Entmischungen in Schmelzen aus Schwermetalloxyden, Silikaten und Phosphaten: Neues Jahr. für Min., Abh., v. 81, p. 315–364.

Fischer, R. P., 1946, German iron ores yield vanadium: Am. Inst. Mining En-gineers Tech. Pub. 2070.

Fisher, L. W., 1929, Origin of chromite deposits: Econ. Geology, v. 24, p. 691–721.

Geijer, Per, 1910, Igneous rocks and iron ores at Kiirunavaara, Lousavaara and Toulluvaara: Econ. Geology, v. 5, p. 699–718.

————, 1931a, The iron ores of the Kiruna type: Sveriges Geol. Undersökning, ser. C, no. 367.

————, 1931b, Pre-Cambrian geology of the iron-bearing region of Kiruna-Galli-vare-Pajala: Sveriges Geol. Undersök-ning, ser. C, no. 366, p. 185–221.

————, 1960, The Kiruna iron ores: 21st Internat. Geol. Cong., Guide to excur-sions A25 and C20, p. 3–17.

————, and Magnusson, N. H., 1952, The iron ores of Sweden: 19th Internat. Geol. Cong., Symposium sur les gise-ments de fer du monde, v. 2, p. 483–485.

Gillson, J. L., 1956, Genesis of titaniferous magnetites and associated rocks of the Lake Sanford district, New York: Am. Inst. Mining Engineers Trans., v. 205, p. 296–301.

————, 1960, Intriguing examples of geol-ogy applied to industrial minerals: Econ. Geology, v. 55, p. 629–644.

Guild, P. W., 1947, Petrology and struc-ture of the Moa district, Oriente Prov-ince, Cuba: Am. Geophys. Union Trans., v. 28, p. 218–246.

Hammond, Paul, 1951, Allard Lake ilmen-ite deposits: Geol. Soc. America Bull., v. 62, p. 1448.

————, 1952, Allard Lake ilmenite de-posits: Econ. Geology, v. 47, p. 634–649.

Hawley, J. E., 1962, The Sudbury ores: their mineralogy and origin: Mineral-ogical Assoc. of Canada, Ottawa; Cana-dian Mineralogist, v. 7, pt. 1.

Hutton, C. O., 1945, Vanadium in the Taranaki titaniferous iron-ores: New Zealand Jour. Sci. and Technology, v. 27, p. 15–16.

International Nickel Company, 1946, Geol-ogy of the Sudbury district, Ontario, *in* The operations and plants of the In-ternational Nickel Company of Canada, Limited: Canadian Mining Jour., p. 322–331.

Newhouse, W. H., 1936, Opaque oxides and sulphides in common igneous rocks: Geol. Soc. America Bull., v. 47, p. 1–52.

Ramdohr, Paul, 1940, Die Erzmineralien in gewöhnlichen magmatischen Ge-steinen: Preuss. Akad. Wiss., Abh. no. 2.

Sampson, Edward, 1929, May chromite crystallize late?: Econ. Geology, v. 24, p. 632–641.

————, 1931, Varieties of chromite de-posits: Econ. Geology, v. 26, p. 833–839.

Schneiderhöhn, Hans, 1958, Die Erzla-gerstätten der Frühkristallisation, v. I: Stuttgart, Gustav Fischer.

Singewald, J. T., Jr., 1917, The role of

mineralizers in ore segregations in basic igneous rocks: The Johns Hopkins Univ. Contrib. to Geol., March 1917, p. 24–35.

Stephenson, R. C., 1948, Titaniferous magnetite deposits of the Lake Sanford area, New York: Am. Inst. Mining Engineers Trans., v. 178, p. 397–421.

Stutzer, O., 1907, Geologie und Genesis der lappländischen Eisenerzlagerstätten: Neues Jahr. für Min., Geol., und Paläon., supp. v. 24, p. 548–675.

Thayer, T. P., 1946, Preliminary chemical correlation of chromite with the containing rocks: Econ. Geology, v. 41, p. 202–217.

Tolman, C. F., Jr., and Rogers, A. F., 1916, A study of the magmatic sulfid ores: Stanford Univ. Press, Stanford.

Uytenbogaardt, W., 1954, On the opaque mineral constituents in a series of amphibolitic rocks from Norra Storfjället, Vasterbotten, Sweden: Arkiv för Mineralogi och Geologi, v. 1, no. 5–6, p. 527–543.

Vaasjoki, O., 1947, On the microstructure of titaniferous iron ore at Otanmäki: Comm. Géol. de Finlande, Pentti Eskola Memorial Volume, Bull. 140, p. 107–114.

Vogt, J. H. L., 1894, Beiträge zur genetischen Classification der durch magmatische Differentiationsprocesse und der durch Pneumatolyse entstandenen Erzvorkommen: Zeit. prakt. Geol., v. 2, p. 381–399.

Williams, David, 1942, Rio Tinto, Spain, in Newhouse, W. H. (ed.), Ore deposits as related to structural features: New Jersey, Princeton Univ. Press, p. 258–262.

Yates, A. B., 1948, Properties of International Nickel Company of Canada, in Structural geology of Canadian ore deposits: Canadian Inst. Mining Metallurgy, p. 596–617.

CHAPTER 10 **Pegmatites**

PEGMATITES ARE UNUSUALLY COARSE-GRAINED igneous or metamorphic rocks. The igneous pegmatites apparently form from the residual, volatile-rich fractions of magmas, whereas the metamorphic pegmatites represent the more mobile constituents of a rock that are concentrated during metamorphic differentiation. Any and all shapes have been assumed by pegmatites, but they are typically in dike-like or lensoid masses. Most pegmatites are small—from a few feet to tens of feet in the longest dimension; few form extensive and continuous tabular bodies such as the deep-seated veins, though exceptional deposits over a mile long are known. Igneous pegmatites characteristically solidify late in the history of igneous activity. They tend to be associated with plutonic rocks or with hypabyssal masses from which the volatile fractions could not readily escape. The great majority of pegmatites, whether of igneous or metamorphic origin, developed in deep-seated, high-pressure environments. They are rare in unmetamorphosed sediments and are seldom found with shallow intrusives, lavas, or tuffs. As with the deep-seated vein deposits, pegmatites generally do not develop conspicuous alteration halos.

The igneous pegmatites that are best known and most commonly described are intermediate to silicic in composition. They are highly colored, conspicuous bodies whose coarse textures and unusual mineral compositions make them favorite mineral collecting grounds. Ferromagnesian pegmatites, associated with gabbroic or more mafic rocks, are fairly common. Yet they do not stand out as noticeably as the silicic pegmatites, and they seldom contain minerals of economic value. Furthermore, mafic plutons are not as abundant as silicic plutons. For these reasons, the mafic pegmatites have been described as rare.

Studies in geothermometry indicate that pegmatites form over a wide range of temperatures. Much of the literature reports a temperature of about 575°C, on the assumption that the quartz forms near the alpha-beta inversion point. However, liquid inclusions have indicated a temperature of about 150°C for many pegmatites (Ingerson, 1947), whereas other geo-thermometers record temperatures up to 700°C. The consensus of reports suggests that most pegmatites are formed between 700°C and 250°C (Jahns, 1955).

Pegmatites are classified as *simple* and *complex*, with reference to mineralogy and genesis. Originally, simple pegmatites were defined as those having undergone no hydrothermal replacement; complex pegmatites were defined as those containing rare minerals introduced by late-stage hydrothermal fluids (Landes, 1933). But these definitions no longer hold. Subsequent applications of these terms have caused them to be redefined. Thus *simple pegmatites* are those having simple mineralogy and no well-developed zoning; *complex pegmatites* are those containing a complex, or assemblage, of rare minerals arranged in a zonal sequence. In practice, both sets of definitions are applicable, because few pegmatites of truly simple mineralogy have undergone hydrothermal alteration.

Simple Pegmatites

The vast majority of pegmatites are of the simple variety. They consist dominantly of coarse-grained quartz and feldspars with subordinate mica, and they are ordinarily uniform from wall to wall, both in composition and in texture. Except where they can be mined for feldspars or micas, they have no economic value and are of interest principally in helping to unravel the geologic history of a region. Simple pegmatites result from metamorphic differentiation or from one comparatively short period of igneous activity. The palingenesis of sediments would produce a melt corresponding chemically to a mixture of quartz, potash feldspars, and muscovite; it is probable that many simple pegmatites are of this origin. Most of the larger simple pegmatites are of igneous origin, whereas the pegmatites formed by metamorphic processes are typically small and irregular. Lit-par-lit types —-pegmatites intertongued with metamorphic rocks—are common; in places they appear to grade into the country rock.

Complex Pegmatites

Complex pegmatites result from igneous processes, rather than from recrystallization or palingenesis associated with metamorphism. Much has been written regarding their origin, and they are thought generally to have formed as a result of one long, continuous period of crystallization, during which the first-formed minerals reacted with a progressively changing residual magmatic fluid. Recent studies support the view that this progressive change involves the development of a gaseous phase within the silicate melt (Jahns and Burnham, 1958).

A special feature of some complex pegmatites is the presence of giant crystals within the inner zones. Abnormally large crystals of quartz, feldspars, micas, beryl, apatite, tourmaline, and other pegmatite minerals have been reported. Individual crystals are measured in feet and even tens of feet. Jahns (1953) argues that evidence for a replacement origin of these large crystals is lacking and contends that they must have crystallized directly from a volatile-rich pegmatitic liquid under delicately balanced thermal and chemical conditions. That is, the crystals must have grown rapidly, and the ions must have been able to diffuse readily through the pegmatitic fluid.

Many complex pegmatites are mined for metallic or rare earth constituents, though not all zoned pegmatites contain these elements in appreciable quantities. Pegmatites are small in volume when compared to most other types of igneous rocks, and the minerals for which they are mined are commonly present only as accessory constituents. Some of these accessory minerals are of great value and are energetically sought, even when present in small amounts. In fact, pegmatites are the only known source of some metals. They contain tantalum, niobium, beryllium, lithium, cesium, uranium, cerium, lanthanum, thorium, yttrium, and many other rare elements in a host of uncommon and complex minerals, as well as the better-known collectors' items such as topaz, garnet, spodumene, monazite, tourmaline, cassiterite, tantalite, columbite, beryl, and lepidolite. A very long list could easily be offered. Small, uneconomic amounts of the sulfides (such as chalcopyrite, molybdenite, and sphalerite) are widely distributed in pegmatites.

Since World War II, uses for the rare minerals and metals have been greatly expanded; these materials are in short supply, and many have been classified as critical for national defense. The greatly increased demand for pegmatite minerals has encouraged an intensified search, which has, in turn, resulted in considerable information about the genesis of pegmatites. Some of the studies have been published, and contribute much to our knowledge of this interesting rock type (Johnston, 1945; Cameron and Shainin, 1947; Cameron et al., 1949; Jahns, 1946, 1951, 1955; Hanley et al., 1950; Page et al., 1953; Brotzen, 1959).

ZONING

The complex pegmatites show a great variety of textural, structural, and mineralogical characteristics, but they also have certain features in common. Foremost among the latter features is the zoning. Nearly all complex pegmatites may be described in terms of textural and mineralogic variations that define concentric zones or shells (Fig. 10-1). Contacts between the zones are generally gradational, though in places they are abrupt. Ideally, there are four zones, designated from outside inward as the *border zone,* the *wall zone,* the *intermediate zone,* and the *core.* All four zones are seldom present in any one pegmatite, but in exceptional instances even more zones have been mapped; additional zones are always described as subdivisions of the intermediate zone. The zones are seldom of uniform thickness around any one pegmatite—a zone may be thick on one side of a body and thin or absent elsewhere. Furthermore, individual deposits are irregular and are not arranged in nicely symmetrical layers, though the zones generally reflect the shape of the pegmatite body, and the outer zones are typically more regular and continuous than the inner zones (Cameron et al., 1949).

The border zone is thin (a few inches or less) in most pegmatites; in some deposits it cannot be recognized. It is a selvage, or transition, between the inner, more characteristic pegmatitic materials and the wall rocks, and is typically aplitic in texture. Fine-grained feldspars, quartz, and muscovite are the most common minerals found in border zones; accessory minerals may include garnet, tourmaline, beryl, or even some of the rare species. But the valuable metallic constituents are absent from this zone. Some border zones are thought to be the chilled margins of pegmatitic masses, as evidenced by a chemical composition similar to that of the pegmatite as a whole; other border zones differ distinctly from the bulk composition of the entire pegmatite (Cameron et al., 1949).

Wall zones are well developed in many pegmatites and are absent in others. In general, the wall zones and border zones contain the same minerals—though

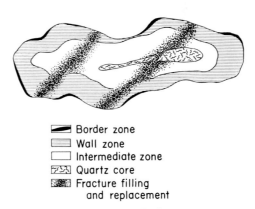

■ Border zone
▭ Wall zone
▢ Intermediate zone
▨ Quartz core
▧ Fracture filling
   and replacement

FIGURE 10-1. *Idealized plan of pegmatite body showing the distribution of zones and other superimposed units.*

the proportions may differ—and the wall zone is characteristically coarser textured and thicker than the border zone. The wall zone is, in turn, generally finer grained than the intermediate zones and the core. The essential minerals of most wall zones include plagioclase, perthite, quartz, muscovite, and subordinate (but often important) amounts of tourmaline, biotite, apatite, beryl, and garnet. The metallic constituents may be present; in a few exceptional deposits they have been of economic value. Mica and beryl are the principal commercial minerals recovered from the wall zones.

Since the intermediate zone includes the greatest concentration of metallic minerals, it is unfortunate that most pegmatites pass directly from the border or wall zones into the core and do not have an intermediate zone. Conversely, in other pegmatites as many as five or six subdivisions of the intermediate zone can be defined. Different parts of the intermediate zone are generally designated by letter or number; or if only two or three subdivisions are present, they are called the outer, middle, and inner intermediate zones. The intermediate subzones are noted for their varied mineralogy and occasional giant crystals, though the dominant minerals are again feldspars, quartz, and micas. It is in these zones that the minerals of uranium, thorium, lithium, cesium, niobium, tantalum, and rare earth metals are concentrated.

Many pegmatites contain a solid massive core of barren white quartz, coarse-grained quartz with feldspar, or quartz with large, euhedral crystals of tourmaline or spodumene. The core is generally near the center of a pegmatitic body and may form discontinuous pods along a central axis. It is ordinarily barren of metallic minerals, though a few exceptions are known.

In places quartz-filled fractures are superimposed upon the zones or confined within a single zone. The veins may define parallel systems or radial patterns, or they may fill irregular, random fractures. In some deposits the veins are confined to thin joint surfaces, but in others a large part of the original pegmatite is replaced by minerals that were introduced along the fractures (see Fig. 10-1). Some of these superimposed vein-filling and replacement materials contain commercial amounts of the metallic elements.

Zoning in the complex pegmatites has been known for many years, and several hypotheses for explaining it have been advanced. Any theory must acknowledge certain fundamental relationships, among which are the arrangements of the zones; the gradational to abrupt contacts; the transection or replacement of outer zones by inner zones, but not vice versa; the progressive sodium enrichment of plagioclases toward the inner zones; and the consistency in paragenesis of both the zones and the mineral assemblages from one pegmatite to another (Cameron et al., 1949).

Three possibilities have been advanced to explain these phenomena. One explanation holds that the zonal structure is formed by fractional crystallization in place under disequilibrium conditions. Thus the reaction between crystals and rest liquid would be incomplete, creating successive layers of contrasting composition (Brögger, 1890, p. 230). Crystallization within a partially closed system that undergoes repeated pressure releases and consequent resurgent boiling may account for the transgressions of younger zones upon older ones. This hypothesis is supported both in theory and in mineralogical details by Bowen's reaction principle. It is certainly a plausible explanation for those pegmatites that correspond to Bowen's reaction series from the border to the core. The pegmatite from the San Gabriel Mountains (Fig. 10-2) is a good example. It is a mafic pegmatite within coarse-grained norite. The deposit consists of a wall zone with augite-labradorite, an outer intermediate zone of hornblende-labradorite, an inner intermediate one of andesine-hornblende, and a core of perthite-quartz-albite-epidote. Grain sizes increase gradually from the outer zone through the intermediate zone, and the core is a relatively coarse mixture of graphic

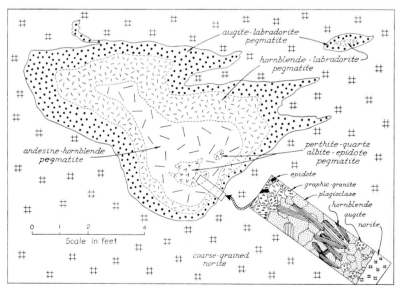

FIGURE 10-2. *Zoning of minerals in a gabbroic pegmatite from the western San Gabriel Mountains, California. (From Jahns, 1954, figure 3.)*

granite, albite, and epidote (Jahns, 1954). This sequence implies both fractional crystallization according to Bowen's series and a gradual increase in the volatile content, or at least mobility, of the rest melt.

A second explanation for zoning suggests that progressively changing solutions deposit materials along the walls of open channels (Hunt, 1871). This hypothesis does not depend upon crystal fractionation and conditions of disequilibrium. The pegmatitic fluids would be expected to vary in composition for any of a number of reasons, such as magmatic differentiation at the source and contamination with wall rocks or other fluids in transit.

The third hypothesis suggests that complex pegmatites are developed in two stages: (1) formation of a simple pegmatite by the direct crystallization of a pegmatitic fluid, (2) partial or complete replacement of the pegmatite as hydrothermal solutions pass through it (Hanley et al., 1950; Cotelo Neiva, 1954). The first stage is thought to take place within a relatively closed system; the second, in an open system.

Most modern workers agree with either the first or the third hypothesis or with some combination of the two (Schaller, 1933; Landes, 1933; Derry, 1931; Cameron et al., 1949). A strong argument against the possibility that zones develop along an open channel—as proposed in the second hypothesis—lies in the fact that many interior zones are completely enclosed within outer zones; since the zones become progressively younger toward the center, it would be physically impossible for this arrangement to develop in an open system. The third hypothesis—the two-stage system—has also been objected to on the grounds that the replacement would have to develop from the outside of a pegmatite toward its core; the zones would represent progressively thinner shells of replacement in fluids of changing composition, in which case the paragenetic sequence would be reversed. In contrast, zoned replacement veins (throughgoing systems), develop from a central fissure. If pegmatite zones do result from replacement reactions in fluids of variable composition, the universal similarity of zonal sequences would seem to be fortuitous rather than a necessary result of the processes involved (Cameron et al., 1949).

The source of fracture-filling and replacement material is generally unknown, but in certain instances the fluids can be related to one of the inner zones. Secondary minerals that transect all zones must have been derived from outside the immediate pegmatitic system, in which case the pegmatite would fit both the first and third hypotheses; but the zoning itself would not have been developed by later replacement processes. Thus the general concept of a pegmatitic system is one in which the zones develop from the walls inward, within a restricted system. The role of a gaseous phase may be of critical importance in this model. Late in the pegmatitic process, hydrothermal fluids that are probably related in various ways to the pegmatite travel through fractures and react with the older minerals. This modern concept of the processes involved in making complex pegmatites is precisely as Brögger had pictured it in 1890.

The vast majority of igneous pegmatites lie near the borders of intrusive masses, either within the igneous rock or in the nearby country rock. To a large extent, the position and size of these pegmatites are controlled by the structure and fracture pattern in the border areas. But in spite of the great amount of work that has been done with pegmatites, very little is actually known about their methods of emplacement.

According to Gevers (1936), the pegmatites of Namaqualand, South Africa, not only possess internal zoning, but the bodies themselves are distributed in zones and around an associated granitic batholith. Gevers classes the Namaqualand pegmatites as interior or core pegmatites, marginal or hood pegmatites, and exterior or roof pegmatites. The interior pegmatites are small, scattered, and generally barren of economic minerals. They become increasingly scarce with depth into the batholith. Marginal pegmatites occur within the upper or outer shell of the batholith. They are abundant and reach large dimensions. Late-phase hydrothermal alteration effects have developed economic concentrations in many of these pegmatites. The most abundant types, and those most rewarding to prospectors, are the exterior pegmatites. They are defined as those outside the parent granite body, though some of them grade into the marginal pegmatites. The exterior pegmatites are distributed over a zone several miles wide (depending upon the size of the parent batholith), and many of them are highly mineralized.

The relationships pointed out by Gevers fit into a generalization stated by Emmons (1940, p. 22). He noted that the valuable pegmatites are in and near the tops of batholiths—within the intrusives or injected into their roofs. This observation seems to agree with the latest field data. Heinrich (1953) found, further, that the simple pegmatites tend to be near or within the batholithic source and the complex pegmatites beyond. He suggested that the complex pegmatites form from the latest pegmatitic fluids and consequently are more mobile and have a greater rare-element content than the fluids producing simple pegmatites. This explanation acknowledges that the complex pegmatites characteristically possess the minerals of economic importance. As with all generalizations in geology, however, there are exceptions. Tôrre de Assunção pointed out (1944) such an exception in Portugal, where the valuable pegmatites are concentrated in the core of a nepheline syenite pluton.

Pegmatites are studied for reasons other than their mineralogy—they are transition materials between ordinary intrusive, granitoid masses and the veins and mineral deposits derived from hydrothermal fluids. With the exception of the pegmatites formed by metamorphic differentiation and related processes, it is generally accepted that most pegmatites are rest magmas—the residual volatile-rich fractions left after the main magmatic mass has solidified. The pegmatite residues crystallize in place or are squeezed off into available openings, where they solidify. Theoretically, it would seem that pegmatites should grade into hydrothermal deposits, especially into quartz veins of hypothermal environments. Many writers state that transitions between pegmatites and quartz veins are known or even common (Schneiderhöhn, 1941; Bateman, 1950), but this appears to be largely a matter of semantics. Actual transitions between typical, individual pegmatite bodies and typical quartz veins are few; most transitions involve swarms of veins and dikes (Shand, 1943). Many examples of the transitions are similar to that of the Passagem lode in the state of Minas Gerais, Brazil, and to some extent to the veins in Georgia (U.S.A.). In these areas the veins are predominately quartz, but they contain minor, scattered amounts of garnet, kyanite, tourmaline, apatite, muscovite, phlogopite, biotite, feldspars, and a few other high-temperature minerals. The Passagem lode is considered to be a vein of deep-seated origin, though an early description classified it as a pegmatite because of its mineral composition and coarse texture (Hussak, 1898). Minerals other than quartz are not abundant, however, nor have variations in the character of vein material been noted at depth or along its lateral extent. Deposits of the Southern Piedmont are similar; they are not typical pegmatites. One exception was found at the Old Franklin pit in Clay County, Alabama; here a zone of quartz stringers was mined for gold, and one narrow vein graded into what seems to be a characteristic simple pegmatite. The composition of veins in the Passagem lode and in the Southern Piedmont is similar to the composition of the enclosing rocks (Ross, 1935). Apparently, the composition of the veins is due in part to contamination from materials mobilized metamorphically from within the country rock.

Petaca District, New Mexico

In terms of economic considerations as well as description, pegmatites of the Petaca district, in northern New Mexico, provide ideal examples for study. The Petaca district comprises an area about 15 miles long and 4 miles wide, trending north-south in Rio Arriba County. The pegmatites there lie within an exposure of Precambrian rocks thought to be a southern extension of the San Juan Mountains (Jahns, 1946).

Careful studies of the Petaca pegmatites were made during World War II, and these studies were reported in detail by Jahns (1946). His descriptions form the basis for the following summary.

The pegmatites intrude Precambrian quartzites, quartz-mica schists, granite, and subordinate amphibole schists, andalusite schists, staurolite schists, and metamorphosed rhyolites. The granite, known as the Tusas Granite (Just, 1937), definitely intrudes the metamorphic rocks, and appears to be the source from which the pegmatitic fluids migrated. Nearly all the commercial pegmatites are in the schists and quartzites, beyond the granite contact. Small, irregular pegmatites within the granite are of little or no economic value. The commercial pegmatites reach dimensions of 1400 feet by 275 feet in plan, but most of them are a few hundred feet long and a few tens of feet wide.

More than fifty pegmatites are exposed in the Petaca district. There are simple pegmatites in the Tusas Granite and simple sills and dikes as well as irregularly shaped, cross-cutting complex pegmatites in the metamorphics. Only the latter are of general commercial value. Folds and minor structures controlled the emplacement of many of the pegmatites. Associated with the pegmatites are swarms of quartz veins. The veins and pegmatites apparently have a common origin in the granite, but most of the veins are younger. Some quartz veins cut through the outer zones of pegmatites and merge with their cores; rare examples can be found where veins gradually change along strike from pure quartz to a quartz vein with feldspathic walls.

The pegmatites are primarily of interest for their mica, but they also contain significant concentrations of beryllium, columbium, tantalum, bismuth, uranium, thorium, and the rare-earth metals. Mineralogically, the Petaca pegmatites consist of microcline, quartz, albite, and muscovite, plus accessory amounts of biotite, spessartite ($Mn_3Al_2Si_3O_{12}$, a garnet), fluorite, beryl, columbite-tantalite [$(Fe,Mn)(Nb,Ta)_2O_6$], samarskite [$(Fe,Ca,UO_2)(Ce,Y)(Nb,Ta)_6O_2$], monazite, ilmenite, magnetite, uraninite, lepidolite, tourmaline, and copper sulfides, plus rare occurrences of apatite, native bismuth, bismuthinite, microlite [$(Ca,Na)_2(Ta,Cb)_2(O,OH,F)_7$], cassiterite, fergusonite [$(Y,Er,Ce)(Nb,Ta)O_4$], gadolinite ($Be_2FeY_2Si_2O_{10}$), galena, phenakite (Be_2SiO_4), phlogopite, pyrite, scheelite, topaz, and many secondary products of these minerals.

Most of the commercial pegmatites in the Petaca district are internally zoned and display superimposed replacement minerals. The border zones generally consist of fine- to medium-grained microcline and quartz with subordinate mica and, in places, garnet, fluorite, and beryl. They range from less than an inch to several feet in thickness. Locally, the pegmatitic fluids reacted with the country rocks, developing gradational, mica-rich border zones.

Wall zones of coarse microcline and quartz, with accessory mica, garnet, fluorite, and beryl, are as much as several feet thick. In some pegmatites the wall zones form complete shells, but in others they were only partly developed or were partly removed by reaction with fluids that formed the intermediate zones.

As many as three intermediate zones can be mapped in the Petaca pegmatites, though some deposits have no intermediate zone. The intermediate zones characteristically form hood-like units along the crests of plunging pegmatite bodies, and seldom encompass the whole core; as a result, these zones vary greatly in thickness. The outer intermediate zone is commonly coarse graphic granite; the middle intermediate zone is coarse blocky microcline; and the inner intermediate zone is generally massive quartz containing sporadic giant microcline crystals.

The cores are found near the troughs of plunging pegmatites. They consist of massive quartz, quartz containing large microcline crystals, or, in some cases, coarse-grained microcline-quartz pegmatite. Usually they are situated in the thickest part of the pegmatite; structurally they consist of single ellipsoidal or pipe-like masses or series of disconnected pods.

Studies of the mineral paragenesis indicate that the zones developed progressively from the border to the core. Minerals of the outer zones were corroded and replaced by later pegmatitic fluids with which they were no longer in equilibrium; veins of the late fractions cut the peripheral zones. In general, microcline, garnet, and beryl formed early; albite, muscovite, monazite, columbite-tantalite, bismuth, and the sulfides formed later; quartz developed during all stages. The latest minerals to form were samarskite, uraninite, and smoky quartz.

Some of the pegmatites were essentially restricted to fractures, but others permeated the walls and left noticeable alteration zones along gradational contacts. In places the wall rock was replaced by pegmatite, leaving relict, oriented stringers or ghosts of schist and quartzite. Figure 10-3 was drawn

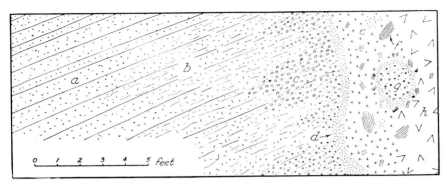

FIGURE 10-3. *Diagramatic sketch showing typical gradational relations between pegmatite and country rock. Petaca district, New Mexico. (a) Slabby micaceous quartzite. (b) Quartzite with muscovite-rich partings and disseminated small flakes of muscovite. (c) Mica-impregnated quartzite with metacrysts of microcline and albite-oligoclase. (d) Fine-grained mica-rich contact zone of pegmatite. (e) Medium-grained microcline-quartz-albite-oligoclase-muscovite pegmatite. (f) Large block of muscovite. (g) Inclusion of altered quartzite (lithologically similar to that in unit c). (h) Coarse-grained microcline-quartz pegmatite. (From Jahns, 1946, figure 5.)*

by Jahns (1946) to demonstrate the typical effect of pegmatitic saturation in the quartzite. The alteration zone averages only a few feet in thickness and projects along permeable parting planes in the quartzite.

Jahns (1946) concluded that the Petaca pegmatites formed in two stages —an early magmatic stage and a later hydrothermal stage. The early stage produced the zoned pegmatites, which are of relatively simple mineralogy. The hydrothermal stage produced most of the albite, muscovite, and rare minerals. These residual fluids must have been rich in soda, silica, alumina, and significant quantities of columbium, tantalum, beryllium, thorium, uranium, fluorine, bismuth, copper, sulfur, and the rare earths. The hydrothermal fluids traveled along fractures and reacted with the previously formed pegmatitic minerals, leaving behind new minerals of a replacement origin. It was during this hydrothermal stage that most of the metals of economic interest were produced.

References to Selected Pegmatite Deposits

Winnipeg River Area, Manitoba, Canada

Davies, J. F., 1957, Geology of the Winnipeg River area (Shatford Lake-Ryerson Lake) Lac du Bonnet mining division, Manitoba: Manitoba Dept. Mines and Nat. Resources, Mines Branch, Pub. 56-1.

Derry, D. R., 1931, The genetic relationships of pegmatites, aplites, and tin veins: Geol. Mag. (Great Britain), v. 68, p. 454–475.

Springer, G. D., 1950, Mineral deposits of the Cat Lake-Winnipeg River area; Lac du Bonnet division, Manitoba:

Manitoba Dept. Mines and Nat. Resources, Mines Branch, Pub. 49-7.

Stockwell, C. H., 1933, The genesis of pegmatites of southeast Manitoba: Roy. Soc. Canada Trans., 3rd ser., v. 27, sec. 4, p. 37–51.

Wright, J. F., 1930, Tin, lithium, and beryllium deposits of southeast Manitoba: Canadian Mining Jour., v. 51, no. 22, p. 514–517.

——, 1932, Geology and mineral deposits of a part of southeastern Manitoba: Canadian Geol. Survey Mem. 169.

Rajputana, India

Crookshank, H., 1945, Mica, beryl and columbite-tantalite in Rajputana: Imperial Inst., London, v. 43, no. 3, p. 228–235.

——, 1948, Minerals of the Rajputana pegmatites: Mining Geology and Metallurgical Inst. India Trans., v. 42, p. 105–189.

Das, Bhagwan, 1954, Characters of productive pegmatites: Indian Mining Jour., v. 2, no. 8, p. 13–15.

Krishnan, M. S., 1946, Beryllium: Geol. Survey of India Rec., v. 76, no. 13.

Sethi, M. L., 1956, Mineral resources of Rajasthan: Rajasthan Dept. Mines and Geology, B. 4.

Wadia, D. N., 1958, Occurrences of beryllium and zirconium in India: Internat. Conf. Peaceful Uses Atomic Energy, 2nd Geneva, Proc., v. 2, p. 107–109.

References Cited

Bateman, A. M., 1950, Economic mineral deposits: New York, John Wiley & Sons, Inc., p. 54–55.

Brögger, W. C., 1890, Die Mineralien der Syenitpegmatitgänge der Südnorwegischen Augit- und Nephelinsyenite: Zeit. für Krist. und Min., v. 16, p. 215–235.

Brotzen, O., 1959, On zoned granitic pegmatites: Stockholm Contrib. in Geology, v. 3, p. 71–81.

Cameron, E. N., Jahns, R. H., McNair, A. H., and Page, L. R., 1949, Internal structure of granitic pegmatites: Econ. Geology Mon. 2.

——, and Shainin, V. E., 1947, The beryl resources of Connecticut: Econ. Geology, v. 42, p. 353–367.

Cotelo Neiva, J. M., 1954, Pegmatitos com cassiterite e tantalite-columbite da Cabracao (Ponte do Lima-Serra de Arga): Univ. de Coimbra (Portugal), Memorias e Noticias, no. 36.

Derry, D. R., 1931, The genetic relationships of pegmatites, aplites, and tin veins: Geol. Mag. (Great Britain), v. 68, p. 454–475.

Emmons, W. H., 1940, Principles of economic geology: New York, McGraw-Hill Book Co., Inc.

Gevers, T. W., 1936, Phases of mineralization in Namaqualand pegmatites: Geol. Soc. South Africa Trans., v. 39, p. 331–378.

Hanley, J. B., Heinrich, E. W., and Page, L. R., 1950, Pegmatite investigations in Colorado, Wyoming, and Utah, 1942–44: U.S. Geol. Survey Prof. Paper 227.

Heinrich, E. W., 1953, Zoning in pegmatite districts: Am. Mineralogist, v. 38, p. 68–87.

Hunt, T. S., 1871, Notes on granitic rocks: Am. Jour. Sci., v. 101, p. 82–89, 182–191.

Hussak, Eugene, 1898, Der goldführende, kiesige Quarzlagergang von Passagem in Minas Geraes, Brasilien: Zeit. prakt. Geol., v. 6, p. 345–357.

Ingerson, Earl, 1947, Liquid inclusions in geologic thermometry: Am. Mineralogist, v. 32, p. 375–388.

Jahns, R. H., 1946, Mica deposits of the Petaca district, Rio Arriba County, New Mexico: New Mexico Bur. Mines and Mineral Resources Bull. 25.

——, 1951, Geology, mining, and uses of strategic pegmatites: Am. Inst. Mining Engineers Trans., v. 190, p. 45–59.

——, 1953, The genesis of pegmatites:

Am. Mineralogist, v. 38, p. 563–598, 1078–1112.

———, 1954, Pegmatites of Southern California: California Div. Mines Bull. 170, p. 37–50.

———, The study of pegmatites: Econ. Geology (50th Anniv. Volume), p. 1025–1130.

———, and Burnham, C. W., 1958, Experimental studies of pegmatite genesis: Melting and crystallization of granite and pegmatite: Geol. Soc. America Bull., v. 69, p. 1592–1593.

Johnston, W. D., Jr., 1945, Beryl-tantalite pegmatites of northeastern Brazil: Geol. Soc. America Bull., v. 56, p. 1015–1069.

Just, Evan, 1937, Geology and economic features of the pegmatites of Taos and Rio Arriba Counties, New Mexico: New Mexico Bur. Mines and Mineral Resources Bull. 13.

Landes, K. K., 1933, Origin and classification of pegmatites: Am. Mineralogist, v. 18, p. 33–56, 95–103.

Page, L. R. et al., 1953, Pegmatite investigations 1942–45, Black Hills, South Dakota: U.S. Geol. Survey Prof. Paper 247.

Ross, C. S., 1935, Origin of the copper deposits of the Ducktown type in the Southern Appalachian region: U.S. Geol. Survey Prof. Paper 179, p. 24–26.

Schaller, W. T., 1933, Pegmatites, *in* Ore deposits of the western states (Lindgren volume): Am. Inst. Mining Engineers, p. 144–151.

Schneiderhöhn, Hans, 1941, Lehrbuch der Erzlagerstättenkunde: Jena, Gustav Fischer, p. 114–120.

Shand, S. J., 1943, Eruptive rocks: New York, John Wiley & Sons, Inc., p. 8–9.

Tôrre de Assunção, C. F., 1944, Algumas observações petrológicas nas Caldas de Monchique: Lisboa, Univ., Mus. e Lab. Min. e Geol., Bol., s. 4, no. 11–12, p. 55–66.

CHAPTER 11 **Igneous Metamorphic Deposits**

Rocks intruded by igneous masses are recrystallized, altered, and replaced by heat and fluids emanating from the intrusives. The resulting changes are known as igneous metamorphism, pyrometamorphism, pyrometasomatism, or contact metamorphism. Each of these terms means roughly the same thing, but igneous metamorphism is less restrictive than the others. Pyrometamorphism refers only to the thermal effects; pyrometasomatism is restricted to replacement reactions; and contact metamorphism implies proximity to the actual igneous contact, whereas the alteration products may be found at great distances from any known intrusive mass. Igneous metamorphism, then, includes all forms of alteration associated with the intrusion of igneous rocks; and for this reason it is the preferred term.

Igneous metamorphism is most widely developed around the borders of small- to moderate-sized, discordant, intrusive masses of intermediate composition, such as monzonites and granodiorites, but metamorphic effects are also found to a lesser extent around other types of intrusives, whether silicic or mafic (Edwards and Baker, 1953). Ore deposits of igneous metamorphic origin are thought to form under high temperatures and pressures, deep within the earth. They are exposed at the surface only after appreciable uplift and erosion.

Characteristics of the igneous metamorphic zone depend upon the nature of the intruded rock and upon the nature of the emanations given off by the intrusive. Some resistant rocks (such as quartzites) may be unchanged, even right at the contact; others (such as carbonates) may be altered up to several miles from the pluton. Two types of alteration are recognized: (1) recrystallization, or rearrangement of the constituents already in the rocks, and (2) addition of materials from the igneous source. Most igneous metamorphic aureoles show both types. Considerable discussion has arisen as to the source of metasomatic materials, because many of the small intrusives are altered by the same processes as the bordering rocks. These added materials may have been derived from the local intrusive mass, in which case the resulting ore deposits are likely to be small. The ores may also have separated at depth within the parent magma chamber, and the exposed intrusive mass might then be a small appendage of a large pluton; that is, it would be a cupola in which the more mobile constituents accumulated. If the small intrusive body had solidified before the metamorphic processes were completed, the igneous rock itself would be altered or endomorphosed (Lindgren, 1905; Barrell, 1907).

Igneous metamorphic effects are best developed in limestones and shales, the most striking metamorphic aureoles being in the carbonate rocks. Sandstones may be recrystallized, but in general they are unreactive and relatively unaltered except where they contain argillaceous or calcareous facies. In clastic sequences metamorphism is likely to be more widespread where the intrusive mass cuts shale beds, which become baked and hardened or recrystallized into a dense, sugary rock known as hornfels. Most hornfels are apparently products of simple thermal metamorphism, though in places small additions (especially of silica) have been made. Shaly rocks in igneous metamorphic aureoles are commonly knotty or nodular, the small knots forming around grains of garnet, cordierite, or other porphyroblasts.

Skarn or tactite zones are developed where materials have been added from intrusive bodies. Skarn was defined originally by Swedish miners as the amphibole contact rock with which the magnetite ores of Sweden are associated. The term tactite was introduced by Hess (1919) to include all metasomatic products of igneous metamorphism. In present-day usage both terms are common and are used synonymously for any silicate rock of complex mineralogy formed in the contact aureole.

The assemblage of alteration products normally depends upon the character of the rocks invaded, although where large amounts of materials have been added (for example, in ore deposits) the minerals formed may bear little relation to the invaded rock. Generally, the minerals of skarn zones are both diagnostic and conspicuous. In limestones, for example, the skarn is characterized by lime-rich minerals, such as grossularite or andradite, wol-

lastonite, epidote, tremolite, and hedenbergite (or salite). The dolomites
develop serpentine, diopside, the humite-chondrodite group, and other
minerals that are comparatively rich in magnesium. In addition to these
minerals, the skarns in carbonate hosts are likely to contain a variety of
other minerals, from the garnet and scapolite families to such species as
ilvaite and jeffersonite (a manganese-zinc pyroxene). The carbonate rocks
near contacts or skarn zones are generally crystalline or sugary, and many
of them have been bleached white.

As would be expected, the alteration products of shales are high in
alumina, the characteristic minerals including biotite, ottrelite $[H_2(Fe,Mn)$
$Al_2SiO_7]$ and other micas, andalusite, sillimanite, hornblende, actinolite,
garnets, scapolite, cordierite, and many others.

Silica is probably the most abundant compound added to igneous metamorphic zones. It may enter into the composition of one or more of the
silicate minerals, or it may replace the host completely, producing quartz
or chert. The silica sometimes forms small, inconspicuous, isolated crystals,
and elsewhere produces massive deposits of cryptocrystalline quartz. Silicification is common in both carbonate rocks and shales.

In contrast to the mineralogy of skarns, the ore minerals are usually simple sulfides and oxides. The sulfides include sphalerite (commonly the
iron-rich variety), galena, chalcopyrite, bornite, and in places molybdenite.
A few igneous metamorphic zones are comparatively iron-free, but most
contain abundant pyrite gangue or even large amounts of the oxide ores,
magnetite and hematite. Scheelite is also found in many igneous metamorphic deposits, and at the Emerald mine in British Columbia the ore
occurs in both the skarn and the intrusive rocks.

Igneous metamorphic ore deposits are essentially restricted to the carbonate rocks; they are unusual or absent in shales and high-silica sediments. The oxide minerals are commonly within the skarn, and seem to
form an integral part of this metamorphic rock. In places the oxides are
concentrated next to the intrusive, but elsewhere they are found along the
outer border of the skarn zone. Most of the sulfides are concentrated along
the periphery of the skarn, near the contact with the carbonate host.
In general, the sulfide minerals were emplaced after the skarn, which they
replace. Many of the original sedimentary textures and structures are preserved after the double replacement by skarn and ore, though in some
deposits the second replacement obscures the evidence, and relict textures
can be found only after diligent searching.

The presence of abundant oxide minerals in igneous metamorphic zones presents problems in chemistry. We know, for example, that most or at least half the iron in mafic igneous rocks is in the ferrous state, and hence that the iron concentrated in residual liquids also must be largely in the reduced form; yet all of the iron in specular hematite and part of the iron in magnetite is in the ferric state. How is the iron oxidized within the environment of igneous metamorphism? Butler (1923, 1927) suggested that the iron is oxidized according to the reaction

$$3FeO + CO_2 \rightleftharpoons Fe_3O_4 + CO$$

by carbon dioxide liberated from the carbonate host rocks during intrusion and replacement. The oxidation reaction is favored by the high temperatures characteristic of igneous metamorphic zones, and the reversed reaction is favored under lower-temperature conditions and lower carbon dioxide pressures. The early, near-pluton deposition of magnetite and specular hematite and the later, more distant deposition of ferrous compounds (sulfides, carbonates, and silicates) strongly favors the above argument. It has been pointed out, however, that the iron is probably not in solution as FeO. Accordingly, Shand (1947) proposed that iron travels as an aqueous colloidal solution of ferrous hydroxide. Upon dehydration, the ferrous hydroxide is oxidized to magnetite:

$$3Fe(OH)_2 \rightleftharpoons Fe_3O_4 + 2H_2O + H_2$$

This reaction was proposed for the oxidation process in general, and not specifically for igneous metamorphic environments, where the presence of colloids is not very probable, especially since the replacement nature of the ores demands widespread diffusion of the mineralizers. Perhaps the answer is a compromise between these two hypotheses or a modification of either one. The modern concept of free ions in solution, rather than molecules of compounds, can be applied to Butler's equation; similarly, it is reasonable that even a true solution of $Fe(OH)_2$, as Fe^{+2} and $2OH^-$, will become oxidized at elevated temperatures. Both reactions have been supported experimentally, but it is possible that neither the compound FeO nor the colloid $Fe(OH)_2$ was the actual substance in question. (The presence of a colloid may have been assumed rather than proved: what was prepared as a colloid may not have remained in this state under the high-temperature reached during the reactions. As regards the compound FeO, early studies used molecular symbols for the same reactions that now require ionic equations.)

Central District, New Mexico

The Central district, in southwestern New Mexico, is a highly mineralized area that supports mining of various types, including disseminated copper deposits, replacements of zinc in limestone, and zinc-lead-copper veins, as well as iron and zinc ores of igneous metamorphic origin. The district has been well studied and, as a consequence, is unusually well known (Lindgren et al., 1910; Paige, 1916; Schmitt, 1933, 1942; Spencer and Paige, 1935; Lasky and Hoagland, 1950; Horton, 1953).

Sedimentary, metamorphic, and igneous rocks, ranging in age from Precambrian to Recent, provide the Central district with a varied geologic column. There are Precambrian granites, gneisses, schists, and hornfels; Paleozoic limestones and shales underlain by a basal unit of sandstone; and Upper Cretaceous to Tertiary clastics and igneous rocks. The igneous rocks include diorite sills; andesite intrusives and associated pyroclastics; quartz diorite sills and laccoliths; composite stocks of granodiorite and quartz monzonite; dikes of quartz monzonite, granodiorite, and quartz latite; rhyolite pyroclastics; and basalt flows (Lasky and Hoagland, 1950; Hernon et al., 1953). Metallization is related to the granodiorite-quartz monzonite stocks and dikes; it took place in the Late Cretaceous or Early Tertiary, though a minor amount of mineralization accompanied Late Tertiary igneous activity. There are three stocks in the immediate area: the Hanover-Fierro stock, the Santa Rita stock, and the Copper Flat stock (Fig. 11-1).

Although the regional geology is complex, we can say that the district lies on the northeast limb of a broad, shallow syncline modified by minor folds and local domes associated with the stocks and laccoliths. Faulting is also complex. The area was subjected to at least six periods of faulting, ranging in age from pre-stock to post-lava flows. Recurrent movement took place along many of the faults during several or all of these episodes.

The Hanover-Fierro stock is the largest of the three plutons. Somewhat oval in shape, it extends about $2\frac{1}{2}$ miles in a north-south direction and averages $\frac{1}{2}$ mile or more in width. The town of Hanover lies at the south end, Fierro, at the north. The Santa Rita stock is about one mile southeast of Hanover, and the Copper Flat stock, the smallest of the three, is about two miles southwest of Hanover. Each of the stocks is surrounded by an igneous metamorphic aureole, chiefly manifested by replacement skarns in limestones and shales but also by alteration of the older igneous rocks. Differences in the compositions of intruded rocks caused considerable differ-

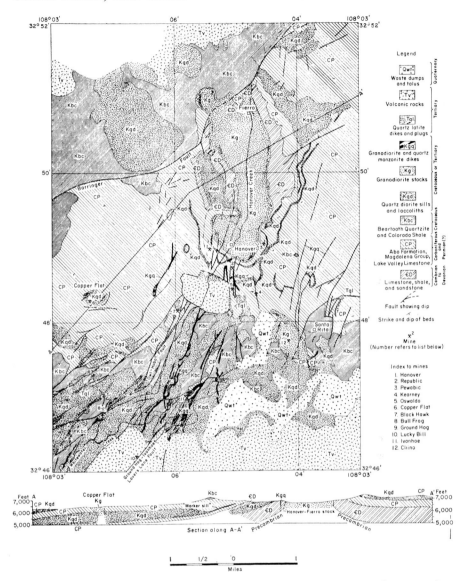

FIGURE 11-1. *Generalized geologic map and section of the Central mining district, New Mexico. (After Lasky and Hoagland, 1950; Hernon et al., 1953.)*

ences in the alteration products formed in the igneous metamorphic zones. For example, the higher magnesium content in the older Paleozoic rocks along the northern end of the Hanover-Fierro stock, and the higher calcium content of the younger rocks near the south end of the stock, resulted in striking differences in the metamorphic products formed at the two extremities. At Fierro the igneous metamorphic zone contains abundant serpentine, wollastonite, tremolite, and magnetite, whereas at Hanover the mineral assemblage is garnet, epidote, hedenbergite, tremolite, ilvaite, and sphalerite. Some of the metamorphic minerals are restricted to certain host rocks—notably epidote, which selects aluminous rocks such as shales and argillaceous limestones, and sphalerite, which favors the pure limestones (Schmitt, 1939). Furthermore, there is a zonation of alteration within the skarn aureole itself; near the intrusives there is a garnet-pyroxene-ore zone, which is separated by marble from an outer zone of actinolite-tremolite skarn (Lasky and Hoagland, 1950).

The localization of igneous metamorphic ores was controlled not only by proximity to the intrusive bodies but also by structure. The ore-bearing fluids ascended most readily along fractures, and as a consequence the skarn and ore zones are most extensive near these structures. In general, the metamorphic aureole is confined to within several hundred feet of intrusives, but apophyses along faults and dikes extend out much farther. Between Hanover and Santa Rita, the metamorphic zones actually merge into a single, continuous band.

Both zinc and iron occur as separate deposits of igneous metamorphic origin in the Central mining district. The largest and richest zinc ore bodies are in the upper crinoidal part of the Lake Valley Limestone (known locally as the Hanover Limestone) of Mississippian age. Lesser amounts of sphalerite are known in other limestone formations, but the Lake Valley Limestone contains an 18-foot shale bed (the Parting Shale), which served as an efficient dam to ascending ore fluids. Much of the ore at Hanover is concentrated within the limestone immediately below the Parting Shale, though locally the mineralization extends into the shale and, in places, through it into the limestone above.

In effect, it was the skarn zone that was localized beneath the Parting Shale, and the skarn, in turn, controlled the deposition of ore minerals. Thus the igneous metamorphic deposits are generally found within the skarn, which they replace. Lasky and Hoagland (1950) made the observation that the ore bodies at Copper Flat lie well within the garnet-pyroxene zone, but at Hanover they are at the outermost edge of this zone, against the marble but still as a replacement of skarn. Consequently, most of the Hanover ore bodies have at least one marble wall. Zinc ores are also found in the limestones at considerable distances from skarns, beyond the zone of igneous metamorphism; these deposits are lower temperature ores and are classified as true vein or replacement deposits.

Some of the igneous metamorphic sphalerite deposits are relatively large. A typical ore body in the Pewabic mine, near the southeast edge of the Hanover-Fierro stock, was localized along the intersection of a thrust fault and a vertical fracture zone, forming a cigar-shaped mass about 40 feet in diameter and 600 feet long (Schmitt, 1939). An analysis of zinc ore from the Hanover area is given in Table 11-I. As in the case for most mining districts, the earliest ore produced (which the analysis represents) was higher grade than the more recent shipments, though the mineral composition of ores has not varied. In the past, the ore brought a premium price because of its extremely low lead content, but as the deposits are worked farther and farther from the intrusive contacts, the amount of galena increases, with the result that lead is now an important constituent of the ores.

TABLE 11-I

Analysis of Early Ore from Hanover, New Mexico

Constituent	Percent
Zn	17.49
Pb	0.13
Fe	6.19
Mn	0.94
CaO	8.09
MgO	1.81
CO_2	3.37
S	10.19
Insoluble	49.77
TOTAL	97.98

SOURCE: After Spencer and Paige (1935).

Igneous metamorphic deposits of iron ore have also been mined in the Central district. In contrast to the sphalerite, which occurs near the outer fringe of the metamorphic aureole, the magnetite is concentrated next to the igneous contacts (Spencer and Paige, 1935). Magnetite is found in many places throughout the district, but the principal commercial deposit is at Fierro, near the northern end of the Hanover-Fierro stock, especially

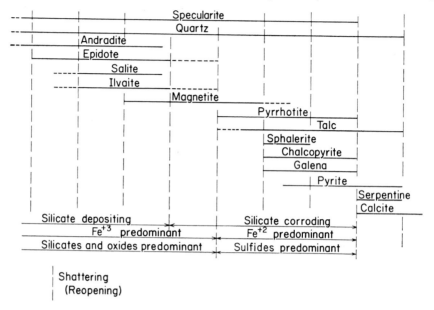

FIGURE 11-2. *Paragenesis of the Pewabic ores. (After Schmitt, 1939, figure 4.)*

where the contact of the igneous rock is parallel to the bedding. The best ores are concentrated in the Lower Ordovician El Paso Limestone. Lesser amounts of ore are found in the Cambrian Bliss Sandstone. The magnetite ore bodies are roughly tabular masses that appear to conform to the stratification of the rocks. They alternate with layers of serpentine, wollastonite, and lesser amounts of garnet, hedenbergite, tremolite, and epidote. Small veinlets of pyrite and chalcopyrite can be found within much of the magnetite, representing a slightly later phase of mineralization. Schmitt (1939), studying the paragenesis of the Pewabic ores, ascertained that the silicates and oxides preceded the sulfides and that ferric iron predominated during the early silicate-oxide phase, in contrast to ferrous iron, which predominated during the sulfide phase (Fig. 11-2). Specular hematite was the first ore mineral deposited and was contemporaneous with the silicates, but, in general, metallization followed the formation of skarn.

The skarn and ore deposits are not products of the accompanying stocks. The stocks solidified before the ores were deposited and, in places, were altered to skarn along with the country rocks. During the episode of mineralization, the stocks were intruded by granodiorite dikes, which in turn are partly mineralized. Evidently, the skarn and ore deposits are due largely to hydrothermal fluids that were generated within the same mag-matic chamber as the stocks, and each was intruded in sequence into the overlying rocks. The postulated hydrothermal activity is evident through-out the district. It began when the stocks were emplaced and continued in augmenting proportions through subsequent periods of fracturing, intrusion of dikes, and ore deposition. All of these phenomena represent phases of an extended period of igneous activity (Spencer and Paige, 1935; Jones et al., 1961). The presence of disseminated veinlets of copper ore in the Santa Rita stock emphasizes that the ore-bearing fluids ascended from depth and were not direct differentiates of the stocks themselves. Further support for this supposition is afforded by the presence of ore away from the stocks and by the similarity between distant ore and that in the skarn.

Iron Springs District, Utah

The magnetite deposits of the Iron Springs district, just west of Cedar City in southwestern Utah (Fig. 11-3), furnish another example of igneous metamorphic deposition (Leith and Harder, 1908; Young, 1947; Mackin, 1947; Mackin and Ingerson, 1960). This district was mentioned in Chapter 2, in connection with deuteric leaching as a source of metals; here it is of interest with regard to the manner of ore deposition.

Ore deposition in the Iron Springs district is associated with three intru-sive masses: Iron Mountain, Granite Mountain, and Three Peaks. The intrusives are aligned in a northeast direction, and each is oval in plan, is 3–5 miles long, and has its long axis trending parallel to the regional alignment. In addition to replace-ment ores along the borders of the intrusives, there are vertical veins of magnetite within the plutons. Much more ore has been obtained from Iron Mountain and Granite Mountain than from Three Peaks. These de-posits differ from the magnetite bod-ies at Fierro, New Mexico, in that most of the Iron Springs ores replaced the limestone directly, rather than re-placing a previously deposited skarn.

FIGURE 11-3. *Index map of the Iron Springs district, Utah.*

The lowest stratigraphic unit exposed in the district is a massive, 200- to 300-foot, blue and gray limestone of Jurassic age, known as the Homestake Formation. It includes a 15- to 25-foot basal siltstone and is capped by 5–10 feet of argillaceous limestone, distinctive for its ripple marks and mudcracks. Overlying the Homestake Formation is the Entrada Formation of Upper Jurassic age. The Entrada consists of maroon and gray shales interlensed with medium- to coarse-grained arkosic sandstone. It varies in thickness from 50 to 220 feet, the variation being due to erosion. The eroded surface of the Entrada is covered disconformably by a basal conglomerate, which grades upward into a sequence of variegated, fresh-water limestones, shales, sandstones, and conglomerates of the Iron Springs Formation, a Cretaceous unit measuring up to 5000 feet in thickness. The Iron Springs Formation is folded, eroded, and overlain unconformably by the Claron Formation, a Cretaceous to Eocene assemblage of coarse boulder conglomerates, gray and red sandstones and shales, and white to pink limestones. The pre-Claron period of folding and erosion left the Iron Springs Formation with a variable thickness of 1000–5000 feet; rarely is the full 5000-foot section preserved. At places, the Iron Springs and Entrada were completely removed, so that the Claron Formation rests directly on the Homestake (Mackin, 1947).

The three intrusive bodies are all of the laccolithic type. They were intruded along the base of the Homestake Formation, which they dome upward along with the overlying sediments. The three laccoliths are similar in composition, consisting principally of quartz monzonite (Mackin, 1954) or granodiorite porphyry (Mackin and Ingerson, 1960). They possess fine-grained chilled borders and, although they lack noteworthy assimilation effects along the contacts, they definitely resulted from the forceful injection of a viscous melt (Mackin, 1947).

Mackin (1947), through careful observations and field mapping, delineated three zones within the laccoliths, each reflecting a different phase of the crystallization process. Around the borders of each intrusive is a peripheral shell of fine-grained quartz monzonite, 100 to 200 feet thick. It is a resistant rock, forming ledges above the interior zone. This peripheral rock is finer-grained, less friable, and higher in magnetite content than the quartz monzonite of the interior zone. It contains fresh biotite and hornblende phenocrysts.

The interior phase of the quartz monzonite is coarser grained, and the biotite and hornblende have undergone deuteric alteration. Owing to the alteration effects, this rock lacks resistance to weathering; it characteristically forms low, crumbly knobs or flat, barren stretches. In contrast to the peripheral quartz monzonite, little fresh rock crops out within the interior zones.

Both the interior zone and the peripheral shell of each laccolith are jointed along radial and concentric planes. The joints are spaced from a few feet to a few tens of feet apart. In general, the radial joints strike at nearly right angles to the concentric joints. In the interior and peripheral zones there is no selvage (alteration) associated with the joints.

Mackin (1947) described a third zone in the laccoliths, which he called the zone of selvage joints. This zone separates the interior from the peripheral shell, forming areas of rugged topography. The rock on each side of individual joints is bleached through a zone ranging from a fraction of an inch to more than six inches in width (Fig. 11-4). Differential weathering within the zone of selvage joints produces a ribbed physiography, because each selvage zone forms a hard surface crust that stands in relief above the surrounding quartz monzonite. This bleached crust grades, within half an inch, into the same kind of soft, deuterically altered quartz monzonite that is characteristic of the interior zone. Mafic minerals within the selvage zones have been bleached to light green or white. About 20 percent of the rock volume in this zone of selvage joints has been bleached. Differences between the three laccolithic zones seem to be due to the nature and degree of deuteric alteration, rather than to any differences in the original rock type.

The selvage joints are of radial, concentric, and oblique types. The radial set is a continuation of the radial joints in the interior zone, which strike normal to the intrusive contacts and have vertical dips. In contrast, the concentric joints strike parallel to the igneous contacts and dip into the intrusives, normal to the contacts. Curved joints that swing from radial to concentric are classified as oblique (Fig. 11-5). Possibly 30–50 percent of the selvage joints contain magnetite with accessory pyroxene, apatite, calcite, and hematite. Comb structures and vugs indicate that the fissures were filled rather than replaced. The veins are unusually abundant. There are thousands of veins less than 4 inches wide; scores of them several feet wide; and some over 10 feet wide. Most of the larger veins occupy the radial joints, but some also fill concentric and oblique joints. In general, the radial veins are wedge-shaped, thickening toward the margins of the laccoliths, both in plan and in cross section.

Chemical analyses indicate that the iron deposited in fissures and as replacements of limestone was derived from the zone of selvage joints.

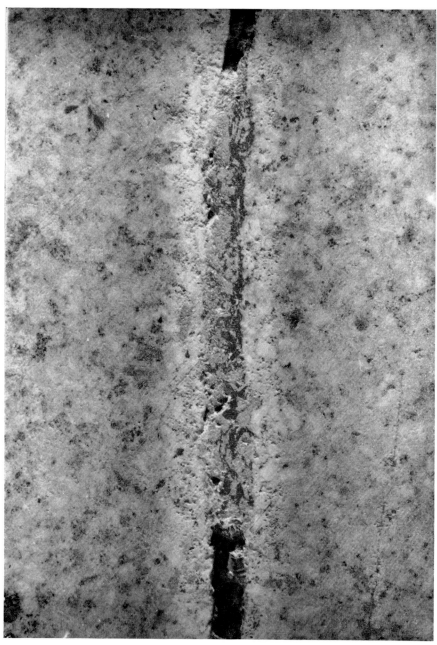

FIGURE 11-4. *Selvage joint through the Three Peaks granite, showing the bleached zone bordering a magnetite veinlet.* ×4. (*Specimen collected by A. S. Radtke; photo by W. J. Crook.*)

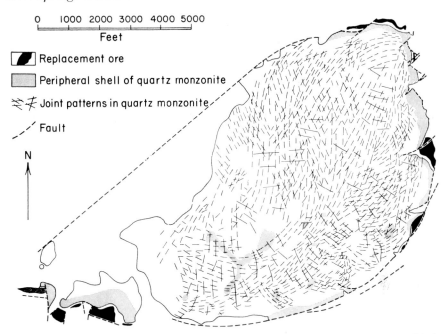

0   1000 2000 3000 4000 5000
                 Feet

▰ Replacement ore

▦ Peripheral shell of quartz monzonite

≋ ≢ Joint patterns in quartz monzonite

⟋⟋ Fault

N

FIGURE 11-5. *Map of quartz monzonite outcrops on Granite Mountain, Utah, showing the joint pattern and areas of peripheral-shell facies. Note the relationship between replacement ore bodies and peripheral-shell facies. (After Mackin, 1954.) See Figure 11-6 for the relationship of quartz monzonite and ore to sedimentary rocks.*

The deuterically altered interior zone contains about the same amount of iron as the fresh peripheral zone—that is, about 3 percent; but the bleached selvage zones are all relatively deficient in iron. It is believed that the volume of rock leached could have supplied more than enough iron to account for the deposits in and around the laccoliths.

Detailed mapping shows that the ore deposits are associated with bulges in the roofs of laccoliths (Mackin, 1947, 1954). Where the intrusive was not arched strongly upward, both the joints and the surrounding limestones are barren of ore. Apparently, there was a critical period during crystallization of the magmas when fracturing of the roof permitted egress of the volatiles. The Three Peaks laccolith has a relatively flat roof, and did not provide joints through the periphery for escaping mineralizers; consequently, this intrusive has only a thin zone of selvage joints and is relatively unproductive in iron. It is especially noteworthy that roof pendants in the Three Peaks laccolith are barren, in contrast to Granite Mountain and Iron Mountain, where they are highly mineralized. Only where late-intrusion tension

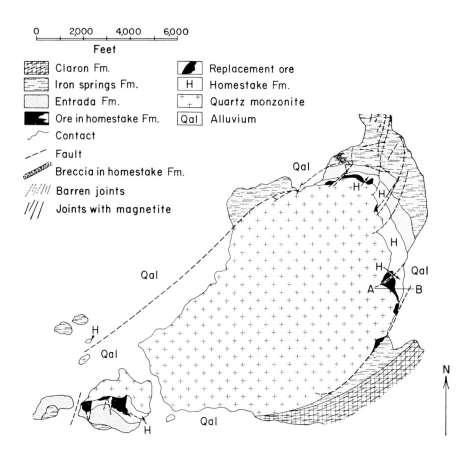

0   2,000   4,000   6,000
Feet

Claron Fm.

Iron springs Fm.

Entrada Fm.

Ore in homestake Fm.

Contact

Fault

Breccia in homestake Fm.

Barren joints

Joints with magnetite

Replacement ore

H   Homestake Fm.

Quartz monzonite

Qal   Alluvium

Qal

Qal

H

H

Qal

H

H

A   B

Qal

Qal

Qal

H

N

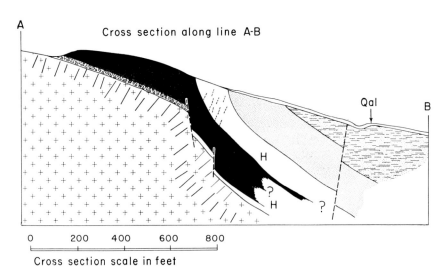

A

Cross section along line A-B

Qal

B

H

H

H

?

?

0   200   400   600   800

Cross section scale in feet

cracks and breccia zones tapped the selvage zone was ore deposited beyond the laccolithic contact. The iron-rich fluids capable of moving from the zone of selvage joints through the peripheral shell were left as igneous metamorphic deposits in the Homestake Limestone.

Replacement ore bodies in the Homestake Limestone measure as much as 1000 feet in dip and strike dimensions and are as much as 230 feet thick in places. They are pod-shaped bodies scattered irregularly along the igneous contact. In general, the ore is separated from quartz monzonite by the basal siltstone member of the Homestake Formation, and the outer limits of ore conform to the bedding only where the entire thickness of limestone was replaced (Fig. 11-6).

Ore deposition was not preceded by the development of skarn, though mica, quartz, garnet, and a few lime silicates are found with the ore. A minor amount of pre-ore silicification took place, but it did not control the localization of ore. Apatite is found in both the vein and the replacement ores; it is concentrated along the footwall side of igneous metamorphic deposits. Copper and iron sulfides are minor constituents in the replacement ores, and they are confined to the parts of ore bodies farthest from the intrusive.

In summary, Mackin (1947, 1954) believes that the Iron Springs ores originated locally within the laccoliths. They were leached from ferromagnesian minerals during late stages of igneous activity, leaving behind areas of bleaching and alteration. Before the interiors of the laccoliths were completely crystallized, but after the outer zones had solidified enough to support tension cracks, upward surges of the interior crystal mush developed bulges in the roofs of the laccoliths, causing distension and local jointing. The entire history of laccolithic emplacement was a sequence of roof rupturing, rather than a sudden release of the tensile forces across the whole intrusive. The shearing and brecciation that accompanied jointing eased some of the dilative forces. Wherever the peripheral shell was breached by joints or breccia zones, the iron-bearing interior fluids ascended into the overlying limestones, forming replacement deposits. If the ore-bearing fluids could have moved freely out of the laccoliths, a continuous blanket of iron ore probably would have been developed. The actual occurrence of ore, however, is sporadic, reflecting the fact that only local avenues were available to tap the mineralizers during this critical phase of crystallization.

FIGURE 11-6. *Facing page. Geologic map and cross section of Granite Mountain, Utah. (After Mackin, 1947, figure 12.)*

Remnants of the peripheral shell can be found along the eroded tops of laccoliths, suggesting that the original sedimentary cover was not far above the present surface of quartz monzonite. At the time of igneous intrusion and ore deposition, the overlying strata were 3000–6000 feet thick (Mackin, 1954). Thus the ores were formed at relatively shallow depths for an igneous metamorphic environment. The ore solutions selectively replaced only limestone and bypassed a bed of siltstone, implying a chemical control of ore deposition. If the limestone had not been available, the ore-bearing fluids presumably would have migrated some distance from the laccoliths before precipitating the iron.

References to Selected Igneous Metamorphic Deposits

Marysville District, Montana

Barrell, Joseph, 1907, Geology of the Marysville mining district, Montana: U.S. Geol. Survey Prof. Paper 57.

Knopf, Adolph, 1950, The Marysville granodiorite stock, Montana: Am. Mineralogist, v. 35, p. 834–844.

Pardee, F. G., and Schrader, F. C., 1933, Metalliferous deposits of the greater Helena mining region, Montana: U.S. Geol. Survey Bull. 842.

Oslo, Norway

Goldschmidt, V. M., 1911, Die Kontaktmetamorphose im Kristianiagebiet (Norway): Norske videnskaps akademia i Islo, Mathematisk-natur-videnskapelig klasse, Skrifter, no. 1.

Vogt, J. H. L., 1894, Ueber die durch pneumatolytische Processe an Granit gebundenen Mineral-Neubildungen: Zeit. prakt. Geol., v. 2, p. 458–465.

Vogt, J. H. L., 1895, Beitrage zur gene-

tischen Klassifizierung der durch magmatische Differentiationsprocesse und der durch Pneumatolyse entstandenen Erzvorkommen: Zeit. prakt. Geol., v. 3, p. 145–156, 367–370, 444–459, 465–484.

Von Groddeck, A., 1879, Die Lehre von den Lagerstätten der Erze: Leipzig.

Suian District, Korea

Higgins, D. F., 1918, Geology and ore deposits of the Collbran contact of the Suian mining concession, Korea: Econ. Geology, v. 13, p. 1–34.

Kato, B., 1910, Journeys through Korea; Contrib. 2, the geology and ore deposits of the Hol-gol gold mine: Imperial Univ. of Tokyo, College of Sci. Jour., v. 27.

Watanabe, Takeo, 1943, Geology and mineralization of the Suian district, Tyosen (Korea): Hokkaido Imperial Univ., Jour. Faculty Sci., ser. IV, v. 6, nos. 3–4.

References Cited

Barrell, Joseph, 1907, Geology of the Marysville mining district, Montana: U.S. Geol. Survey Prof. Paper 57.

Butler, B. S., 1923, A suggested explanation of the high ferric oxide content of limestone contact zones: Econ. Geology, v. 18, p. 398–404.

———, 1927, Some relations between

oxygen minerals and sulphur minerals in ore deposits: Econ. Geology, v. 22, p. 233–245.

Edwards, A. B., and Baker, G., 1953, Scapolitization in the Cloncurry district of north-western Queensland: Geol. Soc. Australia Jour., v. 1, p. 1–33.

Hernon, R. M., Jones, W. R., and Moore,

S. L., 1953, Some geological features of the Santa Rita quadrangle, New Mexico: Guidebook of Southwestern New Mexico, 4th Field Conference, New Mexico Geol. Soc., p. 117–130.

Hess, F. L., 1919, Tactite, the product of contact metamorphism: Am. Jour. Sci., v. 198, p. 377–378.

Horton, J. S., 1953, Geology of the Hanover mine: Mining Eng., v. 5, p. 1228–1229.

Jones, W. R., Hernon, R. M., and Pratt, W. P., 1961, Geologic events culminating in primary metallization in the Central mining district, Grant County, New Mexico: U.S. Geol. Survey Prof. Paper 424-C, p. 11–16.

Lasky, S. G., and Hoagland, A. D., 1950, Central mining district, New Mexico: 18th Internat. Geol. Cong., Symposium on the geology, paragenesis, and reserves of the ores of lead and zinc, p. 97–110.

Leith, C. K., and Harder, E. C., 1908, The iron ores of the Iron Springs district, southern Utah: U.S. Geol. Survey Bull. 338.

Lindgren, Waldemar, 1905, The copper deposits of the Clifton-Morenci district, Arizona: U.S. Geol. Survey Prof. Paper 43.

————, Graton, L. C., and Gordon, C. H., 1910, The ore deposits of New Mexico: U.S. Geol. Survey Prof. Paper 68, p. 305–318.

Mackin, J. H., 1947, Some structural features of the intrusions in the Iron Springs district, Utah: Utah Geol. Soc. Guidebook to the geology of Utah, no. 2.

————, 1954, Geology and iron ore deposits of the Granite Mountain area, Iron County, Utah: U.S. Geol. Survey Mineral Inv. Field Studies Map MF 14.

————, and Ingerson, Earl, 1960, An hypothesis for the origin of ore-forming fluid: U.S. Geol. Survey Prof. Paper 400-B, p. 1–2.

Paige, Sidney, 1916, The Silver City Folio: U.S. Geol. Survey Folio 199.

Schmitt, H. A., 1933, The Central mining district, New Mexico: Am. Inst. Mining Engineers Contrib. 39 (Class I, Mining Geology).

————, 1939, The Pewabic mine: Geol. Soc. America Bull., v. 50, p. 777–818.

————, 1942, Certain ore deposits in the Southwest; Central mining district, New Mexico, in Newhouse, W. H. (ed.), Ore deposits as related to structural features: New Jersey, Princeton University Press, 73–77.

Shand, S. J., 1947, The genesis of intrusive magnetite and related ores: Econ. Geology, v. 42, p. 634–636.

Spencer, A. C., and Paige, Sidney, 1935, Geology of the Santa Rita mining area, New Mexico: U. S. Geol. Survey Bull. 859.

Young, W. E., 1947, Iron Springs, Iron County, Utah: U.S. Bureau of Mines Rept. of Investigations 4076.

CHAPTER 12

Hypothermal Deposits

HYPOTHERMAL DEPOSITS form at high temperatures and great depths, where connection with the surface is impeded. The general temperature range is 300–500°C. Textures and structures indicative of replacement are commonly well developed, whereas vugs and open-fissure fillings, so characteristic of the shallower deposits, are scarce or absent. The rocks may be sheeted or sheared, often so thoroughly that the deposits contain many shadowy fragments of the wall rocks. Most hypothermal ores are coarse-grained, though there are some notable exceptions to this generalization; for example, the Sullivan mine in British Columbia contains large ore bodies of galena and sphalerite with an aphanitic texture. Wall-rock alteration is usually inconspicuous around hypothermal deposits, because the great depth of this environment precludes a significant temperature differential between the ore-bearing fluids and the wall rocks. For this same reason, the veins and their accompanying alteration products are likely to grade into the country rock, rather than have sharp boundaries.

The ore minerals most commonly present in the hypothermal zone are gold, wolframite, scheelite, pyrrhotite, pentlandite, pyrite, arsenopyrite, löllingite, chalcopyrite, sphalerite, galena, stannite, cassiterite, bismuthinite, uraninite, and the cobalt and nickel arsenides. Small amounts of fluorite, barite, magnetite, ilmenite, and specularite may be present. Pyrite, probably the most common sulfide in all ore zones, is widely distributed in hypothermal deposits.

Many minerals of the igneous metamorphic zone continue without interruption into the hypothermal zone. Gangue minerals and products of wall-rock alteration include black tourmaline (schorl), phlogopite, muscovite (commonly stained green with trace amounts of chromium), biotite, zinnwaldite, topaz, apatite, sillimanite, hedenbergite, hornblende, tremolite, actinolite, cummingtonite, the spinels (especially magnetite and gahnite), kyanite, and the feldspars. Many of these minerals are characteristic of igneous metamorphic deposits but are also found with hypothermal veins. Garnets may be present, but they more commonly form in scattered individual crystals rather than in the massive bodies that characterize igneous metamorphic deposits. Similarly, quartz forms in both environments, but it is likely to be more abundant and more conspicuous in the vein deposits.

Locally, deposits of the hypothermal zone grade into pegmatites. For example, the deposit at the Passagem mine, Minas Gerais, Brazil, has been described both as a pegmatite dike and as a hypothermal vein. The latter description is preferable, however, because of the great extent and regularity of the body and because of the great predominance of quartz over the other minerals.

The hypothermal and mesothermal zones are defined and distinguished on the basis of arbitrary criteria; as a result, their ore, gangue, and alteration minerals should be expected to show some duplication, especially within the transition environment or along the cooler fringes of hypothermal deposits. Actual gradations from hypothermal to mesothermal ores have been found within individual mining districts. Several ore minerals are common to both environments, the most notable being chalcopyrite, sphalerite, galena, pyrrhotite, stannite, and uraninite. Alteration minerals commonly grade from high-temperature varieties into typical mesothermal species. In general, the lower temperature minerals are present in small amounts, forming a zone outside (on the wall-rock side) of the zone of hypothermal alteration products. Sericite mica is a good example; it is characteristic of mesothermal alteration zones but is also found along the fringes of many hypothermal veins. Even chlorite is present in some hypothermal deposits, though it is more commonly found in ores of the epithermal zone. In fact, chlorite is one of the most abundant alteration products at the Homestake mine in South Dakota (Noble, 1950; Noble and Harder, 1948) —a deposit whose origin has been well-established as hypothermal. Carbonates are widely distributed in many deposits; they are generally ankeritic, but calcite, dolomite, siderite, and rhodochrosite are found locally.

Quartz is probably the most common gangue mineral. In many deposits the quartz is dark gray or bluish gray; in others it may be white or glassy. The color is usually due to myriads of tiny vacuoles and inclusions. At Hog Mountain, Alabama, the quartz is pervaded with these fluid inclusions and

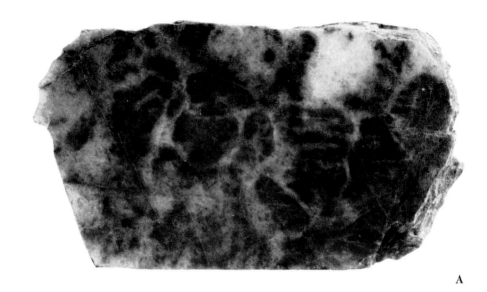

A

B

C

FIGURE 12-1. *Gold-bearing quartz from Hog Mountain, Alabama.*
    (A) *Sugary quartz formed around fragments of dark blue quartz. Depth 60 feet.* ×1.2.
    (B) *Remnants of dark blue quartz in sugary quartz. Depth 20 feet.* ×1.2.
    (C) *Sugary quartz on outcrop.* ×1.8.

appears to be under a form of internal stress (Pardee and Park, 1948, p. 48–49). During mining operations, small razor-sharp chips of this bluish quartz sometimes burst free from the walls and flew violently through the workings. Weathering of the quartz causes fractures to develop between vacuoles, releasing the gases and liquids and creating a sugary texture. Additional weathering removes the sharp edges of individual grains, with the result that eventually the rock superficially resembles a sandstone (Fig. 12-1). Within about 50 feet of the surface, the quartz at Hog Mountain contains bluish remnants in a sugary matrix.

As would be expected in deposits formed under high temperatures and pressures, hypothermal ore bodies tend to assume irregular shapes. Many deposits, however, are roughly tabular or vein-like. They commonly occupy attenuated crests of folds or shear zones, and they also have a tendency to follow drag folds and to replace the country rocks selectively. The development of large, extensive lodes is favored at great depths, because in this environment there are no abrupt changes in temperature and pressure. Accordingly, the large, persistent veins and replacement masses are characteristically hypothermal. But the reverse is not true; hypothermal deposits may also occur as small pods or stringers. For example, the Kolar gold fields in Mysore, India, have been worked to depths of more than 10,500 feet below the surface, with little or no change in the character of mineralization throughout this range (Bichan, 1947). Deposits such as those of the Southern Piedmont in the United States, however, are small and of limited economic value (see Fig. 4-13, p. 80). They have been described as the roots or remnants of deposits that were formerly more extensive, but the field evidence does not support such a conclusion. The deposits are in schists, which should be expected to develop only small, irregular, discontinuous openings under hypothermal conditions. Moreover, the same kinds of deposits are found in the same environment throughout an extensive area.

Ores of the hypothermal zone are deposited at considerable depths and are brought to the surface only through orogenic processes and erosion. Consequently, these ores are more abundant in metamorphic rocks and in rocks of the older geologic periods. They are generally found near masses of plutonic igneous rocks, though some large deposits cannot be linked genetically with any particular plutons.

Morro Velho, Brazil

The Morro Velho mine is an excellent example of a hypothermal gold deposit. It is at the town of Nova Lima, just south of Belo Horizonte, in the State of Minas Gerais, Brazil (Fig. 12-2). Extending about 8700 feet below the collar of the shaft, Morro Velho is one of the deepest mines in the world, though it is exceeded in depth by several mines in the Witwatersrand district of South Africa and by the Champion Reef in Mysore, India.

Even though the Morro Velho mine has been worked for over two centuries and has been in continuous operation since 1834, little has been published regarding the geology. Early reports by Henwood (1844, 1871) and Scott (1903) describe the general occurrence of ore and the history of mining, but most subsequent studies have been kept within the mining companies. Probably the most complete description was contributed by Oliviera (1933). Several short notes have been issued (Lindgren, 1933; Derby, 1903), including a brief but excellent description of the property by Matheson (1956).

The Morro Velho mine was purchased in 1834 by British interests, after over 100 years of small-scale mining. Under this management, Morro Velho became one of the largest, deepest, and most productive gold mines in the world. Its recent history, however, has been relatively unspectacular.

FIGURE 12-2. *Index map of Brazil, showing the location of the Morro Velho mine at Nova Lima, the Raposos mine, and the Passagem mine at Ouro Preto.*

The country rock at Morro Velho is in the Nova Lima Series, of Precambrian age. It is a sequence of metamorphosed sediments and volcanics, principally mica schists, phyllites, and iron formation, but containing lenses of micaceous, dolomitic marble and pure-white marble. West of Morro Velho, the Nova Lima Series is overlain unconformably by quartzites, schists, phyllites, metaconglomerates, and carbonates of the Minas Series, which is also Precambrian in age. Extensive areas of granitic rocks and gneisses surround the metamorphosed sediments, and all rock types have been intruded by diabase dikes. The older literature reports the plutonic rocks as pre-Nova Lima Series in age; but there are several ages present, and Matheson (1956) and Gair (1958) suggest that some are younger than the Minas Series, which they seem to intrude. If Matheson and Gair are correct, the youngest plutons (about 500 million years old; Herz, 1959) may have supplied the mineralizing fluids that deposited the Morro Velho gold. A general map and detailed studies of the older rocks have been published as part of a program to map the itabirites of the region (Departamento Nacional da Produçao Mineral, 1959). In spite of this extensive work, very little is known of the stratigraphic and structural details of the Nova Lima Series.

Within the immediate mine area, the Nova Lima Series consists of metamorphosed graywackes, shales, sandstones, conglomerates, and a lens of quartzite or calc-silicate granulite consisting dominantly of quartz and ankerite (Gair, 1958). This granulite is known locally as the Lapa Sêca. The sediments are tightly folded into easterly-plunging structures, and there is a regional schistosity striking north-northeast across the bedding.

The shape of the main Morro Velho ore body is probably best described as a flattened rod, which stands edgewise and plunges eastward with the folded sediments (Fig. 12-3). Its maximum thickness exceeds 45 feet, and its flat sides average 500 to 600 feet in width. The ore body is continuous from the surface to the deepest workings, its plunge diminishing gradually from about 45° at the top to about 15° at the bottom. This single ribbon of ore has been mined along the plunge for about three miles. Selectively replacing the Lapa Sêca, the lode apparently occupies a sheared or attenuated zone along the axial plane of a tight fold. Its plunge is parallel to the neighboring fold axes and to several smaller ore bodies found along the strike of the Lapa Sêca. In many ways the main lode resembles a saddle reef, but not as strikingly so as the associated ore bodies, which conform closely to the crests of adjacent folds.

The ore is dominantly quartz containing massive sulfides, of which pyrrhotite is the most abundant. Some of the ore is more than half sulfides. Arsenopyrite and pyrite are conspicuous and widely distributed, and a small amount of chalcopyrite is normally present; the arsenic in arseno-

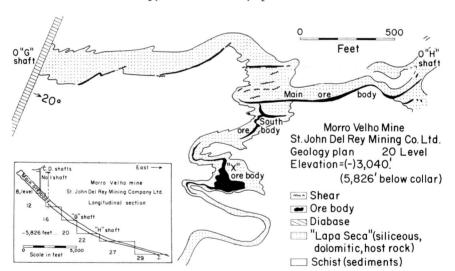

FIGURE 12-3. *Plan and section through the Morro Velho mine. (After Matheson, 1956, figure 2.)*

pyrite is recovered as a valuable by-product. Wolframite and schleelite are accessories, and rare occurrences of tetrahedrite, bornite, sphalerite, galena, and stibnite have been reported. In addition to abundant quartz, the gangue includes smaller amounts of tourmaline, garnet, kyanite, ankerite, sericite, and albite.

Gold is almost uniformly distributed along the lode, averaging about 0.25–0.30 ounces per ton. It is very fine grained and is seldom seen, but is known to be concentrated with the arsenopyrite and pyrrhotite rather than with the other sulfides. Although the main ore body is about three miles long, there are no perceptible changes from one end to the other. Ore from the deepest workings is indistinguishable from ore mined at the surface. Even the arsenic-gold ratio stays remarkably constant (Lindgren, 1933). The only variations in mineralogy that have been noted can be attributed to differences in the host rocks and have no relation to distance along the plunge. Studies of the fineness of gold as a function of depth have not been made.

Veins branch from the main quartz body into the hangingwall. These branch veins vary in thickness, but many are 3–4 feet thick. During the early days of mining, little attention was paid to them, because the main lode contained large amounts of easily obtained ore. Today, however, the smaller veins furnish a supply of comparable grade that is cheaper to mine than ore from the deep levels.

The deposit has been developed along a sequence of vertical shafts and drifts (see Fig. 12-3), hence the deeper levels have no direct communication with the surface. Small amounts of water are pumped from the upper levels, but the deeper workings are far below any aquifers. The lower levels are very dry and dusty, and water for drilling must be piped down from above. Wall-rock temperatures increase steadily with depth, reaching about 140°F at the bottom of the mine. Owing to the extremely hot and uncomfortable conditions, the miners must make frequent retreats to the shaft for fresh air and rest. Even at a depth of about 6600 feet (on the 22nd level) the rock temperature is said to be about 125°F. In order to improve working conditions, 60,000–80,000 cubic feet of conditioned air, at 45°F and 40 percent humidity, is pumped underground every minute. Because of the working difficulties and the high costs of deep mining, operations in recent years have been restricted to the branch veins in the hangingwall of upper levels, above a depth of about 7000 feet.

About three miles by road east-northeast of the Morro Velho mine, there is another deposit known as the Espirito Santo and Raposos mine, or simply

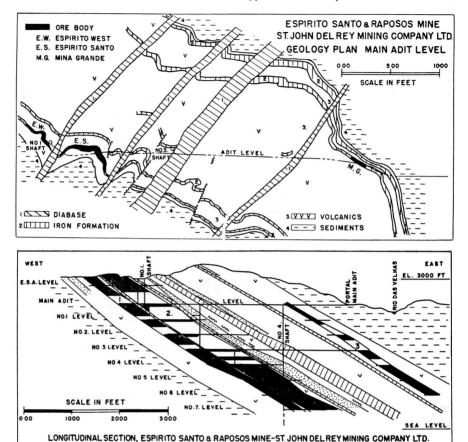

FIGURE 12-4. *Geologic plan and section of the Espirito Santo and Raposos mine.* (*After Matheson, 1956, figures 4 and 5.*)

the Raposos mine. This deposit is similar to Morro Velho, except that the host rock is principally sideritic iron formation instead of sideritic quartzite. Two separate ore shoots are being mined, each resembling a somewhat irregularly dipping, flattened and slightly contorted, rod-shaped body that appears to occupy the nose of a plunging fold (Figs. 12-4 and 12-5). The workings of the Raposos mine are about 5000 feet stratigraphically above the workings of the Morro Velho mine, and the ore bodies in the two mines are parallel; yet by 1955 no exploration work between them had been attempted. If the ore bodies occupy noses of the same fold, or even of nearby folds, the possibility of finding additional ore shoots or saddle reefs between the two known bodies is promising. Gold values in ores from the Raposos mine are slightly less than in Morro Velho ores, due to a smaller sulfide content in the quartz veins. In addition, the Raposos ore bodies are smaller, but they seem to persist in depth. This mine was started in 1934; by 1952 some of the workings had reached 2500 feet (Matheson, 1956).

The Morro Velho and Raposos mines have much in common with the Passagem mine, which is near the old town of Ouro Preto, about 45 miles southeast of Belo Horizonte (Fig. 12-2). This mine is developed on a quartz vein that has a mineral suite similar to that at Morro Velho but contains a higher percentage of tourmaline and other high-temperature minerals. Passagem's quartz vein varies from 5 to 45 feet in thickness, but the wider zones are relatively barren of gold. On the average it is thinner than the Morro Velho lode. Hussak (1898) described the Passagem vein as a pegmatite; Derby (1911) considered it a pegmatite that had been reopened and then invaded by ore-bearing fluids. The deposit is still cited by many

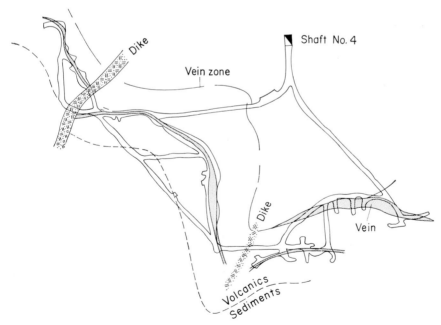

FIGURE 12-5. *Espirito Santo mine, Brazil. Detailed plan 1500 (No. 5) level. (From Matheson, unpublished figure.)*

geologists as an example of a mineralized pegmatite (Schneiderhöhn, 1941, p. 120). Quartz gangue dominates in the vein, but isolated crystals and small concentrations of tourmaline, muscovite, oligoclase, and other pegmatite-like silicates are not rare. Since the continuity and structure are more like those of a vein, it seems preferable to classify the deposit as a vein—a vein that possibly represents a gradation into pegmatite.

Broken Hill, New South Wales, Australia

Another type of hypothermal deposit can be illustrated by the Broken Hill district, in westernmost New South Wales (Fig. 12-6). One of the principal lead-zinc-silver producing areas of the world, Broken Hill—originally staked (mistakenly as a tin claim) in 1883—exceeded the billion-dollar mark in production over a decade ago. The district produces more than a million tons of ore annually and has maintained a steady, developed ore reserve of 12–13 million tons (Andrews, 1948). Average ore yields about 15 percent lead, 12 percent zinc, and five ounces of silver per ton (King and O'Driscoll, 1953). In addition to these metals, the Broken Hill mines annually produce about 60,000 tons of sulfuric acid, about 200 tons of cadmium, and lesser amounts of gold, antimony, copper, and cobalt.

The Broken Hill district has been studied by many able geologists, and excellent reports concerning all phases of the geology are available (Jaquet, 1894; Andrews, 1922; Gustafson et al., 1950; King and Thomson, 1953; King and O'Driscoll, 1953; Stillwell, 1953; Carruthers and Pratten, 1961).

The district is a semi-arid region of sandy plains and rough, rocky ridges. Precambrian rocks underlie the entire district, and in the immediate area the rocks are highly contorted.

The Precambrian rocks are divided into two series, the Willyama and the Torrowangee, which are separated by a widely recognized unconformity. The Willyama Series (probably Lower Precambrian) was originally a thick sequence of sandstones and shales. Before (or possibly dur-

FIGURE 12-6. *Index map of Australia showing the location of Broken Hill.*

ing) metamorphism, the sediments were intruded by pegmatites and sills of granite and gabbro. Regional metamorphism converted this assemblage to sillimanite-biotite-garnet gneisses; serpentines; itabirites; granulites; quartzites; augen gneisses; amphibolites; and sericite, andalusite, hornblende, and staurolite schists. The pegmatites range from large masses to irregular veinlets and lit-par-lit replacements or injections (Gustafson et al., 1950; King and Thomson, 1953). Andrews (1948) noted that the ore-bearing zone coincided with the centrolineal belt of maximum metamorphic intensity.

Unconformably overlying the Willyama Series is a thick section of Proterozoic sediments that includes claystones, quartzites, shales, limestones, conglomerates, and several types of glacial deposits. These rocks constitute the Torrowangee Series. Locally, near its base, the Torrowangee Series is metamorphosed, but in general post-Willyama metamorphic effects are minor.

The regional structure consists of irregular complex basins separated by ridges or sharp arches in which there are zones of intense plastic flowage and shearing. The rocks of the Willyama Series must have been deeply buried and subjected to intense heat and directed pressures. Deformation was apparently most intense in the weak, plastic strata, because they are strongly attenuated and closely folded between the layers of more competent materials. During this period, the rocks were metamorphosed and migmatized. Granite gneiss, aplite, and pegmatites formed in great abundance, in most cases probably as products of granitization. Ultramafics were intruded near the end of the orogenic period, and still later, diabase dikes were emplaced.

The Broken Hill lode is along one of the narrow zones of intense folding, attenuation, and faulting. It lies between a complex basin on the east and a wide arch on the west. A three-mile, north-south line of massive gossan defines the outcrop exposure of the lode, which plunges beneath the surface at both ends. The strike of the ore body is north-northeast, parallel to the metamorphosed sediments. In this area the Willyama Series consists of tightly folded sillimanite-garnet gneisses that include subordinate thin quartzite beds and numerous folded sills of augen gneiss (granite), amphibolite (gabbro), and pegmatite. Postfolding peridotites, granites, and pegmatites are also present. Younger pegmatite dikes were intruded after considerable erosion had taken place, and it is thought that the ore-bearing fluids followed shortly (Gustafson et al., 1950).

Folding in and near the lode is intense, as shown by the extremely complex structures that resulted from plastic deformation (Figs. 12-7 and 12-8). All the folds are deep and isoclinal, with nearly vertical limbs. The regional pitch is, in general, southerly, though the north end plunges abruptly to the north. There are also second-order folds across the main structures, causing abrupt reversals of pitch and divergent plunges in adjacent folds. Vertically plunging kinks or buckles, as well as crushed zones, cut and offset the major folds; these modifications were produced by postfolding, pre-ore fault movements (Gustafson et al., 1950).

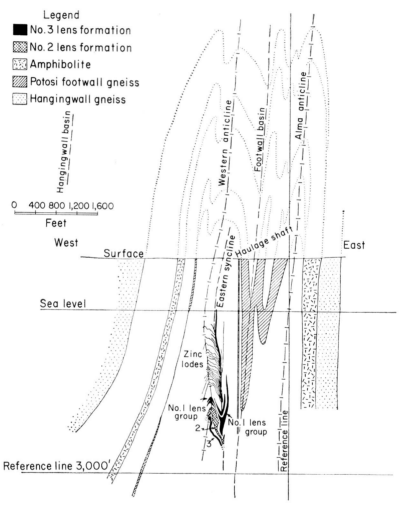

FIGURE 12-7. *Cross section, Broken Hill lode. (After King and O'Driscoll, 1953, figure 2.)*

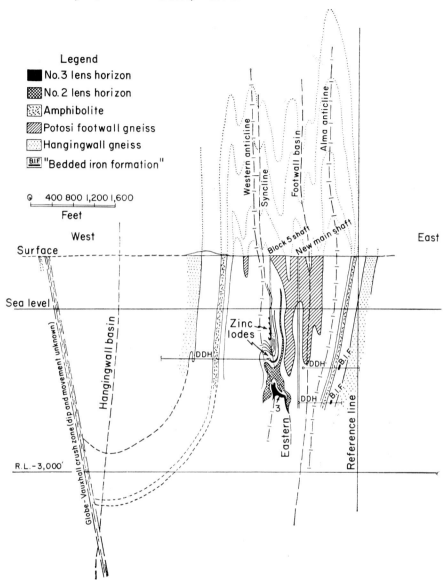

FIGURE 12-8. *Cross section, Broken Hill lode. (After King and O'Driscoll, 1953, figure 3.)*

The ore-bearing zone is actually a composite lode of two or more replaced beds of contorted gneiss, nestled one above the other. It consists of massive lead-zinc sulfide bodies that, before erosion, formed a long, continuous, irregularly shaped ribbon of ore 2000–3000 feet high and of variable thick-

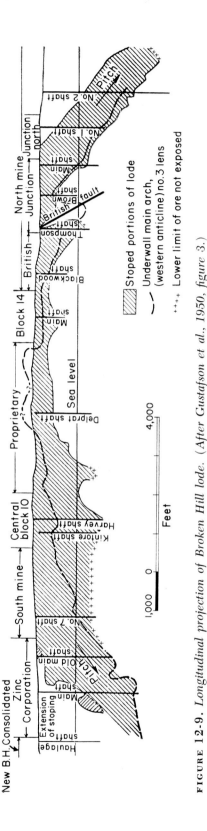

FIGURE 12-9. *Longitudinal projection of Broken Hill lode. (After Gustafson et al., 1950, figure 3.)*

ness. In longitudinal section it describes a flat arc pitching downward at each end (Fig. 12-9). The principal deposits resulted from the selective replacement of two closely adjacent, highly folded strata (Fig. 12-10). Each lode, or lens, is distinguished by details of its gangue mineralogy and metal ratios. Number 2 lens (the upper) is characterized by calcite, bustamite [$(Mn,Ca)SiO_3$], wollastonite, and both rhodonite and hedenbergite with low refractive indices. In contrast, Number 3 lens (the lower) contains fluorite, garnet, rhodonite, and pyroxmangite [$(Mn,Fe)SiO_3$], the latter three all distinguished by high refractive indices. Both lodes contain other minerals in common, including garnets with low to intermediate refractive indices, quartz, potash feldspar, apatite, rutile, and species of rare occurrence. Moreover, the lower horizon has relatively high zinc-lead and silver-lead ratios compared to those in the upper horizon, and rhodonite is much more abundant in the lower lens than in the upper lens. At the south end of the district there are several horizons of ore above the Number 2 lens, each of which has a mineral assemblage similar to the deeper lodes.

Broken Hill ore is mined principally for sphalerite and galena, but it also contains lesser amounts of tetrahedrite, pyrrhotite, marcasite, chalcopyrite, arsenopyrite, löllingite, dyscrasite (Ag_3Sb), pyrargyrite, gudmundite (FeSbS), and cubanite ($CuFe_2S_3$). Stillwell (1953) has reported rare occurrences of many other minerals, including wolframite, scheelite, molybdenite, cobaltite, pyrite, stannite, breithauptite (NiSb), niccolite, bornite, jamesonite, native gold, and native antimony. This mineral assemblage is somewhat anomalous in that it appears to represent formation over a wide temperature range. Arsenopyrite, pyrrhotite, wolframite, and cobaltite are typical hypothermal minerals; tetrahedrite, bornite and jamesonite are usually found in mesothermal deposits; and pyrargyrite and marcasite typify the epithermal environment. The paragenesis of these minerals is obscure, a fact that complicates the problem further (King and O'Driscoll, 1953). Petrographic studies have indicated that the sulfides followed the principal gangue minerals and that the pyrrhotite and arsenopyrite were deposited before the zinc, lead, and silver minerals, but Ramdohr (1950, 1953) suggested the mineral relationships are due to postdepositional recrystallization during the period of metamorphism. If Ramdohr is correct, the ores may represent a metamorphosed epithermal deposit or, as King and Thomson (1953) advocate, a metamorphosed syngenetic deposit. Geothermometry will not solve this controversy, because the ores should indicate high temperatures whether they are hypothermal or metamorphic. The presence of chalcopyrite-cubanite exsolution textures indicates a temperature of deposition above 400–450°C (Gustafson et al., 1950), if the deposit is hydrothermal; and what has been interpreted to be partial fusion of antimony indicates a temperature of about 630°C (Ramdohr, 1950), if the antimony was altered during metamorphism. The low-temperature minerals, such as pyrargyrite and marcasite may be supergene additions to the primary mineralogy, in which case the problem is greatly simplified.

Although each lens has a characteristic mineral assemblage of its own,

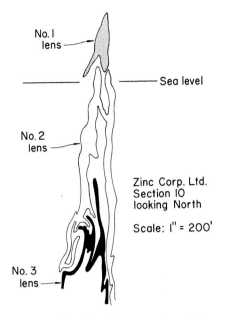

FIGURE 12-10. *Cross section of the ore-bearing strata, Broken Hill, showing the relationships of three lenses. (After Ramdohr, 1950, figure 3.)*

the ore deposits are, in general, remarkably uniform throughout the entire length of the lode. Differences between the lenses seem related to original variations in host rock rather than to zoning effects. A possible hypogene zonation is reflected in slightly greater concentrations of both pyrrhotite and arsenopyrite at the south end of the lode, suggesting that the ore-bearing fluids migrated up the pitch from the south (Gustafson et al., 1950).

Wall-rock alteration is not widespread, nor is it uncommon to find ore against relatively unaltered gneiss. However, some of the gneiss around lodes has been silicified, garnetized, or sericitized. Bleached zones are left in the walls where biotite and sillimanite have been replaced by sericite. The most extensive alteration is replacement by silica, and where silicification has been thorough, the gneisses have the appearance of fine-grained quartzites (Gustafson et al., 1950).

The genesis of Broken Hill ore has been debated by two strongly opposed schools, one advocating a hydrothermal origin and the other a syngenetic origin. According to the hydrothermal theory, the ore was emplaced by hot fluids that moved up the dip along the crests of folds, replacing two or more favorable stratigraphic horizons; folding and metamorphism are believed to have taken place before the ore was deposited. The alternative hypothesis is that the ores were deposited as chemical sediments along with the surrounding rocks and were subsequently folded and recrystallized during metamorphism. Even the syngenetic ore would show some replacement textures, because metamorphism would mobilize it or at least force it to flow in plastic fashion from the limbs to the crests of folds. Both hypotheses are supported by careful geologists who are thoroughly acquainted with the area, and neither hypothesis can account for all the questions.

The syngenetic hypothesis proposed by King and Thomson (1953) is relatively novel for the Broken Hill lode. Whether advocating igneous or metamorphic processes, sponsors of earlier theories had all argued that the ore is genetically related to the granites and pegmatites. But King and Thompson were impressed by the persistence of Number 2 and Number 3 Lenses, which contain dissimilar mineral assemblages in spite of being stratigraphically close. They suggested that the selective replacement of two favorable strata by two different ore fluids (as reflected in the Zn:Ag:Pb ratios) along $3\frac{1}{2}$ miles of highly contorted rocks would not be so perfect. The transmission of ore-bearing fluids along the lode presents a further problem, in that the mechanism of transport for such large quantities of solutions along a three-mile replacement lode is difficult to envisage. Consequently, King and Thomson suggested that the ores were deposited with the Willyama sediments and were later folded, metamorphosed, and granitized. This interpretation has been supported by absolute age determinations based upon the lead isotope ratios of the galenas, which indicate that most of the lead was formed 1400–1600 million years ago and did not experience a complex geochemical history prior to deposition (Russell et al., 1957; Russell and Farquhar, 1960). Some of the ores, however, give anomalous ages, and hence support the hypothesis that at least part of the mineralization is epigenetic.

Gustafson (1954) pointed out the difficulties inherent in hypothesizing a syngenetic origin, not the least of which is explaining the source of the metals. He argued against a premetamorphism age for the mineralization, because the ore and gangue minerals show no effects of differential stress. Petrofabric studies of the quartz gangue support Gustafson's contention that ore deposition took place after metamorphism (den Tex, 1958). It has also been pointed out that the sulfides have replaced some postmetamorphism dikes. Away from the ore the dikes are fresh, cutting clearly across the metamorphosed rocks; but in at least one mine the dikes are uralitized and mineralized (Stillwell and Edwards, 1956).

The advocates of a hydrothermal origin feel that ore deposition was controlled by wall-rock chemistry as well as structure. Attenuation along the crests of folds having left these zones relatively permeable, they acted as conduits for ore-bearing fluids migrating up the pitch. Further localization was caused during the period of ore deposition by repeated fracturing in the favorable strata (Gustafson et al., 1950). Crumpling of the weak beds between layers of stronger rocks produced irregular, saddle-shaped structures that nearly parallel the original bedding. According to the hydrothermal theory, the ores were deposited as replacements of the favorable beds along this zone of maximum deformation.

Until a source for the metals can be demonstrated, the genesis of Broken Hill ores will be continuously debated. There is neither a convincingly related pluton nor a logical source for syngenetic metals. The evidence seems to favor the theory that ore deposition took place after the Willyama Series was metamorphosed; consequently, the hydrothermal theory is presently the most popular. The classification of Broken Hill is a further problem, because of the ore mineralogy, which includes both high- and low-temperature species. However, the mineral assemblage is dominantly a high-temperature suite, and the physical characteristics are typically hypothermal. It is a large, relatively unzoned deposit, and it shows only limited wall-rock alteration. Moreover, the deposit is intimately associated with (and probably genetically related to) a replacement pegmatite, which implies a deep-seated, high-temperature environment. Acknowledging the possibility that the few lower temperature minerals may be secondary, most advocates of a hydrothermal origin classify the Broken Hill lode as hypothermal.

References to Selected Hypothermal Deposits

Homestake Mine, Lead, South Dakota

Gustafson, J. K., 1933, Metamorphism and hydrothermal alteration of the Homestake gold-bearing formation: Econ. Geology, v. 28, p. 123–162.

McLaughlin, D. H., 1931, The Homestake enterprise. Ore genesis and structure: Eng. Mining Jour., v. 132, p. 324–329.

———, 1949, The Homestake mine: Canadian Mining Jour., v. 70, no. 12, p. 49–53.

Noble, J. A., 1950, Ore mineralization in the Homestake gold mine, Lead, South Dakota: Geol. Soc. America Bull., v. 61, p. 221–251.

———, and Harder, J. O., 1948, Stratigraphy and metamorphism in a part of the northern Black Hills and the Homestake mine, Lead, South Dakota: Geol. Soc. America Bull., v. 59, p. 941–975.

———, and Slaughter, A. L., 1949, Structure of a part of the northern Black Hills and the Homestake mine, Lead, South Dakota: Geol. Soc. America Bull., v. 60, p. 321–352.

Paige, Sidney, 1923, The geology of the Homestake mine: Econ. Geology, v. 18, p. 205–237.

Wright, L. B., 1937, Gold deposition in the Black Hills of South Dakota and Wyoming: Am. Inst. Mining Engineers Trans., v. 126, p. 390–425.

Sudbury, Ontario, Canada

Coleman, A. P., 1913, The nickel industry: Canadian Dept. Mines, Mines Branch, Bull. 170.

Collins, W. H., 1934, The life history of the Sudbury irruptive: I, petrogenesis: Roy. Soc. Canada Trans., v. 28, sec. 4, p. 123–177.

———, 1936, The life history of the Sudbury irruptive: III, environment: Roy. Soc. Canada Trans., v. 30, sec. 4, p. 29–53.

———, and Kindle, E. D., 1935, The life history of the Sudbury irruptive: II, intrusion and deformation: Roy. Soc. Canada Trans., v. 29, sec. 4, p. 29–47.

Hawley, J. E., 1962, The Sudbury ores: their mineralogy and origin: Mineralogical Assoc. of Canada, Ottawa.

International Nickel Company Staff, 1946, The operations and plants of International Nickel Company of Canada Limited: Canadian Mining Jour., v. 67, no. 5, p. 322–331.

Stonehouse, H. B., 1954, An association of trace elements and mineralization at Sudbury: Am. Mineralogist, v. 39, p. 452–474.

Symposia, 1948, 1957, in Structural geology of Canadian ore deposits: Canadian Inst. Mining Metallurgy, v. 1, p. 580–626; v. 2, p. 341–376.

Thompson, J. E., 1956, Geology of the Sudbury basin: Ontario Dept. Mines, 65th Ann. Rept., pt. 3, p. 1–56.

———, and Williams, Howel, 1959, The myth of the Sudbury lopolith: Canadian Mining Jour., v. 80, p. 3–8.

Walker, T. L., 1897, Geological and petrographical studies of the Sudbury nickel district of Canada: Geol. Soc. London Quart. Jour., v. 53, p. 40–66.

Wandke, Alfred, and Hoffman, Robert, 1924, A study of the Sudbury ore deposits: Econ. Geology, v. 19, p. 169–204.

Yates, A. B., 1938, The Sudbury intrusive: Roy. Soc. Canada Trans., ser. 3, v. 32, sec. 4, p. 151–172.

Kolar Gold Field, Mysore, India

Bichan, W. J., 1947, Structural principles controlling the occurrence of ore in the Kolar gold field: Econ. Geology, v. 42, p. 93–136.

Dougherty, E. Y., 1939, Some geological features of Kolar, Porcupine, and Kirkland Lake: Econ. Geology, v. 34, p. 622–653.

Emmons, W. H., 1937, Gold deposits of the world: New York, McGraw-Hill Book Co., Inc., p. 378–382.

LeGraye, Michel, 1942, Origine et Formation des Gisements d'Or: Liege, p. 74–76.

Narayanaswami, S., Ziauddin, Mohamed, and Ramachandra, A. V., 1960, Structural control and localization of gold-bearing lodes, Kolar gold field, India: Econ. Geology, v. 55, p. 1429–1459.

Pryor, Thomas, 1923, The underground geology of the Kolar gold field: Inst. Mining Metallurgy (London) Trans., v. 33, p. 95–135.

Smeeth, W. F., and Iyengar, P. S., 1916, Mineral resources of Mysore: Mysore Dept. Mines and Geology Bull. 7, p. 1–55.

Smith, A. M., 1904, The geology of the Kolar gold field: Inst. Mining Metallurgy (London) Trans., v. 13, p. 152–180.

Tufty, Barbara, 1957, Kolar gold field mines, rock bursts feature at all levels, plastic flow at great depths: Canadian Mining Jour., v. 78, no. 11, p. 87–91.

References Cited

Andrews, E. C., 1922, The geology of the Broken Hill district: Geol. Survey of New South Wales, Mem., Geol. no. 8.

———, 1948, Geology of Broken Hill, New South Wales: 18th Internat. Geol. Cong., Symposium on the geology, paragenesis, and reserves of the ores of lead and zinc, p. 117–122.

Bichan, W. J., 1947, Structural principles controlling the occurrence of ore in the Kolar gold field: Econ. Geology, v. 42, p. 93–136.

Carruthers, D. S., and Pratten, R. D., 1961, The stratigraphic succession and structure in the Zinc Corporation Ltd. and New Broken Hill Consolidated Ltd., Broken Hill, New South Wales: Econ. Geology, v. 56, p. 1088–1102.

Departamento Nacional da Produçao Mineral, 1959, Esbôço Geológico do Quadrilátero Ferrífero de Minas Gerais, Brasil: Dept. Nac. Prod. Min., Pub. Especial.

Derby, O. A., 1903, Notes on Brazilian gold-ores: Am. Inst. Mining Engineers Trans., v. 33, p. 282–287.

———, 1911, On the mineralization of the gold-bearing lode of Passagem, Minas Geraes, Brazil: Am. Jour. Sci., v. 32, p. 185–190.

Gair, J. E., 1958, Age of gold mineralization at the Morro Velho and Raposos mines, Minas Gerais: Soc. Bras. Geol., Bol., v. 7, no. 2, p. 39–45.

Gustafson, J. K., 1954, Discussion: geology of Australian ore deposits, Broken Hill: Econ. Geology, v. 49, p. 783–786.

———, Burrell, H. C., and Garretty, M. D., 1950, Geology of the Broken Hill ore deposit, N. S. W., Australia: Geol. Soc. America Bull., v. 61, p. 1369–1437.

Henwood, W. J., 1844, Descriptive notice of the Morro Velho mine, Province of Minas Geraes: and on the relations between the structure of the containing rocks and the directions of the shoots of gold in Brazilian mines: Roy. Geol. Soc. Cornwall Trans., v. 6, p. 143–146.

———, 1871, On the gold-mines of Minas Geraes, in Brazil: Roy. Geol. Soc. Cornwall Trans., v. 8, pt. 1, p. 168–370.

Herz, Norman, 1959, Igneous rocks, in Esbôço Geológico do Quadrilátero Ferrífero de Minas Gerais, Brazil: Dept. Nac. Prod. Min., Pub. Especial, p. 85–94.

Hussak, Eugene, 1898, Der goldführende, kiesige Quarzlagergang von Passagem in Minas Geraes, Brasilien: Zeit. prakt. Geol., v. 6, p. 345–357.

Jaquet, J. B., 1894, Geology of the Broken Hill lode and Barrier Ranges mineral field: Geol. Survey of New South Wales Mem. 5.

King, H. F., and O'Driscoll, E. S., 1953, The Broken Hill lode, *in* Edwards, A. B. (ed.), Geology of Australian ore deposits: Melbourne, Australasian Inst. Mining Metallurgy, p. 578–600.

——, and Thomson, B. P., 1953, The geology of the Broken Hill district: *in* Edwards, A. B. (ed.), Geology of Australian ore deposits: Melbourne, Australasian Inst. Mining Metallurgy, p. 533–577.

Lindgren, Waldemar, 1933, Mineral deposits (4th ed.): New York, McGraw-Hill Book Co., Inc., p. 676–677.

Matheson, A. F., 1956, The St. John del Rey Mining Company, Limited, Minas Geraes, Brazil: Canadian Mining Metall. Bull., v. 77, p. 1–7.

Noble, J. A., 1950, Ore mineralization in the Homestake gold mine, Lead, South Dakota: Geol. Soc. America Bull., v. 61, p. 221–252.

——, and Harder, J. O., 1948, Stratigraphy and metamorphism in a part of the northern Black Hills and the Homestake mine, Lead, South Dakota: Geol. Soc. America Bull., v. 59, p. 941–975.

Oliviera, E. P. de, 1933, Jazida de ouro de Morro Velho, Minas Geraes, Brasil: Acad. Brasil Sci., Annaes, v. 5, no. 1, p. 21–40.

Pardee, J. T., and Park, C. F., Jr., 1948, Gold deposits of the Southern Piedmont: U.S. Geol. Survey Prof. Paper 213.

Ramdohr, Paul, 1950, Die Lagerstätte von Broken Hill in New South Wales im Lichte der neuen geologischen Erkenntnisse und erzmikroskopischer Untersuchungen: Heidelberger Beit. zur Min. und Pet., v. 2, p. 291–333.

——, 1953, Über Metamorphose und sekundäre Mobilisierung: Geol. Rund., v. 42, no. 1, p. 11–19.

Russell, R. D., and Farquhar, R. M., 1960, Dating galenas by means of their isotopic constitutions—II: Geochim. et Cosmochim. Acta, v. 19, p. 41–52.

——, and Hawley, J. E., 1957, Isotopic analyses of leads from Broken Hill, Australia, with spectrographic analyses: Am. Geophys. Union Trans., v. 38, p. 557–565.

Schneiderhöhn, Hans, 1941, Lehrbuch der Erzlagerstättenkunde: Jena, Gustav Fischer.

Scott, H. K., 1903, The gold-field of the State of Minas Geraes, Brazil: Am. Inst. Mining Engineers Trans., v. 33, p. 406–444.

Stillwell, F. L., 1953, Mineralogy of the Broken Hill lode, *in* Edwards, A. B. (ed.), Geology of Australian ore deposits: Melbourne, Australasian Inst. Mining Metallurgy, p. 601–626.

——, and Edwards, A. B., 1956, Uralite dolerite dykes in relation to the Broken Hill lode: Melbourne, Australasian Inst. Mining Metallurgy Proc., no. 178, p. 213–232.

Tex, E. den, 1958, Studies in comparative petrofabric analysis: the Broken Hill lode and its immediate wall rock: Melbourne, Australasian Inst. Mining Metallurgy (F. L. Stillwell Anniv. Volume), p. 77–104.

CHAPTER 13

Mesothermal

Deposits

MESOTHERMAL DEPOSITS are formed at moderate temperatures and pressures. The ores are deposited at about 200–300°C from solutions that probably have at least a tenuous connection with the surface. In effect, the mesothermal zone is distinguished by both hypothermal and epithermal characteristics; it is an intermediate rather than a distinctive zone. Probably no single mineral is diagnostic of the mesothermal zone, because each can be found elsewhere, but the absence of typically hypothermal or typically epithermal minerals is an important criterion for mesothermal deposits. Although most mesothermal deposits show abundant replacement phenomena, the textures are not definitive, because a few vugs and open-cavity fillings are commonly present. The ores occur in many environments and in numerous forms. The host rock may be igneous, metamorphic, or sedimentary, the latter probably being the most common host. The disseminated, or "porphyry," copper deposits are also classified in the mesothermal zone. Veins and pipes are common structural forms, but where they cut carbonate rocks, mantos and irregular replacement bodies may develop. Many deposits have sharp boundaries; others grade into the country rock. Veins commonly develop *ribbon structures*—layering parallel to the walls—formed by the partial replacement of host rock along repeatedly opened shears (Fig. 13-1).

The most abundant products of mesothermal deposits are probably copper, lead, zinc, silver, and gold. Among the more characteristic ore minerals are chalcopyrite, enargite, bornite, tetrahedrite, tennantite, sphalerite, galena, and chalcocite, as well as many less common minerals. Gangue

0   5 inches

FIGURE 13-1. *Ribbon rock. Hamme tungsten mine, North Carolina. Black is hubnerite; white is quartz.*

minerals include quartz, pyrite, and the carbonates. A typical copper-lead-zinc deposit may include all of the above-named minerals plus others.

Extensive alteration zones surround many mesothermal deposits; alteration products include sericite, quartz, calcite, dolomite, pyrite, orthoclase, chlorite, and clay minerals. Secondary orthoclase and clay minerals have been recognized in many disseminated copper deposits. Some of these minerals, such as chlorite and the clays, are more characteristic of epithermal zones, but they are also common along the outer fringes of mesothermal deposits. Lindgren (1933, p. 530) pointed out that mesothermal deposits do not contain garnet, topaz, pyroxenes, amphiboles, or tourmaline, which are high-temperature minerals, nor do they contain the zeolites, which are stable only at lower temperatures.

Many mesothermal deposits are closely related to igneous rocks, both spatially and genetically; for others, no genetic association has been recognized. This is to be expected for all hydrothermal ores; the farther they are from their source, the more difficult it is to locate that source. Hence the genetic ties of mesothermal deposits are commonly more obscure than they are for hypothermal deposits, and are more readily proved than they are for epithermal ores. The copper deposits of Matahambre, Cuba, for example, are 2½ miles from the nearest outcrops of igneous rocks (Pennebaker, 1944). Other mesothermal ores, as evidenced by the disseminated copper deposits, occur in the plutons with which they are associated—in the upper cupolas of quartz monzonite or granodiorite masses.

The variety of mesothermal deposits makes it difficult to characterize this zone by describing a few examples. Most of the ores, however, are in veins or replace favorable beds, or they permeate the rocks as disseminated veinlets and spots. We have chosen to describe the Coeur d'Alene district as an example of vein deposits; Magma, Arizona, as an example of both vein and replacement ore; and Chuquicamata, Chile, as an example of a disseminated copper deposit.

Coeur d'Alene, Idaho

The Coeur d'Alene district in nothern Idaho (Fig. 13-2), one of the largest lead-zinc-silver districts in the world, is an excellent example of a mesothermal deposit. It has produced more than one billion dollars worth of ore since it was discovered in 1879. Most of the production has come from lead-zinc-silver ores, though in recent years— since the discovery of tetrahedrite deposits in the southern part of the district—copper and antimony have been added to the metals produced in quantity. Several good descriptions of the deposits are available (Ransome and Calkins, 1908; Umpleby and Jones, 1923; McKinstry and Svendsen, 1942; Sorenson, 1947, 1951; Shenon, 1948).

The mines of the Coeur d'Alene district extend over an area measuring 25 miles from east to west and 10 miles from north to south (Fig. 13-3). At the northern extreme, the mines were

FIGURE 13-2. *Index map of Idaho, showing location of the Coeur d'Alene district.*

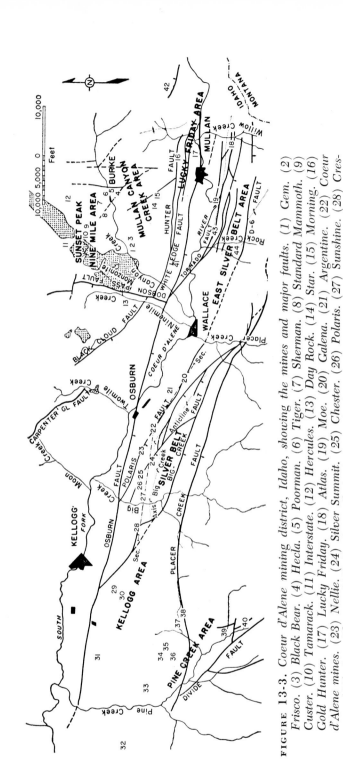

FIGURE 13-3. *Coeur d'Alene mining district, Idaho, showing the mines and major faults.* (1) *Gem.* (2) *Frisco.* (3) *Black Bear.* (4) *Hecla.* (5) *Poorman.* (6) *Tiger.* (7) *Sherman.* (8) *Standard Mammoth.* (9) *Custer.* (10) *Tamarack.* (11) *Interstate.* (12) *Hercules.* (13) *Day Rock.* (14) *Star.* (15) *Morning.* (16) *Gold Hunter.* (17) *Lucky Friday.* (18) *Atlas.* (19) *Moe.* (20) *Galena.* (21) *Argentine.* (22) *Coeur d'Alene mines.* (23) *Nellie.* (24) *Silver Summit.* (25) *Chester.* (26) *Polaris.* (27) *Sunshine.* (28) *Crescent.* (29) *Last Chance.* (30) *Bunker Hill.* (31) *Page.* (32) *Hypotheek.* (33) *Liberal King.* (34) *Denver.* (35) *Sidney.* (36) *Pittsburg.* (37) *Nevada Stewart.* (38) *Highland Surprise.* (39) *Douglas.* (40) *Constitution.* (41) *Golconda.* (42) *Snowstorm.* (43) *Gem State.* (44) *Rock Creek.* (*After Sorenson, 1951, figure 1.*)

worked in the early days for gold ores. Near the center, the principal commodities recovered are lead and zinc; the southern edge of the district contains copper-silver ore. Thus Coeur d'Alene exhibits district zoning.

There are three groups of rocks in the district: the Upper Precambrian sediments of the Belt Series, igneous rocks that intrude the Belt Series, and unconsolidated clastics of Tertiary and Quaternary age. The Belt Series consists principally of quartzites, argillites, and calcareous rocks, reaching a maximum thickness of 20,000 feet or more. Abundant mud cracks, ripple marks, cross-bedding, and stromatolites indicate that most of this sequence is of shallow-water origin. For purposes of mapping, the Belt Series has been divided into six lithologic units. In chronologic order, these units are: the Prichard Formation, made up of some 12,000 feet of black argillite and argillaceous quartzite; the Burke Formation, an 1800–2400 foot sequence of gray to white quartzite, some of which is argillaceous; the Revett Formation, 2100–3400 feet of massive gray to white quartzite with some interbedded argillaceous quartzite; the St. Regis Formation, consisting of thin-bedded purple to purplish-gray argillite and quartzite; the Wallace Formation, about 4500–6000 feet of gray-black calcareous argillite and white to gray calcareous quartzite; and the Striped Peak Formation, which comprises 1500 feet or more of purple, pink, and green quartzite and calcareous argillite, and apparently contains no ore (Sorenson, 1951).

During the Laramide orogeny, the Coeur d'Alene district was strongly folded and faulted. A late phase (postfolding) of this deformation involved the intrusion of monzonite stocks, accompanied by diabase and lamprophyre dikes and sills (McKinstry and Svendsen, 1942). The monzonite stocks, which actually vary from diorite and quartz monzonite to syenite, appear to be satellitic relatives of the Idaho batholith (Umpleby and Jones, 1923). At least one diabase sill predates the monzonite, and even the folding; but the lamprophyre dikes, and probably most of the diabase dikes, are younger than the monzonite.

In spite of its age and the degree of folding, the Belt Series has undergone surprisingly little metamorphism. The argillites have a slaty cleavage, and the arenites are mostly quartzitic, but, in general, the metamorphic effects are minor. Nevertheless, the sediments around the borders of some monzonite stocks show igneous metamorphic alteration in the form of bleaching, sericitization, and even granitization (Anderson, 1949).

As shown in Fig. 13-3, the district is cut by several west-northwesterly faults, the most pronounced being the great Osburn fault. This structure can be traced well beyond the Coeur d'Alene district. It dips 55–65° south and has some 15,000 feet of normal, dip-slip offset, with possibly much more strike-slip displacement (Shenon, 1948). The actual fault zone is 100–200 feet wide and consists of sheared, brecciated, and powdered rock. South of the Osburn fault, there are many parallel and oblique faults, which appear to be second-order structures caused by the Osburn faulting. All the second-order faults dip south. Tensional stresses set up by movements along these major structures developed local openings through which the mineralizing fluids ascended (Sorenson, 1951). The major structural elements differ on opposite sides of the Osburn fault. To the south, the fold axes trend east-west, or parallel to the faults; but north of the Osburn fault, both the folds and the faults strike north to northwest.

Most of the ore deposits lie along fractures and shear zones within the Belt Series. Minor amounts of mineralization are found in the monzonite stocks and diabase dikes, proving their pre-ore age. In contrast, the lamprophyre dikes were intruded after the ore had been deposited. Concentrations of ore lie along areas of strong structural deformation and within the brittle, brecciated rock units (Sorenson, 1951; McKinstry and Svendsen, 1942). Where the rocks were brittle and the bedding planes were oriented obliquely to the directions of shear, open-fissure zones were produced. Thus the quartzites are more favorable hosts than the argillites; for example, in the Polaris mine many fissures are mineralized within the St. Regis Formation but not along their continuations in the Wallace Formation (Fig. 13-4).

The ore minerals include galena, sphalerite, tetrahedrite, chalcopyrite, pyrrhotite, magnetite, arsenopyrite, and minor amounts of bornite, chalcocite, stibnite, boulangerite, bournonite, gersdorffite ($NiAsS$), scheelite, and uraninite. Arsenopyrite is considered an indicator of economically favorable areas, because it apparently describes envelopes around ore shoots (Mitcham, 1952a). Quartz, siderite, other carbonates, pyrite, and, locally, barite are the principal gangue minerals. These ore and gangue minerals form a typical mesothermal assemblage. Geothermometric studies have been somewhat inconclusive, but they indicate the general mesothermal temperature range (Fryklund and Fletcher, 1956).

The lead-zinc ore contains an average of approximately 10 percent combined lead and zinc and about 1 ounce of silver per unit of lead (Shenon, 1948). This does not mean, however, that the silver is in the galena; actually, it is in the tetrahedrite, which, in turn, tends to be associated with galena (Warren, 1934).

The mineral paragenesis is difficult to establish for the district as a

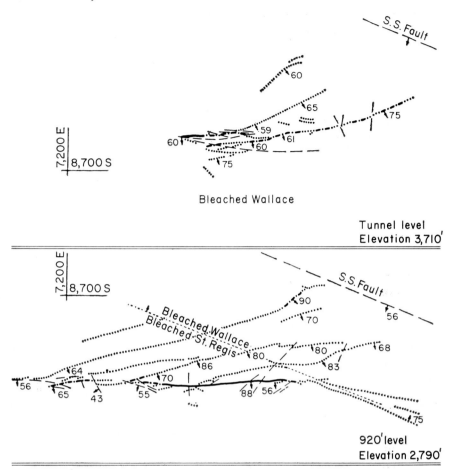

Bleached Wallace

Tunnel level
Elevation 3,710'

920' level
Elevation 2,790'

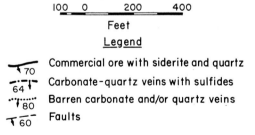

100 0   200   400

Feet

Legend

Commercial ore with siderite and quartz

Carbonate-quartz veins with sulfides

Barren carbonate and/or quartz veins

Faults

FIGURE 13-4. *Plan of the 920-foot and tunnel levels of the Polaris mine. (After Sorenson, 1951, figure 3.)*

whole; but, in general, the gangue minerals were deposited early, and most of them continued to be deposited throughout the sulfide phase. Magnetite, pyrrhotite, and arsenopyrite were among the earliest ore minerals; tetrahedrite, galena, and sphalerite were intermediate in the sequence; and chalcopyrite was one of the last to be deposited (Hosterman, 1956; Anderson, 1940; Ransome and Calkins, 1908). The accessory minerals have not been included in this paragenetic sequence, because their order of deposition is not clear; indeed, the paragenesis of even the principal minerals is questionable. A few of the accessory minerals apparently formed as reaction products between two other compounds; for example, bournonite seems to represent an intermediate step in the replacement of tetrahedrite by galena (Anderson, 1940).

Much of the mineralization lies within zones of altered (bleached) country rock. The altered zones trend parallel to anticlinal axes and faults and, in general, have been good guides to ore deposits. Most workers attribute the bleaching to potash metasomatism and the alteration of argillaceous materials to sericite, but recent studies have discredited this hypothesis, pointing out that the unaltered argillites contain as much sericite as the bleached rock (Anderson, 1949; Sorenson, 1951; Mitcham, 1952a, 1952b). In addition to the controversial sericite, the bleached zones contain disseminated pyrite, quartz, carbonate minerals, and, in shallow zones, chlorite.

The Coeur d'Alene ores have long been considered a product of the Laramide orogeny, but lead isotope studies suggest that the principal metallization took place either during Precambrian times or that the galena was derived from a lead source of Precambrian age (Long et al., 1960). According to exponents of the Laramide orogeny, monzonite stocks intruded the previously folded Belt Series, and subsequent hydrothermal fluids worked their way up along the major faults, which were repeatedly opened as the deeper parts of the source batholith continued crystallizing. Within this deeper source, the late magmatic fractions contained concentrations of potassium, lead, zinc, copper, silver, gold, iron, sulfur, arsenic, and other elements. The earliest phase of mineralization took place within the pluton itself, where the outer shell underwent deuteric alteration by potassium-rich solutions; the original rock was probably dioritic in composition and was deuterically altered to monzonite and syenite (Anderson, 1949). Perhaps some sericitization of the country rocks accompanied this process, but probably not to the degree assumed in the earliest studies. The significant fact is that sericite was one of the few persistently stable minerals in the alteration halo, reflecting the mesothermal conditions of the environment. The metallization process took place during the latest phase of hydrothermal activity, and the intrusion of lamprophyre dikes marked the close of the igneous period.

Magma Mine, Arizona

The Magma mine, at Superior, Arizona (Fig. 13-5), has both vein and replacement ores that were deposited in the mesothermal environment. Copper, silver, gold, zinc, and some lead, have been produced from the mine (Ransome, 1912; Short and Ettlinger, 1927; Short et al., 1943). The early operations were restricted to a pair of rich veins, but around 1950 an extensive deposit of replacement ore was discovered.

Well-exposed rocks of Precambrian and Paleozoic age, overlain to the east with angular discordance by Tertiary dacitic volcanics, make up the geologic column in the Superior district. The Precambrian rocks include a metamorphic complex known as the Pinal Schist and a younger sequence of conglomerates, shales, quartzites, and some limestones. The latest Precambrian is represented by the Troy Quartzite, which uncomformably overlies the older Precambrian sediments. Deposition of the Troy Quartzite was followed by deformation and erosion that produced a widespread unconformity, although at the Magma mine there is no angular discordance at the top of the Precambrian section. A pair of diabase sills was intruded into the Upper Precambrian rocks; these sills total 3100 feet in thickness. Intrusion of the diabase probably took place in Precambrian time (Peterson, 1962), although not all reports agree on this point (Sell, 1960).

The Cambrian is represented by a quartzite that is lithologically similar to the Troy, with which it has been confused; this Cambrian quartzite is 425 feet thick in the mine area (Short et al., 1943) and is probably equivalent to the Bolsa Quartzite, or Abrigo Formation, of

FIGURE 13-5. *Index map of Arizona, showing location of the Magma mine at Superior.*

southern Arizona (Krieger, 1961; D. W. Peterson, personal communication, 1963). Other Paleozoic units include 340 feet of Devonian Martin Limestone, 420 feet of Mississippian Escabrosa Limestone, and over 1200 feet of Pennsylvanian Naco Limestone (Short et al., 1943). Post-Carboniferous dikes of quartz monzonite porphyry and younger (Late Cenozoic) basalt dikes are also found in the mine area. The quartz monzonite is mineralized where it is cut by the principal vein, but the basalt was intruded long after the ores were deposited.

The sediments were faulted and tilted during the Laramide orogeny. East-west faults, which formed normal to regional compressive forces, were utilized by quartz monzonite magmas and shortly thereafter acted as passageways for ascending ore fluids. Apparently, the faulting continued into the period of ore deposition. Owing to these movements, the quartz monzonite porphyry was brecciated, and repeated opening of the fault zone admitted the ore-bearing solutions. The quartz monzonite and ore are thought to have originated in a buried plutonic mass of batholithic dimensions (Ettlinger, 1928). A quartz diorite stock that crops out less than two miles north of the Magma mine (Short et al., 1943) is believed to be part of this batholith. Post-ore faulting, associated with the period of dacitic igneous activity, produced structures trending predominantly north to northwest. Tilting of the strata to the east may have resulted from this period of deformation.

Two parallel east-west faults contain the vein deposits at Magma. The bulk of ore has been recovered from shoots along the Main, or Magma, vein, a fault zone with about 500 feet of vertical displacement and even more strike-slip offset (Short and Wilson, 1938). At the surface, the fault plane strikes east-west and dips about 65°N; but below the 900-foot level it dips 78°S and finally changes in strike to N80°E (Short et al., 1943). Most of the ore is in one large, continuous shoot that plunges steeply to the west along the Magma vein, but there are smaller, isolated zones to the east and west (Fig. 13-6). Mineralization is found along 9000 feet of strike and as deep as 5000 feet. On individual levels, the main shoot extends more than 2000 feet along the fault. The ore filled open spaces along the fault zone, which ranges from less than a foot to over 40 feet in width (Wilson, 1950), but replacement of the breccia and sheared material accounts for the bulk of mineralization (Wilson, 1950; Short et al., 1943). Another mineralized fault, known as the Koerner vein, is located about 1100 feet south of the Magma vein; although parallel in structure and identical in ore mineralogy

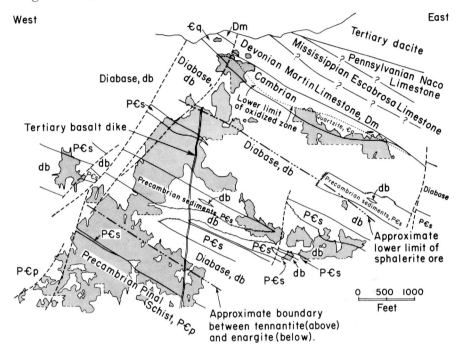

West

East

Tertiary dacite

Diabase, db

€q

Dm

Devonian Martin Limestone, Dm

Mississippian Escabrosa Limestone

?Pennsylvanian Naco Limestone

Diabase, db

Cambrian

Lower limit of oxidized zone

PЄs

Tertiary basalt dike

PЄs

db

PЄs

db

db

Diabase, db

Precambrian sediments, PЄs

Quartzite, €q

Precambrian sediments PЄs

db

Diabase

db

db

PЄs

PЄs

PЄs

db

Approximate lower limit of sphalerite ore

PЄp

Precambrian Pinal Schist, PЄp

PЄs

db

Diabase, db

PЄs

PЄs

db

PЄs

0   500   1000

Feet

Approximate boundary between tennantite(above) and enargite(below).

FIGURE 13-6. *Longitudinal section along the Magma vein, showing the main ore shoot and smaller shoots. (Courtesy of Magma Copper Company.)*

to the Magma vein, the Koerner deposit is much smaller and is no longer being mined.

The width of ore along the veins is partly dependent upon the brittleness and reactivity of the wall rocks. Wide, rich shoots are found in diabase, which became permeable where brecciated by faulting, but the less competent Pinal Schist caused branching along the faults. Moreover, certain carbonate beds also favored the deposition of massive replacement ores (Wilson, 1950).

One section of Martin Limestone was especially favorable for ore deposition—a 30- to 50-foot thickness beginning about 20 feet stratigraphically above the Bolsa Quartzite. Not only was this section replaced for as much as 30 feet on both sides of the Magma vein, but it was the host for an extensive manto of ore located east of the vein deposits, between the Magma and Koerner faults (Webster, 1958).

The manto deposit is localized along an east-west vein that appears to be a subsidiary southern branch of the Magma fault. Replacement was confined

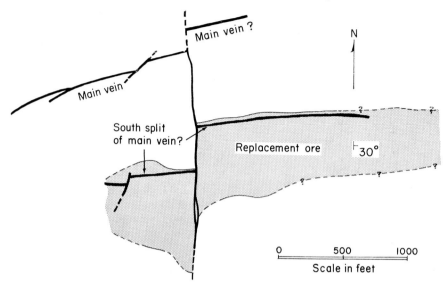

FIGURE 13-7. *Generalized plan of veins and manto, projected to the 2550-foot level, Magma mine, Arizona. (After Webster, 1958, figure 3.)*

to a single stratigraphic section in the Martin Limestone, forming a manto deposit that averages about 20 feet thick and dips 30°E with the sediments. The bed is continuously replaced by sulfides for some 750 feet south of the vein and as much as 200 feet north of the vein. The extent of replacement along the dip has not been ascertained, but it exceeds 5000 feet. Developments to date indicate that the manto fingers out updip at about the 2000 foot level (Webster, personal communication, 1962). A north-south fault of post-ore age divides the manto into two segments, with an apparent strike-slip component that amounts to about 400 feet of left-lateral displacement (Fig. 13-7).

Both the veins and the replacement mantos consist of massive sulfide ore—bornite, chalcopyrite, pyrite, sphalerite, enargite, tennantite, galena, chalcocite, digenite, and stromeyerite. But these minerals are not distributed evenly throughout the deposits. In places, the veins are richest in copper where they pass through diorite. In contrast, the upper, eastern part of the Magma vein is deficient in copper and enriched in sphalerite. Marked differences in ore mineralogy seem to define zones parallel to the bedding, and as a result the zonal distribution of ore forms a pattern that is inclined to the east (Fig. 13-6). However, the mineralogical zones do not conform to individual lithologic units. The upper zone is characterized by zinc and silver mineralization; the middle zone, by chalcocite-bornite-chalcopyrite-tennantite ore; and the lowest zone, by enargite, bornite, pyrite, and chalcopyrite (Short and Wilson, 1938; Webster, 1958). In general, the manto contains specularite, pyrite, chalcopyrite, bornite, chalcocite, and minor amounts of quartz, magnetite, and barite. Silver, gold, zinc, and lead minerals characterize the middle zone (Webster, 1958).

Paragenetic studies indicate that pyrite was the earliest sulfide deposited, and it clearly replaces the hematite (Fig. 13-8). Sphalerite, and possibly enargite, was next. Galena and stromeyerite were deposited later, probably at about the same time as the principal copper minerals—tennantite, bornite, chalcopyrite, and digenite (Short et al., 1943).

Wall-rock alteration—sericitization and silicification—accompanied the deposition of ores. It was most intensely developed in the diabase sills, but it also affected the schists and clastic sediments (Short et al., 1943). Some of the limestone beneath the manto is bleached (Webster, 1958), but in general the carbonates are relatively unaltered.

Although there is some correlation between ore mineralogy and type of wall rock, the overall zoning seems independent of the stratigraphy. If the zones were controlled by wall-rock chemistry, they should correspond to single lithologic units. In the Magma vein, however, zone boundaries fall

FIGURE 13-8. *Pyrite pseudomorphous after specular hematite, manto ore. Magma mine, Superior, Arizona. White is pyrite, black and gray are gangue, light gray is hematite.* ×240. (*Courtesy of Ray Robison.*)

within stratigraphic units—within the diabase, for example—rather than along contacts. In general, the mineral assemblages that constitute the deeper ores were formed at higher temperatures than those of the shallow ores. This relationship suggests that the zoning was produced by a temperature gradient. Ascending isotherms should approach horizontality at any appreciable distance from the heat source; accordingly, the occurrence of ore zoning parallel to bedding indicates that the ore was probably deposited before the beds were tilted.

Near the surface, the ores were oxidized, and where pyrite was available to produce ferric sulfate and sulfuric acid, meteoric waters leached some of the copper, carrying it down to a supergene enrichment zone. The oxidized zone dips eastward, roughly parallel to the sediments. This is further evidence that tilting took place after the ores were deposited (Short and Ettlinger, 1927; Wilson, 1950).

In summary, the Magma ores were deposited by ascending fluids that traveled along the east-west faults shortly after quartz monzonite dikes had been introduced along these same structures. The thickness and width of any portion along the ore shoot were dependent upon the degree of brecciation and shearing that had taken place, which in turn was a function of the physical and chemical properties of wall rocks and their susceptibility to alteration. The ores were distributed zonally, due to a decreasing thermal gradient or to the wall-rock chemistry, or both. Where the ore fluids encountered a thin, reactive section of the lower Martin Limestone, they formed highly selective massive replacement deposits. Essentially all of the ore mineralization, from the earliest sphalerite to the latest copper minerals, took place under mesothermal conditions.

Chuquicamata, Chile

Chuquicamata, in the Atacama Desert of northern Chile (Fig. 13-9), is one of the greatest copper deposits known (López, 1939, 1942). The mine is 130 miles northeast of Antofagasta and about 90 miles from the coast, at an elevation of 9500 feet in the foothills of the main Andes Mountains. Because it is an extremely arid region, large amounts of water-soluble sulfate minerals have been preserved in the zone of oxidation. Chuquicamata is an excellent example of a disseminated or "porphyry" copper deposit, and, along with other deposits of this type, it is classed as mesothermal. Copper ornaments found in the graves of local Indians indicate that the deposits were worked in a small way before the Spanish conquistadors arrived

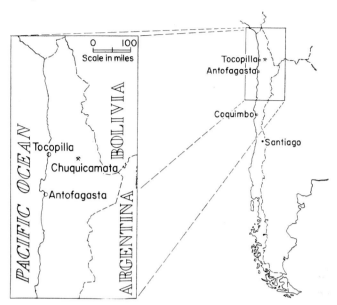

FIGURE 13-9. *Index map of Chile, showing the location of Chuquicamata.*

(Taylor, 1935). Small amounts of shaped turquoise also are found in places along the outcrops. The earliest mining on an appreciable scale—confined principally to narrow but rich veins—was done chiefly by English and Chilean companies between 1879 and 1912. The mass of disseminated ore now providing the bulk of copper production is currently being worked by the Chile Exploration Company, a subsidiary of the Anaconda Mining Company.

The mineralization is apparently related to a period of faulting, folding, and igneous intrusion during the Late Mesozoic or Early Tertiary. Upper Jurassic sediments and older metamorphic rocks were first gently folded and covered with a series of volcanic flows, and then strongly deformed as the Andean batholith was being intruded. After considerable erosion had exposed the plutonic rocks, the area was again uplifted, and more volcanics were deposited. Slight warping and volcanism have continued into Recent time (Taylor, 1935; Jarrell, 1944).

Near Chuquicamata the Andean batholithic complex is represented by three nested stocks, or possibly three facies of a single batholith. The plutonic rocks were intruded along the crest and eastern limb of a broad anticline, forming an elongated mass some 20 miles long by 4 miles wide, with a northerly or northeasterly trend. The occurrence of similar localized

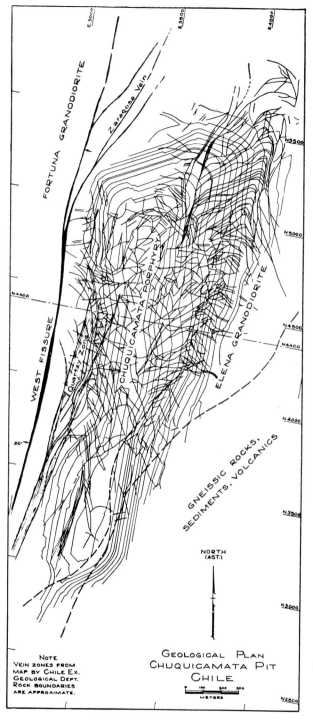

FIGURE 13-10. *Geologic plan of Chuquicamata, Chile. (After Perry, 1952.)*

outcrops of granitic rocks along a narrow belt 95 miles long suggests that they are cupolas of an underlying batholith that erosion has just begun to expose (Perry, 1952). The three facies of granitic rocks at Chuquicamata include two apparently different granodiorites, known as the Fortuna Granodiorite and the Elena Granodiorite, and a highly altered quartz monzonite, called the Chuquicamata Porphyry. In the mine area (Fig. 13-10), the Chuquicamata Porphyry is an elongate, tabular mass, separating the two different kinds of granodiorite. All contacts between quartz monzonite and granodiorite are either faults or gradational and altered zones; consequently, the genetic relationships between facies cannot be determined. Fortuna Granodiorite is unaltered and is separated from altered Chuquicamata Porphyry by a strong fault zone. East of this fault, known as the West Fissure, the Chuquicamata Porphyry and part of the Elena Granodiorite are mineralized. In general, the large open-pit operation is confined to a highly sheared zone in the Chuquicamata Porphyry, between the two granodiorites.

The Chuquicamata Porphyry is made up of several varieties of altered rock. Some parts of it are characterized by plagioclase or orthoclase phenocrysts; other parts are almost aplitic in texture. The rock is laced with stringers of orthoclase and quartz. This altered porphyry is strikingly similar to the hosts for other great disseminated copper deposits (Perry, 1952).

Two strongly sheared zones define the western and eastern limits of the mineralized zone. These shears vary in strike from N10°E to as much as N76°E, forming a violin-shaped ore body with the neck pointed south. Between the eastern and western shear zones, there are several intermediate shear zones and a complex system of tension fractures, most of which form a horsetail pattern branching toward the northeast from the shears. López (1939, 1942) suggested that the shears and tension fractures are all related to a simple shearing couple acting horizontally in a north-south direction. Thus the maximum stresses would have been oriented northeast-southwest, parallel to the horsetail tension fractures. Another prominent set of tension fractures strikes northwest, roughly normal to the horsetail fissures. During shearing, secondary tensional stresses would be set up on opposite sides of a shear plane. The opposing tension fractures at Chuquicamata look suspiciously like products of these secondary forces, especially where they turn into the shear zones.

Several intergradational types of alteration have been described at Chuquicamata (Taylor, 1935; López, 1939; Perry, 1952). They include silicification, sericitization, chloritization, albitization, and epidotization (Fig.

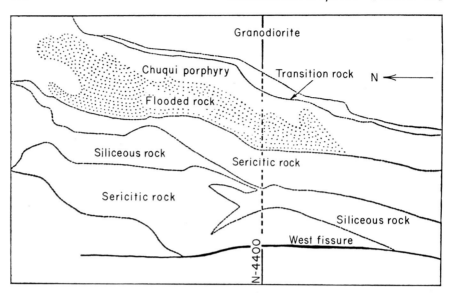

FIGURE 13-11. *Alteration facies at Chuquicamata, Chile. (After López, 1939, figure 2.)*

13-11). Taylor (1935) classified the altered rocks within five categories: (1) siliceous rock, (2) sericitic rock, (3) normal rock, (4) flooded rock, and (5) transition rock. The siliceous rock consists almost entirely of quartz and sericite, and the original texture is completely obliterated; repeated phases of silicification are recorded by interstitial quartz and cross-cutting veinlets. A wide belt of siliceous rock strikes nearly parallel to the West Fissure along the west side of the Chuquicamata Porphyry. The sericitic rock is marginal to the silicified zone; it consists of Chuquicamata Porphyry containing sericitized feldspars and veinlets of quartz. Normal rock retains the original porphyritic texture, though some of the feldspars are albitized or sericitized. The large orthoclase crystals and quartz "eyes" that characterize normal rock are thought to be relict phenocrysts rather than products of alteration. Flooded rock is similar to normal rock except that it has been permeated with hydrothermal quartz. Between the fresh Elena Granodiorite on the east and the normal facies of Chuquicamata Porphyry, there is a narrow zone of transition rock; it consists of Elena Granodiorite containing chloritized ferromagnesians, slightly sericitized and albitized feldspars, a little epidote, and veinlets of specular hematite. In general, the alteration is most intense along the western border of the Chuquicamata Porphyry and dies out gradually toward the east (Taylor, 1935; López, 1939, 1952).

The open-pit ore body is about two miles long and has a maximum width of 3600 feet. Copper minerals were introduced after the rock had been fractured, altered, and fractured again. They fill the fracture systems and permeate veinlets throughout the rock mass. Most of the ore that has been mined is oxidized, but supergene-enriched sulfide zones and primary hypogene ore are also recovered. Listed in paragenetic order, the minerals of the hypogene veinlets are quartz, pyrite, enargite, chalcopyrite, bornite, and tennantite-tetrahedrite (López, 1939). The bulk of hypogene copper is contained in enargite. A zonal distribution of the primary minerals has been established, with molybdenum along the west, enargite in the sericitized rock, and tennantite-tetrahedrite along the east (López, 1939). The pattern seems to reflect deposition from west to east. Supergene enrichment formed chalcocite and covellite at the expense of all other sulfides. The oxidized zone contains many rare minerals, most of which are soluble but are preserved in the extreme aridity of the Atacama Desert. Sulfates, oxides, and carbonates characterize the oxidized zone. The copper minerals include cuprite, melaconite (CuO), native copper, brochantite [$Cu_4SO_4(OH)_6$], antlerite [$Cu_3SO_4(OH)_4$], kröhnkite [$Na_2Cu(SO_4)_2 \cdot 2H_2O$], chalcanthite ($CuSo_4 \cdot 5H_2O$), natrochalcite [$NaCu_2(SO_4)_2OH \cdot H_2O$], cuprocopiapite [$CuFe_4(SO_4)_6(OH)_2 \cdot nH_2O$], salesite ($CuIO_3OH$), turquoise, leightonite [$K_2Ca_2Cu(SO_4)_4 \cdot 2H_2O$], lindgrenite [$Cu_3(MoO_4)_2(OH)_2$], chenevixite [$Cu_2Fe_2(AsO_4)_2(OH)_4 \cdot H_2O$], bellingerite [$3Cu(IO_3)_2 \cdot 2H_2O$], atacamite [$Cu_2Cl(OH)_3$], and numerous other species (Jarrell, 1944; Bandy, 1938; Palache and Jarrell, 1939; Berman and Wolfe, 1940). Sulfates of iron are also abundantly developed in the oxidized zone. The presence of chlorine and iodine in some of the compounds has been attributed both to wind transport of these halides from the ocean (Jarrell, 1944) and to recent volcanism (Bandy, 1938).

Chuquicamata has experienced a complex history of oxidation, leaching, and supergene enrichment. During the Late Tertiary uplift of the area, the climate changed from humid to arid, and the water table fluctuated radically. Copper leached from the oxidation zone was carried down to the water table, where it was reprecipitated as a sulfide enrichment of the primary ore. As the land surface was eroded, the water table and its associated supergene ore moved downward through the hypogene ores. The sudden change to an arid climate quickly lowered the water table and left the supergene zone high and dry above the newly established water table. Subsequent leaching has, in general, been slow, but where the ore contained sufficient pyrite to react with the water and form sulfuric acid, and where there was very little feldspathic material to neutralize this acid, the copper was leached. Consequently, the belt of silicified rock along the western side of the Chuquicamata Porphyry is barren of ore. Similarly, where the porphyry is thoroughly sericitized, it is relatively impermeable and has shielded patches of hypogene ore from the leaching action of descending waters (Jarrell, 1944). The sulfide-enriched blanket that was developed before the period of final uplift contains less pyrite than the hypogene ore, because the supergene copper was deposited at the expense of iron in pyrite. As a result, when this sulfide zone was stranded above the water table, it could not generate enough sulfuric acid to dissolve the copper minerals and carry them down to the new zone of enrichment. Instead, the copper was merely oxidized in place to sulfates, forming the present oxidized ore body. The hypogene ore that had previously underlain the supergene blanket contained sufficient pyrite to leach its copper away, and as a result the rich zone of oxide ore is separated in places from the present zone of supergene enrichment by a layer of iron-oxide waste. Furthermore, the old supergene enriched zone was not uplifted uniformly; it was tilted, leaving its south end lower than its north end. The present-day water table truncates this surface, isolating some sulfides in the north and submerging part of the oxidized zone in the south.

The Chuquicamata ores owe their concentration to several factors. First, there must have been a special supply of copper in the source batholith. Second, the West Fissure must have tapped this supply and conducted the ore-bearing fluids up into the cupola. Third, alternating periods of silicification and fracturing prepared the rock for ore deposition; the ore ascended along the West Fissure, spreading eastward when it reached the altered and fractured zone. Finally, the copper was leached and redeposited by meteoric waters, concentrating what would otherwise have been a more dispersed zone of mineralization.

Recent developments at Chuquicamata include a drainage tunnel driven 1300 feet below the original surface; this tunnel lowered the water table, allowing the zone of supergene enrichment to be developed. As a result, mining is now in the sulfide zone below the oxidized ores, and Chuquicamata promises to be a major producer of copper for many years.

References to Selected Mesothermal Deposits

Butte, Montana

Hart, L. H., 1935, The Butte district, Montana: 16th Internat. Geol. Cong.,

Copper resources of the world, v. 1, p. 287–305.

Lindgren, Waldemar, 1927, Paragenesis

of minerals in the Butte veins: Econ. Geology, v. 22, p. 304–307.

Locke, Augustus, Hall, D. A., and Short, M. N., 1924, Rôle of secondary enrichment in genesis of Butte chalcocite: Am. Inst. Mining Engineers, Trans., v. 70, p. 933–963.

Ray, J. C., 1914, Paragenesis of the ore minerals in the Butte district, Montana: Econ. Geology, v. 9, p. 463–482.

Sales, R. H., 1910, Superficial alteration of the Butte veins: Econ. Geology, v. 5, p. 15–21.

——, 1914, Ore deposits at Butte, Montana: Am. Inst. Mining Engineers Trans., v. 46, p. 3–109.

——, and Meyer, Charles, 1948, Wall rock alteration at Butte, Montana: Am. Inst. Mining Engineers Trans., v. 178, p. 9–35.

——, 1949, Results from preliminary studies of vein formation at Butte, Montana: Econ. Geology, v. 44, p. 465–484.

——, 1951, Effect of post-ore dike intrusion on Butte ore minerals: Econ. Geology, v. 46, p. 813–820.

Weed, W. H., 1912, Geology and ore deposits of the Butte district, Montana: U.S. Geol. Survey Prof. Paper 74.

Mount Isa, Queensland, Australia

Blanchard, Roland, 1942, Mount Isa ore geology, *in* Newhouse, W. H. (ed.), Ore deposits as related to structural features: New Jersey, Princeton Univ. Press, p. 148–154.

——, 1948, The alleged mineral zoning at Mount Isa: Am. Inst. Mining Engineers Trans., v. 178, p. 107–133.

——, and Hall, Graham, 1937, Mount Isa ore deposition: Econ. Geology, v. 32, p. 1042–1057.

——, 1942, Rock deformation and mineralization at Mount Isa: Australasian Inst. Mining Metallurgy Proc., no. 125, p. 1–60.

Carter, E. K., Brooks, J. H., and Walker, K. R., 1961, The Precambrian mineral belt of north-western Queensland: Australia Bur. Mineral Resources, Geol., and Geophys. Bull. 51.

Carter, S. R., 1948, Mount Isa geology, paragenesis and ore reserves: 18th Internat. Geol. Cong., Symposium on the geology, paragenesis, and reserves of the ores of lead and zinc, p. 125–134.

——, 1953, Mount Isa mines, *in* Edwards, A. B. (ed.), Geology of Australian ore deposits: Melbourne, Australasian Inst. Mining Metallurgy, p. 361–377.

——, 1958, Notes on recent Mount Isa ore discoveries: Australasian Inst. Mining Metallurgy (F. L. Stillwell Anniv. Volume), p. 61–75.

Grondijs, H. F., and Schouten, C., 1937, A study of the Mount Isa ores: Econ. Geology, v. 32, p. 407–450.

Hall, Graham, 1939, Geology as applied to the mining of silver-lead-zinc ores at Mount Isa: Melbourne, Australasian Inst. Mining Metallurgy Proc., no. 115, p. 215–234.

Knight, C. L., 1953, Regional geology of Mount Isa, *in* Edwards, A. B. (ed.), Geology of Australian ore deposits: Melbourne, Australasian Inst. Mining Metallurgy, p. 352–360.

Love, L. G., and Zimmerman, D. O., 1961, Bedded pyrite and micro-organisms from the Mount Isa Shale: Econ. Geology, v. 56, p. 873–896.

Murray, W. J., 1961, Notes on Mount Isa geology: Melbourne, Australasian Inst. Mining Metallurgy Proc., no. 197, p. 105–136.

Stillwell, F. L., and Edwards, A. B., 1945, The mineral composition of the Black Star copper ore body, Mount Isa, Queensland: Melbourne, Australasian Inst. Mining and Metallurgy Proc., no. 139, p. 149–159.

Ajo, Arizona

Bryan, Kirk, 1925, The Papago country, Arizona: U.S. Geol. Survey Water Supply Paper 499, p. 208–210.

Gilluly, James, 1935, The Ajo district, Arizona: 16th Internat. Geol. Cong., Copper resources of the world, v. 1, p. 228–233.

——, 1937, Geology and ore deposits of the Ajo quadrangle, Arizona: Arizona Bur. Mines, Geol. Ser. No. 9, Bull. 141.

——, 1942, The mineralization of the Ajo copper district, Arizona: Econ. Geology, v. 37, p. 247–309.

——, 1946, The Ajo mining district,

Arizona: U.S. Geol. Survey Prof. Paper 209.

Joralemon, I. B., 1914, The Ajo copper-mining district: Am. Inst. Mining Engineers Trans., v. 49, p. 593–609.

Schwartz, G. M., 1947, Hydrothermal alteration in the "porphyry copper" deposits: Econ. Geology, v. 42, p. 319–352.

References Cited

Anderson, A. L., 1949, Monzonite intrusion and mineralization in the Coeur d'Alene district, Idaho: Econ. Geology, v. 44, p. 169–185.

Anderson, R. J., 1940, Microscopic features of ore from the Sunshine mine: Econ. Geology, v. 35, p. 659–667.

Bandy, M. C., 1938, Mineralogy of three sulphate deposits of northern Chile: Am. Mineralogist, v. 23, p. 669–760.

Berman, Harry, and Wolfe, C. W., 1940, Bellingerite, a new mineral from Chuquicamata, Chile: Am. Mineralogist, v. 25, p. 505–512.

Ettlinger, I. A., 1928, Ore deposits support hypothesis of a central Arizona batholith: Am. Inst. Mining Engineers Tech. Pub. 63.

Fryklund, V. C., Jr., and Fletcher, J. D., 1956, Geochemistry of sphalerite from the Star mine, Coeur d'Alene district, Idaho: Econ. Geology, v. 51, p. 223–247.

Hosterman, J. W., 1956, Geology of the Murray area, Shoshone County, Idaho: U.S. Geol. Survey Bull. 1027-P.

Jarrell, O. W., 1944, Oxidation at Chuquicamata, Chile: Econ. Geology, v. 39, p. 215–286.

Krieger, M. H., 1961, Troy Quartzite (Younger Precambrian) and Bolsa and Abrigo Formations (Cambrian), northern Galiuro Mountains, southeastern Arizona: U.S. Geol. Survey Prof. Paper 424-C, p. 160–164.

Lindgren, Waldemar, 1933, Mineral deposits (4th ed.), New York, McGraw-Hill Book Co., Inc.

Long, Austin, Silverman, A. J., and Kulp, J. L., 1960, Isotopic composition of lead and Precambrian mineralization of the Coeur d'Alene district, Idaho: Econ. Geology, v. 55, p. 645–658.

López, V. M., 1939, The primary mineralization at Chuquicamata, Chile: Econ. Geology, v. 34, p. 674–711.

————, 1942, Chuquicamata, Chile, in Newhouse, W. H. (ed.), Ore deposits as related to structural features: New Jersey, Princeton Univ. Press, p. 126–128.

McKinstry, H. E., and Svendsen, R. H., 1942, Control of ore by rock structure in a Coeur d'Alene mine: Econ. Geology, v. 37, p. 215–230.

Mitcham, T. W., 1952a, Indicator minerals, Coeur d'Alene silver belt: Econ. Geology, v. 47, p. 414–450.

————, 1952b, Significant spatial distribution patterns of minerals in the Coeur d'Alene district, Idaho: Science, v. 115, p. 11.

Palache, Charles, and Jarrell, O. W., 1939, Salesite, a new mineral from Chuquicamata, Chile: Am. Mineralogist, v. 24, p. 388–392.

Pennebaker, E. N., 1944, Structural relations of the copper deposits at Matahambre, Cuba: Econ. Geology, v. 39, p. 101.

Perry, V. D., 1952, Geology of the Chuquicamata orebody: Mining Engineering, v. 4, p. 1166–1168.

Peterson, D. W., 1962, Preliminary geologic map of the western part of the Superior quadrangle, Pinal County, Arizona: U.S. Geol. Survey Mineral Inv. Field Studies Map, MF 253.

Ransome, F. L., 1912, Copper deposits near Superior, Arizona: U.S. Geol. Survey Bull. 540, pt. 1, p. 139–158.

————, and Calkins, F. C., 1908, The

geology and ore deposits of the Coeur d'Alene district, Idaho: U.S. Geol. Survey Prof. Paper 62.

Sell, J. D., 1960, Diabase at the Magma mine, Superior, Arizona: Arizona Geol. Soc. Digest, v. 3, p. 93–97.

Shenon, P. J., 1948, Lead and zinc deposits of the Coeur d'Alene district, Idaho: 18th Internat. Geol. Cong., Symposium on the geology, paragenesis, and reserves of the ores of lead and zinc, p. 78–80.

Short, M. N., and Ettlinger, I. A., 1927, Ore deposition and enrichment at the Magma mine, Superior, Arizona: Am. Inst. Mining Engineers Trans., v. 74, p. 174–222.

Short, M. N., Galbraith, F. W., Harshman, E. N., Kuhn, T. H., and Wilson, E. D., 1943, Geology and ore deposits of the Superior mining area, Arizona: Arizona Bur. Mines, Geol. Ser. No. 16, Bull. 151.

Short, M. N., and Wilson, E. D., 1938, Magma mine area, Superior, *in* Some Arizona ore deposits: Arizona Bur. Mines, Geol. Ser. No. 12, Bull. 145, p. 90–98.

Sorenson, R. E., 1947, Deep discoveries intensify Coeur d'Alene activities: Eng. Mining Jour., v. 148, no. 10, p. 70–78.

————, 1951, Shallow expressions of Silver Belt ore shoots, Coeur d'Alene district, Idaho: Am. Inst. Mining Engineers Trans., v. 190, p. 605–611.

Taylor, A. V., Jr., 1935, Ore deposits at Chuquicamata, Chile: 16th Internat. Geol. Cong., Copper resources of the world, v. 2, p. 473–484.

Umpleby, J. B., and Jones, E. L., Jr., 1923, Geology and ore deposits of Shoshone County, Idaho: U.S. Geol. Survey Bull. 732.

Warren, H. V., 1934, Silver-tetrahedrite relationship in the Coeur d'Alene district, Idaho: Econ. Geology, v. 29, p. 691–696.

Webster, R. N., 1958, Exploration extends Magma's future: Mining Engineering, v. 10, p. 1062–1065.

Wilson, E. D., 1950, Superior area, *in* Arizona zinc and lead deposits, Part I: Arizona Bur. Mines, Geol. Ser. No. 18, Bull. 156, p. 84–98.

CHAPTER 14 **Epithermal**

Deposits

THE EPITHERMAL DEPOSITS are products of direct magmatic origin formed at shallow depths and at low temperatures. Deposition normally takes place within 3000 feet of the surface, in the temperature range 100–200°C. Most epithermal deposits are in the form of vein fillings, irregular branching fissures, stockworks, or breccia pipes. Replacement is recognized in many of the ores, but open-space fillings are commonly present and in some deposits are the dominant form of emplacement. Drusy cavities, comb structures, crustifications, and symmetrical banding are generally conspicuous. The fissures have a direct connection with the surface, allowing the ore-bearing fluids to flow with comparative ease; in fact, some hot springs and steam vents are probably the surface expressions of underlying epithermal systems. Colloidal textures are also characteristic of the epithermal zone, reflecting the moderate temperatures and free circulation.

A few of the deposits can be related directly to deep-seated intrusive bodies, but this relationship is demonstrable only where special conditions of erosion have taken place. In most cases, the epithermal deposit is removed by erosion before the source pluton is exposed. Consequently, many deposits in this zone have no observable association with intrusive rocks. The majority of epithermal ores are in or near areas of Tertiary volcanism, especially near volcanic necks and other structures that tap the underlying reservoirs of magma. Because these deposits are formed near the surface they are most abundant in rocks of recent geologic age, otherwise they would ordinarily have been removed by erosion. The combination of youth and volcanic environment results in the presence of hot waters in some mines;

for example, hot waters were encountered at depth in the Comstock Lode of Nevada.

The country rocks near epithermal veins are likely to be extensively altered, although the vein walls may be sharply defined. Relatively high porosity allows the associated fluids to permeate the wall rocks for great distances, and a favorable temperature differential promotes reactions between the host and invading solutions. As a result, the wall-rock alteration is typically both widespread and conspicuous. Among the principal alteration products are chlorite, sericite, alunite, zeolites, adularia, silica, and pyrite. Chlorite is probably the most common alteration mineral in this zone. In intermediate to mafic volcanics, propylitization is the dominant process, propylite being an aggregate of secondary chlorite, pyrite, epidote, sericite, carbonates, and albite. The silica and pyrite of epithermal alteration halos are generally fine grained. Carbonate minerals—especially calcite, dolomite, and rhodochrosite—are also found as alteration products. Furthermore, the clay minerals are abundant and conspicuous (Sudo, 1954), forming zones of different colors parallel to the walls of veins. Sericite is more characteristic of mesothermal deposits, but it is not uncommon in epithermal ores; where present, the sericite is normally subordinate to chlorite, forming a narrow zone of relatively high-temperature alteration adjacent to the veins.

The gangue minerals in epithermal veins include quartz (sometimes amethystine), chalcedony, adularia, calcite, dolomite, rhodochrosite, barite, and fluorite. Typical hypothermal minerals, such as tourmaline, topaz, and garnet, are absent.

Ore minerals characteristic of epithermal deposits include the sulfantimonides and sulfarsenides of silver (polybasite, stephanite, pearceite, pyrargyrite, proustite, and others), the gold and silver tellurides (petzite $[(Ag,Au)_2Te]$, sylvanite $[(Au,Ag)Te_2]$, krennerite $[(Au,Ag)Te_2]$, calaverite $(AuTe_2)$, hessite (Ag_2Te), and so on), stibnite, argentite, cinnabar, and native mercury. Some of the world's richest concentrations of native gold and electrum (the natural gold-silver alloy), were deposited under epithermal conditions; these are the famous bonanza deposits, such as Goldfield, Nevada, and Hauraki, New Zealand. Other epithermal bonanza deposits contain gold tellurides and silver sulfides, sulfosalts, and selenides. The famous native copper deposits of the Keweenaw Peninsula in northwestern Michigan, deposited in propylitized basaltic lavas and interbedded conglomerates, are also classified as epithermal. Galena, sphalerite, chalcopyrite, and other sulfides commonly found in the mesothermal zone extend into the epithermal zone, but rarely in large concentrations. By definition, the high-temperature minerals characteristic of hypothermal veins and igneous metamorphic deposits are not present in epithermal ores.

It is not uncommon to find large, highly colored gossans (iron oxide cappings) covering epithermal ores. During weathering, the widespread pyrite in the altered wall rock is oxidized to limonite and hematite, forming a conspicuous guide to ore deposits.

Many famous epithermal deposits could be described as examples of this category—some have been mined out, and others are still producing ore. Such districts as Cripple Creek in Colorado; Tonopah, Goldfield, and the Comstock Lode in Nevada; Keweenaw Point in Michigan; Almadén in Spain; Zacatecas, Guanajuato, and Pachuca in Mexico; and the Chinese antimony deposits are among the most noted. Rather than describe a single district chosen at random, or all of the districts in general, we describe three select types in order to demonstrate the major differences and similarities among epithermal deposits. These types are represented by the Chinese antimony deposits, the Spanish mercury ore of Almadén, and the bonanza silver deposits at Pachuca, Mexico.

Chinese Antimony Deposits

The world's principal resources of antimony lie in southern and southwestern China, in the provinces of Hunan, Kweichow, Kwangsi, Kwangtung, and Yunnan (Fig. 14-1). The deposits lie in three crudely defined belts that trend east-west and which, in general, are associated with Late Mesozoic to Early Tertiary plutonic rocks, principally quartz diorites. The northern belt, extending from northeastern Kweichow through northern Hunan, is the richest; the southern belt, which reaches from southern Yunnan to central Kwangsi, is the least productive. The central belt follows a mountain range, which also marks the Kweichow-Kwangsi and Hunan-Kwangtung borders. Hunan, the chief source, contains the richest deposits and about 88 percent of the reserves (di Villa, 1919; Tegengren, 1921; Juan, 1946).

All the deposits are in sedimentary rocks. There are veins in shales, slates, sandstones, and quartzites, and there are replacement lodes in limestones and dolomites. Most of the ores are in Paleozoic rocks, but the Hunan ores are in Devonian clastics and Carboniferous carbonates. The Kweichow ores are in Precambrian slates, and some small deposits in Yunnan are in Triassic rocks.

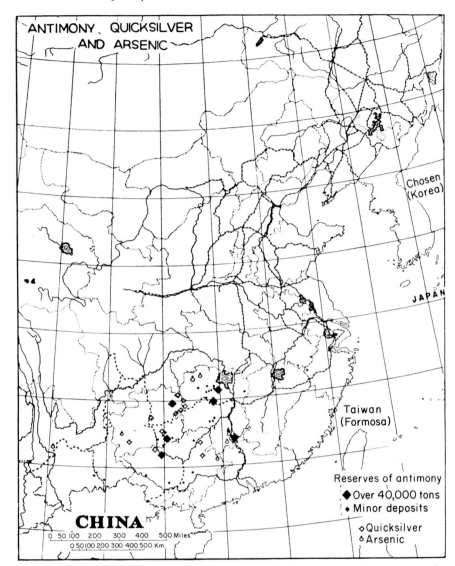

FIGURE 14-1. *Index map of China, showing the location of the antimony deposits. (After Juan, 1946, plate 7.)*

There are two principal kinds of antimony deposits in this extensive region: stibnite-quartz veins in clastic host rocks, and stibnite-galena-arsenopyrite replacement deposits in carbonate rocks. Although some of the most productive mines are in replacement ores, the dominant ore is the stibnite-quartz vein variety.

The veins are restricted to zones of shearing or brecciation. In many places individual fissures open into stockworks or irregularly distributed veinlets. Apparently the slates favor continuous veins, and the quartzites favor stockwork deposits. Few of the veins are uniform in their content of stibnite, which occurs sporadically in pockets or bunches. Quartz, which forms crystal-lined vugs in many places, is generally the only gangue mineral. Cinnabar and pyrite are found in some of the stibnite veins, but only in subordinate amounts. Because of differences in host rocks, stockworks predominate in Hunan, and veins carry the ore in Kweichow. The average vein is about one foot wide, widths of more than three feet being exceptional. Stibnite-quartz ore ranges from 6 to 25 percent stibnite; it is hand-sorted to much higher grades. Because no effort has been made to mine or explore beyond a few hundred feet in depth, the vertical extent of vein ore is unknown.

Replacement deposits of stibnite in carbonate country rocks form irregular pods, with associated galena, arsenopyrite, and pyrite. Relatively continuous and uniform veins carrying the same minerals as the replacement deposits are also found in limestones. The stibnite content of limestone deposits is generally higher than that of stibnite-quartz veins; it ranges from 20 to 57 percent (Juan, 1946).

In mountainous country along the Tzu River, central Hunan, there are several vein deposits, known as the Panshih mines (di Villa, 1919). The tilted sediments (clay, slates, shales, and quartzites) have been intruded by granites, which caused widespread jointing but only slight igneous metamorphism. Vertically dipping veins cut obliquely through the eastward striking sediments. The veins are very narrow, seldom exceeding 15 inches in width, and consist of stibnite in a gangue of quartz or interlaminated schist and quartz. Economic quantities of antimony are restricted to short shoots within narrow footwall seams, which, in turn, are accompanied by a strong clay selvage. The deepest of the mines has been developed to a depth of about 600 feet. The lower levels show that the ore shoots decrease in length, even though well-defined fissures continue to greater depths.

Not far from the Panshih mines, in the rugged country between the Tzu and Yuan rivers, there are stibnite deposits associated with gold-bearing quartz (di Villa, 1919). These are the Wushih mines, located about 50 miles east of Shenchow Fu. The deposits are veins in folded slates, shales, and a few interbedded quartzites. Originally, the mines were worked for gold, and the stibnite was discarded as waste (the quartz gangue contains 0.20–0.25 ounces of gold per ton). Quartz veins having sharply defined, regular footwalls and indistinct hangingwalls carry the stibnite, which is generally concentrated along the footwall side. The principal veins are persistent in both strike and dip, the deepest workings being at the water table, 540 feet from the surface. In places, the veins are as much as five feet wide, and hand-sorted ore from these wide sections carries 20–30 percent antimony. At depth, the shoots contract sharply, and stibnite gives way to pyrite.

The Hsi-K'uang-Shan district in central Hunan contains the largest and richest structure in the entire district (Tegengren, 1921; di Villa, 1919). Gently folded dolomitic limestones and a few beds of shale, sandstone, and low-grade bituminous coal overlie a quartzitic sandstone that contains the ore deposits. The ore bodies are concentrated along the crest of a gentle anticline, the development of which caused jointing and brecciation in the brittle quartzites sandwiched between shales. A distance of about one mile is mineralized with seams and large pockets of stibnite ore. The most favorable ore bed is a quartzite exposed along the upthrown side of a prominent fault escarpment. This bed, more than 150 feet thick, contains several favorable strata, and as a result the deposits seem scattered throughout this rock unit. Most of the stibnite is in veins, irregular veinlets, or lenticular bodies; veins of pure stibnite more than a foot wide are not uncommon. Open-space filling was apparently the dominant process of ore deposition (Tegengren, 1921). Three miles south of Hsi-K'uang-Shan a smaller deposit exists along the same fault. The ore is nearly pure, containing only a fraction of one percent of combined arsenic, lead, and copper. It consists of long, radiating or columnar crystals of stibnite, which has been oxidized in places to stibiconite ($SbSb_2O_6OH$).

The Chinese antimony deposits, especially those of Hunan Province, are said to have been mined since the sixteenth century, yet most of the workings are shallow, being confined to the zone above the water table. Large-scale, systematic mining was started in 1927, but hand sorting and hand labor are still used in large amounts. The available resources are said to be adequate for many years.

Almadén, Spain

The Almadén mine, about 130 miles southwest of Madrid in the western part of Ciudad Real Province, is another famous epithermal deposit (Fig. 14-2). It is the world's richest mercury mine, and has had this status as long as mercury or cinnabar has been sought. The deposits were well known to

FIGURE 14-2. *Index map of Spain, showing the location of the Almadén district.*

the ancients, who used the cinnabar as a paint pigment. According to Bennett (1948), the cinnabar was used as far back as the fourth century B.C., but the tenth-century Moors were the first to distill mercury on a commercial scale. In recent years the deposits have been a fruitful source of income to the Spanish government, which owns and operates the mines (De Kalb, 1921; Hernandez Sampelayo, 1926; Menendez y Puget, 1949; Schuette, 1931).

The rocks near Almadén consist of Lower Paleozoic clastics intruded by Tertiary(?) diabases and silicic porphyries (Almela Samper, 1959; Almela Samper et al., 1962). Slates of unknown age underlie a thick, cross-bedded quartzite of Ordovician (Ordoviciense inferior) age. A prominent ridge trending east-west to west-northwest just south of Almadén is formed by the quartzite, which dips vertically and is about 900 feet thick. Upper Ordovician sandstones, slates, and quartzites overlie the ridge-forming quartzite unit, and Silurian (Gotlandiense) graptolitic shales and beds of sandstone and quartzite follow in sequence. The ore-bearing zone lies within a quartzite bed near the top of the Silurian section. In detail, this unit actually consists of quartzite and slates with basalt sills and lava flows. Overlying the mineralized strata is a white quartzite about 150 feet thick that has arbitrarily been chosen as the base of the Devonian; it forms a minor ridge that parallels the thick Ordovician quartzite. Slates and sandstones, with a few beds of fossiliferous limestone, overlie the Devonian(?) quartzite. These sediments are well established as Devonian. Just north of Almadén shallow intrusives of diabase and various types of porphyries crop out within the Devonian rocks. One small quartz porphyry outcrop has been found near the ore deposits; it seems to intrude the Silurian rocks conformably.

All the strata are either vertical or dip steeply to the north (Fig. 14-3). The stratigraphy has baffled most workers, thus the true structural configuration is still in doubt; however, at least a few isoclinal folds have been worked out. The intrusives are poorly exposed, but the available outcrops describe belts parallel to the sediments, which in turn strike generally east-west. East of Almadén there are some prominent strike-slip faults, one of which has about $2\frac{1}{2}$ miles of right-lateral displacement and supports a Tertiary(?) dike along part of its length (Almela Samper, 1959).

Much confusion has been created in published discussions of the igneous activity associated with ore deposition at Almadén. Some of the studies conclude that there are no igneous rocks near the ore deposits; others insist that there is an intimate association between the cinnabar and altered dikes (De Kalb, 1921; Ransome, 1921; Van der Veen, 1924). Probably much of the controversy is a result of the fact that some of the data are based upon brief visits to the mine or upon petrographic studies of museum specimens and samples collected by proxy. Consequently, the intrusive silicic porphyries and diabases that crop out just north of Almadén have been overlooked in most of the arguments. Almela Samper (1959) has possibly solved the problem by mapping around the mine, rather than within it. The large intrusive masses are clear evidence that there has been igneous activity in the area; they are younger than the ore-bearing strata and therefore represent a logical answer to the problem of ore genesis.

The problem is further confused by the presence of a strange "breccia" in the vicinity of the mercury deposits. Locally, this rock is known as "piedra frailesca" (friar-like rock), after its textural resemblance to the

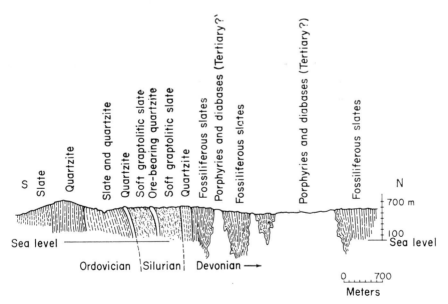

FIGURE 14-3. *Cross section, approximately north-south, through the Almadén district. (After Almela Samper, 1959.)*

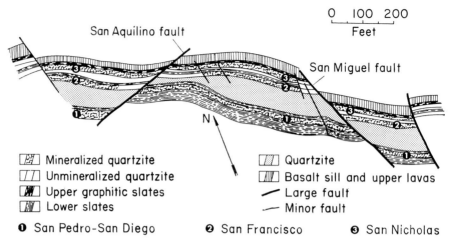

FIGURE 14-4. *Plan of the 14th level, Almadén mine, Spain. (Courtesy of A. Almela Samper, 1962.)*

robes of Franciscan monks. It is this rock that has been the center of debate and the basis for disagreement about the presence or absence of evidence indicating igneous activity. The piedra frailesca is a fine-grained granulated rock containing fragments of quartzite, slate, porphyry, and limestone (Almela Samper, 1959). It is known in several places near Almadén but seems to be restricted to a single stratigraphic position (Almela Samper and Febrel, 1960). Mercury deposits show a striking spatial relationship to the thickest zones of piedra frailesca. Near the principal workings at Almadén, the piedra frailesca forms a cone, or wedge-shaped structure, some 800 feet wide at the surface and absent or inconspicuous in the deepest workings. Petrographically, the matrix of piedra frailesca has the appearance of crushed quartzite (Ransome, 1921); accordingly it has long been considered a tectonic breccia. Almela Samper and Febrel (1960) made a careful study of this rock and concluded that it is a basaltic tuff formed contemporaneously with associated lava flows. This interpretation precludes the possibility that the piedra frailesca and the mercury deposits are cogenetic, because the period of metallization followed an episode of post-basalt volcanism. An alternative hypothesis might be that the piedra frailesca represents material formed by explosive gaseous penetrations—that is, products of fluidization (for example, compare the description of piedra frailesca with the pseudoaplite of Tsumeb, South-West Africa, p. 90, and the pipe at Black Peak, Arizona, p. 74). The presence of both igneous and sedimentary fragments in the material; the pipe, or cone, shapes; and the association of mineral deposits suggests this interpretation, though it has not been advanced by any of the geologists who have examined the rocks in the field.

The ore at Almadén consists predominantly of cinnabar, but contains subordinate amounts of native mercury and pyrite (Van der Veen, 1924; Raynaud; 1941). Gangue minerals include quartz, calcite, dolomite, barite, and natrolite (or a related zeolite). Three closely spaced quartzite strata contain the ore bodies (Fig. 14-4). These beds are separated by 10–20 feet of slate near the surface, but at depth they appear to merge. The three ore-bearing quartzites dip from vertical to 70°N (Fig. 14-5). In stratigraphic order (from south to north), the lodes are named San Pedro-San Diego, San Francisco, and San Nicolás; they are, respectively, 17–36 feet wide, 8 feet wide, and 10 feet wide on the lower levels, where all of them are about 1000 feet long (De Kalb, 1921). The vein material is brecciated quartzite cemented with quartz, a small amount of sericite, and zeolite. Pyrite is widely distributed, even in the adjacent slates. Weathering of the pyritized slate produces conspicuous outcrops that distinguish this slate from nonpyritiferous slate.

Rich zones, one to three meters wide, are restricted to the central

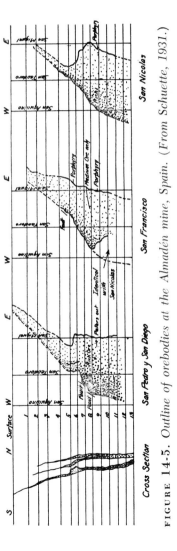

FIGURE 14-5. Outline of orebodies at the Almadén mine, Spain. (From Schuette, 1931.)

plane of the lodes, and the values decrease gradually toward the walls.
Until 1928, mining was confined to the area between two cross faults that
cut the ore bodies on the east and west sides, but underground exploration
beyond these faults has proven the extension of ore. The true configuration
of the ore bodies is not yet known, and early reports that their lengths were
less at depth than at the surface are no longer valid (Menendez y Puget,
1949). However, the three mineralized beds apparently converge and become thinner at depth (Bennett, 1948).

Petrographic studies have demonstrated clearly that the cinnabar re-

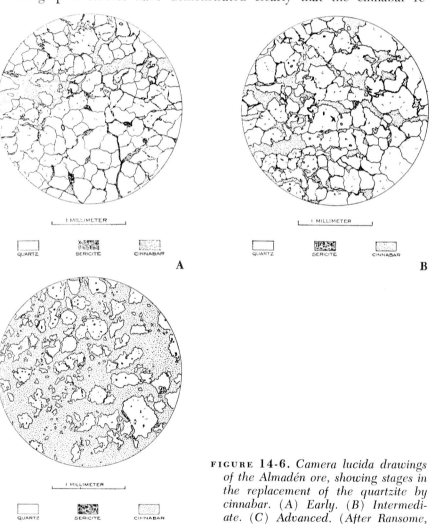

FIGURE 14-6. *Camera lucida drawings
of the Almadén ore, showing stages in
the replacement of the quartzite by
cinnabar. (A) Early. (B) Intermediate. (C) Advanced. (After Ransome,
1921. Figures 22–24.)*

places quartzite and is not merely an interstitial filling around grain borders (Beck, 1909; Ransome, 1921; Raynaud, 1941). This relationship was well illustrated by Ransome (1921) (see Fig. 14-6). Silicification, pyritization, and sericitization preceded the period of ore deposition. Subsequent fracturing of the rocks permitted the mercurial fluids to penetrate the quartzite beds, where cinnabar was deposited at the expense of sericite, quartz, and pyrite. The zeolite was deposited at the same time as the cinnabar.

The Almadén mine is unique among the quicksilver deposits of the world. Most mercury deposits contain irregular pockets of ore, unevenly distributed throughout brecciated and highly altered surficial materials. Almadén is the deepest and most continuous mine of its type. But even here, the evidence of near-surface deposition abounds. Although replacement of the quartzite has accounted for most of the ore, the cinnabar was introduced into the host rock through innumerable small fissures, leaving vugs, druses, and banded open-space fillings. Nearly all mercury mines are epithermal, but further evidence for this classification of the Almadén cinnabar is the presence of a contemporaneous zeolite. The sericite, which might represent a slightly higher temperature, was deposited before the cinnabar. The age of metallization cannot be accurately determined, but is thought to be late in the geologic history and related to a fairly recent period of thermal spring activity in the area (Menendez y Puget, 1949). If this conclusion is correct, the ore must have been deposited very close to its present depth of burial. In all respects, then, the Almadén mercury deposits conform to their classification as epithermal.

Mineralization is traceable on the surface for a distance of more than 12 miles, with numerous scattered showings of cinnabar, but most of the mining activity is confined to the immediate area of Almadén. The grade of ore averages about 6 percent mercury, a grade that is 3–4 percent above that of all competitors. Since 1499, date of the earliest records, the total production from Almadén has been about 240,000 metric tons of mercury, and the reserves are adequate for at least another century of continuous production.

Pachuca-Real del Monte District, Mexico

The famous bonanza silver districts of Pachuca and Real del Monte are about 60 miles north-northeast of Mexico City (Fig. 14–7). They would represent a single district were they not effectively separated by the crest of the Sierra de Pachuca. Pachuca lies along the west flank of the mountain

FIGURE 14-7. *Index map of Mexico, showing the location of the Pachuca-Real del Monte district.*

range; Real del Monte is on the east flank, only about $3\frac{1}{2}$ miles away. Because Real del Monte receives about twice as much rainfall as Pachuca, their geographies differ considerably. But geologically they represent two ends of a single mineralized area (Ordoñez, 1902; Wisser, 1937, 1942; Winchell, 1922; Geyne, 1956).

The Sierra de Pachuca is made up of Tertiary volcanic rocks overlying Cretaceous sediments. Thick andesite flows and associated tuffs and breccias constitute the bulk of these volcanics. They are overlain by rhyolites and dacites, which in turn support local basalt flows. Arranged chronologically, the major events include extrusion of andesites, followed by alternating dacites and andesites; extrusion of rhyolites; deposition of ores; and extrusion of basalts. The volcanic rocks total about 6500 feet in thickness. Dikes of andesite, dacite, and rhyolite of premineralization age strike generally N75°W across the district. The most abundant dikes are rhyolitic, representing the last phase of igneous activity just before the ore-bearing fluids were introduced (Geyne, 1956).

Fossil plants found in the volcanic rocks make it possible to date the periods of igneous activity fairly closely. The andesites are Oligocene to Miocene; the rhyolites, Late Miocene or Early Pliocene; and the younger lavas, Pliocene. The age of ore, then, is probably Early Pliocene, slightly younger than the rhyolites.

The structure has been studied in great detail, because the ore deposits are localized along faults. Regionally, the volcanic rocks describe a broad, shallow syncline, but in the immediate mining district the bedding varies in dip from horizontal to 40–50° in all directions. East-west and northwest-southeast faults dominate the structural pattern, which is emphasized further by the northwest-southeast dike system (Fig. 14-8). In addition to the east-west faults, the eastern part of the district, in Real del Monte, has a well-developed set of mineralized faults that strike north-south. Apparently, the parallel fracture zones represent faulting under conditions of regional stress. The dikes ascended along the earliest fractures, but faulting continued throughout the period of mineralization. Nearly all of the east-west faults have steep dips and normal displacements. The north-south faults formed near the end of the period of east-west faulting, just at the time of ore deposition. These late faults have very little displacement, but recurrent movements and the timing made them especially favorable as avenues for ascending ore fluids (Wisser, 1942; Geyne, 1956).

The ore deposits are in quartz veins along the faults, forming shoots where local conditions favored the development of breccias or wide zones. Paragenetically, the hypogene sulfide sequence is pyrite, sphalerite, galena, chalcopyrite, argentite, acanthite, polybasite, and stephanite (Bastin, 1948; Geyne, 1956). Chalcocite, covellite, and bornite occur locally, but their presence is believed to represent secondary enrichment of the copper sulfides. By far the most abundant compound of silver is acanthite (Ag_2S), which was formed as a product of both hypogene and supergene processes. Other secondary minerals include native silver, silver chlorides and bromides, malachite, azurite, anglesite, and oxides of manganese and iron.

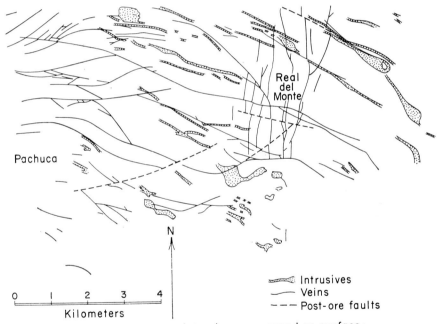

Real del Monte

Pachuca

N

0   1   2   3   4
Kilometers

Intrusives
Veins
Post-ore faults

Intrusives as mapped on surface;
veins and faults projected to the common level.

FIGURE 14-8. *Veins, faults, and intrusives in the Pachuca-Real del Monte district, Mexico. The paired lines and spotted areas are dikes and other intrusives, mostly rhyolite but including some dacite; the solid lines are veins along faults; and the broken lines are post-ore faults. (After Geyne, 1956, figures 3 and 4.)*

Besides quartz, the veins contain calcite, dolomite, rhodochrosite, rhodonite, bustamite, and barite.

Propylitization is the most widespread type of wall-rock alteration. It affects extensive areas of the volcanics. Minor amounts of sericitized, kaolinized, pyritized, and silicified wall rocks serve as valuable guides to the presence of ore deposits (Thornburg, 1952; Geyne, 1956).

The minable ore shoots reach more than 3000 feet in length, but the vertical dimensions are generally shorter (Fig. 14-9). As a result of leaching by meteoric waters, most of the ore bodies do not reach the surface. Except where they have been exposed in Recent deep canyons, the tops of the ore deposits are encountered anywhere from 60 feet beneath the surface (in the east-west fault system) to more than 800 feet beneath the surface (in the north-south faults), and the ore shoots continue down 1000–2000 feet lower. The reasons for localization of ore along the veins cannot always be ascertained. Some shoots occupy the intersections of faults; others are in open zones where the faults changed attitude or formed branches, loop structures, and feather joints. In some places ore was deposited along the contacts between veins and rhyolite dikes (Wisser, 1942; Geyne, 1956; Thornburg, 1945). Veins average 3–5 feet in width, but the silver and gold values typically extend into the wall rocks as disseminations or as stringers that trend parallel to the veins. Consequently, the average stopes are 8–10 feet wide (Thornburg, 1952).

The evidence for shallow, low-temperature deposition of ore minerals is abundant. Repeated movements along the faults caused brecciation of the early quartz, allowing later quartz and ore minerals to enter. Banded veins, vugs, and replacement textures are all common. Some of the quartz is even chalcedonic, indicating deposition from a colloidal system. At depth the veins branch, the quartz content diminishes, and the ore values decrease

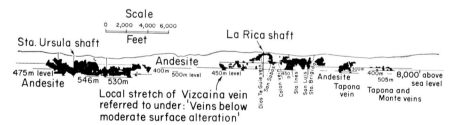

FIGURE 14-9. *Longitudinal section along the Vizcaina-Tapona vein, looking northerly, Pachuca-Real del Monte district, Mexico. (After Thornburg, 1952, figure 6.)*

abruptly. Geyne et al. (1963) estimate that the zone of ore deposition was between 300 and 1000 meters below the original ground surface.

Oxidation and supergene leaching have removed the ore minerals from the upper parts of veins. Much of the silver that was dissolved from the zone of oxidation was reprecipitated beneath the water table at the expense of iron, copper, and sulfur. This supergene-enriched zone accounts for some of the most valuable ore in the district.

Metallization is related to an underlying magmatic source, expressed at the surface in the form of rhyolite dikes and small stocks or plugs. Some of the tectonic features are related to these stocks; the contemporaneity of fault movement and ore deposition implies a cogenetic source for the magmas and mineralizing fluids.

Since about 1526, when the Pachuca-Real del Monte district was first discovered, an estimated 40,000 tons of silver have been produced. Approximately one ounce of gold is recovered for every 200 ounces of silver, thus the district has supplied an appreciable amount of gold as a by-product. As evidence of this productivity, most of which has been achieved during the present century, the district is honeycombed with some 1200–1300 miles of underground workings.

References to Selected Epithermal Deposits

Comstock Lode, Nevada

Bastin, E. S., 1923, Bonanza ores of the Comstock Lode, Virginia City, Nevada: U.S. Geol. Survey Bull. 735-C.

Becker, G. F., 1882, Geology of the Comstock Lode and the Washoe district: U.S. Geol. Survey Mon. 3.

Calkins, F. C., and Thayer, T. P., 1939, Preliminary map and mimeographed text of the Comstock Lode district, Nevada: U.S. Geol. Survey.

Coats, Robert, 1940, Propylitization and related types of alteration of the Comstock Lode: Econ. Geology, v. 35, p. 1–16.

Gianella, V. P., 1934, New features of the geology of the Comstock Lode: Mining and Metallurgy, v. 15, no. 331, p. 298–300.

———, 1936, Geology of the Silver City district and the southern portion of the Comstock Lode, Nevada: Univ. of Nevada Bull., v. 30, no. 9.

Thompson, G. A., 1956, Geology of the Virginia City quadrangle, Nevada: U.S. Geol. Survey Bull. 1042-C.

Lake Superior Copper Deposits

Broderick, T. M., 1929, Zoning in Michigan copper deposits and its significance: Econ. Geology, v. 24, p. 149–162, 311–326.

———, 1931, Fissure vein and lode relationships in Michigan copper deposits: Econ. Geology, v. 26, p. 840–856.

———, and Hohl, C. D., 1935, Differentiation in traps and ore deposition: Econ. Geology, v. 30, p. 301–312.

———, 1935, The Michigan copper district: 16th Internat. Geol. Cong., Copper resources of the world, v. 1, p. 271–284.

———, and Eidemiller, H. N., 1946, Recent contributions to the geology of the Michigan copper district: Econ. Geology, v. 41, p. 675–725.

Butler, B. S., Burbank, W. S., et al.,

1929, The copper deposits of Michigan: U.S. Geol. Survey Prof. Paper 144.

Cornwall, H. R., 1951, Differentiation in lavas of the Keweenawan Series and the origin of the copper deposits of Michigan: Geol. Soc. America Bull., v. 62, p. 159–202.

Lane, A. C., 1909, The Keweenawan Series of Michigan: Michigan Geol. Biol. Survey Pub. 6, ser. 4, v. 1–2.

Stoiber, R. E., and Davidson, E. S., 1959, Amygdule mineral zoning in the Portage Lake lava series, Michigan copper district: Econ. Geology, v. 54, p. 1250–1277, 1444–1460.

Hauraki Peninsula, New Zealand

Bell, J. M., and Fraser, Colin, 1912, The geology of the Waihi-Tairua Subdivision, Hauraki Division: New Zealand Geol. Survey Bull. 15.

Finlayson, A. M., 1909, Problems in the geology of the Hauraki gold fields, New Zealand: Econ. Geology, v. 4, p. 632–645.

Jarman, Arthur, 1916, The geology of the Waihi Grand Junction mine: Inst. Mining Metallurgy (London) Trans., v. 25, p. 3–40.

Morgan, P. G., 1924, The geology and mines of the Waihi district, Hauraki gold field, New Zealand: New Zealand Geol. Survey Bull. 26.

Park, James, 1897, The geology and veins of the Hauraki goldfields, New Zealand: New Zealand Inst. Mining Engineers Trans., v. 1, p. 1–105.

Von Bernewitz, M. W., 1934, The Waihi; one of the world's greatest gold-silver mines (New Zealand): Chem. Engineering Mining Rev., v. 26, p. 197–201, 233–236.

Cripple Creek, Colorado

Cross, Whitman, and Penrose, R. A. F., Jr., 1895, The geology and mining industries of the Cripple Creek district, Colorado: U.S. Geol. Survey, 16th Annual Rept., pt. 2, p. 1–209.

Koschmann, A. H., 1947, The Cripple Creek district, Teller County, *in* Vanderwilt, J. W. (ed.), Mineral resources of Colorado: State of Colorado Mineral Resources Board, p. 387–395.

———, 1949, Structural control of the gold deposits of the Cripple Creek district, Teller County, Colorado: U.S. Geol. Survey Bull. 955-B.

Lindgren, Waldemar, and Ransome, F. L., 1906, Geology and gold deposits of the Cripple Creek district, Colorado: U.S. Geol. Survey Prof. Paper 54.

Loughlin, G. F., 1927, Ore at deep levels in the Cripple Creek district, Colorado: Am. Inst. Mining Engineers Tech. Pub. 13, *and* Trans., v. 75, p. 42–73.

———, and Koschmann, A. H., 1935, Geology and ore deposits of the Cripple Creek district, Colorado: Colorado Sci. Soc. Proc., v. 13, no. 6, p. 217–435.

Lovering, T. S., and Goddard, E. N., 1950, Cripple Creek district, *in* Geology and ore deposits of the Front Range, Colorado: U.S. Geol. Survey Prof. Paper 223, p. 289–312.

References Cited

Almela Samper, Antonio, 1959, Esquema geológico de la zona de Almadén (Ciudad Real): Inst. Geol. y Min. de España, Bol., v. 70, p. 315–330.

———, Alvarado, M., Coma, J., Felgueroso, C., and Quintero, I., 1962, Estudio geológico de la región de Almadén: Inst. Geol. y Min. de España, Bol., v. 73, p. 197–327.

Almela Samper, Antonio, and Febrel, T., 1960, La roca frailesca de Almadén: un episodio tobáceo en una formación basáltica del Siluriano superior: Inst. Geol. y Min. de España, Notas y Comun., no. 59, p. 41–72.

Bastin, E. S., 1948, Mineral relationships in the ores of Pachuca and Real del Monte, Hidalgo, Mexico: Econ. Geology, v. 43, p. 53–65.

Beck, R., 1909, Lehre von der Erzlagerstätten (3rd edition): Berlin, v. 1, p. 521.

Bennett, Evan, 1948, Almadén, world's

greatest mercury mine: Mining and Metallurgy, v. 29, p. 6–9.

De Kalb, Courtenay, 1921, The Almadén quicksilver mine: Econ. Geology, v. 16, p. 301–312.

Geyne, A. R., 1956, Las rocas volcánicas y los yacimientos argentíferos del distrito minero de Pachuca-Real del Monte, Estado de Hidalgo: 20th Internat. Geol. Cong., Excursions A-3 and C-1, p. 47–57.

————, Fries, Carl, Jr., Segerstrom, Kenneth, Black, R. F., Wilson, I. F., and Probert, Alan, 1963, Geology and mineral deposits of the Pachuca-Real del Monte district, State of Hidalgo, Mexico: Mexico, D. F., Consejo de Recursos Naturales no Renovables, Publ. 5E.

Hernandez Sampelayo, P., 1926, Minas de Almaden: 14th Internat. Geol. Cong., Guidebook, Excursion B-1.

Juan, V. C., 1946, Mineral resources of China: Econ. Geology, v. 41, p. 399–474.

Menendez y Puget, Laureano, 1949, The riches of Almadén: Mining World, v. 11, no. 7, p. 34–36; no. 8, p. 38–41; no. 9, p. 35–37.

Ordoñez, Ezequiel, 1902, The mining district of Pachuca, Mexico: Am. Inst. Mining Engineers Trans., v. 32, p. 224–241.

Ransome, F. L., 1921, The ore of the Almadén mine: Econ. Geology, v. 16, p. 313–321.

Raynaud, J., 1941, Le minerai de la mine d'Almaden (Espagne): Soc. Geol. Belgique Bull., v. 64, p. 226–237.

Schuette, C. N., 1931, Occurrence of quick-silver orebodies: Am. Inst. Mining Engineers Trans., Gen. Vol., p. 403–488.

Sudo, Toshio, 1954, Types of clay minerals closely associated with metalliferous ores of the epithermal type: Tokyo Kyoiku Daigaku Science Reports, v. 3, no. 23, p. 173–197.

Tegengren, F. R., 1921, The Hsi-K'uang-Shan antimony mining fields, Hsin-Hua district, Hunan: Geol. Survey of China Bull., no. 3, p. 1–26.

Thornburg, C. L., 1945, Some applications of structural geology to mining in the Pachuca-Real del Monte area, Pachuca silver district, Mexico: Econ. Geology, v. 40, p. 283–297.

————, 1952, The surface expression of veins in the Pachuca silver district of Mexico: Am. Inst. Mining Engineers Trans., v. 193, p. 594–600.

Van der Veen, R. W., 1924, The Almaden mercury ores and their connection with igneous rocks: Econ. Geology, v. 19, p. 146–156.

di Villa, E. M., 1919, The examination of mines in China: North China Daily Mail, Tientsin, p. 71–73.

Winchell, H. V., 1922, Geology of Pachuca and El Oro, Mexico: Am. Inst. Mining Engineers Trans., v. 66, p. 27–41.

Wisser, Edward, 1937, Formation of the north-south fractures of the Real del Monte area, Pachuca silver district, Mexico: Am. Inst. Mining Engineers Trans., v. 126, p. 442–487.

————, 1942, The Pachuca silver district, Mexcio, *in* Newhouse, W. H. (ed.), Ore deposits as related to structural features: Princeton Univ. Press, New Jersey, p. 229–235.

CHAPTER 15

Telethermal

Deposits

SOME ORE DEPOSITS are formed by hydrothermal fluids that have migrated a long distance from the magmatic source—so far, in fact, that they have lost most of their heat and most of their potential to react chemically with the surrounding rocks. These terminal phases of the hydrothermal plumbing system are called *telethermal fluids* (Greek, *tele;* far). The term tele-magmatic has also been used for these deposits, but telethermal is preferred. Generally, the telethermal deposits cannot be established as cogenetic, or even contemporaneous, with nearby igneous activity. Some geologists consider all of them as products of cold waters and meteoric processes. This zone represents the shallow environment, where temperatures and pressures are low and where the general characteristics of minerals will be similar whether precipitated from descending meteoric waters or from ascending hydrothermal fluids diluted by ground waters or connate waters.

The mineralogy of telethermal ores is simple and nondiagnostic. It includes such minerals as sphalerite and galena, chalcopyrite, pyrite, marcasite, chalcocite, and very minor amounts of other sulfides. Native copper is deposited in the telethermal zone, and the oxide minerals are practically unlimited in variety. Oxides of uranium, vanadium, and copper are especially conspicuous and include carnotite $[K_2(UO_2)_2(VO_4)_2 \cdot nH_2O]$, tyuyamunite $[Ca(UO_2)_2(VO_4)_2 \cdot nH_2O]$, autunite $[Ca(UO_2)_2PO_4)_2 \cdot 10–12H_2O]$, torbernite $[Cu(UO_2)_2(PO_4)_2 \cdot 8–12H_2O]$, hewettite $(CaV_6O_{16} \cdot 9H_2O)$, tenorite, cuprite, and many others. The list of telethermal uranium minerals is impressive and contains many species that remained undiscovered until the last decade. Gangue minerals include calcite, dolomite, quartz, fluorite, and barite—the latter two reaching economic proportions at places. In some districts, telethermal galena, sphalerite, barite, and fluorite all occur together in minable quantities.

One of the characteristics of telethermal deposits is the paucity of associated wall-rock alteration effects. In contrast to the epithermal zone, which favors widespread wall-rock alteration, the telethermal zone generally exhibits no alteration or only limited silicification, pyritization, and carbonatization. Cryptocrystalline silica may replace limestones near the ores, and scattered pyrite crystals may define a zone of reduced iron in clastic sediments, but the alteration halo is rarely conspicuous enough to be a noteworthy guide to undiscovered ore bodies. Argillization of porous sediments, however, may effectively bleach wide zones near telethermal deposits, although the development of this alteration typically predates the period of ore deposition, reducing the degree of correlation between bleached zones and ore bodies.

Textures and structures are also nondiagnostic, because the ores are deposited by replacement as well as by open-space filling, and the minerals may be aphanitic to very coarse-grained. The evidence for open-cavity filling generally abounds. Crystal-lined vugs, comb structures, and rhythmically banded ores are common. In carbonate rocks replacement is the dominant form of ore deposition, although many permeable limestones and dolomites contain ores that fill pore spaces and other cavities. Similarly, the telethermal sandstone uranium deposits are well known for their content of fossil logs and bones replaced by carnotite and other uranium minerals.

Structurally, the telethermal deposits are likely to be simple. They were formed a long distance from the magmatic centers and commonly a long way from areas of diastrophism. Circulation of fluids and deposition of ores were controlled by fault systems rather than by tight folds. Most of the ores are in flat-lying beds and show little or no evidence for deposition from ascending fluids. Their general appearance and character are such that they could readily be interpreted as products of meteoric or sedimentary processes. Furthermore, many of the ore bodies have been reworked and owe their present positions to the action of circulating ground waters. This is especially true for the uranium and copper deposits in sandstones.

Many large deposits are classified as telethermal, including such districts as Kennecott copper, Alaska; Mansfeld copper-lead-zinc, Germany; Mississippi Valley and Tri-State lead-zinc and fluorite; Colorado Plateau and Wyoming uranium-vanadium; Mascot-Jefferson City zinc, Tennessee; and Upper Silesian lead-zinc. The recurrence of certain ore types is remarkable; the list includes copper, lead, zinc, fluorite, uranium, and vanadium deposits, or various combinations of these commodities. To illustrate two different types of ores, we describe the Colorado Plateau sandstone uranium deposits and the Upper Silesian lead-zinc replacement ores. Nearly all of the deposits classified as telethermal have characteristics similar to either or both of these examples.

Colorado Plateau Uranium-Vanadium Deposits

The uranium-vanadium deposits of the southwestern United States, in the area known as the Colorado Plateau, have been of great importance in recent years. Although the deposits have been known since 1899, only since the expanded development of fissionable materials has there been more than desultory interest in the region. The deposits are widely distributed throughout the watershed of the Colorado River in western Colorado, eastern Utah, northeastern Arizona, and northwestern New Mexico (Fig. 15-1). As a result of the intense search for uranium during the past two decades, many articles have been published concerning the deposits. Most of the studies, however, have been detailed descriptions of individual deposits; only a few treat the region as a whole (Hess, 1914; Coffin, 1921; Fischer, 1942, 1950; Kerr, 1958).

Exploration techniques for uranium ores are varied, due to the special properties of uranium minerals and because radioactivity can be detected instrumentally from a distance. The most widely used techniques employ scintillators and geiger counters, but prospecting has also been based upon fluorescent minerals, ground-water and stream analyses, electrical geophysical methods, stratigraphic characteristics, biogeochemistry, and geobotany. Regarding the last, a few species of *Astragalus* (also known as "poison-vetch" or "locoweed") grow only where selenium is available in the soil, and on the Colorado Plateau selenium is characteristically associated with uranium-vanadium ores (Cannon, 1957; Hawkes and Webb, 1962).

The known uranium-vanadium deposits of economic value are most abundant in the Shinarump Conglomerate, Chinle Formation, Entrada Sandstone, Todilto Limestone, and Morrison Formation of the Triassic and Jurassic periods, but many other Mesozoic formations, as well as some Paleozoic and Tertiary rocks, also contain ore deposits. Most of these formations are similar; they consist of continental sandstones, siltstones, conglomerates, and impure limestones (Isachsen et al., 1955; Fischer, 1956).

The ore-bearing formations are generally horizontal, but they are dis-

FIGURE 15-1. *Map of the Colorado Plateau, showing the location of the major uranium deposits. (After Kerr, 1958, figure 2; and Kelley, 1956, figure 30.)*

turbed in places by moderately strong monoclinal and anticlinal folds and by high-angle faults. Major structural basins, such as the San Juan Basin, the Uinta Basin, and the Piceance Basin, delimit relatively barren areas between which there are clusters of ore deposits. A regional northwesterly structural grain has been described, which apparently reflects deep-seated igneous and tectonic movements. It is defined by parallel sets of joints and small faults, as well as alignments of intrusive masses. Yet there seems to be no direct relationship between the distribution of uranium and the regional structure, except insofar as the tectonic history has controlled sedimentation, geomorphology, and igneous activity, and insofar as the ore deposits lie within the uplifted regions between structural basins (Kelley, 1955; Kerr, 1958). Salt domes and various types of igneous intrusives are widely distributed in the Colorado Plateau. The intrusive bodies include laccoliths, sills, dikes, diatremes, volcanic necks, and small stocks. Lava flows and pyroclastics are also present. Nearly every major type of igneous rock is represented on the Colorado Plateau, but most of the larger masses are silicic to intermediate in composition. Except for some Precambrian batholiths, the intrusives all seem to be Laramide or younger. No general spatial distribution between igneous activity and ore deposits can be demonstrated, except where uranium mineralization is associated with diatremes and volcanic collapse structures (Shoemaker, 1956).

Most of the ore bodies are similar in type, regardless of their mineralogy and geographic or stratigraphic position. Some of the deposits are small, irregular pods sporadically distributed within a favorable rock unit, but the larger deposits form mantos several hundred feet wide and more than 10 feet thick. Elongated ore bodies tend to follow buried stream courses or lenses of conglomeratic material. Uranium and vanadium minerals commonly fill pore-spaces in sandstones and conglomerates. Local fragments of lignite or bone material acted as centers of reduction and were replaced by rich concentrations of uranium. In addition, disseminations of replacement ore are found in carbonate rocks, and incrustations of uranium minerals occupy small fractures and bedding planes in shales and limestones (Fischer, 1956).

The principal ore minerals recovered on the Colorado Plateau are carnotite and tyuyamunite—oxidation products of primary uraninite, coffinite $[U(SiO_4)_{1-x}(OH)_{4x}]$, roscoelite $[(Al,V)_2(AlSi_3)(K,Na)O_{10}(OH,F)_2]$, and montroseite $[VO(OH)]$. The associated primary and secondary vanadium-uranium minerals are too numerous to list. Minor amounts of pyrite, marcasite, galena, sphalerite, chalcopyrite, bornite, chalcocite, covellite, and many other sulfide minerals also are found. Native selenium and native arsenic are characteristically associated with the uranium-vanadium ores, and the molybdenum oxide, ilsemannite $(Mo_3O_8 \cdot nH_2O?)$ is also common (Weeks, 1956; Weeks and Thompson, 1954; Kerr, 1958). In general, the ores are low grade and rarely contain as much as 1 percent U_3O_8 and 5 percent V_2O_5.

Local controls of ore deposition are commonly related to permeability and ground-water movements. Lithologic controls are the most noticeable.

Thus the ores may be found along valleys in an old erosion surface, within channel sands, or in sandstones interfingered with shales and mudstones (Wright, 1955; Miller, 1955). Sands that contain abundant carbonaceous matter may be selectively enriched in uranium and vanadium. In places the influence of fracture systems can be seen; for example, at Gallup, New Mexico, deposits formed along the basal side of carbonaceous shales where they are intersected by fractures in the underlying sandstone (Kerr, 1958).

The role of oxidation-reduction processes in uranium transportation and deposition has been recognized by most Colorado Plateau geologists. Uranium and vanadium are relatively soluble in the oxidized forms, as hexavalent uranyl dicarbonate and tricarbonate complexes and as tetravalent vanadium complexes. Geochemical studies indicate that the metals would be most stable in solution within a mildly reducing, neutral to alkaline environment that contains abundant CO_2 (Hostetler and Garrels, 1962). Precipitation takes place under more strongly reducing conditions, such as those produced by the action of carbonaceous material or H_2S.

The origin and processes of concentration of the ores have been the subjects of much discussion and disagreement. Four principal ideas have been advanced. It has been argued that (1) the ores are syngenetic and were deposited with the sediments or as an early diagenetic cement; (2) the uranium and vanadium were leached from overlying or interlayered tuffs and volcanic rocks; (3) ground waters leached the metals from the enclosing sands or from a nearby granitic source, forming deposits where the proper Eh-pH conditions prevailed or where ground-water circulation was impeded; and (4) the ores are products of ascending hydrothermal fluids derived from underlying magmas (McKelvey et al., 1955).

The syngenetic theory is no longer in contention, because radioactive dating methods have shown that the uranium is much younger than the host rocks. Early studies, however, were strongly influenced by the apparent lack of structural control, the obvious association between lithologic features and ore bodies, and the absence of typical hydrothermal minerals (an erroneous observation based on the knowledge that the early mines were all in oxidized ores). Consequently, the syngenetic hypothesis was one of the first proposed (Coffin, 1921; Fischer, 1950) and was in strong contention until recently (Wright, 1955; Fischer, 1956).

The presence of devitrified volcanic ash near most of these uranium deposits has supported the hypothesis that the uranium is a product of ash-leaching by meteoric waters (Waters and Granger, 1953). Not only on the Colorado Plateau, but in other areas of similar uranium deposits, a striking correlation has been noted between volcanic ash and the ore. Uranium deposits in the Dakotas are in lignites that underlie bentonites, the lignites acting as precipitants for the uranium leached by descending meteoric waters (Denson and Gill, 1956). But sandstone hosts should allow greater dispersion by circulating ground waters, hence a further mechanism of concentration is required for the Colorado Plateau ores. It is puzzling why the uranium and vanadium are not taken up in place by the montmorillonite formed by devitrification of the volcanic ash, in which case they would not be leached from the bentonitic beds. Hostetler and Garrels (1962) proposed that the ore-bearing fluids are squeezed out of tuff beds by load compaction; that is, connate waters carry the soluble uranium and vanadium salts out of the tuffs and into more permeable sandstone strata. Thus the Eh-pH conditions need not change until the migrating solutions encounter a reducing environment within the permeable sands.

The problems of mineral distribution and precipitation are more directly considered by advocates of the theory that the ores are deposited by circulating ground waters. In its broadest sense, this theory is independent of the ultimate origin of uranium and vanadium. But in a strict sense, it implies that the ore metals were leached from nearby rocks by the same circulating ground waters. Gruner (1956) proposed that bicarbonated ground waters would leach uranium from Precambrian plutonic rocks and carry it into the interior drainage basins, where it would be deposited under local reducing conditions. The arid or semiarid climates in the Plateau province would favor retention of the ore minerals in favorable strata and would account for a gradual increase in the ore grade. Thus Gruner envisaged a multiple migration-accretion process whereby repeated oxidation and leaching at the source would be accompanied by migration to a depositional site and successive increases in the uranium content of the deposit. It has also been proposed that precipitation results from the reducing action of hydrogen sulfide formed in the sediments by anaerobic bacteria (Jensen, 1958); this precipitating agent would be equally effective for ordinary ground water and for ascending hydrothermal fluids. A similar reducing environment may be produced locally where fluids containing organic compounds diffuse away from centers of carbonaceous debris; the merging of this reducing medium with oxidized uraniferous waters would cause precipitation of uranium minerals and a consequent diffusion of more uranium ions to the reaction front (Huff and Lesure, 1962).

Many lines of evidence favor the hypothesis that ascending hydrothermal fluids supplied the uranium and vanadium and that subsequent modifications were controlled by ground-water action. Deep exploration has disclosed a typically hydrothermal suite of minerals, including galena, alunite, hard pitchblende, gersdorffite (NiAsS), sphalerite, chalcopyrite, and several others (Benson et al., 1952). The mineral associations and the presence of cracked hydrocarbons have been interpreted to reflect abnormally high temperatures, in the general range 100–350°C. Wall-rock alteration effects provide strong evidence in favor of hydrothermal activity. In places dolomite, clays, and silica—in a zonal sequence—have been recognized as alteration products associated with ore deposits. Additional evidence of hydrothermal alteration is furnished by the presence of a chrome-mica clay, recrystallized sedimentary clays, and alunitization. The widespread occurrence of molybdenum is also a possible indication of hydrothermal activity, because most other molybdenum deposits are clearly related to igneous sources. One of the strongest arguments favoring a hydrothermal origin for at least some of the deposits is their spatial and temporal relationship to igneous features, such as diatremes, volcanic vents, and breccia pipes. Tentative absolute age determinations further support an epigenetic origin and imply that the ore deposits and igneous activity are contemporaneous (Kerr, 1958).

The evidence published in favor of the various hypotheses is contradictory and inconclusive. Most workers probably advocate the hydrothermal origin, but they recognize that ground waters and supergene processes have strongly influenced the present ore distributions and mineral associations. At the present time, much work—both mining and geological—is being done in the area, and new facts are being uncovered constantly. It seems likely that these efforts will provide conclusive evidence concerning the origin of the ores. Such evidence will have a profound influence upon decisions to explore at depth. It will probably also help explain the controversial origin of sandstone deposits of such minerals as copper, lead, and silver.

Upper Silesia Zinc-Lead Deposits

The zinc-lead deposits of Upper Silesia, Poland, near the former boundary between Germany and Poland, are an excellent example of telethermal ore in carbonate rocks. Deposits of this type have many characteristics distinct from the sandstone deposits. The principal mines are 10–25 kilometers northwest of Stalinogród—or Katowice, as it was formerly known (Fig. 15-2). These ores have been exploited for more than six centuries, account-

FIGURE 15-2. *Index map of Poland, showing the location of the Upper Silesian lead-zinc deposits.*

ing for a major part of the European production (Stappenbeck, 1928; Wernicke, 1931; Schneiderhöhn, 1941; Beyschlag et al., 1916; Zwierzycki, 1950; Sachs, 1914).

The Upper Silesian ores are in the Muschelkalk Limestone, a Triassic, shallow-water marine formation that includes dolomites and shales as well as limestones. No evidence of igneous activity is known in the region. Concentrations of ore are in the lower 350 feet of the Muschelkalk strata, which were faulted and folded into broad gentle warps during an Early Jurassic orogeny. The ore is irregularly distributed along the deeper parts of these structures, especially where cross-cutting faults have provided avenues for ore-forming solutions. Lower Muschelkalk beds are preserved only in the synclines. Four of these synclines contain most of the ore; they are the Bytom syncline, the Wilkoszyn-Trzebinia syncline, the Chrzanów syncline, and the Tarnowskie-Góry syncline. A small amount of ore is present in the Krzeszowice-Siewierz monocline, an extensive structure that causes the Muschelkalk Limestone to plunge to the northeast under younger sediments (Fig. 15-3). The cross-cutting faults extend upward from the underlying Paleozoic rocks and apparently result from renewed movements along older faults. Displacements in the Muschelkalk Limestone are generally less than 100 feet.

Deposition of the ore was preceded by extensive dolomitization, which is most thoroughly developed along a single limestone bed. The dolomitized zones are widely fractured and brecciated, particularly where they are folded; as a result, they formed a permeable host for the circulating ore fluids.

A somewhat unusual feature of the district is the presence of a clay layer at the base of the dolomitized stratum. Known locally as the "vitriolic clay," it is an impervious bed 20–40 centimeters thick that marks the lower limit of mineralization. Apparently, the clay bed was formed by removal of argillaceous impurities from the limestone during dolomitization and concomitant recrystallization. Concentrated at the base of the dolomite, the clay bed impeded the circulation of ore-bearing fluids. All the dolomite and all the ore are above the clay layer. The deposition of ores above an impermeable clay and near the base of a permeable dolomite is more readily explained as a result of ground-water circulation than as a product of ascending hydrothermal fluids. Nevertheless, the ore-bearing fluids joined the ground-water system via faults, as evidenced by traces of mineralization along the fault planes at depth (Zwierzycki, 1950).

In general, the ore deposits follow the base of the dolomite and form beds 5–13 feet thick. In the Bytom syncline two more ore beds lie stratigraphically above, and within 100 feet of, the principal bed; and another ore bed has been found in several other parts of the district. All of the ore lies within 300 feet of the surface. None of the ore is continuous, even in the principal bed; ore bodies are largest and richest near faults and fissures. Shattering of the dolomite was more extensive along troughs of synclines than along crests of anticlines, hence it is doubtful that extensive ore deposits were removed by erosion of the anticlinal folds. The upper bed, which is connected to the lower bed by veins, forms a horizontal body, irrespective of the enclosing structure, but the other ore bodies conform to the bedding.

The primary minerals include sphalerite, wurtzite, galena, pyrite, marcasite, and small amounts of the arsenic and antimony sulfides, jordanite ($4PbS \cdot As_2S_3$), gratonite ($9PbS \cdot 2As_2S_3$), and meneghinite ($4PbS \cdot Sb_2S_3$). A regional zoning is shown by the lead-zinc ratios; in the rich central areas zinc greatly predominates over lead, but marginal ores contain more lead than zinc. The mines have produced an estimated five to ten times more zinc than lead. A typical analysis of ore from the rich Bytom syncline showed 1.7 percent lead and 10.7 percent zinc. The galena contains very small amounts of silver, some of the sphalerite contains cadmium, and some of the pyrite contains thallium (Zwierzycki, 1950).

Ascending solutions entered the dolomite along faults, and ore deposition took place at low temperatures after the fluids had mixed and migrated with ground waters. The ore minerals were deposited in crevices, solution cavities, and joints within the dolomite, just above the clay stratum or in overlying zones where brecciation was especially prevalent. The presence of encrustations and stalactites of ore shows that much of the deposition took place in open spaces, but, in addition, sulfides replaced the dolomite.

The mineral textures are typically colloidal, both superficially and in

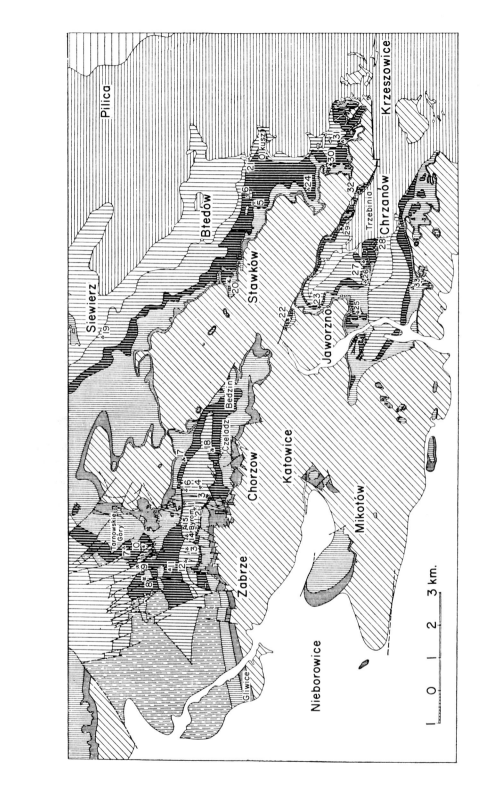

Pilica

Siewierz

Błedów

Stawków

°9

°19

°20

°6

°5

°2

Okusz

°24

°22

°23

°32

°29

Trzebinia

Okusz

°30 °3

°31

Krzeszowice

Chrzanow

°28

°27 °26

°25

°33

Jaworzno

Tarnowskie
Góry

Byrom

Bedzin

Czeladz

°7 °8

Chorzow

Zabrze

Gliwice

Katowice

Mikołów

Nieborowice

1 0 1 2 3 km.

Tertiary	
Cretaceous	
Jurassic with Rhaetic	
Keuper	
Upper and Middle Muschelkalk (limestones, dolomites, and marly dolomites)	

a b

Lower Muschelkalk, upper part
a) limestones b) ore-bearing dolomites

Lower Muschelkalk,
lower part (limestones)

Bunter Sandstone

Paleozoic

✷ **Working mines**

1. Nowa Helena 2. Bolko 3. Nowy Orzeł Biały 4. Orzeł Biały 5. Ulisses 6. Bolesław

✶ **Abandoned mines**

7. Tarnowskie Góry	16. Cecylja-Brzozowice	25. Jelen
8. Płakowice	17. Zychcice	26. Byczyna
9. Repty	18. Rozalia	27. Cezarówka
10. Sucha Gora-Bobrowniki	19. Wiktor-Emanuel	28. Matylda
11. Stolarzowice	20. Anna	29. Gory Luszowskie
12. Miechowice	21. Jozef	30. Galman
13. Maria	22. Dlugoszyn	31. Nowa Góra-Ostrzenioa
14. Nowa Wiktoria	23. Jaworzno	32. Trzebionka
15. Nowy Dwór	24. Cwiek	33. Libiaz

detail (Kutina, 1952; Krusch, 1929). Sphalerite was deposited in rhythmically banded, botryoidal masses that show numerous shrinkage cracks trending both normal and parallel to orbicular surfaces. Liesegang rings are also present, and spectrographic analyses show slight differences in the iron content between the light and dark bands. According to Krusch (1929), the zinc sulfide was originally deposited as a colloidal gel that gradually crystallized to wurtzite and finally to sphalerite. Marcasite was deposited contemporaneously with the zinc sulfide; it too exhibits colloidal textures, such as spherical shapes and desiccation cracks. Galena was probably deposited from a true solution; it forms alternating layers with sphalerite and marcasite, indicating that both chemical precipitation and flocculation of colloids took place in the same hydrothermal system. Younger generations of galena were deposited after the zinc-iron sulfide phase was completed.

Along the shallow edges of the syncline and on the Krzeszowice-Siewierz monocline, the ore beds are deeply oxidized to a product known locally as galman. In places the zone of galman is as much as 60–100 feet thick. The higher solubility of zinc caused the zinc and iron to separate during weathering. Relatively pure iron oxides are concentrated along the outcrops, and zinc enrichment zones lie beneath. Enrichment of cadmium also accompanied oxidation. The most abundant oxidation products are smithsonite, hemimorphite, cerussite, and limonite, but minor amounts of other minerals, such as anglesite, goslarite ($ZnSO_4 \cdot 7H_2O$), tarnowitzite [$(Ca,Pb)CO_3$], and phosgenite ($PbCl_2 \cdot PbCO_3$) are also found (Zwierzycki, 1950).

The origin of the Upper Silesian ores has been widely discussed, and few workers are in agreement. Certainly the ores were deposited at low temperatures, and the presence of mineralized fissures continuing from the Muschelkalk Limestone downward into the Paleozoic rocks is strong evidence ascending solutions deposited the ore. But Sachs (1914) argued that the ores were deposited from descending solutions that were dammed against the vitriolic clay and precipitated by organic matter in the clay; and Stappenbach (1928) envisioned a process of lateral secretion whereby artesian waters leached syngenetic metals from the limestones and reconcentrated them as ore deposits. Krusch (1929) and Kutina (1952) emphasized the colloidal structures and textures and attributed great significance to colloidal transportation. At some mines the evidence for colloidal deposition is so striking that this origin remains virtually unchallenged. Other deposits in the district indicate that part, but not all, of the zinc sulfides and marcasite were precipitated as colloids. Summing up the evidence, we can say that the Upper Silesian ores were undoubtedly formed near the surface at low temperatures, and it is probable that the metals came from a distant magmatic source. These are the essential criteria of a telethermal deposit. A comparison with the Mississippi Valley lead-zinc deposits and similar ones will show a striking uniformity in this type of mineralization.

References to Selected Telethermal Deposits

Tri-State District, Mississippi Valley, United States

Bastin, E. S. (ed.), 1939, Contributions to a knowledge of the lead and zinc deposits of the Mississippi Valley region: Geol. Soc. America Spec. Paper 24.

Behre, C. H., Jr., Heyl, A. V., Jr., and McKnight, E. T., 1950, Zinc and lead deposits of the Mississippi Valley: 18th Internat. Geol. Cong., pt. 7, p. 51–69.

Fowler, G. M., 1942, Ore deposits in the Tri-State zinc and lead district, *in* W. H. Newhouse (ed.), Ore deposits as related to structural features: Princeton Univ. Press, New Jersey, p. 206–211.

———, and Lyden, J. P., 1932, The ore deposits of the Tri-State district: Am. Inst. Mining Engineers Trans., v. 102, p. 206–251.

———, 1935, The ore deposits of the Tri-State district—discussion: Econ. Geology, v. 30, p. 565–575.

Newhouse, W. H., 1933, The temperature of formation of the Mississippi Valley lead-zinc deposits: Econ. Geology, v. 28, p. 744–750.

Ohle, E. L., 1958, Some considerations in determining the origin of ore deposits of the Mississippi Valley type:

Am. Inst. Mining Engineers Preprint 5817A6.

Ridge, J. D., 1936, The genesis of Tri-State zinc and lead ores: Econ. Geology, v. 31, p. 298–313.

Stoiber, R. E., 1946, Movement of mineralizing solutions in the Picher field, Oklahoma-Kansas: Econ. Geology, v. 41, p. 800–812.

French Morocco

Aubert de la Rue, E., 1928, Observations sur quelques gisements marocains de plomb et de zinc: Paris, Mines et Carrières.

Blondel, F., 1935, Le plomb, le zinc, et l'argent: Les Resources Minerales de la France d'Outre-mer, Paris, p. 1–82.

Bouladon, J., 1952, Plomb et zinc: 19th Internat. Geol. Cong., Monographies Regionales, 3rd ser., no. 1, Géologie des Gites Minéraux Marocains, p. 179–216.

Claveau, Jacques, Paulhac, Jean, and Pellerin, Jean, 1952, The lead and zinc deposits of the Bou Beker-Touissit area, eastern French Morocco: Econ. Geology, v. 47, p. 481–493.

Jouravsky, G., Permingeat, F., Bouladon, J., and Agard, J., 1950, Deux types de gisements de plomb au Maroc Français: 18th Internat. Geol. Cong., pt. 7, p. 222–233.

References Cited

Benson, W. E., Trites, A. F., Jr., Beroni, E. P., and Feeger, J. A., 1952, Preliminary report on the White Canyon area, San Juan County, Utah: U.S. Geol. Survey Circular 217.

Beyschlag, F., Vogt, J. H. L., and Krusch,

Paul, 1916, The deposits of the useful minerals and rocks (v. II), translated by S. J. Truscott: London, Macmillan and Co., Ltd., p. 723–730.

Cannon, H. L., 1957, Description of indicator plants and methods of botanical prospecting for uranium deposits on the Colorado Plateau: U.S. Geol. Survey Bull. 1030-M.

Coffin, R. C., 1921, Radium, uranium, and vanadium deposits of southwestern Colorado: Colorado Geol. Survey Bull. 16.

Denson, N. M., and Gill, J. R., 1956, Uranium-bearing lignite and its relation to volcanic tuffs in eastern Montana and North and South Dakota: U.S. Geol. Survey Prof. Paper 300, p. 413–418.

Fischer, R. P., 1942, Vanadium deposits of Colorado and Utah: U.S. Geol. Survey Bull. 936-P.

———, 1950, Uranium-bearing sandstone deposits of the Colorado Plateau: Econ. Geology, v. 45, p. 1–11.

———, 1956, Uranium-vanadium-copper deposits on the Colorado Plateau: U.S. Geol. Survey Prof. Paper 300, p. 143–154.

Gruner, J. W., 1956, Concentration of uranium in sediments by multiple migration-accretion: Econ. Geology, v. 51, p. 495–520.

Hawkes, H. E., and Webb, J. S., 1962, Geochemistry in mineral exploration: New York and Evanston, Harper and Row.

Hess, F. L., 1914, A hypothesis for the origin of the carnotites of Colorado and Utah: Econ. Geology, v. 9, p. 675–688.

Hostetler, P. B., and Garrels, R. M., 1962, Transportation and precipitation of uranium and vanadium at low temperatures, with special reference to sandstone-type uranium deposits: Econ. Geology, v. 57, p. 137–167.

Huff, L. C., and Lesure, F. G., 1962, Diffusion features of uranium-vanadium deposits in Montezuma Canyon, Utah: Econ. Geology, v. 57, p. 226–237.

Isachsen, Y. W., Mitcham, T. W., and Wood, H. B., 1955, Age and sedimentary environments of uranium host rocks, Colorado Plateau: Econ. Geology, v. 50, p. 127–134.

Jensen, M. L., 1958, Sulfur isotopes and the origin of sandstone-type uranium deposits: Econ. Geology, v. 53, p. 598–616.

Kelley, V. C., 1955, Regional tectonics of the Colorado Plateau and relationship to the origin and distribution of uranium: Univ. of New Mexico Pubs. in Geol., no. 5.

———, 1956, Influence of regional structure and tectonic history upon the origin and distribution of uranium on the Colorado Plateau: U.S. Geol. Survey Prof. Paper 300, p. 171–178.

Kerr, P. F., 1958, Uranium emplacement in the Colorado-Plateau: Geol. Soc. America Bull., v. 69, p. 1075–1111.

Krusch, Paul, 1929, Über kolloidal Vorgänge bei der Entstehung der oberschlesischen Zink-Bleierzlagerstätten: Zeit. des Oberschlesischen Berg- und Huttenmännischen Vereins, Katowice, no. 6–7. Abstract *in* Zeit. der Deutschen Geol. Gesell., v. 81, p. 169–170.

Kutina, Jan, 1952, Mikroskopischer und spektrographischer Beitrag zur Frage der Entstehung einiger Kolloidalstrukturen von Zinkblende und Wurtzit: Geologie, v. 1, p. 436–452.

McKelvey, V. E., Everhart, D. L., and Garrels, R. M., 1955, Origin of uranium deposits: Econ. Geology (50th Anniv. vol.), p. 464–533.

Miller, L. J., 1955, Uranium ore controls of the Happy Jack deposit, White Canyon, San Juan County, Utah: Econ. Geology, v. 50, p. 156–169.

Sachs, A., 1914, Die Bildung schlesischer Erzlagerstätten: Centralblatt für Min., Geol. und Paläont., Jahr. 1914, p. 12–19, 186–190.

Schneiderhöhn, Hans, 1941, Lehrbuch der Erzlagerstättenkunde: Jena, Gustav Fischer, p. 573–579.

Shoemaker, E. M., 1956, Structural features of the central Colorado Plateau and their relation to uranium deposits: U.S. Geol. Survey Prof. Paper 300, p. 155–170.

Stappenbeck, R., 1928, Ausbildung und Ursprung der oberschlesischen Bleizinkerzlagerstätten: Archiv für Lagerstättenforschung, no. 41.

Waters, A. C., and Granger, H. C., 1953, Volcanic debris in uraniferous sandstones and its possible bearing on the origin and precipitation of uranium: U.S. Geol. Survey Circular 224.

Weeks, A. D., 1956, Mineralogy and oxidation of the Colorado Plateau uranium ores: U.S. Geol. Survey Prof. Paper 300, p. 187–193.

————, and Thompson, M. E., 1954, Identification and occurrence of uranium and vanadium minerals from the Colorado Plateau: U.S. Geol. Survey Bull. 1009-B.

Wernicke, Friedrich, 1931, Die primären Erzmineralien der Deutsch-Bleischarley-Grube bei Beuthen O. S.: Archiv für Lagerstättenforschung, no. 53.

Wright, R. J., 1955, Ore controls in sandstone uranium deposits of the Colorado Plateau: Econ. Geology, v. 50, p. 135–155.

Zwierzycki, J., 1950, Lead and zinc ores in Poland: 18th Internat. Geol. Cong., Symposium on the geology, paragenesis, and reserves of the ores of lead and zinc, p. 190–198.

CHAPTER 16 **Xenothermal Deposits**

PLUTONS INTRUDED TO SHALLOW DEPTHS expel high-temperature fluids into low-pressure environments. Under these conditions, the temperature and pressure gradients are exceptionally steep, causing ore fluids to undergo rapid cooling and sudden losses of pressure during their ascent. As a result, the ore minerals are deposited over a short distance and in a confused paragenesis. The earliest minerals to form are high-temperature varieties, but rapid cooling to near-surface temperatures requires the deposition of typical low-temperature minerals during the waning stages of hydrothermal activity. Furthermore, most of the early, high-temperature minerals are out of equilibrium with the cooler phases, and hence are etched and altered as a result of younger mineralization. Thus the pressure and temperature criteria may be complex and confused in this environment. Mixed high- to low-temperature ores deposited near the surface are known as *xenothermal* deposits (Greek, *xeno;* strange or abnormal). This category was introduced by Buddington (1935) as a necessary addition to Lindgren's classification.

Depending upon how fast the temperature and pressure decrease as the ore-bearing fluids ascend toward the surface, the high-temperature and low-temperature minerals may be either "dumped" together or spread along a restricted course. "Dumping" results when minerals that ordinarily are not found together are precipitated practically simultaneously. In some xenothermal deposits, the shallower minerals follow the higher temperature, deeper minerals closely, but the sequence of deposition is recognizable and similar to the normal paragenesis of vein minerals. This type of deposit is said to be *telescoped*, because each zone overlaps the next. Telescoping and dumping characterize xenothermal deposits.

Most xenothermal deposits are associated with volcanic and tuffaceous rocks of comparatively recent age, but they also are found at shallow depths in rocks of all types and ages. The deposits are generally in the form of composite veins, developed by the periodic reopening of fissures and the deposition of progressively lower temperature materials. Telescoped veins show a simple gradation in space, from high-, through intermediate-, to low-temperature minerals. Open-fissure textures tend to predominate over replacement textures, because the systems are throughgoing and there is not enough time for most replacement reactions to take place. The host rocks are typically fractured, crackled, or sheared, and the hydrothermal minerals are generally fine-grained.

The mineralogy of xenothermal deposits is likely to be complex due to the extreme range of temperatures involved. Typical high-temperature minerals, such as cassiterite, wolframite, magnetite, specularite, scheelite, and molybdenite, are found with minerals that are characteristic of low-temperature environments, such as the silver sulfosalts. Furthermore, any of the minerals common to mesothermal deposits may be present in xeno-thermal assemblages. The gangue minerals include such divergent types as orthoclase, tourmaline, topaz, augite, diopside, phlogopite, chalcedony, apatite, and alunite; but beryl, alkali tourmalines, spodumene, and other high-pressure minerals are not formed in the xenothermal environment. Wall-rock alteration ranges from tourmalinization to kaolinization and alunitization, depending upon the temperatures or the phase of hydrothermal activity.

Ikuno-Akenobe District, Japan

The Late Tertiary rocks of Japan contain several excellent examples of xenothermal deposits (Kato, 1928), and one of the best is the Ikuno and Akenobe district in Hyogo Prefecture, southwestern Honshu (Fig. 16-1). This district has produced gold, silver, copper, lead, zinc, tin, tungsten, bismuth, and arsenic from Tertiary volcanic rocks and underlying sediments (Kato, 1920, 1927, 1928; Geological Survey of Japan, 1960; Nakano, 1931; Kondo and Kawasaki, 1943; Yamaguchi, 1939; Sato and Kaneko, 1952).

The mines are in Cenozoic, Mesozoic, and Paleozoic rocks ranging from slates, phyllites, and quartzites at the base, to Mesozoic and Early Tertiary shales, conglomerates, and sandstones, assorted Tertiary volcanics, and

FIGURE 16-1. *Index map of Japan, showing the location of the Ikuno-Akenobe district.*

Quaternary basalt. Mineralization accompanied a late phase of igneous activity, but the basalts postdate the ore. The igneous activity began with the ejection of a rhyolitic tuff breccia, followed by thick rhyolite flows. Overlying the rhyolite is a sequence of pyroxene andesite flows, which are extensively propylitized in places. Numerous dikes of andesite, quartz porphyry, and basalt cut the sedimentary rocks and flows. The ore-bearing veins are younger than some of the dikes and older than others. Late Mesozoic gabbros and diorites intrude the sediments, but these plutonic rocks are not related to the period of ore deposition.

Ikuno and Akenobe are the two principal mines in a regional swarm of veins. The veins are fissure fillings; some lie adjacent to brecciated structures, and others occupy repeatedly opened fractures. Banding and ribbon structures are abundant. Near the Ikuno mine the veins are in Tertiary volcanics, but in the Akenobe province they are in the older metamorphic and plutonic rocks. Nevertheless, the veins in these provinces are similar in nearly all aspects; they are all composite, telescoped fissure fillings that record a sequence of high- to low-temperature surges of mineralization. Each vein may have a slightly different history than the others, but the general succession is the same everywhere—that is, tin and tungsten are followed by copper; then zinc-lead; and finally by silver-gold-quartz.

The principal vein in the Ikuno mine is the Kanagase lode. It strikes roughly north-south and dips 60–80°E. The vein has been followed for about two miles along strike and passes from rhyolite at the surface into the underlying Tertiary sediments. At places the Kanagase vein is as much as 25 feet wide, but it pinches and swells irregularly. It is a typical composite vein, formed by successive depositions along a repeatedly opened fracture (Kato, 1927). Near the surface the vein is principally a copper producer, but within 600 feet of depth, it also carries appreciable amounts of tin and tungsten.

Four successive stages of mineralization are readily distinguished in the

Kanagase vein (Kato, 1927, 1928). The first stage is represented by cassiterite and quartz and minor amounts of pyrrhotite, chalcopyrite, and pyrite that surround and replace the cassiterite and quartz. Small amounts of scheelite fill the interstices between quartz crystals.

Sharply defined veins of wolframite-cassiterite-quartz constitute the second stage. They cut through the earlier cassiterite-quartz veins. Again, there are minor quantities of sulfide minerals and a late-phase addition of scheelite. Tiny crystals of topaz are enclosed in the granular quartz. The sulfides are late in the paragenesis; they fill intergranular spaces and transect even the scheelite.

The third stage consists of massive chalcopyrite in veins and irregular impregnations, with associated quartz, sphalerite, galena, tetrahedrite, and other sulfides. This was the main stage of sulfide deposition. Chalcopyrite and quartz were the first minerals deposited during this stage, and they are in turn cut and replaced by the other sulfides.

The fourth, and last, stage of mineralization is represented by gold-silver-quartz veins that transect all previous stages of mineralization. Some of the veins consist of massive quartz, but wide zones and sporadic stretches contain dark patches caused by minute grains of tetrahedrite, chalcopyrite, pyrite, sphalerite, galena, and other sulfides. The sulfide minerals fill the interstices between quartz grains and associated sericite. Gold and silver occur primarily as trace elements in the sulfides, but native gold has also been found.

Five stages of mineralization have been described in the Akenobe district (Kato, 1927). In chronologic order they are (1) chalcedonic quartz with cassiterite and minor amounts of sulfides; (2) wolframite-cassiterite-quartz with accessory bismuth, fluorite, and topaz; (3) massive chalcopyrite veins; (4) veinlets of sphalerite; and (5) barren quartz. This sequence is almost identical to that in the Kanagase vein.

The ore throughout the district is in composite veins that carry chalcopyrite, bornite, cassiterite, stannite, wolframite, scheelite, native bismuth, bismuthinite, native gold, argentite, pyrite, sphalerite, galena, and arsenopyrite in a gangue of quartz, calcite, chlorite, fluorite, siderite, apatite, sericite, barite, and adularia (Geological Survey of Japan, 1960; Kato, 1927). Wall-rock alteration effects are appreciable and seem to depend upon the host-rock composition. The rhyolites were silicified, the andesites propylitized, and the slates chloritized. Kato (1927, 1928) interpreted many of the textures of both the ore and gangue minerals as products of colloidal deposition. Even the earliest cassiterite is in globular aggregates of radial crystals that appear to be spherulites of recrystallized colloidal gel. Much of the quartz forms botryoidal structures and also has a radial texture. If these minerals were deposited as colloids, they represent an unusually high-temperature example of this type of deposition. Perhaps they reflect the rapid aggregation of solid particles in a system that did not provide sufficient time for equilibrium reactions.

All the veins in this district are related genetically to the Late Tertiary volcanic activity, represented by large volumes of extrusive rhyolite and minor andesitic and felsitic dikes. The hydrothermal fluids apparently represent the latest fraction of an underlying magma that had previously supplied the volcanic materials.

Takahashi and his associates (1955) studied about 70 samples of ore collected from a vertical range of 500 feet in the Akenobe mine. Using the decrepitation method of geothermometry, they found that the temperatures of formation on the 500-foot level averaged about 300°C, whereas those from the 1000-foot level averaged 335°C. The fact that the veins are composite, however, means that the temperature at any one level probably varied widely. Thus the temperature range determined is probably more significant than the average temperature gradient. The maximum temperature was 350°C, and the minimum temperature was 160°C; this range apparently represents a decrease in temperature with time.

The sequence of mineral deposition in the veins agrees well with the standard zonal sequence around igneous centers. The paragenesis shows, further, that the earliest minerals formed at high temperatures and that the latest minerals formed at moderate temperatures. Since all stages of this sequence are found either together or in telescoped zones, the deposit is logically classified as xenothermal, and most workers interpret the ores as the near-surface evidence of an underlying shallow intrusive mass.

Potosí, Bolivia

Any of several tin and tin-silver deposits in central and southern Bolivia could be used as a classic example of xenothermal ore deposition. The Bolivian region as a whole contains many ore districts, ranging over a wide belt along the Eastern Andes of central Bolivia (Fig. 16-2). This belt extends across southwestern Bolivia along a curve that trends north-south to northwest-southeast (Ahlfeld, 1946). It is one of the world's most productive metallogenetic provinces, reaching beyond the borders of Bolivia to attain a total length of about 580 miles. The most intense mineralization,

however, lies within a more restricted area, about 150 miles
long, between Oruro on the
northwest and Potosí on the
southeast. This area of concentration coincides with a major
bend in the Andean Cordillera
(Ahlfeld, 1941). In northern Bolivia, the deposits are hypothermal and mesothermal (Tur-
neaure and Welker, 1947), but
in southern and central Bolivia,
the deposits are characteristically
xenothermal. Tin and silver are
the principal metals recovered
from the xenothermal deposits,
but some also produce tungsten,
lead, zinc, antimony, and gold.

FIGURE 16-2. *Index map of Bolivia, showing the tin-silver belt.*

The entire belt of mineralization is related to Middle(?) Tertiary intrusives—granitic batholiths, stocks, and shallow intrusives that apparently
represent the uppermost cupolas and apophyses of an underlying batholithic
complex. Nearly all of the deposits were emplaced under near-surface
conditions over a wide range of temperatures and at low pressures. Composite veins, sheeted zones, and stockworks carry the ores, and only a
minor amount of erosion followed their emplacement. Lindgren and
Creveling (1928) estimated that the ores of the xenothermal zone were
deposited at a depth of 3000 feet or less.

The ore deposits at Potosí are restricted to an area of about one-half
square mile. As shown in Fig. 16-3, Potosí lies in a region of Paleozoic
(Ordovician) shales overlain unconformably by Tertiary volcanic rocks and
their clastic derivatives. The principal host rock is a quartz porphyry stock
—the Potosí intrusive—which forms a pyramidal hill called Cerro Rico. It is
funnel shaped, decreasing in cross section from about 5600 × 4000 feet at
the surface to about 325 × 325 feet at a depth of 1650 feet (Turneaure,
1960). Although the original composition of the Potosí intrusive was masked
by strong propylitization, sericitization, pyritization, and silicification, petrographic studies have indicated that it was either dacite or quartz latite
(Jaskolski, 1933; Ahlfeld, 1941; Lindgren and Creveling, 1928).

Most of the veins at Potosí fill shear fractures and normal faults of only

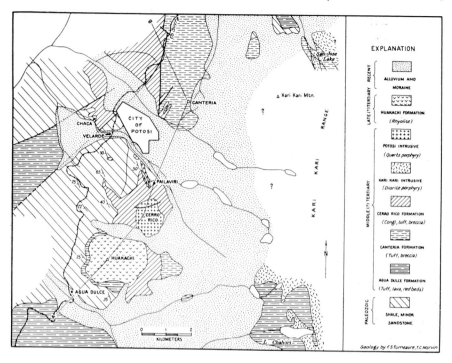

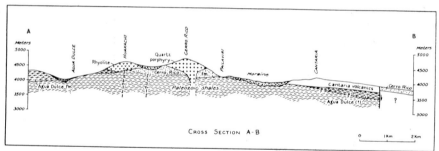

figure 16-3. *Geologic map and cross section of the Potosí district, Bolivia.*
(*After Turneaure, 1960, figures 2 and 3.*)

slight displacement. In general, they strike northeast and dip steeply. The
shallow veins are concentrated within the quartz porphyry, but the deeper
veins are equally abundant in the shales and overlying sedimentary and
pyroclastic rocks (Fig. 16-4). A remarkably productive sheeted zone, made
up of small, parallel veinlets, dips easterly through the crest of Cerro Rico,
reaching a maximum width of over 550 feet and a maximum length of 1150
feet (Turneaure, 1960).

The ores are in composite, anastomosing, veins or lodes as well as in parallel fissures within the sheeted zone. The veins range from three or more feet to only a few inches in width. Several overlapping periods of ore deposition have been recognized, though for descriptive purposes they can be classified as early versus late (Turneaure, 1960). The early mineralization produced cassiterite, pyrite, wolframite, bismuthinite, arsenopyrite, quartz, and minor pyrrhotite. Subsequently, stannite, tetrahedrite, sphalerite, ruby silver, and minor amounts of chalcopyrite, andorite ($AgPbSb_3S_6$), matildite, jamesonite, boulangerite, and galena were deposited. Late-stage alunite veinlets cut the sulfide veins. The characteristic alteration products are chlorite, sericite, quartz, kaolinite, alunite, and possibly tourmaline. Deeper parts of the stock are sericitized; the shallower part is intensely silicified (Turneaure, 1960).

Paragenetic studies have shown that quartz, pyrite, and cassiterite were deposited early, followed by stannite and chalcopyrite, then tetrahedrite and andorite, and finally lead sulfosalts, galena, ruby silver, and the late-stage gangue minerals. This sequence represents a general drop in temperature during the history of mineralization. The early minerals were deposited at 400–500°C, and the late minerals at 100–150° (Turneaure, 1960).

Ahlfeld (1941) argued that the ores were deposited as colloids, emphasizing that "wood tin" is abundant; but the existence of high-temperature colloids is not probable (p. 53), nor do the sulfide textures support this hypothesis. Davy (1920) has observed, however, that the colloidal tin occurs only within oxidized layers, which suggests that it was deposited as a secondary mineral at the expense of stannite.

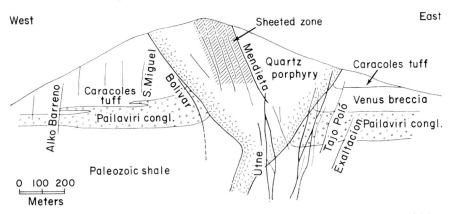

FIGURE 16-4. *Cross section of Cerro Rico, showing the Potosí vein system. (After Turneaure, 1960, figure 15.)*

The general zonal arrangement conforms to the paragenesis. A deep, central zone, characterized by bismuthinite and wolframite, is surrounded by a zone containing silver sulfosalts and, beyond this, by a zone containing lead and zinc minerals (Ahlfeld, 1941).

Ore deposition at Potosí was probably controlled by changes in pressure and temperature rather than by wall-rock chemistry. There is no consistent difference between lodes in altered quartz porphyry, shale, and bedded volcanics. Apparently, metallization occurred wherever the ore-bearing fluids were flushed into a fissure or fracture zone, so that any and all competent formations were favorable hosts. The high-grade ore shoots, complex textures, and unusual mineral assemblages all reflect rapid changes in temperature and pressure.

The accepted view of ore genesis as outlined by Turneaure (1960), is as follows: A centrolineal belt of magma, differentiating at depth, supplied volcanics and shallow intrusives to the long belt of the Bolivian Andes. Early hydrothermal fluids ascended fracture systems developed by stresses along the zone of igneous activity. These fluids altered the host rocks and intrusives, causing extensive chloritization, sericitization, and silicification. Further fracturing allowed high-temperature tin-bearing fluids to enter the altered rocks, forming cassiterite deposits. With waning temperatures, and probably after further differentiation at the source, the vein systems received deposits of sulfides and sulfosalts. The latest ores and gangue minerals were deposited at relatively low temperatures. This picture of ore deposition at shallow depths with temperatures ranging from those characteristic of hypothermal veins to those typical of the epithermal zone is practically a classic example of the xenothermal environment.

References to Selected Xenothermal Deposits

Oruro, Bolivia

Ahlfeld, Federico, 1954, Los Yacimientos Minerales de Bolivia: El Banco Minero de Bolivia y la Corporación Minera de Bolivia, Bilbao.

Campbell, D. F., 1942, The Oruro silver-tin district, Bolivia: Econ. Geology, v. 37, p. 87–115.

Chace, F. M., 1948, Tin-silver veins of Oruro, Bolivia: Econ. Geology, v. 43, p. 333–383, 435–470.

Davy, W. M., 1920, Ore deposition in the Bolivian tin-silver deposits: Econ. Geology, v. 15, p. 463–496.

Lindgren, Waldemar, and Abbott, A. C., 1931, The silver-tin deposits of Oruro, Bolivia: Econ. Geology, v. 26, p. 453–479.

Singewald, J. T., Jr., 1929, The problem of supergene cassiterite in Bolivian tin veins: Econ. Geology, v. 24, p. 343–364.

Turneaure, F. S., 1960, A comparative study of major ore deposits of central Bolivia: Econ. Geology, v. 55, p. 217–254, 574–606.

Mount Bischoff-Renison Bell District, Tasmania

Fisher, N. H., 1953, The Renison Bell tinfield, *in* Edwards, A. B. (ed.), Geology of Australian ore deposits: Melbourne, Australasian Inst. Mining Metallurgy, p. 1179–1184.

Knight, C. L., 1953, Mount Bischoff tin mine: *in* Edwards, A. B. (ed.), Geology of Australian ore deposits: Melbourne, Australasian Inst. Mining Metallurgy, p. 1185–1193.

Stillwell, F. L., and Edwards, A. B., 1943, The mineral composition of the tin-ores of Renison Bell, Tasmania: Melbourne, Australasian Inst. Mining Metallurgy Proc., no. 131–132, p. 173–186.

Weston-Dunn, J. G., 1922, The economic geology of the Mount Bischoff tin deposits, Tasmania: Econ. Geology, v. 17, p. 153–193.

References Cited

Ahlfeld, Federico, 1941, Los Yacimientos Minerales de Bolivia: Ministerio de Economía Nacional, Dirección General de Minas y Petróleo, La Paz.

———, 1946, Geología de Bolivia: Ministerio de Economía Nacional, Dirección General de Minas y Petróleo, La Plata, Argentina.

Buddington, A. F., 1935, High-temperature mineral associations at shallow to moderate depths: Econ. Geology, v. 30, p. 205–222.

Davy, W. M., 1920, Ore deposition in the Bolivian tin-silver deposits: Econ. Geology, v. 15, p. 463–496.

Geological Survey of Japan, 1960, Geology and mineral resources of Japan (2nd ed.): Geol. Survey of Japan, Hisamotocho, Kawasaki-shi, Japan.

Jaskolski, S., 1933, Les gîsements argentostannifères de Potosí en Bolivie: Archiv. de Min., Warsaw, v. 9, p. 47–92.

Kato, Takeo, 1920, A contribution to the knowledge of the cassiterite veins of pneumo-hydatogenetic or hydrothermal origin: Imperial Univ. of Tokyo, College of Sci. Jour., v. 43, art. 5.

———, 1927, The Ikuno-Akenobe metallogenetic province: Japan. Jour. Geol. and Geog., v. 5, no. 3, p. 121–133.

———, 1928, Some characteristic features of the ore deposits of Japan, related genetically to the Late Tertiary volcanic activity: Japan. Jour. Geol. and Geog., v. 6, no. 1–2, p. 31–48.

Kondo, Nobuoki, and Kawasaki, Shigetaro, 1943, Survey of the Ikuno mine: Geol. Survey of Japan Spec. Rept. 3.

Lindgren, Waldemar, and Creveling, J. G., 1928, The ores of Potosí, Bolivia: Econ. Geology, v. 23, p. 233–262.

Nakano, O., 1931, Some microscopic structures of copper ore from the Akenobe mine: Japan. Assoc. Mining, Petroleum, and Econ. Geology Jour., no. 5, p. 217–222: no. 6, p. 21–24.

Sato, K., and Kaneko, J., 1952, Geophysical exploration at Ikuno mine, Hyogo Prefecture: Geol. Survey of Japan Bull., v. 3, no. 10, p. 27–34.

Takahashi, Taro, Takeuchi, Sukune, Nishio, Shigeru, and Imai, Hideki, 1955, Temperature of mineral formation in some types of deposits in Japan, as measured by the decrepitation method (II): Mining Geology (Soc. Mining Geologists of Japan), v. 5, no. 15, p. 9-17.

Turneaure, F. S., 1960, A comparative study of major ore deposits of central Bolivia: Econ. Geology, v. 55, p. 217–254, 574–606.

———, and Welker, K. K., 1947, The ore deposits of the eastern Andes of Bolivia. The Cordillera Real: Econ. Geology, v. 42, p. 595–625.

Yamaguchi, K., 1939, Ore deposits of the Ikuno mine and their zonal arrangement: Japan. Assoc. Mining, Petroleum, and Econ. Geologists Jour., v. 21, p. 257–275; v. 22, p. 25–37.

CHAPTER 17 **Sedimentary**

Deposits

MECHANICAL AND CHEMICAL WEATHERING supply ore materials to basins of deposition just as they supply quartz, clays, and dissolved solids for the production of clastic and nonclastic sediments. Under favorable conditions of transportation, sorting, and deposition, some of the ore materials become sufficiently concentrated to constitute economic deposits. These sedimentary ores are generally classified, first, as chemical precipitates or mechanical accumulations and, second, according to their chemical or mineralogical composition. Whether chemically or mechanically derived, they are *syngenetic* deposits.

Many large and valuable sedimentary deposits have been exploited in recent years, and additional discoveries are to be expected as our knowledge of sedimentary processes grows. Unfortunately, most students of ore deposits are poorly prepared in the study of these processes. The mining industry, however, has begun to appreciate the value of such studies as they apply to syngenetic deposits and to epigenetic ores controlled by primary textures and structures. The emphasis on sedimentary features has been especially strong for such deposits as the Blind River uranium ores in Ontario, Canada, and the Witwatersrand gold ores in South Africa.

Chemical Precipitates

Certain deposits of the metals have been precipitated as primary sediments from surface waters by chemical and biochemical processes (McKelvey, 1950; Mason, 1958). Most elements are amenable to chemical precipitation in one form or another, but only a few of the metals form large deposits as a result of this process. The principal ores of this type include the oxides, silicates, and carbonates of iron and manganese, such as the Lake Superior banded "iron formation" and the oölitic manganese sediments at Chiaturi in the Russian Urals. A few base metal deposits, such as the Kupferschiefer copper-zinc-lead strata at Mansfeld, Germany, are sediments that have accumulated under unusual conditions. The origin of other bedded sulfides is debatable, but many geologists consider them to be syngenetic. Low-grade uranium, vanadium, and rare-element deposits, particularly those associated with marine black shales and phosphorites, also form as chemical sediments.

The chemical precipitation of sediments is controlled by many factors, chief among which are the availability of the ions in question and the pH and Eh of the environment. Oxidation-reduction potentials are related to the oxygen content of the water, which is ordinarily a function of depth and, possibly, nearness to the shoreline. Most dissolved solids are supplied to the depositional basins by streams, and as a consequence the mineral deposits are likely to be thickest and best developed along the shoreline. Reef-like deposits are hence more common than broad, equidimensional sheets.

The role of biochemical processes in the precipitation of ore deposits has been a subject of long-standing debate and remains an unsolved problem (Hem, 1960). It is known that certain bacteria and algae can cause the precipitation of oxide compounds by acting as catalysts for oxidation reactions, from which they derive energy for their life processes. Furthermore, anaerobic bacteria are able to reduce sulfates, producing H_2S, which in turn may cause the precipitation of ore minerals. Sulfide deposits of the base metals will form where the metal ions encounter H_2S, and native sulfur may form through the oxidation of H_2S by inorganic processes or by aerobic bacteria as the gas ascends into an aerated zone (Dessau et al., 1962). Even some oxide deposits may result from the reducing action of H_2S; for example, Jensen (1958) suggested that H_2S produced by anaerobic bacteria caused the reduction of soluble U^{+6} ions to insoluble U^{+4} ions, forming the uraninite ores of sandstone uranium deposits. Iron- and manganese-fixing bacteria have been recognized since the nineteenth century, but their actual role in the formation of ore deposits is unknown. Since most of the reactions they cause will also take place without their aid, although at a slower rate, the physical and chemical environment may be the true controlling factor. The presence of sulfides in the carbonaceous shale facies of basin sediments supports the biogenic hypothesis, but oxide, carbonate, and silicate facies generally lack evidence of organic activities. The problem is clouded by the similarity between the conditions under which microorganisms cause iron and manganese to precipitate and those under which these metals will precipitate inorganically (Beerstecher, 1954).

The distinction between sedimentary ores formed as chemical precipitates and deposits formed by hydrothermal processes may be difficult or nearly impossible to make. The problem is generally a matter of distinguishing pseudomorphous bedding from original bedding or interstitial hydrothermal deposits from diagenetic cement. Fine-grained, banded sulfide ores similar to those of the Rammelsberg district, Germany (see Fig. 17-12, p. 386), are especially difficult to interpret.

SEDIMENTARY IRON ORE DEPOSITS

Several types of iron ore deposits form directly as chemical precipitates. Probably the most widespread is *iron formation*— also known as *taconite* in the Lake Superior district, as *itabirite* in Brazil, as *jaspilite* in Australia, and as *banded ironstone* in the British Empire. Other sedimentary iron ores include oölites (such as the Clinton ores of the eastern United States and the minettes of Alsace-Lorraine), bog iron ores, and iron carbonate beds (otherwise known as "black band" ores).

FIGURE 17-1. *Typical folded iron formation from Gabon, Africa.* ×1.5. (*Photo by Ruperto Laniz.*)

Iron Formation

The term *iron formation* is widely used by geologists, though not always in a consistent way. Deposits of iron formation generally have features in common, but unfortunately each deposit is likely to have some characteristics distinct from those of another area (Gundersen, 1960). Because of these differences, considerable confusion and misunderstanding have arisen over the definition of iron formation. James (1954) attempted to clarify the matter by generalizing the definition; he defined iron formation as "a chemical sediment, typically thin-bedded or laminated, containing 15 percent or more iron of sedimentary origin, commonly but not necessarily containing layers of chert." Since this definition is broad enough to embrace all so-called iron formation, we have adopted it for this book. Most iron formation, however, contains between 25 and 35 percent iron, hence some geologists consider the lower limit of 15 percent as being too low. Furthermore, the presence of thin layers and nodules of chert is considered by many to be an essential characteristic of iron formation (Figs. 17-1 and 17-2). The iron contained in iron formation is present in several compounds, including magnetite, martite, limonite, siderite, chlorite, greenalite $[(Fe^{+2},Fe^{+3})_6Si_4O_{10}(OH)_8]$, minnesotaite $[(Fe^{+2},Mg,H_2)_3(Si,Al,Fe^{+3})_4O_{10}(OH)_2]$, specularite, soft red hematite, stilpnomelane $[K(Fe^{+2},Fe^{+3},Al)_{10}Si_{12}O_{30}(O,OH)_{12}]$, grunerite $[(Fe,Mg)_7Si_8O_{22}(OH)_2]$, fayalite $[Fe_2SiO_4]$, and pyrite.

Most iron formation contains no fossils other than a few algae or nondiagnostic and questionable organisms. It has long been claimed that all iron formation is of Precambrian age, but several Paleozoic deposits have recently been reported (O'Rourke, 1961). Many hypotheses on the origin of iron formation have been based upon the assumption that these ores formed only during the Precambrian. But whether Precambrian or Paleo-

FIGURE 17-2. *Folded iron formation from outcrop, Andrade mine, Minas Gerais, Brazil. Layers of sandy weathered silica fell out when the specimen was moved. Natural size. (Photo by Ruperto Laniz.)*

FIGURE 17-3. *Sketch of a split drill core of iron formation. Bomi Hills, Liberia. Three-fourths natural size.*

zoic, the deposits are all very old. Such ancient rocks have usually experienced a complex tectonic history, and as a result the easily-deformed, thin-bedded iron formation is likely to be intricately distorted or even highly metamorphosed (Fig. 17-3). The apparent lack of similar materials formed during the later geologic periods has led investigators to explain the tremendous accumulations of iron minerals as the result of special Precambrian conditions, which have not recurred since. For example, Lepp and Goldich (1959) suggested that the Precambrian atmosphere was relatively deficient in oxygen and that, as a result, more iron was taken into solution in the ferrous state. But most geologists think that no such explanation is necessary, nor is it reasonable if the Paleozoic iron formations are acknowledged. Perhaps longer periods of crustal stability and deeper peneplanation resulted in a higher degree of chemical weathering during Precambrian and early Paleozoic time. River waters carry large amounts of iron, furnishing a ready and adequate supply for chemical deposition. Since iron is more abundant than calcium in the earth's crust, sedimentary iron should, under the proper conditions, be as extensive as limestone.

Five theories have been advanced to explain the origin of iron formation:

1. Silica and iron accompanied volcanism and were probably poured out on the sea floor from magmatic springs (Van Hise and Leith, 1911).
2. Iron and silica were carried in solution from a nearby land mass and were rhythmically deposited as sediments in water, probably in response to seasonal variations in composition of the water. Various explanations have been offered for the mode of deposition, most of which involve the direct precipitation of silica and iron or one of several biochemical processes.
3. Beds were originally deposited as fine-grained ferruginous tuffs and other iron-rich sediments; these sediments were quickly oxidized and silicified,

more or less contemporaneously with their deposition, under the action of solutions that were partly magmatic in origin (Dunn, 1935, 1941). According to Dunn the silicification gave rise to the banded cherts and jaspers that alternate with more iron-rich layers.

4. Deposits of iron formation in Rhodesia apparently resulted from the supergene leaching, silicification, and ferrugination of carbonatized felsite (Zealley, 1918).

5. Iron formation is due to accumulation in a partly enclosed basin, the precipitation and character of the sediments being controlled by the oxidation-reduction conditions of the depositional environment (James, 1951, 1954).

The first theory—that the iron formation is a direct result of volcanic activity—has received much support and is still favored by many geologists (Van Hise and Leith, 1911; Royce, 1942; Goodwin, 1956). Advocates of this theory point to the common association of volcanic activity and iron formation. Certainly, in many places volcanism was contemporaneous with the accumulation of iron formation. The hot waters associated with the igneous activity might logically furnish a ready supply of iron in solution. However, this relationship between iron formation and volcanic activity is not found everywhere, and as a consequence other theories of origin have been developed. Morro do Urucum, in Western Brazil, is an example of a large district in which volcanism seems to have been absent.

As a result of his work in India, Dunn (1935, 1941) conceived the idea that the silica layers in the iron formation are not sedimentary, but are the product of secondary silicification of materials now represented by ferruginous, chloritic, or carbonaceous shales and phyllites, many of which originated as tuffs. The silicification is thought to have been in part contemporaneous with the deposition of the beds and to have resulted from thermal effects accompanying the volcanism. A low temperature is suggested by the fine-grained textures of the silica. The Rhodesian iron ores, however, have been attributed to the leaching of volcanics by circulating meteoric waters.

The issue seems to involve two problems: (1) what is the source of the iron, and (2) how did the banded deposit form? Of the five theories, three attribute the iron directly to a magmatic source—either thermal volcanic waters or penecontemporaneous leaching of volcanic rocks. The banded deposits are attributed to rhythmic pulsations of volcanic waters, to silicification parallel to the water table, and to seasonal variations in the environment of deposition. Perhaps several of these theories are valid for individual deposits, but none of the theories relating the ores to volcanism can be applied universally.

The recent work of James and others in the Lake Superior region throws doubt on the volcanic source of iron and silica in this area (James, 1951, 1954; White, 1954). These geologists relate both the iron-rich rocks and the volcanism to geosynclinal development during Huronian time. The major environmental requirement for deposition of iron formation is thought to be the closed or restricted basin. This condition coincides in time with a normal stage in evolution of the geosyncline—that is, with the structural development of offshore buckles or swells that subsequently develop into the island arcs characterized by volcanism.

The iron formation (taconite) of the Lake Superior region is divided into four facies—sulfides, oxides, carbonates, and silicates—on the basis of the dominant iron-bearing mineral. Deposition of each facies was largely controlled by the Eh and pH conditions of the environment, especially the oxidation-reduction potential (Fig. 17-4). Low values of pH and Eh favor the deposition of pyrite, whereas high values promote the oxide minerals; carbonates and silicates form under intermediate Eh-pH conditions (Krumbein and Garrels, 1952; Huber, 1958). The deposition of taconite took place in restricted basins, which were separated from the ocean by thresholds that inhibited free circulation and caused the development of abnormal oxidation-reduction environments.

Hough (1958) suggested that the following conditions provided the environment for deposition of iron formation: large, deep, fresh-water lakes; an annual weather cycle such as that in a subtropical or warm-temperate climatic zone; and a watershed in a state of mature geomorphic development. The lakes would have to be of sufficient depth to permit density stratification of the water. During the summer, the lower water zone would be isolated from the atmosphere, making it acidic and slightly reducing and causing iron to be retained in solution. During the winter, convective overturn of the water would bring about a change to oxidizing, alkaline conditions, causing precipitation of the iron. Biochemical precipitation may account for enrichments of silica during the summer, but direct chemical precipitation also may have been seasonally controlled—especially during the Precambrian, when surface waters were possibly saturated with silica (Siever, 1957; Hough, 1958). Furthermore, differential weathering in the source area may increase the supply of iron during the winters and increase the supply of silica during the summers (Alexandrov, 1955).

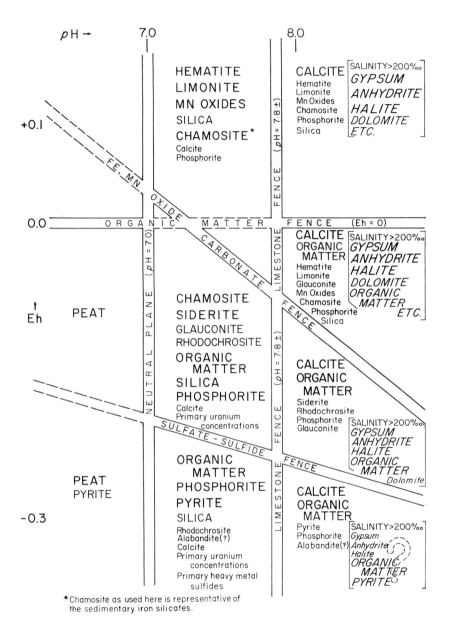

FIGURE 17-4. *Stability fields of the iron facies. (After Krumbein and Garrels, 1952, figure 8.)*

Lake Superior's sulfide facies is represented by black slates containing as much as 40 percent pyrite. The free carbon content of these slates typically ranges from 5 to 15 percent, indicating that ultrastagnation conditions prevailed during deposition. Individual crystals of pyrite are microscopic in size, even in the slate, and as a consequence the iron content is not noticeable in hand specimens. In its uncontaminated form, the carbonate facies consists of interbedded siderite, or iron-rich ankerite, and chert. It is a product of an environment in which the oxygen concentration was sufficiently high to destroy most of the organic material but not high enough to permit the formation of ferric compounds. There are two subfacies of the oxide zone, one characterized by hematite and the other by magnetite. Both minerals are of primary sedimentary origin. The magnetite facies, very common in the Lake Superior region, consists of magnetite interlayered with silica, carbonates, iron silicates, or some combination of these minerals; its mineralogy and associations suggest deposition under weakly oxidizing to moderately reducing conditions. The hematite rock consists of finely crystalline hematite interlayered with chert or jasper; oölitic structures are common in this facies. Evidently the hematite facies accumulated in a strongly oxidizing, near-shore environment similar to that in which younger iron-rich rocks, such as those of the Clinton formation of the eastern United States, were deposited. The silicate facies contains as a major constituent one or more of the hydrous ferrous silicates—greenalite, minnesotaite, stilpnomelane, or chlorite. The silicate facies is most commonly associated with either carbonate- or magnetite-bearing rocks, which suggests that the optimum conditions for deposition ranged from slightly oxidizing to slightly reducing. Figure 17-5 illustrates diagrammatically the depositional zones as proposed by James (1954).

Excellent evidence in support of James's theory was advanced by Gastil and Knowles (1960) as a result of their work in the Wabush Lake area of eastern Canada. They found similar facies in a sequence that implied control by oxygen availability as expressed in terms of water depth or proximity to a shoreline. Figure 17-6 shows this relationship clearly and implies a shoreline to the northwest.

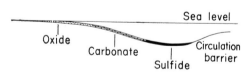

FIGURE 17-5. *Depositional zones in a hypothetical basin in which iron compounds are being precipitated. (After James, 1954, figure 3.)*

Many geologists have felt that ordinary river waters can dissolve and transport sufficient iron to supply the immense

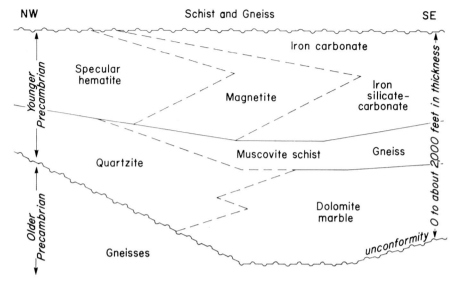

FIGURE 17-6. *Diagramatic section across the Wabush Lake area, showing the distribution of sedimentary facies. (After Gastil and Knowles, 1960, figure 2.)*

amounts in iron formations, and this hypothesis is supported by the available field and laboratory evidence. An important contribution to this problem was made several decades ago by Moore and Maynard (1929), who found that the presence of abundant organic matter will allow cold water to extract and transport enough iron and silica to build up large deposits of iron formation. They held that the iron and the silica traveled and precipitated as colloids protected by organic matter; their experiments showed that a mixture of these sols will form a banded sediment, with an iron-rich layer at the base and nearly pure silica at the top. However, Krauskopf's studies (1956a) have cast doubt on the colloidal nature of the silica.

It has been suggested that iron formation is an epicontinental sediment formed as a chemical precipitate from river waters that entered saline lakes or other closed basins; the absence of clastic diluents implies a land surface that had been reduced to the last limit of peneplanation. The combination of closed basins and peneplanation should be a rare occurrence, and as a consequence the precipitation of iron formation has been restricted to periods of exceptionally perfect base leveling (Woolnough, 1941). Studies in Manchuria by Sakamoto (1950) led to the conclusion that shallow lakes in an oscillating basin, coupled with a monsoon-like climate, were responsible for the banded iron deposits. Periodic fluctuations in the pH of the lake water resulted in cyclic deposition of iron oxides and silica in alternating bands. Sakamoto attributed the iron and silica to mature weathering in the neighboring areas and noted that these materials must have been transported in different ways according to the seasons, in a manner similar to the development of distinct soil horizons in wet and dry climates. He suggested that the iron was carried to lakes during the wet season when the waters were acidic; an arid season would have caused precipitation of the iron and concomitant transportation of silica, due to a sharp rise in pH. Accordingly, a uniform climate would not have produced the banded iron formation.

The layers and nodules of silica in iron formation consist of chert, though in many places—especially where subjected to metamorphism and later to tropical weathering—the silica resembles quartzite or sandstone, and is frequently so called. Examination of many specimens of the silica has led to the conclusion that the material is not a mechanical sediment. In some districts the silica has a mosaic texture (Tyler, 1949), and the iron formation in general is notably lacking in the heavy accessory minerals that should be present in a clastic sediment. As would be expected in any sequence of sedimentary rocks, there are local accumulations of mechanical deposits, hence the chemical precipitates occasionally grade into clastic debris. But by far the vast amount of silica in iron formation is chemically precipitated chert.

Bacteria and biochemistry may be important in the deposition of iron formation, but it is not possible to tell to what extent they are involved, since their actual role is not fully understood. Iron-secreting bacteria exist, and they were apparently active even in Precambrian times (Harder, 1919; Gruner, 1922; Beerstecher, 1954). Under favorable conditions, these microorganisms may be the dominant factor in the process of iron deposition, but not necessarily. The bacteria may speed up an inorganic reaction that would produce the same results if given enough time. Both processes are undoubtedly active in the same environment; the problem that has not been settled is which mechanism—organic or inorganic—produced the most iron in a given deposit.

The observation: "the waste of one generation is the ore of the next" is well exemplified by the story of iron formation. Until about the end of World War II, iron formation was not ore; the iron content was too low and the silica content too high. Iron formation could be mined as ore only in localities where the silica had been leached by weathering or other processes. With the development of fusion or jet-piercing drills and economic methods of concentrating and pelletizing the iron, low-grade taconites became ore almost overnight. As a result of these developments, low-grade direct-shipping ores (50±% iron) find it increasingly difficult to compete. Most iron formation, however, is not ore unless it is situated such that it can be cheaply and easily handled—that is, it must be shallow and near a market, and it must be readily amenable to concentration.

Many districts that are underlain by iron formation contain pods or lenses of high-grade ore, in places totaling millions of tons. These concentrations were formed by leaching of the silica or by addition of iron as a replacement product, either mechanism being the result of metamorphism, hydrothermal fluids, or weathering processes. In many districts where the original rock is itabirite or taconite, only these high-grade products are mined.

Iron ores of unquestioned chemical sedimentary origin, but distinct from iron formation, are mined in many places throughout the world. Of these ores, the oölitic deposits are probably the most valuable. Oölitic ores range considerably in their characteristics. In some the oöids are abundant and make up most of the rock, but in others they are scattered throughout a matrix, such as clay or limestone. The composition of the oöids also varies; they consist of hematite, limonite, siderite, or chamosite.

Oölitic Iron Ores

One of the world's most extensive deposits of oölitic iron ore is found in the Clinton Formation, which crops out sporadically from upper New York State southward into Alabama, where it is covered by the Coastal Plain sediments. The Clinton Formation, of Silurian age, is composed of thin-bedded, iron-stained sandstone, shale, and oölitic hematite. Locally the beds are calcareous and grade into impure limestones (Smyth, 1892; Burchard and Butts, 1910; Alling, 1947). Fossils are abundant, and many have been replaced entirely by hematite. The hematitic beds attain their greatest development in the Birmingham district of Alabama, where they are as much as 20 feet thick.

Three types of ore are mined in the Birmingham district: oölitic, "flax-seed," and fossil ore. As the names imply, the hematite forms oöids in the oölitic ore, generally in a hematite, calcite, or somewhat siliceous matrix; forms small, flat grains or flattened oöids in the flax-seed ore; and replaces the numerous fossils—principally mollusks and bryozoa—in the fossil ore. As a result of the supergene leaching of calcite matrix, much of the ore in the upper parts of the mines is soft; at depth the ores are harder and more siliceous. The hard ores are relatively low grade, the main impurity being calcite. But since calcite is necessary as a fluxing agent, and since coking coals are mined in the nearby Warrior coalfields, the Birmingham deposits can compete successfully with higher grade deposits found elsewhere. With depth the Birmingham ores become increasingly siliceous and more refractory to smelt.

The Clinton Formation is of shallow-water, marine origin (Smyth, 1892; Alling, 1947). It exhibits cross-bedding, mud cracks, animal tracks, oölitic structures, and other shallow-water features, and in places it contains lenses of conglomerate. The hematite is probably of both primary and diagenetic origin, as evidenced by replaced fossils and concentric layers in calcareous oöids (Alling, 1947). The iron was carried into shallow marine basins and was slowly oxidized and precipitated at the same time the other sediments were accumulating. Castaño and Garrels (1950) demonstrated experimentally that aerated river waters with a pH of 7 or lower are able to carry significant quantities of ferrous iron in solution. If such a solution enters a marine environment where solid calcium carbonate is at equilibrium with the sea water, the iron will be precipitated as ferric oxide, both in the water and as a direct replacement of the calcium carbonate. It is precisely this mechanism that is the most popular explanation of the Clinton ores. Hence they are considered to be early diagenetic replacements of calcareous ooze, fossil fragments, and oöids, to which additional contributions were made by direct chemical precipitation.

The oölitic limonite ores of Alsace-Lorraine and of Luxembourg are in Middle Jurassic shales, sandstones, and marls. The ores average between 30 and 35 percent iron in a gangue of calcium carbonate and silica. These ores furnish the bulk of iron used in the Western European iron and steel industry. The oöids consist dominantly of limonite, though siderite, chlorite, and hematite are also present. According to Cayeux (1909), the iron minerals replaced the original calcitic oöids.

A third example of oölitic ore is found at Wabana, along the coast of Newfoundland. These deposits consist of beds a few inches to 30 feet thick that lie within the upper 400 feet of a sequence of Ordovician sandstones and shales. Only the three thickest beds are of economic importance. Shallow-water to subaerial depositional conditions are evidenced by raindrop imprints, oöids, cross-bedding, mud cracks, and the presence of shallow-water marine fossils, such as brachiopods and trilobites. The oöids consist of concentric shells of hematite and chamosite, in places embedded in a matrix of siderite. Both the oöids and the matrix are penetrated by algal borings, and from this it is concluded that the ores were approximately in their present condition before they were covered by younger sediments. The period of iron oxide deposition apparently terminated prematurely, as evidenced by overlying deposits of graptolitic shale, which contains oölitic pyrite (Hayes, 1915, 1928, 1929, 1931). These deposits are exposed along the northwest shore of Bell Island and dip about 9°NNW out under Conception Bay. Mining operations have been carried on for a distance of more than $2\frac{1}{2}$ miles along the dip, placing the deepest workings well out under the bay. The ore averages 51.5 percent iron, 11.8 percent silica, 0.9 percent phosphorus, and 1.5 percent moisture. A potential area of 50 square miles or more is available for mining, of which hardly more than one-tenth has been developed (Lyons, 1957).

Siderite Deposits

Sedimentary beds containing siderite are widely distributed throughout the world. They are commonly known as black-band ores. Efforts to mine these deposits have generally been unsuccessful, because the ores are very low grade, but sedimentary siderite has been worked in Germany and in the British Isles. During the colonial days in the United States, small amounts of iron carbonates were extracted from marine sediments in Ohio, Pennsylvania, and a few other areas.

Bog Ores and Spring Deposits

Bog iron ores occur in small, low-grade deposits with a high content of phosphorus, water, clay, and other impurities. They are of interest mainly because some of them are good examples of the biochemical precipitation of iron minerals. The iron content of bog waters is higher than that of most other surface waters, because the iron is stabilized by humic complexes (Rankama and Sahama, 1950, p. 665). Bacterial action causes the precipitation of ferric oxides and hydroxides from the breakdown of humic iron complexes and ferrous bicarbonate. Supplies of iron are transported to the bog waters by streams and springs. These reactions can be observed in some of the northern glacial lakes. At the present time, bog ores are of very minor economic significance.

Special environmental conditions may account for local concentrations of both calcium carbonate and iron. An analogous example is offered by spring deposits; travertine forms where the spring waters are charged with calcium carbonate, and iron oxide deposits form from iron-rich waters. For

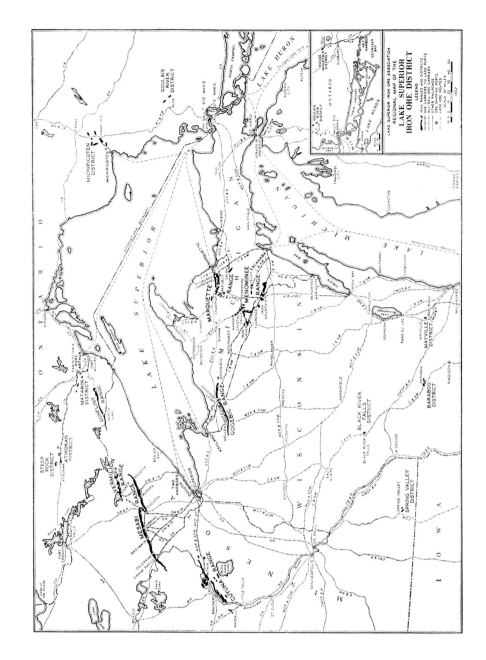

LAKE SUPERIOR IRON ORE ASSOCIATION
REGIONAL MAP OF THE
**LAKE SUPERIOR
IRON ORE DISTRICT**
LEGEND
IRON RANGES AND DISTRICTS
ORE CARRIERS TO LAKE PORTS
OTHER RAILROADS
ORE SHIPPING PORTS
LAKE ORE ROUTES
SCALE OF MILES
10 0 10 20 30 40 50
1952

example, at the Kuchan mine in Hokkaido, Japan, about 5 million tons of limonite were mined where a cold spring flowed from the side of the hill. The ferrous iron in solution was quickly oxidized as soon as the water was exposed to the air, and the ensuing deposit formed a terrace-like embankment.

Lake Superior Region

The Lake Superior region of the north-central United States and southern Canada (Fig. 17-7) is the most productive iron ore province in the world. From the time of the first production in 1884 through 1956, the mines yielded more than 3 billion tons of ore (Wade and Alm, 1957). Although the most accessible ores, and those of the highest quality, have already been mined, the region will continue to produce good ore for many years, but in decreasing amounts. The future of the region is assured by the current development of new economical methods of handling the hard magnetic tacozites from the eastern part of the Mesabi range and the "jasper" ores of the Marquette range.

There are six principal districts—or ranges, as they are called—within the United States sector of the Lake Superior region. These are the Mesabi, the Vermilion, and the Cuyuna in Minnesota, the Penokee-Gogebic across the Wisconsin-Michigan border, and the Marquette and Menominee ranges in Michigan. The Menominee range is further divided into the Iron River, Crystal Falls, and Iron Mountain districts. Of the six ranges, the Mesabi is by far the most productive. Many subordinate deposits, such as the Gunflint range, the Republic trough, the Amasa district, the Baraboo range, and the Florence district, have contributed ore, but in much smaller quantities than the six principal ranges. In Canada the two most productive deposits are the Michipicoten range and the Steep Rock Lake district.

The literature concerning the Lake Superior deposits is voluminous. Probably the most exhaustive treatment of the region as a whole is given in the monograph by Van Hise and Leith (1911), though many other excellent discussions of both the region and individual districts have been published (Gruner, 1930, 1946; Royce, 1938; Tyler, 1949; Dutton, 1952; James, 1954; Grout and Wolff, 1955).

Extensive tracts of land between the various ranges are covered with

---

FIGURE 17-7. *Facing page. Index map of the Lake Superior region, showing the location of each important iron ore district. (After Lake Superior Iron Ore Association, 1952, frontispiece.)*

glacial drift and vegetation. This lack of outcrops has handicapped geological studies, and correlation between the ranges is difficult. Nevertheless, the possibilities of finding new ore beneath the drift and of extending the known ranges into covered territory have been attractive. A great deal of exploration work has been done in an attempt to find new ore, some of which has been successful. In addition to routine geological studies, much geophysical work has been done. Magnetic methods are the most popular; the dip needle and the magnetometer are commonly used, and in recent years much of the region has been mapped on a reconnaissance scale with airborne magnetic equipment. Magnetic techniques have also been helpful in mapping bedrock structure beneath the drift. Due to the fact that most high-grade ores are related to structures—usually folds—the magnetic methods have contributed directly to the discovery of considerable ore.

The Precambrian stratigraphy of the Lake Superior region varies considerably from one district to another. Probably the most comprehensive correlations were made by Leith and his co-workers, in 1935; a modified copy of their correlation chart is reproduced in Table 17-I. The great abundance of slates associated with the iron formation is a conspicuous feature of the stratigraphy. Many of these slates are lithologically similar to one another and are not easy to distinguish in the field. They are also intricately distorted in places. Most of the slates are uniformly gray or black, but a few beds show gradational bedding that resembles varves. Other beds contain a few slate fragments of slightly different color, and locally sandy, or even conglomeratic, beds are recognized. The slates contain appreciable amounts of finely divided carbon and pyrite. In the Menominee range many of the slates ignite spontaneously when exposed to the air, and for this reason they are avoided in the mines wherever possible.

Volcanic materials are widely distributed, particularly in the Huronian and Keweenawan series. Greenstones are the most abundant types of igneous rocks, though intrusive bodies are also common. Many mafic dikes are present, and in the Gogebic range the best ores are concentrated along these intrusives. The Duluth Gabbro borders the western shore of Lake Superior and cuts off the eastern extension of the Mesabi range. Granitic rocks (Giants Range Granite) are also widespread north of the Mesabi range.

Throughout most of the region, the iron formation contains between 25 and 35 percent iron. It is a hard, tough rock that is difficult to break and expensive to beneficiate. The iron is present in the form of hematite, magnetite, siderite, pyrite, or as one of the iron silicates. The direct-shipping ore of the Lake Superior region comes from those areas where natural processes have leached the silica, leaving an enriched iron-bearing product. Only in recent years have methods been developed for mining and concentrating the unenriched taconite. In the eastern part of the Mesabi range the iron formation contains magnetite; this hard rock is crushed, concentrated magnetically, and roasted into high-grade pellets that are in much demand in industry. On the Marquette range a similar process has been developed for hard jasper-hematites, but in this process the iron is concentrated by flotation. The use of unleached taconites is likely to expand in the future.

A major controversy has developed concerning the ways in which silica was removed from iron formation, leaving the high-grade ore deposits. The subject is of vital importance and becomes more and more critical as the mining depths increase. If the silica was leached by cold waters, then the ore should be concentrated either near the present surface or along unconformities where weathering took place during earlier geologic times. If the leaching was caused by hydrothermal waters—possibly associated with volcanic activity—there is a favorable chance that more ore will be encountered at depth. This problem has not been solved, and possibly in the present state of our knowledge it is incapable of solution. Some of the evidence advanced is contradictory, indicating that many of the basic field relationships have not been solved. The current arguments for cold- versus hot-water leaching are listed below.

A. *Evidence and Arguments for Cold-water Leaching of Silica*

1. The ores are near surface, either near the present surface or near an old surface that existed during Precambrian time. Advocates of the cold-water leaching hypothesis emphasize the presence of many unconformities found in the stratigraphic column, which they feel are genetically related to the ores.
2. Much of the ore is concentrated in synclines. This is interpreted to signify leaching by descending waters.
3. The ore bodies grade in depth into unleached iron formation, similar to other deposits known to have been formed by ordinary weathering processes. The fact that supergene leaching can form high-grade deposits in iron formation is demonstrated in other areas. For example, extensive itabirites in the Republic of Gabon, Africa, were leached by surface agencies, and in places the silica has been removed to depths of more than 300 feet.
4. The mineralogy is simple and is what would be expected under meteoric conditions.
5. Comparison has been made with the formation of bauxite-boehmite deposits, where surface waters have leached tremendous quantities of silica.
6. In the Penokee-Gogebic range, ore is found both above and below comparatively impermeable dikes. Here the leaching is attributed to meteoric water

TABLE 17-I

Comparative Stratigraphic Columns from the Principal Districts

Series		Gogebic	Marquette	Menominee
Post-Keweenawan rocks			Upper Cambrian sandstone	Upper Cambrian sandstone
		Unconformity〰	〰〰〰	〰〰〰
Killarney granite		Presque Isle Granite	Silicic intrusives	Silicic intrusives
Keweenawan		Mafic intrusives Sandstones, shales, and conglomerates Silicic flows Mafic flows Quartzite and conglomerate	Mafic intrusives	
		Unconformity〰		
Huronian	Upper	Tyler Slate	Michigamme Slate Upper slates Bijiki iron formation member Lower slates Clarksburg volcanics Greenwood iron formation Goodrich Quartzite	Michigamme Slate (including iron formation) South belt of Quinnesec greenstone
		Unconformity〰	〰〰〰	〰〰〰
	Middle	Mafic intrusives and extrusives Ironwood iron formation	Negaunee iron formation Siamo Slate	Vulcan iron formation
		Palms Quartzite	Ajibik Quartzite	Greenstones (Lake Antoine region)
	Lower	Unconformity〰	〰〰〰	〰〰〰
		Bad River Dolomite Sunday Quartzite	Wewe Slate Kona Dolomite Mesnard Quartzite	Randville Dolomite Sturgeon Quartzite
Algoman granite				
Knife Lake (may be Lower Huronian)				
		Unconformity〰	〰〰〰	〰〰〰
Laurentian granite		Granite and granitoid gneiss	Granite, syenite, peridotite Palmer Gneiss	Granites and gneisses
Keewatin		Greenstones and green schists	Kitchi Schist and Mona Schist	

SOURCE: From Leith et al. (1935).

of the Lake Superior Region

Cuyuna	Mesabi	Vermilion
Cretaceous conglomerate	Cretaceous conglomerate and shale	
~~	~~~~~~~~~~~~~~~~~~~~~	~~~~~~~~~~~~~~~~~~~~~
Silicic intrusives	Embarrass Granite	
Mafic intrusives	Duluth Gabbro	Duluth Gabbro

Virginia Slate
  Upper slates
  Deerwood iron formation
    member
  Lower slates
	Virginia Slate	Rove Slate

	~~?~~~~~~~~~~	~~~~~~~~~~~?~~~~~~~~~~
	Biwabik iron formation Pokegama Quartzite	Gunflint iron formation
	Unconformity~~~~~~~~~~~ Giants Range Granite	~~~~~~~~~~~~~~~~~~~~ Vermilion Granite

	Knife Lake Slate	Knife Lake Slate
		  Slate
		  Agawa iron formation
		    member
		  Ogishke conglomerate
		    member

	~~	~~~~~~~~~~~~~~~~~~~~~ Granite
	Greenstones, schists, and porphyries	Soudan iron formation Ely Greenstone

moving along an old erosion surface. The explanation of ore above the dikes seems difficult for ascending waters.

B. *Evidence and Arguments for Hot-water Leaching of Silica*

1. There are numerous dikes in this region, and the ores are commonly found along or near these igneous rocks.
2. The depth of leached iron formation, especially in the Penokee-Gogebic range, is between 3000 and 4000 feet. This depth of leaching seems too great for waters related to the present surface, and no conclusive evidence has been found that the leaching is related to old erosion surfaces.
3. Where the dikes are inclined at low angles, the ores are likely to be concentrated on the footwall side—a relationship that is common in the Penokee-Gogebic range. (This line of evidence seems to be in direct conflict with argument six of the cold-water hypothesis.)
4. In a few places ore is recovered along the crests of anticlines, which argues against the cold-water evidence that descending fluids selectively leached silica from the synclines.
5. Much smaller quantities of warm water than cold water would be required for the leaching.
6. The presence of manganese ore pipes containing hausmannite (Mn_3O_4), a member of the spinel family, indicates that hydrothermal fluids have been active in the region.

The Mesabi range is by far the leading producer in the region (Fig. 17-8). Most of the ore is a mass of soft, reddish-brown hematite and limonite from which all or nearly all of the silica and other minerals have been leached. Structurally the Mesabi range is simple. Except for a Z-shaped bend near the center of the outcrop area, the ore body strikes east-northeast and dips 4–7°SE in the western part of the area and 6–12°SE in the eastern part. At a depth of a few hundred feet, the ore grades into unleached and unoxidized iron formation, which is partly iron carbonate. The eastern end of the range consists of hard magnetic taconite; the western end consists of soft weathered taconite in which the silica is still retained. Between these extremes the iron is direct-shipping, high-grade material. The soft western taconite is also mined; it is beneficiated to an economic grade by a washing process that removes the silica.

In contrast to the simple structure of the Mesabi range, most of the other districts are structurally complex. The iron formation is intricately folded and faulted, and as a result, detailed knowledge of both the stratigraphy and structure are essential to exploration (Schmidt and Dutton, 1957; Pettijohn, 1946; Dutton et al., 1945).

Different problems were encountered in the Steep Rock Lake deposit of Ontario, because the ore is massive and not clearly bedded. Boulders

FIGURE 17-8. *Aerial view of the Mississippi Group, Mesabi range, Minnesota.*

of ore found along the lakeshore led to the discovery of this deposit, which, between 1938 and 1942, was outlined by exploratory drilling through the ice of Steep Rock Lake. Before the ore could be developed, however, the river had to be diverted and the lake drained. The ores are localized along the contact of limestones and volcanic rocks, which they seem to replace (Roberts and Bartley, 1943a, 1943b; Quirke, 1943). These relationships led early workers to conclude that the iron was introduced by hydrothermal agencies. The hard ores of Steep Rock Lake are similar to the hard ores of the Vermilion and Marquette ranges, suggesting that all three deposits were formed by a similar process. Jolliffe (1955) remapped the Steep Rock Lake deposit after considerable mining had been done and concluded that it is not of replacement origin. He interpreted the deposit as a sedimentary bed of limonite that was modified by hydrothermal fluids. This theory is supported by the stratigraphic position of the ore zone, which lies on an erosion surface; by the presence of gradational facies that are undoubtedly sedimentary in origin; by the mineralogy; and by the paragenesis. Jolliffe

(1955) emphasized that the dominant mineral, goethite, is early in the paragenetic sequence—a position that would be anomalous for hydrothermal ore but normal for a sediment that was later altered by hydrothermal activity.

In general, the mineralogy of the Lake Superior ores is simple. Hematite is the principal mineral and is either the soft, reddish variety—as on the Mesabi range—or the hard, massive variety of the Marquette and Vermilion ranges. Magnetite is commonly present and is the dominant mineral in a few areas. On the Menominee and Cuyuna ranges the ore is composed of soft, yellow to brown limonite plus some soft hematite. Several beds in the Cuyuna range carry as much as 8 percent manganese, which brings them a higher price than the straight iron ore.

SEDIMENTARY MANGANESE DEPOSITS

Manganese behaves chemically in much the same manner as iron—the two elements accumulate in similar environments and under similar conditions. Under oxidizing conditions, pyrolusite or some other form of MnO_2 would be expected to form; at intermediate values of Eh and pH, hausmannite or the manganese carbonates or silicates should be deposited; and in extremely reducing environments, alabandite (MnS) or manganosite (MnO) should form (Krauskopf, 1957). The extremely low Eh-pH conditions necessary for alabandite and manganosite are not likely to be attained in sedimentary environments, but the other minerals are common and seem to be deposited according to their thermodynamic restrictions. Figure 17-9 shows the stability fields for many of the manganese minerals. Although the compounds having complex or variable com-

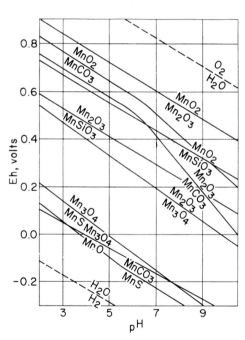

FIGURE 17-9. *Eh-pH diagram for manganese compounds, showing the stability fields for common sedimentary minerals.* (*After Krauskopf, 1957, figures 1 and 3.*)

positions must be generalized by a simple formula, the figure still gives a fairly accurate picture of manganese environments and the facies to be expected under various conditions. For example, the diagram indicates that pyrolusite should be formed in the same environments as manganite and braunite but not under the same conditions as rhodochrosite, alabandite, or hausmannite; the natural mineral assemblages corroborate this expectation.

Both the oxides and the carbonates of manganese are widely distributed throughout the world. The carbonates are generally complex, containing variable amounts of calcium, magnesium, and iron along with the manganese. Many of the manganese oxide deposits are nearly pure, but others contain minor amounts of cobalt, nickel, tungsten, copper, and barium, or extraneous materials such as clay, limestone, chert, and tuff. Manganese silicates ordinarily do not accumulate as sedimentary deposits, although at the San Francisco mine in Jalisco, Mexico, braunite ($Mn^{+2}Mn^{+3}_6SiO_{12}$) is among the most abundant of the sedimentary minerals.

Sedimentary manganese deposits may be classified into three categories:

1. deposits associated with tuff and clastic sediments of volcanic materials;
2. deposits independent of volcanic activities;
3. deposits associated with iron formation.

These three classes are intergradational, and they also grade into deposits of hydrothermal and metamorphic origin. In places it is difficult or impossible to distinguish among the different types of deposits. For example, where hot springs transport manganese to a lake or ocean floor, part of the manganese will precipitate out of the water and become an integral part of the ordinary sediments; but ore that formed near or within the spring orifice may be classified as a hydrothermal deposit. Notwithstanding its limitations, the above classification serves as a convenient outline for studies or descriptions of the genesis of manganese deposits.

According to Mikhalev (1946), all of the principal manganese deposits of the world are either of sedimentary origin or are metamorphosed sediments. He concluded that the deposition of manganese ores takes place in near-shore basins, especially along the peripheries of continents. Within recent years, many manganese deposits that were formerly described as residual products of weathered metamorphic rocks are now considered to be primary sediments; other deposits have resulted from the weathering of metamorphosed sediments (Park, 1956b; Nagell, 1962). Whether residual or primary, the manganese is ultimately a product of sedimentary processes, perhaps modified by metamorphic processes or enriched by weathering.

Many valuable manganese ore deposits, usually consisting of oxide minerals, are interlayered with (and genetically related to) highly altered reddish or greenish andesitic tuffs and clastic sediments of volcanic origin. These beds exhibit characteristic sedimentary features similar to those of the overlying and underlying tuffaceous beds. They are generally classified as sedimentary deposits, although where they are localized along faults, they have been interpreted as hydrothermal (Wilson and Veytia, 1949). The deposits are thin-bedded, with individual layers four inches thick and less. In a few places the beds resemble ordinary banded iron formation, because the manganiferous layers are separated by thin beds and nodules of chert. More commonly, however, the interlayered materials are clays, altered tuffs, or clastic volcanic debris. Locally the layers between manganese strata pinch out, and the manganese becomes massive.

The origin of the manganese oxides that are associated with volcanic processes is of considerable theoretical and economic interest. Hot volcanic materials ejected under water tend to become finely and thoroughly fragmented. The fragments are agitated during volcanic activity, and they are ideally prepared and strategically situated for leaching by volcanically heated lake or sea water or by hydrothermal waters contributed during volcanism. Under these conditions, the ferromagnesian minerals—which contain the manganese—are susceptible to alteration. Volcanic emanations that percolate through the tuff contribute toward decomposition of the ferromagnesian minerals, and conceivably might transport manganese. The dissolved manganese migrates upward to the floor of the lake or sea and is deposited near the top of the tuff bed. These ores may be termed exhalation deposits. If deposition should take place where oxygen is limited or excluded, manganese oxide nodules would form until the available oxygen was exhausted, and the remaining manganese would be deposited as a carbonate or would stay in solution until it migrated to a more oxygen-rich region. The abundance of oxygen is related to water depth and consequently is indirectly related to the shoreline. Manganese deposits thus form under much the same conditions as iron formation, and like many other sediments, they resemble reefs. There is an example of this type in the Elqui River valley in central Chile, where a ribbon-shaped bed of manganese oxides averaging about 8 inches in thickness is enclosed in highly altered volcanic debris. It has been followed in the valley for 18–20 miles along the strike, but as far as can be determined, it is only about one mile wide across the strike. The field evidence indicates that it is a reef-like deposit that

FIGURE 17-10. *Bed of manganese oxides and tuff overlain by massive white lime-stone. Ponupo mine, Oriente Province, Cuba.*

parallels an ancient shoreline. In support of this contention, impure limestones are almost everywhere associated with the manganese and tuffs.

Deposits similar to the Chilean manganese are known in Cuba at Charco Redondo, El Cristo, Ponupo (Fig. 17-10), and Taratana; in Mexico at Paridero and San Francisco in the state of Jalisco (Fig. 17-11); and in the United States near Lake Mead in Nevada and Arizona (Park, 1942, 1956a; Hewett and Webber, 1931; McKelvey et al., 1949).

Silica is a common gangue mineral in the sedimentary beds associated with altered tuffs and other volcanic debris. In Cuba and in Haiti the ores are clearly associated with fine-grained, reddish-brown silica called "bayate." Bayate resembles the jasperoid that is so common in hydrothermal ore deposits of the western United States. It is probably cogenetic with the manganese minerals; field evidence indicates that it is deposited at the orifices or along the channels of hot springs. In Jalisco, Mexico, a similar type of silica has been found along fractures that cross the bed of ore and at places along the edges of the ore body.

Sedimentary manganese deposits that are independent of volcanic processes include both carbonate and oxide minerals. A reasonable explanation

Figure 17-11. *Workings along the outcrop of a bed of manganese oxides. San Franciso mine, Autlán, Mexico.*

for the origin of these beds is that the manganese was leached from surrounding rocks during normal weathering processes; was transported in stream waters to nearly closed and protected basins; and was precipitated by electrolytic coagulation or some other chemical process. The deposition of manganese carried to a lake or sea would be chemically similar to the deposition of manganese contributed by volcanic activities. Again, the ores are commonly concentrated in ribbon-shaped deposits parallel to a shoreline.

Some of the world's largest manganese deposits are sediments that seem to be independent of volcanism. The famous Russian areas of Nikopol, on the Dneiper River, and the Chiaturi field on the south slope of the Caucasus Mountains are of this type. At Chiaturi the ore beds average 4–8 feet in thickness and cover an area of some 50 square miles. Manganese was derived from the weathering of neighboring granites, syenites, and possibly some andesitic volcanics. The ore consists of oölitic and nodular pyrolusite in a matrix of manganese oxides, and the associated sediments are shales, marls, and sandstones (de la Sauce, 1926). Less extensive deposits of this type in the United States are the oxides of Artillery Peak, Arizona, and the carbonate beds of Arkansas, Virginia, and Maine. In general, carbonate beds are uneconomic unless weathered and concentrated as oxides.

The third type of sedimentary manganese ore is associated with iron formation—an association found in many parts of the world. The manganiferous beds commonly contain oxides concentrated in layers separate from the iron-rich beds, as at Morro do Urucum, Brazil; in other deposits, such as the Cuyuna range, Minnesota, and Lagoa Grande, Minas Gerais, Brazil, the manganese is distributed throughout many of the iron-oxide layers.

The voluminous literature dealing with iron formation seldom discusses the origin of the accompanying manganese. Why manganese is separated from iron in some deposits, but is distributed throughout the iron-rich strata in other deposits, has long puzzled geologists. Certainly the association of manganese oxides with iron formation is common enough that an explanation of the origin of the iron formation must also explain the origin of the manganese oxides. Ljunggren (1955) pointed out that manganese and iron separate during precipitation in bogs and during movement of mineral-bearing waters through soils and subsoils. In both Sweden and Finland, iron and manganese have been found as separate precipitates within single lakes or inlets. The degree of separation seems to be directly dependent upon the pH of the waters, because acidic waters will retain dissolved manganese longer than iron, and alkaline or less acidic waters will precipitate the two oxides together (Ljunggren, 1955). The solubilities of both manganese and iron are a function of their oxidation states; in the reduced state they are both readily soluble, but each forms a very insoluble oxide. As Krauskopf (1957) pointed out, the iron compounds found in nature are uniformly less soluble than the corresponding manganese compounds, and the ferrous ion is more easily oxidized than the manganous ion under any naturally occurring Eh-pH conditions. Consequently, iron should be precipitated before manganese from any solution containing both metals, unless the Mn/Fe ratio is very high. Similarly, manganese should be more readily distributed than iron by weathering or meteoric processes. The problem of iron and manganese separation—both within laminae of iron formation and as pure deposits of each metal—has not been solved; but differential oxidation and solubility seem to be the most logical explanation, except perhaps under local conditions.

Manganese silicates are not found in most unmetamorphosed iron formations, in spite of the abundance of silica in these rocks. Possibly the development of silicates is directly related to warm or hot waters, which are essentially absent during the deposition of iron formation.

Bacteria are known to secrete manganese as well as iron, though the extent to which they are operative is debatable. Zapffe (1931) studied the manganese in ground waters and concluded that bacteria may play an active part in the precipitation process; in support of this hypothesis, the sedimentary ores of Tennengebirge, Austria, have been ascribed to bacterial action (Cornelius and Plöchinger, 1952). In addition to bacteria, there may be other organisms, such as algae, that precipitate manganese (Twenhofel, 1950). It has also been suggested that the separation of iron and manganese may be due in part to the presence of bacteria that utilize either one of the metals to the exclusion of the other (Krauskopf, 1957). As with iron, the total effects of bacteria may prove to be considerable, but available evidence is inconclusive, and other processes appear to explain the larger accumulations of manganese satisfactorily.

SEDIMENTARY DEPOSITS OF THE BASE METALS

Wherever there is a source of metal ions and favorable redox conditions for precipitation, an ore deposit has a chance to form. Such conditions may be met in certain basins of deposition where decaying organic debris or bacterial action generates an exceptionally reducing environment and where the accumulation of clastics is practically nil. Several large deposits in the world seem to belong in this category, but in each case there is doubt whether the ore minerals are actually syngenetic. Perhaps the principal objection to this mechanism of ore deposition is the mysterious source of metals; normal sea water does not carry an appreciable supply. Given the base-metal ions, however, there is no chemical objection to precipitation in a sedimentary reducing environment.

European geologists have long advocated a syngenetic origin for the base-metal deposits of the Kupferschiefer near Mansfeld, Germany (Pompeckj, 1920; Schneiderhöhn, 1923; Trask, 1925). Even such ardent magmatists as Lindgren (1933) have been impressed with the strong evidence for a syngenetic origin. The ore minerals are sulfides—bornite, chalcocite, chalcopyrite, galena, sphalerite, tetrahedrite, and pyrite. Minor amounts of silver, nickel, cobalt, selenium, vanadium, and molybdenum have also been recovered. Copper is the most important product of this black, bituminous shale; its content averages as much as 3 percent over wide areas. The Kupferschiefer Formation is only about 2 feet thick, but its extent exceeds 20,000 square miles, representing a long, shallow arm of the Permian sea. Very finely divided sulfides are distributed throughout the cupriferous shale, the greatest concentration being along the lower foot of the bed. The Kupferschiefer overlies a thin conglomerate and is overlain by limestones. It contains marine animal and plant remains, but they do not represent an ecologic assemblage. Apparently, the environment was similar to that of the present Black Sea—shallow, stagnant waters that were not amenable to a flourishing fauna. The ore deposit possibly represents an adsorption of metallic elements from sea water during the slow accumulation of sediments.

Some geologists maintain that many fine-grained, banded sulfide ores similar to those of the Rammelsberg district, Germany (Fig. 17-12), are sediments (Schneiderhöhn, 1953). Although many European geologists have attributed the genesis of these base-metal deposits to syngenetic processes, this theory is not widely accepted in the United States. The principal objection stems from the chemical problem of how the metals were supplied to the basin of deposition. Furthermore, detailed studies of many polished sections of the ores indicate a complex history of replacement, which seems incompatible with a syngenetic origin. Nevertheless, the syngeneticists are supported by much of the field evidence.

Schneiderhöhn (1937), Garlick (1953, 1961), and Davis (1954) have advocated a syngenetic origin for the Northern Rhodesian copper ores. These deposits, averaging several percent copper (as disseminated grains of chalcopyrite, bornite, and chalcocite), are within Precambrian sediments —principally within a carbonaceous shale, but also within nonargillaceous rocks. Early studies concluded that the ores are hydrothermal, but the postulated igneous source has been shown to be older than the host rock (Garlick and Brummer, 1951). The distribution of mineralization—restricted to narrow stratigraphic limits over an area of several hundred square miles —is difficult to explain as a product of hypogene processes, but it seems reasonable for a syngenetic deposit. Extensive ore-bearing strata lie within a sequence of sandstones, arkoses, shales, conglomerates, and dolomites that underwent regional low-rank metamorphism (greenschist facies), grading into the epidote-amphibolite facies in the southern part of the district (Mendelsohn, 1961a). The sediments and ore minerals exhibit a type of zoning that has been interpreted to be parallel to an old shoreline (Garlick, 1953). Basinward from the shore, the facies change from barren quartzite and dolomite to shale and, within the shale, from chalcocite to bornite, then to chalcopyrite, and finally to pyrite. Thus the copper/iron ratio decreases outward from the shoreline. These facies have no relationship to folds or other structures (Mendelsohn, 1961b). In support of the zonal interpretation, Davis (1954) pointed out the apparent transgressive nature of the sedimentary strata and the ore minerals. Nevertheless, there is strong

FIGURE 17-12. *Photograph of banded sulfide ore from the Rammelsberg district, Germany. Natural size.*

evidence that at least some of the ores are epigenetic. The magmatists' arguments emphasize the presence of replacement textures and small veinlets of ore; the syngeneticists argue that some of the ores were mobilized during metamorphism and point out the remarkable stratigraphic persistence of the deposits. Sulfur isotope studies, which are interpreted as indicating a biogenic origin for the sulfur, also seem to favor the syngenetic hypothesis (Jensen and Dechow, 1962). At the present time, the problem is unsettled, because field evidence can be found in support of both hypotheses; but the syngenetic theory is gaining popularity among Rhodesian geologists.

As a loose generalization, it may be stated that the United States geologists do not favor the syngenetic origin of layered base-metal deposits. They feel that this hypothesis may solve some problems, but it also creates others. Until more evidence is obtained, the status of many of these deposits must be considered open to debate (Sales, 1960).

OTHER CHEMICAL PRECIPITATES

Carbonaceous shales, phosphatic shales, and many similar marine sediments contain minor amounts of uranium, vanadium, silver, arsenic, gold, molybdenum, and other metallic elements (Krauskopf, 1955, 1956b). Our knowledge of the metal content of sediments is fragmentary, largely because the amounts of metals are so small that most deposits are not commercial and have not received much attention. Shales appear to contain slightly higher percentages of metals than the other sedimentary rocks, but the sampling and distribution studies that have been made have not been adequate to permit generalizations concerning concentrations and distributions. It has been observed, however, that some metals are enriched in black, carbonaceous marine shales. Krauskopf (1955) found that several elements are enriched more than a thousandfold in selected organic sediments. These elements are concentrated by chemical precipitation in the reducing environment created by organic sediments; by adsorption on clay particles, colloidal gels, and organic debris; and by organic processes such as bacterial action.

Krauskopf (1956b) studied the concentration of zinc, copper, lead, bismuth, cadmium, nickel, cobalt, mercury, silver, chromium, molybdenum, tungsten, and vanadium in sea water and concluded that the seas are greatly undersaturated in each of these metals. Accordingly, direct chemical precipitation of these elements cannot be responsible for the observed concentrations in sediments. Local precipitation of sulfides may remove some of the metals from sea water. This is not, however, the chief control; the concentrations in solution are unrelated to the sulfide solubilities, and some of the metals do not form stable sulfides. Again, it was concluded that adsorption processes supplemented by organic precipitation must be significant factors in removing many of the dissolved metals present in sea water (Krauskopf, 1956b).

In recent years, marine sediments have attracted increased attention because certain types contain appreciable, though as yet noncommercial, amounts of uranium and vanadium (McKelvey and Nelson, 1950; McKelvey et al., 1955). The uranium-bearing black shales are typically rich in organic matter and sulfides. Many of the black shales and phosphorites contain 0.01–0.02 percent uranium, and the alum shale of Sweden is said to carry as much as 0.5 percent uranium. The character of the uranium-bearing mineral in the black shales is not known, but these shales are characteristically more phosphatic than other shales, hence the uranium may be contained as a phosphate or as adsorbed ions on organic matter (McKelvey et al., 1955). In the phosphorites the uranium content increases roughly in proportion to an increase in the phosphate content, implying that the uranium is contained in a phosphatic mineral. The depositional environment of uranium-bearing formations—both the black shales and the phosphorites —is characteristic of low-lying, stable areas, where the influx of clastic material is small. Many of these deposits are associated with diastems or minor unconformities; and, as far as is known, the nonmarine black shales are not uraniferous. The precipitation of uranium in carbonaceous black shales may be brought about by chemical adsorption on apatite, on living or dead plankton (McKelvey et al., 1955), and by reduction of U^{+6} ions to the less soluble U^{+4} ions through the action of biochemically generated H_2S (Goldschmidt, 1954; Jensen, 1958). Quadrivalent uranium ions and divalent calcium ions are approximately the same size, which permits uranium to substitute for calcium in the apatite structure of phosphorites. Consequently, uranium ions will compete for positions with calcium ions, and only the calcite-poor varieties of shale or phosphorite will be able to adsorb appreciable quantities of uranium.

Vanadium is also concentrated in shales and organic sediments (Goldschmidt, 1954). It is typically associated with sedimentary uranium in reducing environments, but unlike the uranium, it forms stable sulfide compounds. Both solid and liquid hydrocarbons have been known to contain highly abnormal concentrations of vanadium, which may be a biochemical precipitate or a product of reduction in sapropelic muds. The patronite (VS_4) of Peru was probably formed by the secondary enrichment of vanadiferous hydrocarbons through natural fractionation in an oil seep. Phosphatic rocks, such as the Phosphoria Formation of the northwestern United States, have yielded concentrations of vanadium, but the vanadium ions seem to be related to organic matter in the sediments rather than to the phosphate minerals (Jacob et al., 1933). The presence of both vanadium and uranium in these carbonaceous sediments is thought to be due to reduction from higher, more soluble stages of valency rather than from direct concentration in plant and animal tissues.

Mechanical Accumulations

Minerals that are chemically stable at the earth's surface are not decomposed by weathering processes. As the surrounding rocks are dissolved and disintegrated, these stable minerals remain in the soil or are carried away by rain, streams, waves, or wind. The lighter particles are moved readily, and as a consequence are dispersed. Other minerals break easily along cleavage or fracture planes, becoming so fine-grained that they, too, are dispersed and lost. But the heavy, stable minerals are left as residual particles in the soil or are transported into sands and gravels of streams and beaches. Further agitation within the stream or beach environments will cause the heavy particles to settle to the bottom layers and concomitantly enrich the deposit by removing the lighter and more brittle gangue materials. The effect is to produce a concentration of the heavy, tough, and chemically resistant minerals. They may accumulate near the outcrops, as residual concentrations; they may be washed into streams and accumulate in sand bars or in riffles and irregularities along the channel floors; or they may reach bodies of water where they are reworked by wave action and are deposited in beach sands. All such concentrations of clastic minerals are called *placers*. Where the slopes below outcrops are steep, or where other conditions encourage movement of the resistant minerals, the particles slide or creep gradually down slope until they reach a stream bed. Here the material is moved more rapidly by running waters. Sorting takes place according to the specific gravities of the particles, the shapes of the grains, the velocity and gradient of the stream, and other factors. The minerals having favorable properties are concentrated at the expense of the lighter, brittle particles, which are broken, scattered, and transported into the deeper basins of deposition.

The most abundant placer minerals include the native metals—especially gold and the platinum group—and many of the heavy, inert oxides and silicates, such as monazite, zircon, cassiterite, chromite, wolframite, rutile, magnetite, ilmenite, and many gemstones. Since sulfides readily break up and decompose, they seldom accumulate in placers; in the few exceptional instances, however, small amounts of relatively insoluble sulfides—for example, the cinnabar at New Almaden, California—have been recovered from placers formed near the lode deposit. Probably magnetite and ilmenite are among the most abundant minerals in placer deposits, but concentrations are rarely sufficiently rich to be of economic interest. Some of the world's greatest tin and diamond deposits are also placers. But the most valuable placer commodity is gold. Placer gold varies widely in composition, depending on the character of the original mineral and its distance from the source lode. Native gold is generally alloyed with silver, or less commonly with copper and other metals. Because both silver and copper are more soluble than gold, they are selectively leached from the alloy. Consequently, gold far removed from its source tends to become purer than the original material. The constant pounding and abrasion that particles of placer gold receive as they travel downstream also result in a gradual reduction in grain size away from the lode.

Placer deposits have formed throughout geologic time, but most productive placers are of Cenozoic age. As a rule, placer deposits are small in volume and form at the earth's surface, usually above the local base level; hence most of them are eventually removed by erosion before they have an opportunity to be buried and preserved. Moreover, the older deposits are likely to be tilted and lithified, so that unless they contain unusually valuable minerals or exceptional concentrations, they cannot compete with the unconsolidated surface materials whose chief virtue may be ease of recovery.

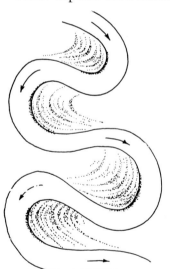

FIGURE 17-13. *Rich streaks of placer ore formed along the inside curves of meanders.*

Fossil placers, or those buried under younger rocks, are mined in many areas. In the Sierra Nevada of California and in the Victoria field of Australia, for example, placer gold deposits have been deeply buried beneath other stream materials and lava flows. Lavas that flowed down stream valleys and covered Mother Lode placer deposits have subsequently been left as residual ridges above the eroded interstream terrane; as a result, the old stream valleys are easy to locate, but the sporadic gold concentrations are difficult to find beneath the flows. If placer deposits were evenly distributed along stream courses, the problem of underground mining would be greatly simplified; but this is not the case. Aside from the concentrations along riffles and other irregularities on the stream bottom, placer minerals tend to accumulate on the insides of curves or meanders. Where a meander migrates downstream, a rich streak of ore will be formed (Fig. 17-13). Finding these pay streaks is enough of a challenge in surface deposits, without extrapolating the techniques to buried placers. Consequently, much of the placer gold covered by lava flows in the Sierra Nevada remains to be discovered.

FLORIDA BEACH SANDS

The world contains many commercial beach placers, but few have received more attention than the titanium deposits of eastern Florida (Martens, 1928, 1935; Creitz and McVay, 1949; Lynd, 1960). Some of the placers have been deposited along existing beaches; others have been left along elevated shorelines of the Florida interior. The two principal deposits are elevated sand bars, one east of Jacksonville and the other, known as Trail Ridge, east of Starke. The average heavy-mineral content in both deposits is very low, and only the combination of low-cost dredging and beneficiation by the efficient Humphrey spiral concentrator has made the operation possible.

Trail Ridge sand concentrates contain staurolite, zircon, sillimanite, tourmaline, kyanite, rutile, andalusite, pyroxene, and small amounts of corundum, gahnite, garnet, and monazite (Creitz and McVay, 1949; Carpenter et al., 1953). Epidote, hornblende, sphene, and other minerals have been identified elsewhere, but have not been reported from Trail Ridge. Most of the titanium at Trail Ridge is in the form of leucoxene, which is an alteration product of ilmenite, sphene, or other titaniferous minerals and consists for the most part of microcrystalline rutile, anatase, or brookite. During the alteration process, some of the titania (TiO_2) apparently goes through an amorphous phase, therefore some of the leucoxene is structureless. A long-standing controversy has centered around the true nature of this titanium mineral. Early studies considered it to be ilmenite (Martens, 1928, 1935). Subsequently it was discovered that the iron/titanium ratio does not match the stoichiometry of ilmenite, and it was suggested that it is a nearly amorphous variety of arizonite (Miller, 1945), which is a ferric iron analogue of ilmenite with the formula $Fe_2Ti_3O_9$. Further work with samples of so-called arizonite has essentially discredited this mineral as a valid species; instead of being a new mineral, the material is apparently a cryptocrystalline alteration product of ilmenite, consisting of a mixture of hematite, ilmenite, anatase, and rutile (Overholt et al., 1950). Possibly the alteration of ilmenite takes two courses: the oxidation of iron to produce the material called arizonite, and the leaching of iron to form leucoxene. But whatever the true mineralogy of the Florida titanium ores, the important fact is that the material—call it leucoxene or altered ilmenite—is more amenable than ilmenite to metallurgical processes for the extraction of titanium.

Concentrations of titaniferous sands are widely distributed in Florida, but most of them are not of commercial grade. Studies of the modern beaches, which are similar in mineralogy and structure to the elevated bars (such as Trail Ridge), have revealed the mode of concentration and source of heavy minerals. The deposits form strips or ribbons parallel to the shoreline. Sand dunes built by wind and storm action form a ridge along the back side of the beach. The major concentrations of heavy minerals are at the foot of the dunes on the ocean side where storm waves have reworked the dune sands (Fig. 17-14). The titanium-bearing beach sands are somewhat finer grained than the normal beach sands; they seem to accumulate where the older dunes are being reworked. Heavy minerals are present throughout most of the sands, but they occur in commercial amounts only where they have been selectively enriched.

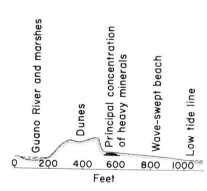

FIGURE 17-14. *Generalized section of beach south of Mineral City, St. John's County, Florida. Vertical scale exaggerated. (After Martens, 1928, figure 28.)*

All the heavy minerals present in the Florida beach sands are also found in the old metamorphic and intrusive rocks of the Southern Piedmont. Geologists who have studied the sands agree that the most likely source of the heavy minerals lies in the Piedmont province, especially parts of Georgia and the Carolinas. Evidently, the sands were transported to the coast by streams and reworked along the coast by southward-moving, lateral shore currents. The heavy sand deposits are found northward for long distances beyond Florida, but in general they become less concentrated (McKelvey and Balsley, 1948). The content of titanium also decreases northward as the magnetite content increases.

Martens (1935) emphasized the fine-grained character of the heavy sands and the presence of coarser fragments of shells and glaucophane from local formations. He suggested that much of the detrital material in the beach sands did not come directly from the older rocks of the Piedmont, but rested for varying lengths of time in some of the Coastal Plain formations. Modifications on the texture and composition of sands can be explained as admixtures from local sources, supplied by the direct wave erosion of the land during high tides and storms. One feature that has caused discussion is that the sand in southern Florida is generally coarser than the sand to the north. Anomalously, then, the grain size seems to increase away from the source of supply. Martens (1935) suggested that the southern beaches winnow out the finer materials more efficiently because the sea floor is steeper in the south than in the north. But the change from fine to coarse grains is fairly abrupt; most of the beaches north of Cape Kennedy are fine-grained, and most of those to the south are coarse-grained. This relationship suggests that the southward-moving longshore currents are deflected oceanward at Cape Kennedy; if this is the case, the beaches to the south must receive most of their sand from direct erosion of the Florida landmass (much of which was derived from the Piedmont region during an earlier cycle of erosion).

WITWATERSRAND GOLD FIELD, SOUTH AFRICA

The Witwatersrand district—or as it is commonly known, the Rand—is in South Africa, near the cities of Johannesburg and Pretoria (Fig. 17-15). The Rand has been by far the most productive gold district in the world, yielding over 12 billion dollars in gold to date and containing large reserves. Although the ore averages only 0.2–0.3 ounce of gold per ton, as much as 20 million ounces of gold have been recovered in a single year (Douglas and Moire, 1961), and the annual production figures have been increasing steadily. Since World War II and the discovery that appreciable amounts of uranium can be recovered as a by-product of the gold, the district has become one of the world's principal sources of fissionable materials. Serious mining was begun in the Witwatersrand district in 1886, when a gold rush started the activity. Since that time, many mines have been developed along some 250 miles of strike on the Witwatersrand conglomerate beds. Several of the mines are operating at depths of more than 9000 feet. The East Rand Proprietary mine, the deepest in the world, operates

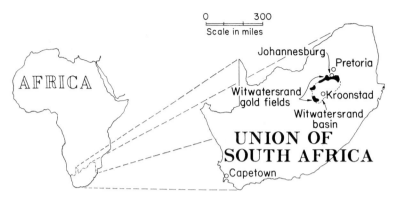

FIGURE 17-15. *Index map of South Africa, showing the location of the Witwatersrand deposits.*

at a depth of more than 11,200 feet. The distance mined down the dip of the ore-bearing strata exceeds $3\frac{1}{2}$ miles. Refrigeration is needed to cool some of the mines, because the rock temperatures at these great depths are as high as 125°F (Barcza and Lambrechts, 1961). Mine waters constitute a further problem in the Rand; about 50 million gallons of water are pumped from the mines each day (Dolan, 1961).

The literature concerning the Witwatersrand district is voluminous (Hargraves, 1960). Every aspect of the deposits has been studied by capable geologists, but some of the fundamental issues are still open to debate. Of special interest to mining geologists is the controversy concerning ore genesis. We have included the Rand deposits under the heading of placer deposits because this is the theory of origin favored among South African geologists, but other authors would list it with the hydrothermal ores. Until the controversial origin is resolved, it is not important which classification is used, as long as this famous district is included and the pertinent arguments presented; any treatment on the origin of ore deposits would be incomplete without a discussion of the Witwatersrand gold ores.

Three theories have been advanced to explain the origin of the gold. One school, including most of the geologists who have worked with these deposits for long periods, maintains that the ores are placers. Most of the supporters of this theory agree that the gold is no longer in the form of simple placer grains; they argue that it was mobilized and recrystallized during metamorphism of the enclosing rocks (Mellor, 1916, 1931; Reinecke, 1927, 1930; Young, 1931; Macadam, 1936; de Kock, 1940; du Toit, 1940; Frankel, 1940; Liebenberg, 1955; Ramdohr, 1958).

A second, much smaller group considers the ores syngenetic, but advocates chemical precipitation of the gold rather than mechanical deposition of placer grains (Penning, 1888; de Launay, 1896; Garlick, 1953). A modification of this process has also been proposed, wherein the gold is considered to be a diagenetic addition to chemically precipitated, syngenetic uranium-carbon deposits (Miholić, 1954). This school also argues that the ores have been reorganized during metamorphism.

The third hypothesis holds that the ores were deposited by hydrothermal fluids that arose directly from an underlying magmatic source (Maclaren, 1908; Hatch and Corstorphine, 1909; Horwood, 1917; Graton, 1930; Davidson, 1953, 1957). This concept has had flashes of popularity, but the Rand geologists have remained opposed to it.

To an outsider unfamiliar with the Rand geology, the tremendous volume of literature and the many conflicting statements made by various writers render the task of reaching an impartial appraisal nearly impossible. The published evidence is contradictory and may be taken to support either the syngenetic placer theory or the epigenetic hydrothermal theory, according to the prejudices of the reader. Under any hypothesis it is difficult to understand why such tremendous amounts of gold are limited to thin conglomerate beds that extend for several hundred square miles. Whichever hypothesis is advocated for the gold, its concentration in the conglomerate beds between barren quartzites is a function of the original character of the sediment. If the gold is placer, it should be concentrated in the coarser materials near the bottoms of channels; if it was introduced in epigenetic fluids, the migration and deposition of gold should have been controlled by the more permeable, coarse-grained beds.

The oldest rocks of the region are Precambrian schists and granitic rocks, making up a basement complex of involved stratigraphy. Overlying the basement is the Dominion Reef System, a thin sequence of basal conglomerates and lava flows. One gold-bearing zone has been discovered in this unit (see Fig. 17-16). Unconformably overlying the Dominion Reef System and basement is the Witwatersrand System, which is divided into lower and upper halves. The Lower Division of the Witwatersrand System consists of shales, quartzites, grits, and conglomerates, with one gold-producing conglomerate bed. These sediments were deposited in a gradually subsiding lake or inland sea.

As the clastic materials accumulated in the center, the edges of the basin became tilted upward and were themselves eroded. Consequently, the basin of deposition was smaller when the Upper Division sediments—mostly

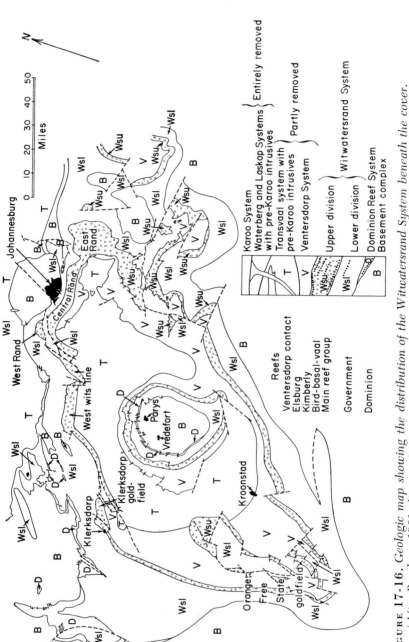

FIGURE 17-16. *Geologic map showing the distribution of the Witwatersrand System beneath the cover.* (After Borchers, 1961, diagram 2.)

quartzites and conglomerates—were being deposited. The Upper Division of the Witwatersrand System contains most of the gold-bearing conglomerates, the most productive horizon being at the base of this unit. Tilting and erosion of the Witwatersrand System, which is some 25,000 feet thick, was followed by igneous activity, forming the Ventersdorp System of lavas and interbedded clastic sediments. The Ventersdorp System varies greatly in thickness, exceeding 10,000 feet in places. Following erosion and subsidence of the Ventersdorp System, a thick sequence of clastics and dolomitic limestones, known as the Transvaal System, was deposited in a new basin. The end of this period was marked by further igneous activity, followed by folding and thrusting. In the center of the Witwatersrand basin, the basement was thrust up, doming and overturning the overlying sediments into a prominent structure known as the Vredefort dome, or Vredefort ring. Erosion stripped the sediments from the top of the dome and left the Witwatersrand System exposed as a pair of concentric circles. At the end of the Paleozoic Era, the Karroo System of shallow marine sediments and coal formations was deposited over the entire area, and it still covers half or more of the Witwatersrand System (Borchers, 1961). The sedimentary rocks are intruded by dikes and small masses of mafic and intermediate igneous rocks, thought to be related to the Ventersdorp volcanics and the Bushveld period of igneous activity, but no granitic rocks younger than the Witwatersrand System have been found. (Early reports that some of the plutonic rocks post date the Rand conglomerates have been discredited.)

The Witwatersrand System forms a large structural trough, which measures about 250 miles in length and 90 miles in width and is aligned in a northeast-southwest direction. The principal ore-bearing conglomerates lie not at the outer fringes of this basin, but within, describing a smaller oval that is roughly 180 by 70 miles in long and short dimensions (Fig. 17-16). The mines are concentrated along the northwest side and at both extremities of the synclinal structure. In general, the sediments dip steeply basinward around the outer edges of the synclinal structure, but in the larger mines flatter dips have been encountered at depth. Nearly vertical beds are common, and an overturned sequence is found along the northwest side of the Vredefort ring. The syncline is complicated by many faults. Large-scale thrust and normal faulting are involved, and small normal faults are abundant. Several of the mines were abandoned because faults complicated the mining operations so badly that the gold could not be recovered economically.

The origin of the Witwatersrand System of conglomerates and quartzites has been the subject of almost as much discussion as the origin of the gold. Several environments of deposition have been visualized, including a marine shoreline, a large delta, an enclosed basin, a piedmont or flood plain, and a region of alluvial fans (Mellor, 1916; Reinecke, 1930; Gevers, 1961). Most workers agree, however, that the clastic materials were derived from basement rocks to the northwest.

The Witwatersrand rocks have been metamorphosed, and, except for the presence of quartz pebbles, the conglomerate beds have little in common with ordinary conglomerates. They are dense and tightly cemented. Many of the pebbles were stretched during metamorphism, although in places a high degree of sphericity has been retained (Fig. 17-17). The spaces between pebbles are occupied by pyrite (locally present in abundance), grains of quartz, sericite, rutile, chlorite, carbon, and sporadic tourmaline. Locally, many of the quartz pebbles are a bluish, opalescent variety. Coarse-grained gold is rare in these deposits; most of the values come from fine-grained, nearly microscopic disseminations within the coarser, cleaner facies of the conglomerates. As would be expected in either deltaic or flood-plain sediments, the conglomerate layers are not uniform throughout the entire district, though they are surprisingly persistent. The general stratigraphic sequence—a normal sequence for rapidly deposited, coarse, clastic sediments—can be recognized on all sides of the Witwatersrand district.

In the Witwatersrand area, ore-bearing conglomerate strata are known as reefs or bankets (the latter term being Dutch for "almond cake," which the conglomerates resemble). There are six major reef horizons in the Witwatersrand System, as well as a minor ore zone within the underlying Dominion Reef System. Most of the gold-bearing reefs are scattered throughout the two-mile thickness of Upper Division quartzites and conglomerates. Attempts have been made to unify the nomenclature and correlate the reefs between mining camps (Jones, 1936). The problem is not simple, because some of the reefs consist of several thin beds irregularly distributed throughout a thick sequence of quartzites. For example, the Main Reef Group, which is the most important zone in the district, includes several ore-bearing conglomerates. In the Central Rand area near Johannesburg, this group includes the Main Reef, the Main Reef Leader, and the South Reef; about 20 miles to the east, in the East Rand field, only the South Reef persists; along the West Wits line, a mineralized zone some 25–50 miles southwest of Johannesburg, a rich gold-uranium conglomerate known as the Carbon Leader carries most of the values in the Main Reef Group; and in the

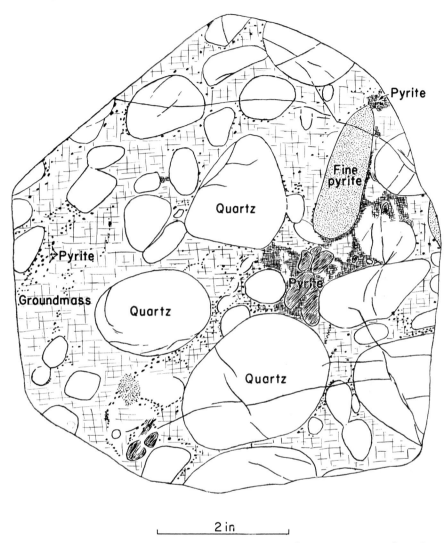

FIGURE 17-17. *Sketch of a hand specimen of conglomerate, Ventersdorp Contact Reef, Witwatersrand gold district, South Africa.*

Klerksdorp area, about 85 miles southwest of Johannesburg, the Main Reef Group consists of two conglomerates, known as the Commonage Reef and the Ada May Reef (Borchers, 1961). Locally, there are ore-bearing conglomerates that resulted from the erosion of previously deposited Witwatersrand rocks; for example, the Black Reef, in the West Rand area (immediately west of the Central Rand field), is a basal conglomerate of the Transvaal System, overlying the Witwatersrand System and the Ventersdorp lavas unconformably (Pegg, 1950).

The ore-bearing reefs vary in thickness, but as a general rule they average only a few feet in thickness, and productive beds more than 10 feet thick are uncommon. Some of the richest reefs are only inches thick. The best gold values are characteristically recovered along the base of the conglomerates, which leads to the suggestion that they represent transgressive shoreline deposits or erosional hiatuses caused by oscillations in the sedimentary basin (Sharpe, 1949).

As early as 1923, the presence of uraninite was noted in the Rand ores (Cooper, 1923). There was no immediate effect of this discovery, because the market for uranium was not large, and the quantities of uraninite reported were small. Near the end of World War II, however, when interest in fissionable materials was gaining momentum, it was discovered that the frequently mentioned "carbon" of the Rand ores is actually a uraninite-carbon aggregate, known as thucholite (Davidson and Bowie, 1951). The changing economics regarding uranium caused geologists to take a second look at the Rand as a source of supply. It was found to contain much more uranium than previously thought. The average ore contains about 0.03 percent uranium (Burger et al., 1962). Relatively low-grade materials are treated for the uranium content where they can be recovered as by-products of the gold ores; but some of the uranium is mined from nonauriferous reefs, and in such deposits, the uranium content must pay the mining costs. Thus, various grades of uranium ore are recovered.

The thucholite, or carbon, has long been recognized as a close companion of the gold, and throughout much of the development of the district, this material was used as a guide to the better ores; where the carbon is richest, the gold values are likely to be best. Some of the gold is molded on carbon. In the so-called buckshot pyrite ore—conglomerate containing abundant pyrite in rounded pebble-like forms—pyrite, carbon, and gold appear to have grown in the order listed, forming concentric layers (Macadam, 1931).

The intimate association between uranium and gold has led some workers to insist that the two metals must have a common origin (Davidson and Bowie, 1951; Liebenberg, 1955). Accordingly, the uranium has been studied in detail, and the genesis problem has been reopened with new strength. As is the case with most lines of evidence in the Rand debate, the uranium has been advanced in support of both the hydrothermalists and the placerists.

There is a wide variety of arguments in favor of the hydrothermal origin of the gold and uranium. Davidson (1953) pointed out that thucholite and uraninite are unstable under surface conditions, making it unlikely that they could have survived erosion at the source and transportation to the site of deposition. Although the thucholite is in rounded grains that appear to be detrital, similar shapes can be found in veins of undoubted hydrothermal origin (Davidson and Bowie, 1951). It has been suggested that the thucholite was formed by the polymerization of hydrocarbon gases under the influence of radioactive bombardment. Methane is abundant in the mine areas, and the association of hydrocarbons with uranium may mean that the thucholite is a secondary product formed where these gases encountered uraninite. Thus the association between gold and carbon may actually be an association between uranium and hydrocarbons, and in turn between uraninite and gold (Davidson and Bowie, 1951). In addition to these arguments, the hydrothermalists emphasize that the gold is seldom found as nuggets. The gold generally occurs in tiny shreds and flakes within the matrix between pebbles, rather than in both the matrix and the pebbles. Furthermore, the gold is very fine-grained throughout the Witwatersrand area; a placer deposit should show a gradual reduction in grain size away from the source. The gangue includes such typically hydrothermal minerals as chlorite, sericite, and tourmaline. Most placer gold is accompanied by black sands, but magnetite and ilmenite are nearly absent from the Witwatersrand deposits. The hydrothermalists also point out that there was volcanic activity after the Rand sediments were deposited; gold-bearing veins of undoubtedly hypogene origin have been mined in nearby areas, hence the possibility of a genetic association with these igneous rocks is not unreasonable. Some geologists maintain that the presence of abundant pyrite means that a comparable supply of sulfur must have been introduced. The hydrothermalists explain the restriction of gold to conglomerates as a function of permeability; the most permeable channels for epigenetic fluids would reasonably be the conglomerate beds, where the interstitial openings are larger than in the quartzites and where the clay is at a minimum (Graton, 1930).

A study of the gold-silver ratios in the ore (Hargraves, 1961) would seem at first to support the hydrothermalist school, because the gold generally increases in fineness with depth. Such zoning implies ascending hydrothermal fluids. The fineness of placer gold normally increases away from the source, because the silver is selectively removed. No such trends have been found in the Witwatersrand fields. The observed zoning there would

result from either an initial hydrothermal system or hydrothermal leaching
of placer gold. If it resulted from the latter, the fineness of gold would be a
function of leaching by ascending hydrothermal fluids during regional
metamorphism. Thus the ultimate problem of gold genesis is not solved by
the presence of vertical zoning.

South African geologists are so united in their defense of a placer origin
for the ores that this hypothesis has been referred to as "a national article
of faith" by a member of the opposing school (Davidson, 1953). The
placerists do not deny the action of hydrothermal fluids on the Witwatersrand sediments, but they ascribe these effects to regional metamorphism
rather than to the infiltration of ore-bearing solutions. They point out that
the Witwatersrand sediments were derived from the basement, which is
known to contain numerous small, gold-bearing quartz veins. The richer
ores are concentrated in gravels—generally in the coarser, cleaner gravels
—but the quartzites, many of which are also clean and permeable, are
essentially gold free. Platinum minerals (especially iridosmine, a natural
alloy of iridium and osmium), diamonds, zircons, tourmaline, chromite, and
other heavy residual minerals are present as nuggets that were favorably
located—for example, within shaly pockets—and escaped destruction during metamorphism. Several of the objections to a placer origin raised by
the hydrothermalists can be attributed to metamorphic effects, brought
about by temperatures as high as 300°C (Ramdohr, 1953). The replacement
textures and shredded appearance of the gold may be the result of mobilization and recrystallization during metamorphism. The lack of magnetite
and ilmenite may be due to a diagenetic reaction (Ramdohr, 1958) or to a
metamorphic reaction involving the iron and sulfur, the latter being abundantly supplied by the black shales; breakdown of the ilmenite by these
processes will also explain why rutile is associated with the deposits. Careful sampling has shown neither enrichment nor increased gold values of the
reefs in the proximity of dikes, though small amounts of gold have been
reworked in the igneous metamorphic aureole, leaving mineralization along
cross-cutting dikes and gash veins. Hydrothermal effects can be observed,
but they are related to fissures; alteration may be shown to grade laterally
from the fractures, but the gold content does not vary with the degree of
hydrothermal alteration. The placerists also point out that no known igneous
source for the gold has been found, and at no place does the ore fill strong,
persistent, cross-cutting fissures.

The presence of uranium minerals with the gold seemed at first to support the epigenetic hypothesis, but recent studies have arrived at the oppo-

site conclusion. The original objection to a placer origin for the uranium was based upon the supposition that uraninite and pitchblende should be unstable under surface conditions; for example, Davidson and Bowie (1951) noted that the uranium is being leached from the mine dumps by meteoric water. But the placerists argue that the mine waters are abnormally acidic and that the presence of detrital pyrite grains with the uraninite presupposes a low redox environment that might favor the chemical stability of uraninite (Ramdohr, 1958). Laboratory studies have shown that uraninite is physically resistant to the abrasive action of stream transport and should be as persistent in a placer deposit as monazite and other common detrital minerals (Koen, 1958). Furthermore, the similar uranium concentrations found in the Blind River district of Ontario seem to be of detrital origin (Robertson and Steenland, 1960). In both districts, the uraninite is in the form of rounded grains that show all the signs of attrition and none of the signs of colloidal deposition. Some thucholite grains in the Witwatersrand ores exhibit the relict octahedral cleavage of crystalline uraninite, and in places they have been shattered cataclastically by compaction; it is unlikely that these features would be shown by colloidally deposited, epigenetic pitchblende (Ramdohr, 1958). It has also been pointed out that the gold-"carbon" association may be a product of the metamorphic redistribution of gold; accordingly, the carbon would be a secondary alteration product of uraninite that acted as a precipitant for gold mobilized during metamorphism. Paragenetic studies corroborate this interpretation (Liebenberg, 1955). One of the most recent—and most devastating—arguments against the hydrothermal origin of the uranium minerals is based upon absolute age determinations of radiogenic lead in galena and detrital monazite. The parent uraninite for the radiogenic lead in galena samples and the detrital grains of monazite are among the oldest materials known (about 3000 million years old) and match the age of granites in the basement rocks (Allsopp, 1961; Nicolaysen et al., 1962; Burger et al., 1962). The absolute age of the Witwatersrand Series is not known, but it is thought to be about 2200 million years old (Gevers, 1961).

Whatever the origin of the gold and uranium ores, their localization is a function of sedimentary textures. The ore concentrations are directly related to the character of the conglomerate beds and are not dependent upon superimposed structures. Until the advocates of a hydrothermal origin provide unequivocal evidence of their theory, the South African geologists will continue directing their exploration programs according to a placer philosophy, because this approach has proved highly successful in the past. But observers on the outside will probably consider the problem unsolved until one of the theories is convincingly refuted.

References to Selected Ore Deposits Formed by Chemical Precipitation

Banded Hematite Ores of India

Dunn, J. A., 1941, The origin of banded hematite ores in India: Econ. Geology, v. 36, p. 355–370.

——, 1942, The economic geology and mineral resources of Bihar province: Geol. Survey of India Mem. 78.

Jones, H. C., 1934, The iron ore deposits of Bihar and Orissa: Geol. Survey of India Mem. 63.

Krishnan, M. S., 1952, The iron ores of India: 19th Internat. Geol. Cong., Symposium sur les gisements de fer du monde, v. 1, p. 503–532.

Weld, C. M., 1915, The ancient sedimentary iron ores of British India: Econ. Geology, v. 10, p. 435–452.

Banded Hematite Ores of Minas Gerais, Brazil

Departamento Nacional da Producao Mineral, 1959, Esbôço Geológico do Quadrilátero Ferrífero de Minas Gerais, Brasil: Dept. Nac. Prod. Min., Pub. Especial.

Derby, O. A., 1910, The iron ores of Brazil: 11th Internat. Geol. Cong., Iron ore resources of the world, p. 813–822.

Dorr, J. Van N., II, 1954, Comments on the iron deposits of the Congonhas district, Minas Gerais, Brazil: Econ. Geology, v. 49, p. 659–662.

——, Guild, P. W., and Barbosa, A. L. M., 1952, Origin of the Brazilian iron ores: 19th Internat. Geol. Cong., Symposium sur les gisements de fer du monde, v. 1, p. 286–298.

Guild, P. W., 1953, Iron deposits of the Congonhas district, Minas Gerais, Brazil: Econ. Geology, v. 48, p. 639–676.

——, 1957, Geology and mineral resources of the Congonhas District, Minas Gerais, Brazil: U.S. Geol. Survey Prof. Paper 290.

Harder, E. C., 1914, The "itabirite" iron ores of Brazil: Econ. Geology, v. 9, p. 101–111.

——, and Chamberlin, R. T., 1915, The geology of central Minas Geraes, Brazil: Jour. Geology, v. 23, p. 341–378, 385–424.

Leith, C. K., and Harder, E. C., 1911, Hematite ores of Brazil and a comparison with hematite ores of Lake Superior: Econ. Geology, v. 6, p. 670–686.

Scott, H. K., 1902, The iron ores of Brazil: London, Jour. Iron and Steel Inst.

Manganese Deposits of Cuba

Burchard, E. F., 1920, Manganese-ore deposits in Cuba: Am. Inst. Mining Engineers Trans., v. 63, p. 51–104.

Norcross, F. S., Jr., 1940, Development of the low-grade manganese ores of Cuba: Am. Inst. Mining Engineers Tech. Pub. 1188.

Park, C. F., Jr., 1942, Manganese deposits of Cuba: U.S. Geol. Survey Bull. 935-B, p. 75–97.

——, and Cox, M. W., 1944, Manganese deposits in part of the Sierra Maestra, Cuba: U.S. Geol. Survey Bull. 935-F, p. 307–355.

Simons, F. S., and Straczek, J. A., 1958, Geology of the manganese deposits of Cuba: U.S. Geol. Survey Bull. 1057.

Straczek, J. A., 1950, Manganeso en Cuba: 1940–45: Bol. Hist. Nat., v. 1, p. 161–168.

Vaughn, T. W., Hayes, C. W., and Spencer, A. C., 1901, Informe sobre un reconocimiento geológico de Cuba: Dirección des Montes, Minas y Aguas, p. 66–74.

Woodring, W. P., and Daviess, S. N., 1944, Geology and manganese deposits of Guisa-Los Negros area, Oriente Province, Cuba: U.S. Geol. Survey Bull. 935-G, p. 357–386.

References to Selected Deposits of Mechanically Accumulated Ores

Sierra Nevada, California

Averill, C. V., 1946, Placer mining for gold in California: California Div. Mines Bull. 135.

Bowie, A. J., Jr., 1879, Hydraulic mining in California: Am. Inst. Mining Engineers Trans., v. 6, p. 27–100.

Gilbert, G. K., 1917, Hydraulic mining débris in the Sierra Nevada: U.S. Geol. Survey Prof. Paper 105.

Hammond, J. H., 1889, Auriferous gravels of California: 9th Ann. Rept., State Mineralogist, California State Mining Bureau, p. 105–138.

Jenkins, O. P., 1932, Geologic map of northern Sierra Nevada showing Tertiary river channels and Mother Lode Belt: California Div. Mines. (Later reprinted with accompanying text on back of map.)

Lindgren, Waldemar, 1911, The Tertiary gravels of the Sierra Nevada of California: U.S. Geol. Survey Prof. Paper 73.

Turner, H. W., 1895, Auriferous gravels of the Sierra Nevada: Am. Geologist, v. 15, p. 371–379.

Malayan Tin Deposits

Adams, F. D., 1929, Tin mining in Malaya: Canadian Inst. Mining Metallurgy Trans., v. 31, p. 115–146.

Fitch, F. H., 1952, The geology and mineral resources of the neighbourhood of Kuantan, Pahang: Geol. Survey Dept. Malaya Mem. 6.

Jones, W. R., 1925, Tinfields of the world: London, Mining Publications, Ltd., p. 161–207.

Roe, F. W., 1951, The geology and mineral resources of the Fraser's Hill area, Selangor, Perak and Pahang, Federation of Malaya, with an account of the mineral resources: Geol. Survey Dept. Malaya Mem. 5.

————, 1953, The geology and mineral resources of the neighbourhood of Kuala Selangor and Rasa, Selangor, Federation of Malaya, with an account of the geology of Batu Arang coalfield: Geol. Survey Dept. Malaya Mem. 7.

Scrivenor, J. B., 1928, Geology of the Malayan ore-deposits: London, Macmillan and Co., Ltd.

References Cited

Alexandrov, E. A., 1955, Contribution to studies of origin of Precambrian banded iron ores: Econ. Geology, v. 50, p. 459–468.

Alling, H. L., 1947, Diagenesis of the Clinton hematite ores of New York: Geol. Soc. America Bull., v. 58, p. 991–1018.

Allsopp, H. L., 1961, Rb-Sr age measurements on total rock and separated-mineral fractions from the Old Granite of the Central Transvaal: Jour. Geophysical Research, v. 66, p. 1499–1508.

Barcza, M., and Lambrechts, J. de V., 1961, Ventilation and air conditioning practice in South African gold mines: Trans of the Seventh Commonwealth Mining and Metallurgical Congress, Papers and Discussions, v. 2, South African Inst. Mining Metallurgy, p. 725–742.

Beerstecher, Ernest, Jr., 1954, Petroleum microbiology: New York, Elsevier Press, Inc.

Borchers, R., 1961, Exploration of the Witwatersrand System and its extensions: Trans. Seventh Commonwealth Mining Metallurgical Cong., Papers and Discussions, v. 2, South African Inst. Mining Metallurgy, p. 489–512; and 1962, Geol. Soc. South Africa Trans., v. 64.

Burchard, E. F., and Butts, Charles, 1910, Iron ores, fuels, and fluxes of the Birmingham district, Alabama: U.S. Geol. Survey Bull. 400.

Burger, A. J., Nicolaysen, L. O., and de Villiers, J. W. L., 1962, Lead isotopic compositions of galenas from the Witwatersrand and Orange Free State, and their relation to the Witwatersrand and Dominion Reef uraninites: Geochim. et Cosmochim. Acta, v. 26, p. 25–59.

Carpenter, J. H., Detweiler, J. C., Gillson, J. L., Weichel, E. C., Jr., and Wood, J. P., 1953, Mining and concentration of ilmenite and associated minerals at Trail Ridge, Fla.: Am. Inst. Mining Engineers Trans., v. 196, p. 789–795.

Castaño, J. R., and Garrels, R. M., 1950, Experiments on the deposition of iron with special reference to the Clinton iron ore deposits: Econ. Geology, v. 45, p. 755–770.

Cayeux, L., 1909, Les Minerais de Fer Oolithique de France, v. 1: Paris, Imprimerie Nationale.

Cooper, R. A., 1923, Mineral constituents of Rand concentrates: Jour. Chem. Soc. South Africa, v. 24, p. 90–95, 264–266.

Cornelius, H. P., and Plöchinger, B., 1952, Der Tennengebirge-N-Rand mit seinen Manganerzen und die Berge im Bereich des Lammertales: Austria Geol. Bundesanstalt, Jahrb., v. 95, p. 145–225.

Creitz, E. E., and McVay, T. N., 1949, A study of opaque minerals in Trail Ridge, Florida dune sands: Am. Inst. Mining Engineers Trans., v. 181, p. 417–423.

Davidson, C. F., 1953, The gold-uranium ores of the Witwatersrand: Mining Mag. (London), v. 88, no. 2, p. 73–85.

———, 1957, On the occurrence of uranium in ancient conglomerates: Econ. Geology, v. 52, p. 668–693.

———, and Bowie, S. H. U., 1951, On thucholite and related hydrocarbon-uraninite complexes, with a note on the origin of the Witwatersrand gold ores: Geol. Survey of Great Britain Bull., no. 3, p. 1–19.

Davis, G. R., 1954, The origin of the Roan Antelope copper deposit of Northern Rhodesia: Econ. Geology, v. 49, p. 575–615.

Dessau, G., Jensen, M. L., and Nakai, N., 1962, Geology and isotopic studies of Sicilian sulfur deposits: Econ. Geology, v. 57, p. 410–438.

Dolan, John, 1961, Water problems of the Transvaal and Orange Free State mines: Trans. Seventh Commonwealth Mining Metallurgical Cong., Papers and Discussions, v. 3, South African Inst. Mining Metallurgy, p. 1357–1388.

Douglas, J. K. E., and Moir, A. T., 1961, A review of South African gold recovery practice: Trans. Seventh Commonwealth Mining Metallurgical Cong., Papers and Discussions, v. 3, South African Inst. Mining Metallurgy, p. 971–1003.

Dunn, J. A., 1935, The origin of iron ores in Singhbhum, India: Econ. Geology, v. 30, p. 643–654.

———, 1941, The origin of banded hematite ores in India: Econ. Geology, v. 36, p. 355–370.

Dutton, C. E., 1952, Memorandum on iron deposits in the United States of America: 19th Internat. Geol. Cong., Symposium sur les gisements de fer du monde, v. 1, p. 371–411.

———, Park, C. F., Jr., and Balsley, J. R., Jr., 1945, General character and succession of tentative divisions in the stratigraphy of the Mineral Hills district: U.S. Geol. Survey Prelim. Rept.

Frankel, J. J., 1940, Notes on some of the minerals in the Black Reef Series: Geol. Soc. South Africa Trans., v. 43, p. 1–8.

Garlick, W. G., 1953, Reflections on prospecting and ore genesis in Northern Rhodesia: Inst. Mining Metallurgy (London) Trans., v. 63, p. 9–20, 94–106.

———, 1961, Ore genesis; the syngenetic theory, *in* Mendelsohn, F. (ed.), The geology of the Northern Rhodesian copper belt: London, Macdonald and Co., Ltd., p. 146–165.

———, and Brummer, J. J., 1951, The age of the granites of the Northern Rhodesian copper belt: Econ. Geology, v. 46, p. 478–497.

Gastil, Gordon, and Knowles, D. M., 1960, Geology of the Wabush Lake area, southwestern Labrador and eastern Quebec, Canada: Geol. Soc. America Bull., v. 71, p. 1243–1254.

Gevers, T. W., 1961, Outline of the geology of Southern Africa: Trans. Seventh

Commonwealth Mining Metallurgical Cong., Papers and Discussions, v. 1, South African Inst. Mining Metallurgy, p. 25–37.

Goldschmidt, V. M., 1954, Geochemistry: Oxford, Clarendon Press.

Goodwin, A. M., 1956, Facies relations in the Gunflint iron formation: Econ. Geology, v. 51, p. 565–595.

Graton, L. C., 1930, Hydrothermal origin of the Rand gold deposits: Econ. Geology, v. 25, Supplement to no. 3, p. 1–185.

Grout, F. F., and Wolff, J. F., Sr., 1955, The geology of the Cuyuna district, Minnesota: a progress report: Minnesota Geol. Survey Bull. 36.

Gruner, J. W., 1922, The origin of sedimentary iron formations: the Biwabik Formation of the Mesabi Range: Econ. Geology, v. 17, p. 407–460.

———, 1930, Hydrothermal oxidation and leaching experiments; their bearing on the origin of Lake Superior hematite-limonite ores: Econ. Geology, v. 25, p. 697–719, 837–867.

———, 1946, Mineralogy and geology of the taconites and iron ores of the Mesabi Range, Minnesota: St. Paul, Minn., Iron Range Resources and Rehabilitation.

Gundersen, J. N., 1960, Lithologic classification of taconite from the type locality: Econ. Geology, v. 55, p. 563–573.

Harder, E. C., 1919, Iron-depositing bacteria and their geologic relations: U.S. Geol. Survey Prof. Paper 113.

Hargraves, R. B., 1960, A bibliography of the geology of the Witwatersrand System: Univ. of the Witwatersrand, Econ. Geology Research Unit Information Circular 1.

———, 1961, Silver content of gold in Witwatersrand conglomerates: Univ. of the Witwatersrand, Econ. Geology Research Unit Information Circular 3.

Hatch, F. H., and Corstorphine, G. S., 1909, The Geology of South Africa: London, Macmillan and Co., Ltd., p. 146–151.

Hayes, A. O., 1915, Wabana iron ore of Newfoundland: Canadian Geol. Survey Mem. 78.

———, 1928, Wabana iron mines and deposits, Newfoundland: Mining and Metallurgy, v. 9, p. 361–366.

———, 1929, Further studies of the origin of the Wabana iron ore of Newfoundland: Econ. Geology, v. 24, p. 687–690.

———, 1931, Structural geology of the Conception Bay region, and of the Wabana iron ore deposits of Newfoundland: Econ. Geology, v. 26, p. 44–64.

Hem, J. D., 1960, Some chemical relationships among sulfur species and dissolved ferrous iron: U.S. Geol. Survey Water-Supply Paper 1459-C, p. 57–73.

Hewett, D. F., and Webber, B. N., 1931, Bedded deposits of manganese oxides near Las Vegas, Nevada: Univ. of Nevada Bull., v. 25, no. 6.

Horwood, C. B., 1917, The gold deposits of the Rand: London.

Hough, J. L., 1958, Fresh-water environment of deposition of Precambrian banded iron formations: Jour. Sedimentary Petrology, v. 28, p. 414–430.

Huber, N. K., 1958, The environmental control of sedimentary iron minerals: Econ. Geology, v. 53, p. 123–140.

Jacob, K. D., Hill, W. L., Marshall, H. L., and Reynolds, D. S., 1933, Composition and distribution of phosphate rock with special reference to the United States: U.S. Dept. of Agriculture Tech. Bull. 364.

James, H. L., 1951, Iron formation and associated rocks in the Iron River district, Michigan: Geol. Soc. America Bull., v. 62, p. 251–266.

———, 1954, Sedimentary facies of iron-formation: Econ. Geology, v. 49, p. 235–293.

Jensen, M. L., 1958, Sulfur isotopes and the origin of sandstone-type uranium deposits: Econ. Geology, v. 53, p. 598–616.

———, and Dechow, E., 1962, The bearing of sulphur isotopes on the origin of the Rhodesian copper deposits: Geol.

Soc. South Africa Trans., v. 65, pt. 1, p. 1–17.

Jolliffe, A. W., 1955, Geology and iron ores of Steep Rock Lake: Econ. Geology, v. 50, p. 373–398.

Jones, G. C., 1936, Correlation and other aspects of the exploited auriferous horizons on the Witwatersrand mining field: Geol. Soc. South Africa Proc., v. 39, p. xxiii–lxi.

Kock, W. P. de, 1940, The Ventersdorp contact reef: Geol. Soc. South Africa Trans., v. 43, p. 85–108.

Koen, G. M., 1958, The attrition of uraninite: Geol. Soc. South Africa Trans., v. 61, p. 183–196.

Krauskopf, K. B., 1955, Sedimentary deposits of rare metals: Econ. Geology (50th Anniv. Volume), p. 411–463.

———, 1956a, Dissolution and precipitation of silica at low temperatures: Geochim. et Cosmochim. Acta, v. 10, p. 1–26.

———, 1956b, Factors controlling the concentrations of thirteen rare metals in sea-water: Geochim. et Cosmochim. Acta, v. 9, p. 1–32b.

———, 1957, Separation of manganese from iron in sedimentary processes: Geochim. et Cosmochim. Acta, v. 12, p. 61–84.

Krumbein, W. C., and Garrels, R. M., 1952, Origin and classification of chemical sediments in terms of pH and oxidation-reduction potentials: Jour. Geology, v. 60, p. 1–33.

Lake Superior Iron Ore Association, 1952, Lake Superior iron ores (2nd ed.): Cleveland, Lake Superior Iron Ore Assn.

Launay, L. de, 1896, Les Mines d'Or du Transvaal: Paris, Baudry et Cie., p. 177–351.

Leith, C. K., Lund, R. J., and Leith, Andrew, 1935, Pre-Cambrian rocks of the Lake Superior region: U.S. Geol. Survey Prof. Paper 184.

Lepp, Henry, and Goldich, S. S., 1959, The chemistry and origin of iron formations: Econ. Geology, v. 54, p. 1348–1349.

Liebenberg, W. R., 1955, The occurrence and origin of gold and radioactive minerals in the Witwatersrand System, the Dominion Reef, the Ventersdorp Contact Reef and the Black Reef: Geol. Soc. South Africa Trans., v. 58, p. 101–254.

Lindgren, Waldemar, 1933, Mineral deposits (4th ed.): New York, McGraw-Hill Book Co., Inc., p. 415–417.

Ljunggren, Pontus, 1955, Geochemistry and radioactivity of some Mn and Fe bog ores: Geol. Fören. Förhandl., Stockholm, v. 77, p. 33–44.

Lynd, L. E., 1960, Titanium, *in* Gillson, J. L. (ed), Industrial minerals and rocks (3rd ed.): Am. Inst. Mining Engineers, p. 863–864.

Lyons, J. C., 1957, Wabana iron ore deposits, *in* Structural geology of Canadian ore deposits (Volume II): Canadian Inst. Mining Metallurgy, p. 503–516.

Macadam, Peter, 1931, The distribution of gold and carbon in the Witwatersrand bankets: Geol. Soc. South Africa Trans., v. 34 (Annexure), p. 81–88.

———, 1936, The heavier metals and minerals in the Witwatersrand banket: Geol. Soc. South Africa Trans., v. 39, p. 77–79.

Maclaren, J. M., 1908, Gold: Its geological occurrence and geographical distribution: London, The Mining Journal, p. 95–98.

Martens, J. H. C., 1928, Beach deposits of ilmenite, zircon and rutile in Florida: Geol. Survey of Florida, 19th Ann. Rept., p. 124–154.

———, 1935, Beach sands between Charleston, South Carolina, and Miami, Florida: Geol. Soc. America Bull., v. 46, p. 1563–1596.

Mason, Brian, 1958, Principles of geochemistry (2nd ed.): New York, John Wiley & Sons, Inc.

McKelvey, V. E., 1950, The field of economic geology of sedimentary mineral deposits, *in* Trask, P. D. (ed.), Applied sedimentation: New York, John Wiley & Sons, Inc., p. 485–505.

————, and Balsley, J. R., Jr., 1948, Distribution of coastal blacksands in North Carolina, South Carolina, and Georgia, as mapped from an airplane: Econ. Geology, v. 43, p. 518–524.

McKelvey, V. E., Everhart, D. L., and Garrels, R. M., 1955, Origin of uranium deposits: Econ. Geology (50th Anniv. Volume), p. 464–533.

McKelvey, V. E., and Nelson, J. M., 1950, Characteristics of marine uranium-bearing sedimentary rocks: Econ. Geology, v. 45, p. 35–53.

McKelvey, V. E., Wiese, J. H., and Johnson, V. H., 1949, Preliminary report on the bedded manganese of the Lake Mead region, Nevada and Arizona: U.S. Geol. Survey, Bull., 948-D, p. 83–101.

Mellor, E. T., 1916, The conglomerates of the Witwatersrand: Inst. Mining Metallurgy (London) Trans., v. 25, p. 226–348.

————, 1931, The origin of the gold in the Rand banket: discussion of Professor Graton's paper: Geol. Soc. South Africa Trans., v. 34 (Annexure), p. 55–69.

Mendelsohn, F., 1961a, Metamorphism, in Mendelsohn, F. (ed.), The geology of the Northern Rhodesian copper belt: London, Macdonald and Co., Ltd., p. 106–116.

————, 1961b, Ore genesis; summary of the evidence, in Mendelsohn, F. (ed.), The geology of the Northern Rhodesian copper belt: London, Macdonald and Co., Ltd., p. 130–146.

Miholić, Stanko, 1954, Genesis of the Witwatersrand gold-uranium deposits: Econ. Geology, v. 49, p. 537–540.

Mikhalev, D. N., 1946, On the great and minor epochs of accumulation of manganiferous sediments: Comptes rendus (Doklady) de l'Academie des Sciences de l'U.S.S.R., v. 54, no. 4, p. 339–341.

Miller, Roswell, III, 1945, The heavy minerals of Florida beach and dune sands: Am. Mineralogist, v. 30, p. 65–75.

Moore, E. S., and Maynard, J. E., 1929, Solution, transportation and precipitation of iron and silica: Econ. Geology, v. 24, p. 272–303, 365–402, 506–527.

Nagell, R. H., 1962, Geology of the Serra do Navio manganese district, Brazil: Econ. Geology, v. 57, p. 481–498.

Nicolaysen, L. O., Burger, A. J., and Liebenberg, W. R., 1962, Evidence for the extreme age of certain minerals from the Dominion Reef conglomerates and the underlying granite in the Western Transvaal: Geochim. et Cosmochim. Acta, v. 26, p. 15–23.

O'Rourke, J. E., 1961, Paleozoic banded iron-formations: Econ. Geology, v. 56, p. 331–361.

Overholt, J. L., Vaux, G., and Rodda, J. L., 1950, The nature of "arizonite": Am. Mineralogist, v. 35, p. 117–119.

Park, C. F., Jr., 1942, Manganese deposits of Cuba: U.S. Geol. Survey Bull. 935-B, p. 75–97.

————, 1956a, On the origin of manganese: 20th Internat. Geol. Cong., Symposium sobre yacimientos de manganeso, v. I, p. 75–98.

————, 1956b, Manganese ore deposits of the Serra do Navio district, Federal Territory of Amapá, Brazil: 20th Internat. Geol. Cong., Symposium sobre yacimientos de manganeso, v. III, p. 347–376.

Pegg, W. C., 1950, A contribution to the geology of the West Rand area: Geol. Soc. South Africa Trans., v. 53, p. 209–227.

Penning, W. H., 1888, The South African gold-fields: Jour. Soc. Arts, v. 36, p. 433–444.

Pettijohn, F. J., 1946, Geology of the Crystal Falls-Alpha iron-bearing district, Iron County, Michigan: U.S. Geol. Survey Prelim. Map 3-181, Strategic Minerals Inv.

Pompeckj, J. F., 1920, Kupferschiefer und Kupferschiefermeer: Zeit. der Deutschen Geol. Gesell. v. 72, p. 329–339.

Quirke, T. T., 1943, Hydrothermal replacement in deep seated iron ore deposits of the Lake Superior region; a discussion: Econ. Geology, v. 38, p. 662–666.

Ramdohr, Paul, 1953, Über Metamorphose

und sekundäre Mobilisierung: Geol. Rund., v. 42, no. 1, p. 11–19.

———, 1958, New observations on the ores of the Witwatersrand in South Africa and their genetic significance: Geol. Soc. South Africa Trans., v. 61 (Annexure), p. 1–51.

Rankama, Kalervo, and Sahama, T. G., 1950, Geochemistry: Chicago, The Univ. of Chicago Press.

Reinecke, Leopold, 1927, The location of the payable ore-bodies in the gold-bearing reefs of the Witwatersrand: Geol. Soc. South Africa Trans., v. 30, p. 89–119.

———, 1930, Origin of the Witwatersrand System: Geol. Soc. South Africa Trans., v. 33, p. 111–133.

Roberts, H. M., and Bartley, M. W., 1943a, Replacement hematite deposits, Steep Rock Lake, Ontario: Am. Inst. Mining Engineers Tech. Pub. 1543.

———, 1943b, Hydrothermal replacement in deep seated iron ore deposits of the Lake Superior region: Econ. Geology, v. 38, p. 1–24.

Robertson, D. S., and Steenland, N. C., 1960, On the Blind River uranium ores and their origin: Econ. Geology, v. 55, p. 659–694.

Royce, Stephen, 1938, Geology of the iron ranges, *in* Lake Superior iron ores: Cleveland, Lake Superior Iron Ore Assn., p. 27–61.

———, 1942, Iron ranges of the Lake Superior district, *in* Newhouse, W. H. (ed.), Ore deposits as related to structural features: New Jersey, Princeton Univ. Press, p. 54–63.

Sakamoto, Takao, 1950, The origin of the Pre-Cambrian banded iron ores: Am. Jour. Sci., v. 248, p. 449–474.

Sales, R. H., 1960, Critical remarks on the genesis of ore as applied to future mineral exploration: Econ. Geology, v. 55, p. 805–817.

Sauce, Wilhelm B. W. de la, 1926, Beitrage zur Kenntnis der Manganerzlagerstätte von Tschiaturi im Kaukasus: Abh. prakt. Geol. und Bergwirtschaftslehre, v. 8.

Schmidt, R. G., and Dutton, C. E., 1957, Bedrock geology of the south-central part of the North range, Cuyuna district, Minnesota, Sheets 1–3: U.S. Geol. Survey Min. Inv. Field Studies Map MF 99.

Schneiderhöhn, Hans, 1923, Chalkographische Untersuchung des Mansfelder Kupferschiefers: Neues Jahr. für Min., Geol. und Paläon., supp. v. 47, p. 1–38.

———, 1937, Die Kupferlagerstätten von Nordrhodesia und Katanga: Geol. Rund., v. 28, p. 282–291.

———, 1953, Konvergenzerscheinungen zwischen magmatischen und sedimentären Lagerstätten: Geol. Rund., v. 42, no. 1, p. 34–43.

Sharpe, J. W. N., 1949, The economic auriferous bankets of the Upper Witwatersrand beds and their relationship to sedimentation features: Geol. Soc. South Africa Trans., v. 52, p. 265–300.

Siever, Raymond, 1957, The silica budget in the sedimentary cycle: Am. Mineralogist, v. 42, p. 821–841.

Smyth, C. H., Jr., 1892, On the Clinton iron ore: Am. Jour. Sci., v. 143, p. 487–496.

du Toit, A. L., 1940, Developments on and around the Witwatersrand: Econ. Geology, v. 35, p. 98–108.

Trask, P. D., 1925, The origin of the ore of the Mansfeld Kupferschiefer, Germany. A review of the current literature: Econ. Geology, v. 20, p. 746–761.

Twenhofel, W. H., 1950, Principles of sedimentation (2nd ed.): New York, McGraw-Hill Book Co., Inc., p. 444–451.

Tyler, S. A., 1949, Development of Lake Superior soft ores from metamorphosed iron formation: Geol. Soc. America Bull., v. 60, p. 1101–1124.

Van Hise, C. R., and Leith, C. K., 1911, The geology of the Lake Superior iron region: U.S. Geol. Survey Mon. 52, p. 499–529.

Wade, H. H., and Alm, M. R., 1957, Mining directory of Minnesota: Univ. of Minnesota, v. 40, no. 9.

White, D. A., 1954, The stratigraphy and structure of the Mesabi Range, Minnesota: Minnesota Geol. Survey Bull. 38.

Wilson, I. F., and Veytia, Mario, 1949, Geology and manganese deposits of the Lucifer district, northwest of Santa Rosalía, Baja California, Mexico: U.S. Geol. Survey Bull. 960-F, p. 177–233.

Woolnough, W. G., 1941, Origin of banded iron deposits—a suggestion: Econ. Geology, v. 36, p. 465–489.

Young, R. B., 1931, The genesis of gold in the Rand banket: Geol. Soc. South Africa Trans., v. 34 (Annexure), p. 1–14.

Zapffe, Carl, 1931, Deposition of manganese: Econ. Geology, v. 26, p. 799–832.

Zealley, A. E. V., 1918, On certain felsitic rocks, hitherto called "banded ironstone," in the ancient schists around Gatooma, Rhodesia: Geol. Soc. South Africa Trans., v. 21, p. 43–52.

CHAPTER 18 **Weathering**

Most ore minerals, especially the sulfides and sulfosalts, are formed at temperatures higher than atmospheric and in reducing environments. Where these minerals are exposed to surface conditions, they break down chemically, forming new compounds or going into solution. Similarly, most rock-forming minerals are not stable at the earth's surface and consequently undergo chemical changes as equilibrium is re-established with the environment. Minor amounts of metals contained in unweathered rock may be concentrated into economic deposits during weathering. Enrichment takes place where the oxidized metallic product is stable and other constituents are selectively leached away. Therefore, depending upon the materials, environments, and products involved, weathering processes may (1) destroy an existing ore deposit, (2) produce one from previously barren or sub-economic rock, or (3) merely change the mineralogy of a deposit.

The chemical effects of meteoric waters on rocks vary according to the minerals being attacked. Even pure water will dissolve minerals to a limited degree; but meteoric waters contain carbon dioxide, which makes the water slightly acidic. Furthermore, waters in the soil zone generally contain appreciable amounts of carbon dioxide as well as humic acids, lowering the pH to 4 or 5 in places. These acidic waters percolate slowly through the zone of aeration on their way to the ground-water table. In transit, or after reaching the zone of saturation, they react with carbonate rocks or feldspars and other silicate minerals to become neutral or slightly alkaline. All minerals are soluble under favorable conditions, and at the earth's surface they eventually break down or are mechanically removed. Mineral solubilities vary over a wide range, and the rates of chemical reactions vary independently; as a result, there is a wide range of effective mineral stabilities. Meteoric waters charged with carbon dioxide and oxygen from the atmosphere will oxidize, hydrate, and carbonatize the rock-forming minerals. The sulfides are converted to sulfates, most of which are soluble, or they are converted to the more stable oxides, native metals, and carbonates. Iron, manganese, and aluminum form oxides and hydroxides that are relatively insoluble at the surface; lead forms a stable sulfate; lead, zinc, and copper are preserved as carbonates in some environments; copper, zinc, nickel, and chromium are retained as silicates; and native gold, copper, and silver may remain as stable minerals in the weathered zone. These elements have all been recovered as residual concentrates and as simple oxidation products near the weathered rock outcrops that contained them (Emmons, 1917).

The mobility of metal ions in the zone of weathering is largely determined by the composition of both the vadose waters and the country rocks (Hawkes and Webb, 1962). Sulfide-free meteoric waters leach such elements as zinc, molybdenum, and uranium from igneous rocks, leaving behind stable oxidation products of iron, aluminum, titanium, chromium, and in places manganese, nickel, cobalt, copper, lead, or antimony. The host-rock environment is especially important in the oxidation of sulfides, because some of the metals that would be leached from a siliceous host rock are retained in calcareous rocks. Molybdenum, zinc, and silver are especially soluble in sulfate solutions, but under favorable conditions they form stable oxidation products in limestones. Similarly, copper, which is relatively mobile in sulfate waters that circulate through siliceous igneous rocks, forms practically insoluble carbonate minerals in calcareous environments. Iron and lead oxidize to stable compounds in both siliceous and calcareous rocks, resulting in their retention in the zone of weathering. Certain elements are dependent upon the presence or absence of a second element for their stability during weathering; for example, molybdenite oxidizes to the relatively insoluble compound ferrimolybdite [$Fe_2(MoO_4)_3 \cdot 7\frac{1}{2}H_2O$] in siliceous, iron-rich environments, but the molybdenum is readily leached where iron is not plentiful.

In tropical climates, where leaching is especially effective, only the most insoluble oxides remain at the surface. Iron and aluminum form such stable compounds and are so abundant in the earth's crust that they are commonly left as residual concentrates. These iron- or aluminum-rich soils are known as *laterites*. Mafic minerals and feldspars break down and release hydrous iron and aluminum compounds, which are relatively insoluble under oxidizing conditions and consequently remain at the outcrop. During oxidation, the soluble components are dispersed, and the iron and aluminum are oxidized in place or redistributed. The oxidation products may be transported in solution under low Eh and pH conditions; for example, iron is soluble as the simple ferrous ion or in the form of organic, sulfate, and hydroxide complexes (Hem and Cropper, 1959; Hem, 1960; Oborn and Hem, 1961). However, the oxidation products are generally redeposited as they form, because there is an immediate increase in the Eh and pH away from oxidizing sulfides in the zone of weathering. Apparently the mineral structures break down, and the oxidation products go into the colloidal state, as evidenced by the presence of orbicular, concretionary structures known as pisolites. Since pisolites form in ways other than from colloidal solutions, their presence alone is not considered as definite proof of a colloidal origin. Not all laterites are pisolitic, but some are made up almost entirely of these pellets (Fig. 18-1).

Iron-rich laterites form over ferromagnesian rocks where the rainfall is heavy and the topography subdued. Flat areas and broad swales are ideal, because the water is retained long enough to dissolve the siliceous components of the soil without eroding the residual materials. Apparently,

FIGURE 18-1. *Pellets in laterite, Moanda manganese deposit, Gabon.*

laterites form most readily between the annual high and low positions of the water table; thus alternating wet and dry seasons are ideal for laterization (Harder, 1952). Laterites have been mined in small amounts as iron ore where the limonitic pellets are abundant and fine-grained soils or clays nearly absent. Very large areas covered with this type of laterite are known in Brazil, Cuba, India, central Africa, the Philippine Islands, and elsewhere in the tropics. Many of the iron-rich laterites overlie serpentine bodies or other rocks that originally were rich in iron and deficient in silica. In order to compete successfully with the world's large sedimentary iron-ore deposits and with high-grade magnetite deposits, the iron laterites must be nearly pure and strategically located. A significant factor in the cost of mining laterites is the presence of 10–30 percent combined water, which has to be transported and must be removed during smelting processes.

In tropical or subtropical environments where the underlying rocks are rich in aluminum and low in other comparatively stable materials, such as iron and silica, concentrations of bauxite are likely to form. Such concentrations are especially common over syenites and nepheline syenites. Bauxites consist of boehmite [$AlO(OH)$], gibbsite [$Al(OH)_3$], diaspore [$AlO(OH)$], and other hydrous aluminum oxides. The formation of clay minerals may be an intermediate step in the breakdown of some feldspars and feldspathoids to bauxite. Bauxites also form over argillaceous carbonate rocks, in an association with the residual clay known as terra rossa; although such concentrations of alumina are generally high in iron, they are mined in places (for example, in the Mediterranean region and in Jamaica). Large reserves of aluminous clays are known in many areas, but owing to the difficulty of separating aluminum from silica, the clays are considered only as potential ore.

Manganese oxides commonly form concentrations of relatively pure mineral over bodies of rock that are rich in manganese and deeply weathered. Many metamorphic rocks contain spessartite garnets and other manganese-bearing silicates and carbonates; in places these minerals are present in large amounts. In India the term *gondite* has been applied to these spessartite-bearing metamorphic rocks. Elsewhere other names have been applied, but gondite has received the widest recognition. Ore is formed where the silica and other valueless materials are removed and the relatively insoluble manganiferous oxides remain at the surface.

Lateritic pellets of manganese oxides are not as common as similar pellets of limonite, but they are found in many places. In Cuba the name *granzon* has been applied to these pellets, and this term is now widely used. Economic concentrations of granzon are commonly found on the surface near manganese ore bodies.

Besides iron, aluminum, and manganese, several other metals form stable oxidation products. Where they reach economic proportions, these metals are mined as ore, but more often they are present as complicating impurities in iron laterites. Many serpentines contain small amounts of nickel, cobalt, and chromium, which are concentrated in the iron-rich laterites, or in the upper parts of the serpentines; in some districts—for example, at Nicaro, Cuba—these metals are recovered as by-products. The nickel is concentrated in the serpentine, just below the laterite, forming ores contain-

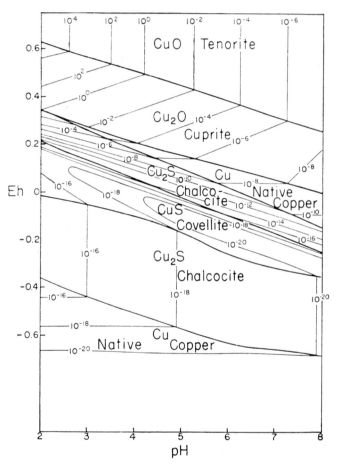

FIGURE 18-2. *Fields of stability of some copper compounds as functions of pH and Eh. Contours are for activity Cu^{+2} + activity Cu^+. (After Garrels, 1954, figure 2.)*

ing about 0.3–1.5 percent nickel. Exceptional deposits, such as those of New Caledonia, contain as much as 6–10 percent nickel. The chromium content of laterites is as much as 1.5–2.5 percent; the cobalt content, 0.2 percent.

Most sulfide minerals are less stable in the zone of weathering than are the rock-forming silicate, oxide, and carbonate minerals. Consequently, the sulfides are oxidized, dissolved, or otherwise altered more readily than the surrounding host rocks, leaving only surface exposures of the weathered products. The exploration for ore deposits thus involves the interpretation of altered surface exposures to help determine the subsurface mineralogy.

The thermodynamic relations in supergene processes are illustrated by diagrams such as those of Garrels (Fig. 18-2). The fundamental process is one of oxidation, but since the oxidation of sulfides produces hydrogen ion and sulfate, both Eh and *p*H are controls. The actual mechanisms of oxidation and dissolution of metal sulfides, however, are not well understood. The sulfide minerals no doubt dissolve ionically under the attack of surface waters, and the constituents then react with dissolved oxygen. The oxidation reaction would be much more sluggish if the materials were not first broken down into the ionic state. Sato (1960) suggested that the oxidation agent is H_2O_2, which forms as an intermediate product during the reduction of oxygen; if the oxidation potential of the environment exceeds that of the H_2O_2-O_2 couple, any metal ions present react with the peroxide to form the metal oxide and water. Both theoretical and experimental evidence substantiate this mechanism. Moreover, field measurements of the Eh and *p*H values in the zone of oxidation fall into a narrow zone just above the standard potential for the H_2O_2-O_2 couple.

Pyrite is the most common sulfide mineral; few sulfide ore deposits lack this compound. The oxidation of pyrite and other iron sulfides generally leaves limonite or hematite and generates sulfuric acid. The normal reaction involved is

(1) $2FeS_2 + \frac{15}{2}O_2 + 4H_2O \longrightarrow Fe_2O_3 + 4SO_4^{-2} + 8H^+$

Actually, iron is dissolved as the ferrous ion or as ferrous sulfate, and ferrous iron is oxidized to insoluble limonite or hematite:

(2) $2FeS_2 + 7O_2 + 2H_2O \longrightarrow 2Fe^{+2} + 4SO_4^{-2} + 4H^+$

(3) $2Fe^{+2} + \frac{1}{2}O_2 + 2H_2O \longrightarrow Fe_2O_3 + 4H^+$

The iron in massive pyrite bodies is likely to be leached, without leaving much hematite or limonite, because the presence of sulfuric acid keeps the *p*H low and may form a reducing environment that retains the iron in the soluble ferrous state. Conversely, waters rich in oxygen may cause pyrite to alter directly to ferric sulfate, without going through a ferrous sulfate stage (equation 4). The Fe^{+2}/Fe^{+3} ratio may vary widely, depending upon both Eh and *p*H. The minerals that form under set conditions of Eh and *p*H will depend upon relative concentrations and the extent to which various solubility products are satisfied.

(4) $$2FeS_2 + \tfrac{15}{2}O_2 + H_2O \longrightarrow Fe_2(SO_4)_3 + SO_4^{-2} + 2H^+$$

Some iron persists at the outcrop as ferric or ferrous sulfate in arid climates, but in general these sulfates are merely temporary transitional states. Iron will migrate in the dissolved state where the solutions remain strongly acidic or deficient in oxygen; a low redox potential favors the stability of ferrous ions in solution, whereas a *p*H below 3 permits ferric ions to remain in the dissolved state. However, such low redox potentials and extremely acidic conditions are unlikely near the surface and above the water table.

The weathering of iron sulfides involves the oxidation of both iron and sulfur. Sulfur in sulfide minerals generally has a valence (oxidation number) of −2; the sulfur in FeS_2 would seem to be an exception, but it is not, because it occurs as S_2^{-2} "molecules" bound to divalent iron. Oxidation to the sulfate radical increases the valence to +6. As an intermediate step, the oxidation process forms native sulfur, rather than the sulfate radical. For example, ferric sulfate solutions react with chalcocite to release copper ions in solution and produce native sulfur (Sullivan, 1930; Sato, 1960):

(5) $$Cu_2S + 4Fe^{+3} + 6SO_4^{-2} \longrightarrow 2Cu^{+2} + 4Fe^{+2} + 6SO_4^{-2} + S$$

This explains the presence of small amounts of native sulfur in many outcrops.

Ferric sulfate and sulfuric acid generated by the oxidation of iron sulfides act as potent solvents for other metallic sulfides. Ferric sulfate oxidizes sulfide minerals to soluble sulfates and during this process is reduced to ferrous sulfate. At the expense of hydrogen ions and oxygen, ferrous sulfate probably is oxidized quickly back to ferric sulfate:

(6) $$2Fe^{+2} + 2H^+ + \tfrac{1}{2}O_2 \longrightarrow 2Fe^{+3} + H_2O$$

Wherever the acidity of the waters percolating through an ore deposit is maintained, such elements as copper, silver, and zinc are leached. In the absence of iron sulfides, ferric sulfate and sulfuric acid do not readily form, hence the oxidation products of other sulfides tend to remain in place. Similarly, the neutralization of acidic waters by reactive wall rocks, such as carbonates, causes dissolved metals to precipitate as stable minerals. Equations

7–21 demonstrate the oxidation of a few common sulfide minerals. Solid reactants and relatively insoluble products are written as stoichiometric compounds; dissolved substances are expressed as ions.

(7) $2FeS$ (pyrrhotite) $+ \frac{9}{2}O_2 + 2H_2O \longrightarrow Fe_2O_3 + 2SO_4^{-2} + 4H^+$

(8) $2CuFeS_2$ (chalcopyrite) $+ \frac{17}{2}O_2 + 2H_2O \longrightarrow$
$$Fe_2O_3 + 2Cu^{+2} + 4SO_4^{-2} + 4H^+$$

(9) $CuFeS_2$ (chalcopyrite) $+ 4Fe^{+3} + 2H_2O + 3O_2 \longrightarrow$
$$Cu^{+2} + 5Fe^{+2} + 2SO_4^{-2} + 4H^+$$

Equations 8 and 9 show two reactions involving chalcopyrite; it may break down directly to iron oxide and an acidic solution of cuprous sulfate, or it may be taken into solution by ferric sulfate. The sulfuric acid generated in these reactions or generated by oxidizing iron sulfides helps take the copper into solution as cupric sulfate. Bornite behaves similarly:

(10) $2Cu_5FeS_4$ (bornite) $+ \frac{27}{2}O_2 + 8H_2O \longrightarrow$
$$Fe_2O_3 + 10Cu^{+2} + 8SO_4^{-2} + 16H^+$$

(11) Cu_5FeS_4 (bornite) $+ 4Fe^{+3} + 4H_2O + 6O_2 \longrightarrow$
$$5Cu^{+2} + 5Fe^{+2} + 4SO_4^{-2} + 8H^+$$

(12) Cu_5FeS_4 (bornite) $+ 4H^+ + 9O_2 \longrightarrow 5Cu^{+2} + Fe^{+2} + 4SO_4^{-2} + 2H_2O$

The simple sulfides that do not contain iron are oxidized directly or dissolved by ferric sulfate and sulfuric acid produced by the oxidation of associated iron sulfides:

(13) Cu_2S (chalcocite) $+ 2H^+ + SO_4^{-2} + \frac{5}{2}O_2 \longrightarrow 2Cu^{+2} + 2SO_4^{-2} + H_2O$

(14) Cu_2S (chalcocite) $+ 2Fe^{+3} + 3SO_4^{-2} + \frac{3}{2}O_2 + H_2O \longrightarrow$
$$2Cu^{+2} + 2Fe^{+2} + 4SO_4^{-2} + 2H^+$$

(15) PbS (galena) $+ 2O_2 \longrightarrow PbSO_4$ (anglesite)

(16) PbS (galena) $+ 2Fe^{+3} + 3SO_4^{-2} + \frac{3}{2}O_2 + H_2O \longrightarrow$
$$PbSO_4 \text{ (anglesite)} + 2Fe^{+2} + 2H^+ + 3SO_4^{-2}$$

In the presence of calcareous rocks, galena oxidizes to the relatively insoluble carbonate, cerussite:

(17) PbS (galena) $+ H_2O + CO_2 + 2O_2 \longrightarrow$
$$PbCO_3 \text{ (cerussite)} + SO_4^{-2} + 2H^+$$

The process may involve two steps: oxidation to anglesite (equation 15) and conversion of anglesite to cerussite:

(18) $PbSO_4$ (anglesite) $+ H_2O + CO_2 \longrightarrow$
$$PbCO_3 \text{ (cerussite)} + SO_4^{-2} + 2H^+$$

The geological evidence of these steps is convincing in cerussite ores, where cores of galena are rimmed in places with transition zones of anglesite. Elsewhere anglesite is absent, and galena appears to alter directly to cerussite. Zinc and silver sulfides are also dissolved in the presence of ferric sulfate:

$$(19) \quad ZnS \text{ (sphalerite)} + 2Fe^{+3} + 3SO_4^{-2} + H_2O + \tfrac{3}{2}O_2 \longrightarrow$$
$$Zn^{+2} + 2Fe^{+2} + 2H^+ + 4SO_4^{-2}$$

$$(20) \quad Ag_2S \text{ (argentite)} + 2Fe^{+3} + 3SO_4^{-2} + H_2O + \tfrac{3}{2}O_2 \longrightarrow$$
$$2Ag^+ + 2Fe^{+2} + 2H^+ + 4SO_4^{-2}$$

In a limestone environment, the zinc sulfate solution reacts to form smithsonite and gypsum:

$$(21) \quad Zn^{+2} + SO_4^{-2} + CaCO_3 + 2H_2O \longrightarrow$$
$$CaSO_4 \cdot 2H_2O \text{ (gypsum)} + ZnCO_3 \text{ (smithsonite)}$$

Cupric sulfate solutions react in a similar manner with carbonate rocks to form the hydrous carbonates of copper—malachite and azurite.

Iron oxides and lead sulfate are relatively insoluble and tend to remain at the outcrops, but most of the oxidation products of other metals are removed in solution and carried downward. Where beds of limestone or other basifying rocks are encountered, the acidic solutions are neutralized, and the more stable carbonates of copper and zinc are formed. In extremely arid countries, such as the Atacama Desert of Chile, water-soluble minerals—sulfates and chlorides of copper and iron—remain in the zone of oxidation.

Native copper is commonly found associated with cuprite (Cu_2O) in the upper parts of oxidized copper deposits. In fact, the association between these oxidation products is so universal that cuprite without disseminated native copper is rare. The reaction producing native copper and cuprite from chalcocite may be written:

$$(22) \quad 2Cu_2S + 8Fe^{+3} + 12SO_4^{-2} + 6H_2O + \tfrac{3}{2}O_2 \longrightarrow$$
$$2Cu + Cu_2O + 8Fe^{+2} + 12H^+ + 14SO_4^{-2}$$

The further oxidation of native copper and cuprite produces tenorite (CuO):

$$(23) \quad Cu + Cu_2O + O_2 \longrightarrow 3CuO$$

Silver behaves much the same as copper in the zone of oxidation but has fewer stable oxidation products. Argentite, the common silver sulfide, is oxidized by and therefore soluble in ferric sulfate solutions (equation 20), and silver sulfosalts are broken down in a similar manner. Consequently, the silver content of sulfide veins is usually carried downward by meteoric waters. Where the climate is somewhat arid, however, the weakly soluble halogen salts, such as cerargyrite (AgCl), bromyrite (AgBr), iodyrite (AgI), and embolite [Ag(Br,Cl)], are left in the oxidized zone. The presence of silver halides in arid or semiarid regions is due to the absence of sufficient water to dissolve the minerals, and usually a windborne supply of salts is available for reaction. Silver carbonates and silver oxides are not found as economic minerals, but native silver is common. The native silver forms as a result of reduction of the silver ion, probably by ferrous iron (Stokes, 1906; Cooke, 1913). Equation 24 shows the reaction between ferrous sulfate and silver sulfate.

$$(24) \qquad 2Ag^+ + 2Fe^{+2} \longrightarrow 2Ag + 2Fe^{+3}$$

Zinc sulfates are very soluble, and as a result the zinc content of most oxidized ore bodies is dispersed in the ground-water system. However, in arid or semiarid climates, zinc may be retained in the oxidized zone as smithsonite, hydrozincite [$Zn_5(CO_3)_2(OH)_6$], hemimorphite [$Zn_4Si_2O_7(OH)_2 \cdot H_2O$], or other carbonate and silicate minerals.

Galena is soluble in ferric sulfate solutions, but the reaction is so sluggish that unoxidized masses of galena are common in areas where other sulfides have been altered or leached. The leaching of galena is retarded, because the common oxidation products—anglesite and cerussite—are also stable in the zone of weathering.

Native gold is inert to most oxidizing environments, but field evidence indicates that solution and short-distance transport of gold take place under favorable conditions (Emmons, 1912). Gold is somewhat soluble as a chloride complex. In acidic solutions and in the presence of a strong oxidizing agent, such as MnO_2, gold is oxidized to Au^{+3}, which combines with chlorine ions to form the stable $AuCl_4^-$ complex. Manganese, an abundant and widespread component of the earth's crust, is present in many gold ores. Enrichments of gold near the surface have been found, suggesting that the gold has been dissolved and reprecipitated ahead of mechanical erosion. The solution and reprecipitation of gold results in the presence of coarse gold along cracks and small openings throughout the upper parts of the vein and the adjacent wall rock.

Antimony forms the relatively stable compounds, valentinite (Sb_2O_3), bindheimite, [$Pb_{1-2}Sb_{2-1}(O,OH,H_2O)_{6-7}$], and stibiconite (also known as cervantite). These minerals are not conspicuous, and, owing to iron oxide staining, are easily mistaken for limonite. Nevertheless, they have been identified in the oxidized zones of many ore deposits. Where antimony is present in complex sulfantimonide minerals, the oxidation products are likely to be complex also. The oxidation of stibnite probably takes places according to the following equations:

(25) Sb_2S_3 (stibnite) $+ 3H_2O + 6O_2 \longrightarrow$

$$Sb_2O_3 \text{ (valentinite)} + 6H^+ + 3SO_4^{-2}$$

(26) $3Sb_2S_3$ (stibnite) $+ 10H_2O + 20O_2 \longrightarrow$

$$2SbSb_2O_6(OH) \text{ (stibiconite)} + 18H^+ + 9SO_4^{-2}$$

Most arsenic compounds, in contrast with those of antimony, are relatively soluble and consequently are leached from the zone of weathering. Traces of rare arsenates, such as conichalcite [$CaCuAsO_4(OH)$] in oxidized copper ores, reflect the former presence of sulfarsenides, but in humid climates these minerals are dissolved with the sulfates.

Oxide minerals also are susceptible to weathering, but usually at a slower rate than the sulfides. Chromite and ilmenite ores persist at the outcrop until they are mechanically removed. But, given time, they eventually oxidize or dissolve. Martite (Fe_2O_3), hematite, and limonite commonly form in the outcrops of magnetite deposits; maghemite (Fe_2O_3) is stable in many lateritic soils.

Oxidation rates vary over a wide range. Cinnabar oxidizes so slowly that for practical purposes it is considered stable in surface outcrops, even though it is thermodynamically unstable under surface conditions. Galena is commonly protected from oxidation in a jacket of anglesite. In contrast, a few other sulfides oxidize so rapidly that they ignite when exposed to the atmosphere. In deposits of massive sulfides, especially pyrrhotite and marcasite, it is not uncommon for the rock to burn as a result of spontaneous combustion. Experience has taught the miners of Iron River, Michigan, to leave a skin of iron ore on the walls of stopes in order to prevent the highly pyritiferous black slate from igniting. High rock and air temperatures are also produced by oxidizing sulfides, making it necessary in some mines to pump refrigerated air underground so that miners can work comfortably. The processes and end products are the same in these situations as they are on surface outcrops. Acidic waters are produced by the oxidation of sulfides; in some districts the mine waters are so acidic that they dissolve mine rails and clothing, creating a major problem for men and equipment. Similarly, large amounts of noxious and strongly corrosive sulfur dioxide fumes are generated where the sulfides burn, and in extreme cases the mines must be abandoned or parts sealed off until the fire exhausts the oxygen supply or burns all of the combustible materials. The burned country rock is generally bleached and altered as if it had been exposed at the surface for a long time.

The leached, oxidized surface exposures of weathered sulfide deposits are known as *gossans*. A thorough understanding of gossans can be of great value to economic geologists, because gossans may retain distinctive characteristics of the underlying sulfide materials. It is desirable to know whether sulfides exist at depth and, further, whether the mineralization is simply pyrite or includes appreciable amounts of copper, zinc, silver, and other valuable sulfides. Consequently, many serious efforts have been made to study gossans quantitatively. The criteria by which gossans are evaluated are vague and poorly understood. Those considered include such features as the shapes of the cavities formerly occupied by sulfides; the structure, texture, and color of the limonite; the quantity of kaolinite and other clay minerals; and the presence of small amounts of metallic oxidation products. Emphasis is usually placed upon the color of the limonite and the configuration of boxworks (the meshwork of porous gossan left after much of the original sulfide is leached). The confident application of gossan studies in exploration, although valuable in some areas, ordinarily requires great skill and a more intimate knowledge of the local ore deposits than most geologists are able to obtain. Extrapolating the characteristics of gossans from one environment to another can be discouraging. Resident geologists, or others familiar through long experience in certain areas, use the color and texture of limonite to indicate whether the underlying rocks are favorable, though seldom is a quantitative approach considered (Locke, 1926). Most geologists agree that gossans should be studied with care; proof of their value has been demonstrated in many mining districts. Lacy (1949) studied the oxidation products at Yauricocha, Peru, and was able to relate individual oxide minerals to their source materials. He divided the oxidation products into residual and transported materials and subdivided these according to the textures developed and the minerals from which they were derived. On the basis of this study, Lacy distinguished among gossans that overlie several kinds of sulfide deposits, including lead-zinc ores, lead-zinc-copper ores, copper-pyrite ores, and massive pyrite bodies.

The presence of gossans does not necessarily mean unaltered sulfides exist at depth. Under relatively low Eh and pH conditions, iron goes into solution in the ferrous state and travels appreciable distances from the oxidation zone. Where these ferrous sulfate solutions encounter limestone or a similar basifying medium, the acid is neutralized, and the iron precipitates

as ferric oxide or ferric hydroxide. Displaced iron oxide zones of this type
are known as *false gossans*. Clearly, then, it is of critical importance to distinguish between false gossans and indigenous gossans.

The depth of oxidation is another problem of significance to mining
geologists. In tectonically stable regions the oxidation zone generally
extends to the water table, especially if the country rocks are permeable.
But recent faulting, a fluctuating water table, or impervious wall rocks may
cause modifications in the pattern of oxidation. The most critical factors are
the position and permanency of the water table, because sulfides are generally stable in the slightly alkaline, moderately reducing environment
found below the ground-water table. In humid climates, the sulfide zone
may be present a few feet from the surface; and in arid environments,
where the water table is likely to be deep, the lower limit of oxidation may
extend two or three thousand feet below the outcrop. At the other extreme,
a rapidly lowered water table may leave sulfides isolated well up in the
zone of oxidation. This is especially common in arid environments, where
there is not enough water to oxidize and dissolve the sulfides.

The role of permeability in oxidation is strikingly demonstrated at the
Tsumeb mine, South-West Africa, where a nearly vertical ore pipe that cuts
through steeply dipping sediments is oxidized in the upper and lower parts
but is unweathered at intermediate levels. Here, deep oxidation was brought
about by ground waters circulating along a permeable, fractured bed that
crops out some distance from the mine but intersects the ore pipe at depth
(see Fig. 4-21, p. 88). The unoxidized part of the pipe is protected from
ground water by relatively impermeable strata. Although sulfides remain
in the oxidized zones, there are relatively sharp changes in the ratio of
oxidized to unoxidized minerals. Between the 1200- and 2400-foot levels,
the ores are largely sulfides, whereas above and below this section of the
pipe, the ores are oxidized. Oxidation along the deep brecciated stratum is
so efficient that the lower part of the pipe is more thoroughly oxidized than
much of the shallow weathered zone (Söhnge, 1963).

Descending waters charged with dissolved substances tend to seek density
levels. This results in a crude stratification of water and explains how concentrations of oxidation products have formed in certain places where deep
circulation of water is doubtful; for example, heavy, mineral-laden, and
perhaps oxygenated, waters settle below the water table (Brown, 1942;
McKnight, 1942).

Many fine-grained oxides, silicates, and carbonates in the zone of oxidation are considered to have traveled as colloids. Typical products of this kind include opal and chalcedony, smithsonite, reniform hematite and limonite, aluminum hydroxides, and manganese oxides. Wad, the amorphous or cryptocrystalline manganese oxide commonly found in residual deposits, is a good example. Some wad gives no pattern with x-ray diffraction equipment and is still in the colloidal state. The composition of wad is indefinite, because the colloidal gel tends to adsorb many elements. Unlike most oxide colloids, colloidal manganese oxides carry a negative charge, so that they attract cations of other metals out of solution. Small amounts of nickel are common in many deposits of wad; copper, cobalt, and barite have also been reported in some. The manganese oxides of the Tocantins district, Brazil, contain as much as 4 percent cobalt (Pecora, 1944). The presence of tungsten, strontium, and a few other metals is considered by Hewett to indicate a history of hydrothermal, and most probably igneous, processes (Hewett and Fleischer, 1960).

Nickel Deposits of New Caledonia

Surface weathering affects mineral deposits in several ways. It may leach away a previously existing ore deposit; it may oxidize the materials in place without changing the grade of ore; and it may create an ore deposit by the residual concentration of materials that originally were dispersed throughout the fresh rock. The nickel deposits of New Caledonia are a product of the last-mentioned process.

The island of New Caledonia, located in the South Pacific, is about 250 miles long and has an average width of only about 30 miles. Nickel deposits were discovered there by Garnier in 1865, and sporadic production has continued since about 1875. Prior to the discovery of the Sudbury district in Ontario, New Caledonia dominated the world's nickel production.

Much of New Caledonia is underlain by an assemblage of ultramafic intrusives—dunite, saxonite, and associated rock types—many of which are partly or entirely serpentinized (Fig. 18-3). The serpentine series, as this igneous complex is known, intrudes Cretaceous and older sedimentary rocks, and is consequently thought to be Tertiary in age. Serpentinization is essentially a process involving hydration of the original ultramafic minerals, accompanied by rearrangement and minor loss of constituents; hydration normally results from deuteric or intrusive metamorphic effects as the hot ultramafics take up water from the intruded country rocks. This mecha-

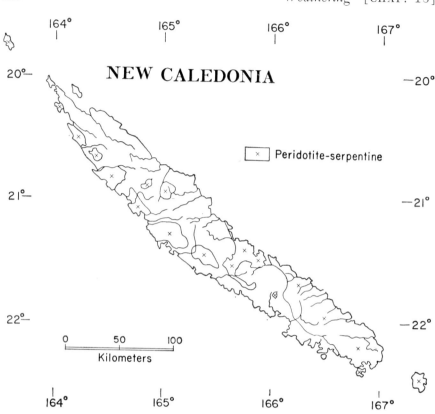

FIGURE 18-3. *Geologic sketch map of New Caledonia. (After Lacroix, 1943.)*

nism of serpentinization appears to be the one that altered the rocks at New Caledonia, because the serpentine is independent of the present topography and of weathering processes.

The mineral deposits of New Caledonia have been described many times, and all studies agree that the nickel was concentrated during laterization of the serpentine (Glasser, 1904; Ontario Nickel Commission, 1917; Berthelot, 1933; Caillère, 1936; Lacroix, 1943; Chételat, 1947; Routhier, 1952). The serpentine series weathers to a typical dark-reddish laterite, producing soil profiles similar to those in other tropical areas (Fig. 18-4). Over much of the surface, the serpentine series is covered with deposits of pisolitic iron oxides. Most of the nodules are about the size of peas, and fine-grained, clayey minerals are nearly absent. Where laterization is complete, the original low-alumina silicates of the ultramafics are destroyed, and silica, calcium, and magnesium are removed. Iron in the laterites is in the form of

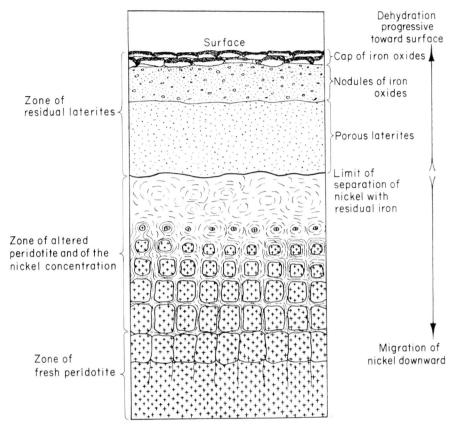

Surface

Dehydration
progressive
toward surface

Cap of iron oxides

Nodules of iron
oxides

Zone of
residual laterites

Porous laterites

Limit of
separation of
nickel with
residual iron

Zone of altered
peridotite and of the
nickel concentration

Zone of
fresh peridotite

Migration of
nickel downward

Peridotite altered mineralized   Fresh peridotite with tenor 0.25 nickel

FIGURE 18-4. *Typical section through nickeliferous laterite deposits, New Caledonia.* (*After Chételat, 1947, figure 4.*)

limonite, carrying 10–25 percent water. The serpentine series and the laterites are readily distinguished on the surface from other formations by differences in vegetation.

The best nickel ores are concentrated below the laterite near the top of the serpentine series, in nearly horizontal zones. But not all the laterite is underlain by ores. Locally the minerals are concentrated in minor fissures that extend downward into the rock below, but these fissures are seldom worth mining. The efficiency of the nickel-concentration process was controlled largely by the topography; the best ores are on gentle slopes and on saddles of spurs extending from the main ridges. Figure 18-4 and Table 18-I clearly show the various stages of laterization and distribution of

TABLE 18-I

Zones in the Nickeliferous Laterite of New Caledonia

Su face

Zone of laterites	Upper laterite	Scoriaceous hematite of the surface. Platy laterite. Pisolites of iron oxides.
	Lower laterite	Generally in place. Iron hydroxides with some clay. Concentrations of cobalt and manganese.

Upper limit of nickel (leached from overlying materials, deposited in underlying materials).

Zone of altered peridotite and concentration of nickel	Migration and concentration of nickel along cracks in the altered peridotite. Concentration of iron and nickel by partial removal of silica and magnesium. Hydration and oxidation of the peridotite minerals.

Fresh peridotite (carrying about 0.25% Ni + Co).

SOURCE: After Chételat (1947), Table 2.

metals in the New Caledonia deposits. The ores are overlain by soil, by decomposed rocks of the serpentine series, or by pisolitic laterites. In general, the zone of nickel concentration lies 1–20 feet below the surface, but there are exceptions where the cover reaches a thickness of 75–100 feet. Most nickel migration has been downward, though lateral migration produced a few deposits near the bases of gentle slopes. Small amounts of cobalt and manganese are concentrated in the lower part of the laterites above the more soluble nickel.

Garnierite, a nickeliferous variety of serpentine, is the principal ore mineral in the New Caledonia deposits. Locally the garnierite is called noumé-ite. Another nickeliferous antigorite (népouite and genthite) is also an important ore mineral. Nickel-bearing saponite, known locally as pimélite, is a third nickel ore. The colors of the minerals range from bright apple green, through light green, to white. Where the iron of the silicates is replaced by nickel, the ore is green, and accordingly is known as green ore; where the magnesium is replaced, the ore is brown, because it retains the color of the iron oxides. Brown ore, known locally as chocolate ore, is now the common material being mined. Up to 10 percent cobalt is present in the amorphous oxide mineraloid, asbolite (cobaltiferous wad). Black manganese oxides, identified as pyrolusite and psilomelane, have been mined locally in small amounts. Talc and sepiolite [$Mg_4(Si_6O_{15})(OH)_2 \cdot 6H_2O$] are the most common gangue minerals, and small amounts of chalcedony—representing colloidal silica leached from the laterite zone—are found in fractures cutting the serpentine series.

The ore averages about 3.5 percent nickel, but higher grade ore was mined during the early days, when 10 percent nickel was not unusual. The present grade is still well above the nickel content of laterites in most other districts. Most of the ore bodies are small (less than 100,000 tons), the largest deposit containing only about 600,000 tons.

Studies of the unaltered serpentine and ultramafics show that the nickel and cobalt content are relatively uniform throughout the district. There seems to be no direct relationship between the grade of the original serpentine series and the metal content of the ores. Thus the presence of ore is strictly a function of favorable topography and the effect of weathering conditions on the serpentine series. The effectiveness of the weathering process is more fully appreciated when we realize that it has concentrated the nickel ten- to thirtyfold from fresh ultramafic rock that contained only 0.2–0.3 percent nickel (Chételat, 1947; Blanchard, 1944). Chételat (1947) pointed out the presence of arsenopyrite and pyrite in the serpentine series and considered the possibility that nickel was a constituent of these sulfides. Other workers think the nickel was contained in the ferromagnesian silicate minerals.

Whatever the original distribution of the nickel, it is clear that weathering caused the enrichment. The best ores are found where chemical weathering was most effective. It has even been noted (Chételat, 1947) that the serpentine is less commonly a source material for nickel ores than other rocks of the ultramafic complex, in spite of the fact that the serpentine contains an equal amount of nickel; the difference is a function of permeability, because the lack of permeability in serpentine tends to inhibit circulation and downward migration of the mineral-bearing waters.

Morro da Mina, Brazil

Morro da Mina, in the Lafaiete district, Minas Gerais, Brazil, has been one of the most productive manganese deposits in the Western Hemisphere. The ore is residual, and consists of manganese oxides formed by the weathering of silicate and carbonate protores. The protore has, by different workers, been called gondite (Park, 1956), queluzite (Derby, 1901), and manganese silicate-carbonate protore (Dorr et al., 1956). Dorr and his co-workers state that the protores are metamorphosed sediments that formed a gradational sequence of cherts, mudstones, and manganiferous carbonates. They are in schists of Precambrian age. The characteristic manganiferous beds have been followed along the strike for more than 40 miles, and probably continue for greater distances. The irregular distribution of the constituents in the original sediments helps to explain the present erratic distribution of manganoan carbonates in the protores. The sediments have undergone intense regional metamorphism, and locally are intruded by granitic igneous masses and by mafic and pegmatitic dikes (Guimarães, 1935). Particularly near the northwestern part of the mine, igneous metamorphism has been superimposed upon the regional metamorphism—a factor that has led observers in the past to relate the mineralization to igneous metamorphic processes. Igneous metamorphism is now thought to have developed tephroite (Mn_2SiO_4) and other silicates, mainly at the expense of manganese carbonates.

The mineralogy of the protores was studied intensively by Horen (1955), who determined spessartite garnets, rhodochrosite and manganoan calcite, rhodonite, tephroite, and a long list of minor minerals, particularly manganese silicates. Pyrite and small amounts of other sulfides, notably alabandite, have been recognized (Park et al., 1951; Ödman, 1955; Horen, 1955). Much of the protore is a nondescript, sandy looking, gray-brown rock that contains mainly small crystals of spessartite interspersed in a cement of manganoan carbonate and minor amounts of fine-grained sulfides. In the deeper parts of the mine workings the protore is cut by veins and irregular masses of bright red rhodochrosite, rhodonite, and smaller amounts of other minerals. The protore averages about 30 percent manganese. In a few places the carbonates make up as much as 70 percent of the rock (Dorr et al., 1956), but in many places carbonates are sparse or absent, and the rock is massive, dense, and impermeable.

The ore at Morro da Mina consists of an assemblage of manganese oxides —a product of the removal of silica and carbonate from the protores by meteoric waters. In very few places does the ore grade downward into the protore; rather, the contact is a sharp, clearly defined, undulating surface that locally extends downward into the protore along fractures, dikes, and water courses. The presence of carbonates and sulfides that are more easily decomposed than the silicates, is thought to aid greatly in the weathering of the protores. Where these materials are present the protore becomes permeable, and decomposition proceeds rapidly and to considerable depths. Ore has been mined to a depth of about 500 feet. Where the carbonates and sulfides are absent in the protores—for example, in those parts of the beds where igneous metamorphism has been active—oxidation is limited, and generally the manganese oxides form only a thin film or at most a few feet of ore.

References to Selected Deposits Formed by Weathering

Cuban Laterites

Cox, J. S., Jr., 1912, The iron-ore deposits of the Moa district, Oriente Province, Island of Cuba: Am. Inst. Mining Engineers Trans., v. 42, p. 73–90.

Guardiola, Ricardo, 1912, Sobre el origen de los criaderos de Mayari: Revista Minera, Metalúrgica y de Ingeniería, v. 63, p. 25–27.

Hayes, C. W., 1912, The Mayari and Moa iron-ore deposits in Cuba: Am. Inst. Mining Engineers Trans., v. 42, p. 109–115.

Kemp, J. F., 1916, The Mayari iron-ore deposits, Cuba: Am. Inst. Mining Engineers Trans., v. 51, p. 3–30.

Leith, C. K., and Mead, W. J., 1916, Additional data on origin of lateritic iron ores of eastern Cuba: Am. Inst. Mining Engineers Trans., v. 53, p. 75–78.

Spencer, A. C., 1908, Three deposits of iron ore in Cuba: U.S. Geol. Survey Bull. 340, p. 318–329.

Weld, C. M., 1910, The residual brown iron-ores of Cuba: Am. Inst. Mining Engineers Trans., v. 40, p. 299–312.

Woodbridge, D. E., 1912, Exploration of Cuban iron-ore deposits: Am. Inst. Mining Engineers Trans., v. 42, p. 138–152.

Jamaican Bauxite

Bramlette, M. N., 1947, Lateritic ore of aluminum in the Greater Antilles: Geol. Soc. America Bull., v. 58, p. 1248–1249.

Burns, D. J., 1961, Some chemical aspects of bauxite genesis in Jamaica: Econ. Geology, v. 56, p. 1297–1303.

Hartman, J. A., 1955, Origin of heavy minerals in Jamaican bauxite: Econ. Geology, v. 50, p. 738–747.

Hill, V. G., 1955, The mineralogy and genesis of the bauxite deposits of Jamaica, B.W.I.: Am. Mineralogist, v. 40, p. 676–688.

Hose, H. R., 1950, The geology and mineral resources of Jamaica: Colonial Geol. and Min. Res., v. 1, no. 1, p. 11–36.

———, 1959, The origin of bauxites in British Guiana and Jamaica: 5th Sess., Inter-Guiana Geol. Conf.

———, 1963, Jamaica type bauxites developed on limestones: Econ. Geology, v. 58, p. 62–69.

Kelly, W. C., 1961, Some data bearing on the origin of Jamaican bauxite: Am. Jour. Sci., v. 259, p. 288–294.

Salas, G. P., 1959, Los depósitos de bauxita en Haití y Jamaica y posibilidades de que exista bauxita en México: México Univ. Nac., Inst. Geol. Bol., no. 59, p. 9–42.

Schmedeman, O. C., 1948, Caribbean aluminum ores: Eng. and Mining Jour., v. 149, no. 6, p. 78–82.

———, 1950, First Caribbean bauxite development, Reynolds Jamaica Mines, Ltd.: Eng. and Mining Jour., v. 151, no. 11, p. 98–100.

Zans, V. A., 1952, Bauxite resources of Jamaica and their development: Colonial Geol. and Min. Res., v. 3, no. 4, p. 307–333; 1954, Geol. Survey Dept. Jamaica Pub. 12.

———, 1957, Geology and mineral deposits of Jamaica: Geol. Survey Dept. Jamaica Pub. 33.

References Cited

Berthelot, Ch., 1933, Le nickel et le chrome dans les colonies françaises: Paris, Chimie et Industrie, v. 29, p. 718–723.

Blanchard, Roland, 1944, Derivatives of chromite: Econ. Geology, v. 39, p. 448.

Brown, J. S., 1942, Differential density of ground water as a factor in circulation, oxidation and ore deposition: Econ. Geology, v. 37, p. 310–317.

Caillère, Simone, 1936, Contribution a l'étude des minéraux des serpentines; Chap. VII, pt. 1, Minéraux de la Nouvelle-Calédonie: Soc. Française de Min. Bull., v. 59, p. 289–298.

Chételat, E. de, 1947, La genèse et l'évolution des gisements de nickel de la Nouvelle-Calédonie: Soc. Géol. France Bull., sér. 5, v. 17, p. 105–160.

Cooke, H. C., 1913, The secondary enrichment of silver ores: Jour. Geology, v. 21, p. 1–28.

Derby, O. A., 1901, On the manganese ore deposits of the Queluz (Lafayette) district, Minas Gerais, Brazil: Am. Jour. Sci., v. 12, p. 18–32.

Dorr, J. V. N., II, Coelho, I. S., and Horen, Arthur, 1956, The manganese deposits of Minas Gerais, Brazil: 20th Internat. Geol. Cong., Symposium sobre yacimientos de manganeso, v. 3, p. 279–346.

Emmons, W. H., 1912, The agency of manganese in the superficial alteration and secondary enrichment of gold-deposits in the United States: Am. Inst. Mining Engineers Trans., v. 42, p. 3–73.

———, 1917, The enrichment of ore deposits: U.S. Geol. Survey Bull. 625.

Garrels, R. M., 1954, Mineral species as functions of pH and oxidation-reduction potentials, with special reference to the zone of oxidation and secondary enrichment of sulphide ore deposits: Geochim. et Cosmochim. Acta, vol. 5, p. 153–168.

Glasser, Edouard, 1904, Rapport a M. le Ministre des Colonies sur les richesses minerales de la Nouvelle-Calédonie: Ann. des Mines, v. 5, p. 29–154, 503–701.

Guimarães, Djalma, 1935, Contribuição ao estudo da origem dos depósitos de minério de ferro e manganês do Centro de Minas Gerais: Rio de Janeiro, Serv. Fom. Prod. Min., Bull. 8.

Harder, E. C., 1952, Examples of bauxite deposits illustrating variations in origin, *in* Problems of clay and laterite genesis: New York, Am. Inst. Mining Engineers, p. 35–64.

Hawkes, H. E., and Webb, J. S., 1962, Geochemistry in mineral exploration: New York and Evanston, Harper and Row.

Hem, J. D., 1960, Some chemical relationships among sulfur species and dissolved ferrous iron: U.S. Geol. Survey Water-Supply Paper 1459-C, p. 57–73.

———, and Cropper, W. H., 1959, Survey of ferrous-ferric chemical equilibria and redox potentials: U.S. Geol. Survey, Water-Supply Paper 1459-A, p. 1–31.

Hewett, D. F., and Fleischer, Michael, 1960, Deposits of the manganese oxides: Econ. Geology, v. 55, p. 1–55.

Horen, Arthur, 1955, Mineralogy and petrology of the manganese protore at the Merid mine, Minas Gerais, Brazil: Geol. Soc. America Bull., v. 66, p. 1575.

Lacroix, M. A., 1943, Les péridotites de la Nouvelle-Calédonie, leurs serpentines et leurs gîtes de nickel et de cobalt; les gabbros qui les accompagnent: Acad. Sci. Paris Mém., v. 66.

Lacy, W. C., 1949, Oxidation processes and formation of oxide ore at Yauricocha: Soc. Geol. Peru (Vol. Jubilar), XXV Aniv., pt. II, Fasc. 12.

Locke, Augustus, 1926, Leached outcrops as guides to copper ore: Baltimore, The Williams & Wilkins, Co.

McKnight, E. T., 1942, Differential density of ground water in ore deposition: Econ. Geology, v. 37, p. 424–426.

Oborn, E. T., and Hem, J. D., 1961, Microbiologic factors in the solution and transport of iron: U.S. Geol. Survey Water-Supply Paper 1459-H, p. 213–235.

Ödman, O. H., 1955, Morro da Mina manganese deposit and its protore: Engenharia Mineraçao e Metalurgia, Feb. 1955, p. 57.

Ontario Nickel Commission, 1917, Nickel deposits of the world: Ontario Nickel Comm., p. 234–264.

Park, C. F., Jr., 1956, On the origin of manganese: 20th Internat. Geol. Cong., Symposium sobre yacimientos de manganeso, v. 1, p. 75–98.

——, Dorr, J. V. N., II, Guild, P. W., and Barbosa, A. L. M., 1951, Notes on the manganese ores of Brazil: Econ. Geology, v. 46, p. 1–22.

Pecora, W. T., 1944, Nickel-silicate and associated nickel-cobalt-manganese-oxide deposits near São José do Tocantins, Goiaz, Brazil: U.S. Geol. Survey Bull. 935-E, p. 247–305.

Routhier, Pierre, 1952, Les gisements de fer de la Nouvelle-Calédonie: 19th Internat. Geol. Cong., Symposium sur les gisements de fer du monde, v. II, p. 567–587.

Sato, Motoaki, 1960, Oxidation of sulfide ore bodies: Econ. Geology, v. 55, p. 928–961, 1202–1231.

Söhnge, P. G., 1963, The geology of the Tsumeb mine: Geol. Soc. South Africa Trans., in press.

Stokes, H. N., 1906, Experiments on the solution, transportation and deposition of copper, silver and gold: Econ. Geology, v. 1, p. 644–650.

Sullivan, J. D., 1930, Chemistry of leaching chalcocite: U.S. Bur. Mines Tech. Paper 473.

CHAPTER 19 **Supergene Sulfide**

Enrichment

THE CHEMICALS RELEASED by the breakdown of minerals in the zone of oxidation either remain in place as stable compounds or are carried in solution with the meteoric waters that migrate downward to the phreatic zone. The dissolved materials may be repeatedly deposited as they descend to the ground-water table, but if they are soluble, they will eventually be carried out of the oxidized zone. Rain waters and solutions that pass through organic-rich soil zones become slightly to moderately acidic, and waters near oxidizing sulfides may be strongly acidic. Reaction of these acidic solutions with carbonates and the rock-forming silicates causes them to become neutral or alkaline. Below the ground-water table the circulation is very slow, permitting this basifying process to reach completion; consequently, most ground waters are alkaline and have a low Eh. As would be expected, many compounds that are soluble in acidic oxidizing waters are precipitated where the solutions become basic and reducing. Meteoric waters that percolate through the zone of oxidation into the zone of ground-water saturation undergo these changes in chemistry. Accordingly, some of the metals dissolved near the surface are precipitated below the ground-water table (Emmons, 1917; Garrels, 1954). This process is important to economic geology and the mining industry, because it means that the metals leached from the oxidized upper parts of mineral deposits may be expected at depth; and of even greater importance, it provides a mechanism by which a small percentage of metal can be leached from a large volume of rock and—provided the conditions are favorable below the ground-water table —can be redeposited as a higher grade deposit in a smaller volume of rock. Such a process is known as *supergene enrichment*. The primary, subeconomic material underlying the enriched zone is known as protore. Ideally, then, there are three fundamental zones in a near-surface ore deposit: the oxidized zone, the supergene enriched zone, and the hypogene zone or protore (Fig. 19-1).

Supergene enrichment is effective in concentrating dispersed metals, and many disseminated copper deposits owe their economic success to this process. Several factors are involved in the development of a supergene-enrichment zone. Where ground water is actively circulating, the dissolved metals may be widely dispersed. Where the rocks are not permeable, meteoric waters will not be able to leach the oxidation products and carry them down to the ground-water zone. Where erosion is rapid, the ground-water table may be lowered so fast that oxidation of the sulfides above cannot keep pace. Where the water table is not lowered through the disseminated mineralization—that is, where the topography is in old age—the process will be at a standstill, and enrichment will cease. Thus the development of an appreciable concentration involves a balance between the rates of oxidation and erosion as well as a fairly sluggish ground-water system.

The tendency to classify minerals as supergene or hypogene should be avoided as far as possible. Certain minerals are characteristic of high-temperature environments, and others are characteristic of low-temperature environments, but there are exceptions. The availability of the chemical components and the Eh-pH environment may be controlling factors. For example, a certain mineral may be rare or unknown as a product of supergene processes because the proper redox conditions are uncommon to the phreatic zone; but, at least locally, almost any Eh is possible below the

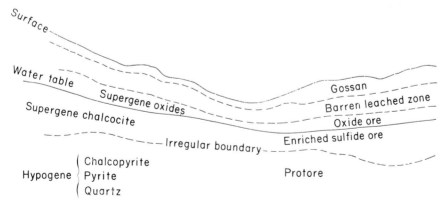

FIGURE 19-1. *Diagramatic sketch of a deposit containing chalcopyrite, pyrite, and quartz, showing the effects of weathering.*

ground-water table, therefore the possibility that this species may form should not be ruled out unconditionally. Specular hematite is commonly considered a high-temperature mineral, yet at the Mountain Home property west of Hanover, New Mexico, plates of specular hematite as much as one-half inch wide are found in limestone above the water table; they are not found at depth and are thought to be of supergene origin. Similarly, Brown (1936) has shown that at Balmat, New York, magnetite forms by the weathering of pyrite; magnetite had long been considered a high-tempera-ture mineral, hence this observation was at first difficult for many geologists to accept. In the Southern Piedmont gold deposits of the southeastern United States, there are doubly terminated quartz crystals in the subsoil above the ground-water table. The quartz crystals contain skeleton out-lines marked by limonite; similar quartz is not found at depth. Sulfide min-erals that are characteristic of the hypothermal and igneous metamorphic zones may be used as indicators of hypogene deposition, but again the possible exception must be anticipated. For example, pyrrhotite is a typical high-temperature mineral, but thermodynamic considerations indicate that it can form under very restricted (and unlikely) supergene conditions (Garrels, 1960).

Metallic elements have certain definite affinities for sulfur—affinities that are related to the solubilities of their sulfide compounds. Any metal in solu-tion that has a stronger affinity for sulfur than another metal will precipitate as a sulfide at the expense of the more soluble metal sulfide. The sequence of stabilities of the heavy-metal sulfides was first established in 1888 by Schürmann, and accordingly the order of affinites for sulfur, or relative solu-bilities of the sulfide compounds, is known as Schürmann's series (Table 19-I). Any metal in the series will replace another that is lower in the series. Thus copper in solution will replace the iron in pyrite or the zinc in sphal-erite. In general, the farther apart the elements are in the series, the more complete the replacement and the greater the rate of reaction. Furthermore, different metals will be selectively replaced according to their relative posi-tions in Schürmann's series; for example, silver-bearing solutions will react with sphalerite more readily than they will with covellite or chalcocite.

Schürmann's series has been applied to all ore deposits, both hypogene and supergene. Theoretically, the relationships should be valid in either environment, but hypogene fluids are complicated by so many factors that strict adherence to Schürmann's series should not be expected. The simple relations of the series are especially unlikely in high-temperature, high-pressure systems. Under conditions of supergene deposition, however, where

TABLE 19-I

Schürmann's Series

Increasing affinity for sulfur		Increasing solubility as sulfide
	palladium	
	mercury	
	silver	
	copper	
	bismuth	
	cadmium	
	antimony	
	tin	
	lead	
	zinc	
	nickel	
	cobalt	
	iron	
	arsenic	
	thallium	
	manganese	

SOURCE: From Schürmann (1888).

the expected relationships are usually found, Schürmann's concept is an extremely useful one.

The best examples of supergene leaching and enrichment are found in pyrite-bearing silver and copper deposits. Upon exposure to weathering and attack by meteoric waters, such deposits yield dilute solutions rich in sulfuric acid and silver or copper sulfate, according to the reactions expressed in equations *1, 8–14,* and *20,* in Chapter 18. As this solution descends to the ground-water level, oxygen is gradually exhausted; consequently, the solution changes slowly from an oxidizing agent to a reducing agent. Furthermore, reactions with alkaline constituents will neutralize or basify the descending solutions. Thus the Eh and pH of the meteoric waters change from oxidizing and acidic where the sulfides are initially attacked to reducing and basic below the ground-water table. In the reducing environment the primary sulfide minerals generally remain stable, but they may react according to Schürmann's series with the dissolved metals brought down from the zone of oxidation.

Pyrite is an important mineral both above and below the ground-water table. It weathers to ferric sulfate and sulfuric acid in the zone of oxidation, enabling the meteoric waters to dissolve the ore metals. Below the ground water table, pyrite acts as a host for deposition of the ores, because iron sulfide is relatively soluble and readily relinquishes its sulfur to invading ions of copper and silver. Stokes (1907) showed experimentally how the reaction between copper ions and pyrite may take place in supergene copper enrichment; his reaction, known as Stokes' equation, is given below:

$$5FeS_2 + 14Cu^{+2} + 14SO_4^{-2} + 12H_2O \longrightarrow 7Cu_2S \text{ (chalcocite)}$$
$$+ 5Fe^{+2} + 24H^+ + 17SO_4^{-2}$$

The excess acid is neutralized, and the chalcocite remains in the enriched zone. Stokes considered this a generalization of the actual process, but the field evidence supports his interpretation (Fig. 19-2).

The rates of supergene reactions are controlled by many factors. In the presence of abundant calcite or other carbonate minerals, the oxidizing solutions may be neutralized before the ground-water level is reached, and an enriched oxidized zone will result. The character of the sulfides also influences the reaction rate. Pyrrhotite, for example, reacts much faster than pyrite; where pyrrhotite is the primary sulfide below the water table, a supergene chalcocite zone is likely to be thin but high grade. Such a condi-

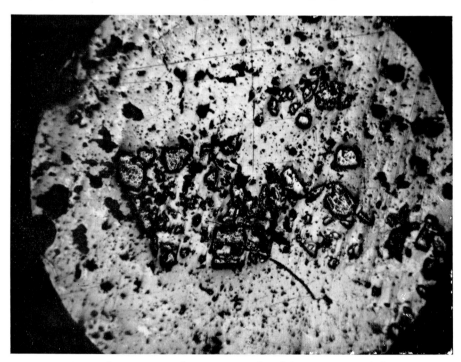

FIGURE 19-2. *Photomicrograph of pyrite replaced by supergene chalcocite. Darwin, California.* ×30. (*Photo by Ruperto Laniz.*)

tion was encountered in the deposits at Ducktown, Tennessee, where the primary ore contains pyrrhotite with subordinate amounts of chalcopyrite. The enriched zone formed just below the ground-water table, for a thickness of 2–8 feet. In this zone the chalcocite replaced the pyrrhotite almost entirely, and the ore was unusually rich (Emmons and Laney, 1926). In contrast, where the protore contains pyrite and chalcopyrite, as it does in many disseminated copper deposits, it is not uncommon to find enriched zones extending several hundred feet or more beneath the ground-water level.

Copper sulfides also replace the sulfides of zinc and lead, in accordance with Schürmann's series. Many deposits of sphalerite and galena contain small amounts of copper minerals, reworked during weathering and concentrated as supergene products below the water table. The thickness of these zones is generally intermediate between the thicknesses of supergene enriched zones in pyrite and pyrrhotite protores.

Supergene chalcocite is commonly soft and powdery. It is referred to as "sooty" chalcocite, as distinguished from the massive, gray, crystalline chalcocite found in hypogene ores. But not all supergene chalcocite is necessarily sooty in character; it may be massive and indistinguishable from hypogene chalcocite. In addition to chalcocite, other copper sulfides form by supergene processes. Covellite and bornite are not uncommon; chalcopyrite and several of the more complex copper salts of arsenic and antimony also form under special conditions of supergene enrichment. In general, though, supergene sulfides are of simple mineralogy compared to hypogene sulfides.

The chemistry of silver is similar to that of copper, although there are no insoluble silver carbonate compounds to retain silver in the oxidized zone of limestone host rocks. Where halogens are available, as in arid climates, the silver may form insoluble halides above the ground-water table, but silver is ordinarily taken into solution as a sulfate. The supergene minerals, as well as the textures and structures of the deposits, are similar to those formed under epithermal conditions. Consequently, it is sometimes impossible to distinguish between hypogene and supergene deposits of silver. The need for such a distinction is obvious: supergene deposits are likely to be rather shallow, blanket types, whereas hypogene deposits may persist in depth. The most common supergene sulfide compound is Ag_2S. Above $180°C$, Ag_2S forms the isometric mineral argentite; at lower temperatures, monoclinic Ag_2S (acanthite) is more stable (Roy et al., 1959). The presence of isometric crystals of Ag_2S will accordingly indicate a hypogene origin; but the presence of monoclinic Ag_2S proves only that deposition took place below 180°C, and cannot be used to distinguish between supergene and low-temperature hypogene ores. Nor can this criterion be applied to most published descriptions of silver deposits, because, in the past, few geologists attempted to distinguish between the polymorphs of Ag_2S; unless the mineral occurred in elongated crystals of obvious nonisometric habit, it was generally called argentite. The ruby silvers (pyrargyrite and proustite) are more likely to be hypogene than supergene, yet the possibility that they can form as supergene minerals rules out their use as positive criteria of hypogene deposition. The general observation that supergene assemblages are typically less complex than hypogene assemblages may be of value in the interpretation of silver deposits, but this criterion is of little value when it stands alone.

Other minerals, such as those of lead and zinc, have been reported to form enriched sulfide zones, but there are no extensive commercial deposits of these supergene ores. Lead sulfate and lead carbonate are relatively insoluble, and as a result they are left in the oxide zone. Zinc also forms a stable carbonate, but the zinc content of sulfide ores is often leached from the zone of oxidation. Many examples of supergene zinc sulfides have been described, perhaps the most noteworthy being the Horn Silver mine in Utah (Butler et al., 1920) and the Balmat-Edwards district of New York (Brown, 1936). Zinc deposition below the water table forms either wurtzite or a light-colored sphalerite. No large deposits of supergene zinc sulfides— comparable to supergene copper and silver—are known; evidently, most zinc remains in solution to be dispersed in the ground-water system.

Chañarcillo, Chile

Many examples of supergene-enriched silver deposits could be given, including the famous bonanza deposits of the western hemisphere. Today, these deposits are nearly exhausted; most of them are abandoned and are largely of historical interest. Deposits of this type extend from the United States southward through Mexico, Central America, and along the western slopes of the Andes in South America. One of the outstanding districts was Chañarcillo, where more than $100 million worth of silver was produced (Moesta, 1928; Whitehead, 1919, 1942; Segerstrom, 1962).

Chañarcillo is in the Atacama Desert of Chile, about 32 miles south of Copiapó, in the arid foothills along the western side of the Interior Valley (Fig. 19-3). The district was discovered in 1832 (Miller and Singewald,

1919). During the boom years, from 1860 to 1885, it produced about $2\frac{1}{2}$ million kilograms of silver. Much of the silver was recovered from high-grade masses; one piece of nearly pure native silver weighed over 200 pounds, and another mass of embolite [Ag(Cl,Br)] with native silver weighed 45,000 pounds and contained 75 percent silver.

The rocks in the immediate area of the mine consist of an alternating sequence of Cretaceous limestones and volcanic tuffs intruded by a swarm of diorite dikes and a small granodiorite stock (Segerstrom, 1962). Both the dikes and the stock are highly altered, and parts of the stock consist of diopside, wollastonite, epidote, and similar metamorphic minerals. Narrow copper veins are close to the stock; the silver is farther away.

Although Chañarcillo lies on the axis of a broad regional fold, the dips of the rocks are slight. The rocks are cut by many fractures, which were probably formed in connection with the folding; these fractures contain the ore deposits. Most of the fractures are parallel to the fold axis, but others cut it at angles of about 45°. The fractures are steeply dipping and of great continuity both in depth and along the strike; at least the upper portions of these fissures were open during metallization (Whitehead, 1919, 1942).

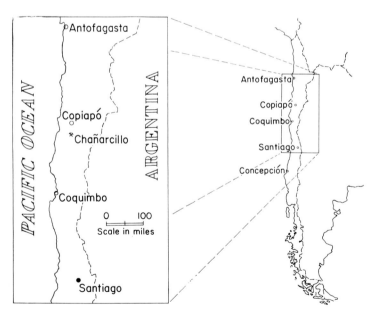

FIGURE 19-3. *Index map of Chile, showing the location of the Chañarcillo district.*

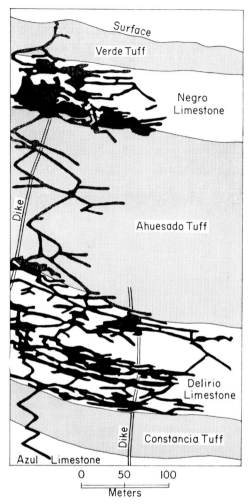

FIGURE 19-4. *Cross section through the Constancia mine, Chañarcillo, Chile, showing the concentration of ore in limestones and the extensions of ore parallel to the bedding. (After Whitehead, 1919, figure 2.)*

The primary veins vary in width from about 1 inch to 3 feet. Hypogene minerals include pyrite, sphalerite, chalcopyrite, galena, arsenopyrite, cobalt arsenides, pearceite ($Ag_{16}As_2S_{11}$), freibergite [$(Cu, Ag)_3 SbS_3$], proustite (Ag_3AsS_3), polybasite ($Ag_{16}Sb_2S_{11}$), and pyragyrite (Ag_3SbS_3) in a gangue of calcite, barite, quartz, and siderite. The veins extend through the rock sequence to the greatest depths explored, but the best ores were concentrated in the purest beds of limestone, but small ore zones were also formed where veins intersect fissures and dikes (Fig. 19-4). The major veins are aligned along the axial plane of the anticlinal structure; there seems to be a direct correlation between proximity to the crest of this fold and continuity or richness of the parallel veins.

After the hypogene minerals were deposited, the rocks were faulted. In general, the faulting was of only small magnitude; the major structure—a normal fault with about 150 feet of displacement—divides the Chañarcillo district into northern and southern parts. During this period of faulting the ore-bearing veins were reopened, permitting subsequent erosion and weathering to redistribute the silver minerals in the near-surface parts of the veins.

The shapes and sizes of the primary ore bodies were not significantly changed by supergene sulfide enrichment; they were merely enriched in silver content at the expense of iron, antimony, arsenic, and sulfur. The zone of supergene enrichment ranges in thickness from a minimum of 130 feet in the northern part of the district to a maximum of 500 feet in the south (Whitehead, 1942). Descending meteoric waters precipitated their silver content when they reached the primary ore beneath the ground-water table; accordingly, the upper parts of the supergene sulfide zones were selectively enriched, and the ore grade diminished from the top to the bottom of the bed. Enrichment was also extensive along faults and water courses. The enrichment processes obliterated the primary minerals in the richest zones, but pseudomorphous relationships between hypogene and supergene minerals were characteristic in all of the enriched ores.

Supergene minerals include stephanite (Ag_5SbS_4), "argentite" (acanthite?), dyscrasite (Ag_3Sb), native silver, stromeyerite ($AgCuS$), and minor amounts of pearceite and polybasite (Whitehead, 1919). Enrichment was due to the replacement of early sulfides by secondary sulfides, antimonides, and native silver; little replacement of the gangue minerals was noted. As a rule, the supergene minerals are richer in silver than the hypogene minerals.

Studies of the supergene sulfide paragenesis have clarified the processes of enrichment. In the early stages of enrichment, ruby silvers (pyrargyrite and proustite) were replaced by "argentite" (acanthite?), stromeyerite, stephanite, and small amounts of polybasite and pearceite. Because pyrargyrite was more susceptible to replacement than proustite, it was the first hypogene mineral attacked. The replacement processes were clearly recorded in concentric bands of supergene minerals formed around unaltered cores of the ruby silvers. Dyscrasite and native silver were restricted to zones of intense enrichment; they formed irregular dendritic masses, which developed most readily in pyrargyrite but also replaced proustite, pearceite, and polybasite as enrichment progressed. Further supergene enrichment eventually resulted in the complete replacement of primary minerals, until native silver and dyscrasite replaced even the earlier supergene minerals in the upper part of the enriched zone. The most intense enrichment was represented by veins of massive dyscrasite and native silver, which usually replaced other sulfides but locally filled open spaces or replaced calcite along cleavage planes.

Above the supergene sulfide ores, and separated from them by a thick bed of tuff (Fig. 19-4), is a second bed of limestone, containing oxidized ores. In contrast to the supergene-enriched lodes, the oxidized ore bodies were changed from their original configurations. The veins were thickened to as much as 30 feet and became irregular in shape, rather than elongated.

Oxidation processes resulted in the development of silver halides, which were zoned according to relative solubilities. Cerargyrite (AgCl), the least soluble, formed the upper zone; embolite [Ag(Br,Cl)] defined the intermediate zone; and iodyrite (AgI) formed the lower zone (Miller and Singewald, 1919, p. 277). Bromyrite (AgBr) and iodembolite [Ag(Cl,Br,I)] were also common oxidation products. In places the oxidized ores cropped out, but elsewhere they were overlain by a bed of tuff. The oxidized ore minerals were deposited both as a replacement of calcite and sulfides and as open-cavity fillings, replacement being the dominant process. As the ground-water level was lowered slowly through the silver-bearing rocks, the oxidized zone gradually encroached on the supergene-enriched sulfide zone. Thus parts of the oxidized ores—native silver and dyscrasite—were replaced by silver halides. After the halides were formed, there was a short period during which the oxidation processes were reversed; native silver and small amounts of argentite coated, transected, and replaced some of the silver halides (Whitehead, 1919).

Whitehead (1919) studied the chemistry of the enrichment processes and concluded that sulfuric acid and ferric sulfate, mixed with halides (which were probably wind-blown from the sea), were the active solvents and reagents. The abundant calcite quickly neutralized the acid, but enough ferric sulfate was present to facilitate the leaching process.

Very little hypogene ore has been mined in the Chañarcillo district, even though the primary veins contained 60–150 ounces of silver per metric ton. Oxidation and supergene enrichment increased the silver content 25–80 percent, forming deposits with 100–240 ounces of silver per ton. The remoteness of Chañarcillo prohibited the mining of anything but high-grade ores, and the primary veins were further excluded because of their depth and the presence of considerable water in the lower levels. Thus, owing both to their nearness to the surface and to their higher content of silver, the supergene-enriched zones contained the most favorable mineralization for mining, and Chañarcillo owed its economic success to the processes of supergene enrichment.

Miami, Arizona

Supergene enrichment has been an especially important process in the history of most disseminated or "porphyry" copper deposits. There are several deposits of disseminated copper in the Miami (or Globe-Miami) district, Arizona; each has been affected by supergene enrichment (Ran-

some, 1919; Tenney, 1935; Peterson et al., 1951; Peterson, 1954).
Miami is in southeastern Arizona, near the center of the great,
southwestern United States copper province (Fig. 19-5).

The principal ore bodies at
Miami form an irregular, elongated mass of disseminated copper that extends for 2 miles along
a schist-granite contact (Fig.
19-6). Evidently, the mineralizing fluids ascended along the
granite contact, where late-magmatic turbulence or post-intru-
sion tectonics created repeatedly
opened veinlets in the contact
zone. Most of the ore is in the
schist (Pinal Schist, of Precambrian age), but some copper is

FIGURE 19-5. *Index map of Arizona, showing the location of the Miami district.*

mined from a porphyritic facies of the granite—the Schultze Granite of
Tertiary(?) age. On the western end of the mineralized zone is the Live
Oak ore body; near the center, the Inspiration ore body; and on the eastern
end, the Miami ore body. Live Oak and Inspiration are largely overlain by
a sheet of granite porphyry.

Hypogene mineralization formed an assemblage of ore sulfides and alteration products that typifies the disseminated copper deposit (see Chapter
13). The unenriched protore in the Miami ore body averages about 1 percent copper (Ransome, 1919) and consists of pyrite, chalcopyrite, and
molybdenite distributed along minute veinlets throughout the schist and
granite porphyry. Other ore bodies in the district contain much less copper
in the protore than that directly under the Miami ore body. The alteration
products include pyrite, quartz, sericite, orthoclase, and clay minerals
(Schwartz, 1947).

Supergene enrichment increased the grade of ore from 1 percent or less
to as much as 5 percent in localized zones. In the early days of mining,
when the upper, high-grade part of the supergene-enriched ore was recovered, the ore averaged more than 2 percent copper; today, materials that
have been only weakly enriched are being mined. The Pinal Schist is more

SG   Schultze Granite

GC   Gila Conglomerate

PS   Pinal Schist

TD   Tertiary dacite

----- Contacts

⌒   Faults

Ore-bearing zone

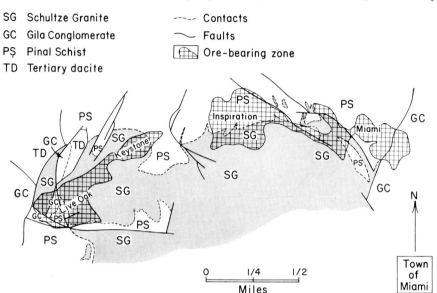

FIGURE 19-6. *Outline of the disseminated copper ore bodies at Miami, Arizona, and their relation to the contact between Pinal Schist and Schultze Granite. (After Ransome, 1919, plates 31 and 39.)*

permeable than the Schultze Granite, and as a result it was more amenable to supergene enrichment. Leaching was relatively complete in the oxidized zone of the schist, but the oxidized zone in granite typically retains its copper in the form of malachite and chrysocolla. Accordingly, supergene sulfide enrichment was more thorough in the schist. The supergene-enriched

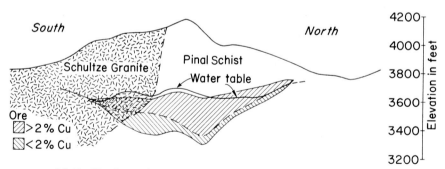

FIGURE 19-7. *North-south cross section through the Inspiration orebody, showing the shape of the ore zone, the relationship of high-grade ore to lower grade ore, the thickness of the ore-bearing zone in Pinal Schist, and the relationship between the top of the supergene enriched zone and the ground water table. (After Ransome, 1919, plate 41.)*

zone starts abruptly beneath the gossan, anywhere from 100 to 600 feet below the surface; it indicates the position of the water table at the time of supergene enrichment (Fig. 19-7). The copper content increases abruptly at the chalcocite zone and tapers off gradually down to the protore (Fig. 19-8). This reflects the fact that supergene sulfide enrichment started at the water table and continued downward to the limit of ground-water circulation or until the supply of copper ions in solution was depleted. Insipient enrichment took place along grain boundaries and tiny cracks in pyrite and chalcopyrite. Further replacement of the primary sulfides by chalcocite increased the copper tenor until the upper zone, the richest, contained about 3 percent copper. The effects of supergene enrichment are found as far as 1200 feet below the surface (Lindgren, 1933).

Chalcocite is practically the only supergene sulfide mineral in the Miami district. It replaced both pyrite and chalcopyrite, but chalcopyrite was more susceptible to replacement. In the upper parts of the supergene zone, both the chalcopyrite and the pyrite were completely replaced by chalcocite, and intermediate stages are represented by chalcocite envelopes around remnant cores of pyrite. Small amounts of covellite are found in places; it represents

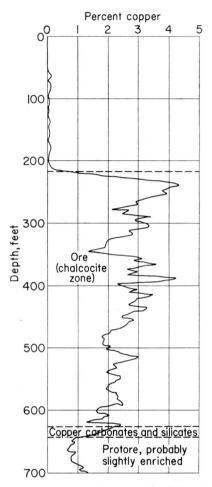

FIGURE 19-8. *Assay graph of No. 2 shaft, Miami copper mine, showing the copper content in the oxidized zone, supergene enriched zone, and protore. The thin zone of oxidized ore beneath the chalcocite zone is anomalous. (After Ransome, 1919, plate 47, graph 4.)*

the first step in the enrichment of chalcopyrite. In the Copper Cities deposit, $3\frac{1}{2}$ miles north of Miami, supergene enrichment did not progress far, because the protore was not exposed to weathering processes until recently

(Peterson, 1954). Here, pyrite is preserved in the enrichment zone; even the chalcopyrite is only partly replaced by chalcocite.

All the ore mined in the Miami district has been taken from supergene-enriched deposits. In the early days of mining, when the cut-off grade was 1.5 percent copper, even the exceptionally rich protore beneath the Miami ore body could not be mined economically. With the development of modern mining and metallurgical techniques, the limits of ore grade have gradually been dropped, with the result that rock containing only 0.5 percent copper can be mined profitably under favorable conditions. Thus the Copper Cities deposit is now being mined even though it has been enriched only slightly above the tenor of the protore (which averages 0.4 percent copper). In each deposit, then, the copper has been mined as soon as the definition of ore grade has been broadened to include the supergene-enriched part of each deposit. Where leaching and supergene enrichment were thorough, a thick, high-grade chalcocite zone was produced; these deposits were mined first. Deposits that were not favorably weathered and enriched had to await economic changes before becoming classified as ore. Today some of the marginal materials are leached artificially with acidic solutions, and the copper is recovered from collecting basins in the lower levels of the workings.

References to Selected Supergene Deposits

Rio Tinto, Spain

Bateman, A. M., 1927, Ore deposits of the Rio Tinto (Huelva) district, Spain: Econ. Geology, v. 22, p. 569–614.

Finlayson, A. M., 1910, The pyritic deposits of Huelva, Spain: Econ. Geology, v. 5, p. 357–372, 403–437.

Herrero Aleixandre, Andres, 1947, Mining in Spain's Huelva district: Eng. Mining Jour., v. 148, no. 10, p. 90–92.

Rutherford, W. P., 1953, El campo de piritas de Huelva (con referencia especial a los macizos de la "Zarza"): Minería y Metalurgía (Madrid), no. 151, p. 11–20.

Williams, David, 1934, The geology of the Rio Tinto mines, Spain: Inst. Mining Metallurgy (London) Trans., v. 43, p. 593–678.

———, 1942, Rio Tinto, Spain, in Newhouse, W. H. (ed.), Ore deposits as related to structural features: New Jersey, Princeton Univ. Press, p. 258–262.

———, 1950, Gossanized breccia-ores, jarosites, and jaspers at Rio Tinto, Spain: Inst. Mining Metallurgy (London) Bull., no. 526, p. 1–12.

Williams, Gordon, 1932, The genesis of the Perrunal-La Zarza pyritic orebody, Spain: Inst. Mining Metallurgy (London) Trans., v. 42, p. 3–80.

Ely, Nevada

Bateman, A. M., 1935, The copper deposits of Ely, Nevada: 16th Internat. Geol. Cong., Copper resources of the world, v. 1, p. 307–321.

Fournier, R. O., 1959, Mineralization of a portion of the porphyry copper deposit near Ely, Nevada: Econ. Geology, v. 54, p. 1348.

Lawson, A. C., 1906, The copper deposits of the Robinson mining district, Nevada: Univ. of California Publ., Dept. Geol. Bull., v. 4, p. 287–357.

Pennebaker, E. N., 1942, The Robinson mining district, Nevada, *in* Newhouse, W. H. (ed.), Ore deposits as related to structural features: New Jersey, Princeton Univ. Press, p. 128–131.

Schwartz, G. M., 1947, Hydrothermal alteration in the "porphyry copper" deposits: Econ. Geology, v. 42, p. 319–352.

Spencer, A. C., 1913, Chalcocite enrichment: Econ. Geology, v. 8, p. 621–652.

———, 1917, The geology and ore deposits of Ely, Nevada: U.S. Geol. Survey Prof. Paper 96.

Whitman, A. R., 1914, Notes on the copper ores at Ely, Nevada: Univ. of California Publ., Dept. Geol. Bull., v. 8, p. 309–318.

Neihart, Montana

Bastin, E. S., 1923, Supergene processes at Neihart, Montana: Econ. Geology, v. 18, p. 87–93.

Hurst, M. E., 1922, Supergene processes at Neihart, Montana: Econ. Geology, v. 17, p. 383–388.

Schafer, P. A., 1935, Geology and ore deposits of the Neihart mining district, Cascade County, Montana: Montana Bur. Mines and Geology Mem. 13.

Weed, W. H., 1901, The enrichment of gold and silver veins: Am. Inst. Mining Engineers Trans., v. 30, p. 424–448.

References Cited

Brown, J. S., 1936, Supergene sphalerite, galena, and willemite at Balmat, N.Y.: Econ. Geology, v. 31, p. 331–354.

Butler, B. S., Loughlin, G. F., Heikes, V. C. et al., 1920, The ore deposits of Utah: U.S. Geol. Survey Prof. Paper 111, p. 521–527.

Emmons, W. H., 1917, The enrichment of ore deposits: U.S. Geol. Survey Bull. 625.

———, and Laney, F. B., 1926, Geology and ore deposits of the Ducktown mining district, Tennessee: U.S. Geol. Survey Prof. Paper 139.

Garrels, R. M., 1954, Mineral species as functions of pH and oxidation-reduction potentials, with special reference to the zone of oxidation and secondary enrichment of sulphide ore deposits: Geochim. et Cosmochim. Acta, v. 5, p. 153–168.

———, 1960, Mineral equilibria at low temperature and pressure: New York, Harper & Brothers.

Lindgren, Waldemar, 1933, Mineral deposits (4th ed.): New York, McGraw-Hill Book Co., Inc., p. 849–850.

Miller, B. L., and Singewald, J. T., Jr., 1919, The mineral deposits of South America: New York, McGraw-Hill Book Co., p. 273, 274, 277.

Moesta, F. A., 1928, El mineral de Chañarcillo: Bol. Minero, Santiago de Chile, v. 40, p. 167–182. (Translation of 1870 article.)

Peterson, N. P., 1954, Copper Cities copper deposit, Globe-Miami district, Arizona: Econ. Geology, v. 49, p. 362–377.

———, Gilbert, C. M., and Quick, G. L., 1951, Geology and ore deposits of the Castle Dome area, Gila County, Arizona: U.S. Geol. Survey Bull. 971.

Ransome, F. L., 1919, The copper deposits of Ray and Miami, Arizona: U.S. Geol. Survey Prof. Paper 115.

Roy, Rustum, Majumdar, A. J., and Hulbe, C. W., 1959, The Ag$_2$S and Ag$_2$Se transitions as geologic thermometers: Econ. Geology, v. 54, p. 1278–1280.

Schürmann, Ernst, 1888, Ueber die Verwandtschaft der Schwermetalle zum Schwefel: Justus Liebig's Annalen der Chemie, v. 249, p. 326–350.

Schwartz, G. M., 1947, Hydrothermal alteration in the "porphyry copper" deposits: Econ. Geology, v. 42, p. 319–352.

Segerstrom, Kenneth, 1962, Regional geology of the Chañarcillo silver mining district and adjacent areas, Chile: Econ. Geology, v. 57, p. 1247–1261.

Stokes, H. N., 1907, Experiments on the action of various solutions on pyrite and marcasite: Econ. Geology, v. 2, p. 14–23.

Tenney, J. B., 1935, Globe-Miami district

(Arizona): 16th Internat. Geol. Cong., Copper resources of the world, v. 1, p. 189–201.

Whitehead, W. L., 1919, The veins of Chañarcillo, Chile: Econ. Geology, v. 14, p. 1–45.

————, 1942, The Chañarcillo silver district, Chile, *in* Newhouse, W. H. (ed.), Ore deposits as related to structural features: New Jersey, Princeton Univ. Press, p. 216–220.

CHAPTER 20 **Metamorphism of Ores**

A GREAT DEAL of confusion exists in the literature on the metamorphism of ore minerals, especially the sulfides, sulfosalts, and native metals. The stability ranges of the metallic minerals under conditions of high temperatures and high pressures are practically unknown. Accordingly, a distinction is seldom made between ores that have been subjected to mild metamorphic processes and those that have gone through intense, high-grade metamorphism. Until more is known of the stability ranges and decomposition conditions for many of the common ore minerals, the discussion of metamorphic processes as applied to ores will continue to be somewhat futile.

The criteria by which metamorphism of sulfide ore bodies is recognized are unsatisfactory and inconclusive. Certain textures are thought to be products of dynamothermal metamorphism, but they are generally open to alternative interpretations (Bastin, 1950; Edwards, 1954; Betekhtin, 1958). For example, the banding in many so-called metamorphosed ores actually may be a product of dynamic metamorphism, or it may be relict foliation that was retained through the replacement of a schist or gneiss.

Arguments about the origin and geologic history of the lead-zinc deposits at Broken Hill, New South Wales (see Chapter 12), exemplify the type of uncertainty that exists in this realm of study. Broken Hill has been described by many careful geologists as old deposits that were rearranged and recrystallized during intense regional metamorphism (Andrews, 1922; Ramdohr, 1950, 1953; King and Thomson, 1953). The ores conform to the contorted bedding of Precambrian sediments. High-grade metamorphic rocks and the associated aplites and pegmatites attest to the severity of deformation during metamorphism. The folding took place under conditions of considerable plasticity and was succeeded by faulting while flowage was still possible. King and Thomson (1953), who advocated a syngenetic origin for the metals, argued that during metamorphism the zinc-lead deposits were recrystallized and structurally concentrated along particular fold axes. Ramdohr (1950, 1953) also thought the ores were involved in the high-grade metamorphism that affected the enclosing sediments, though he suggested that the lead and zinc were deposited as epithermal replacement ores before metamorphism. Other workers have classified the ores as hypothermal and consider them to be postmetamorphism in age (Gustafson et al., 1950; Gustafson, 1954). According to this interpretation, the ore and gangue minerals replace foliated metamorphic rocks and therefore possess inherited banding. Gustafson (1954) points out that the ore minerals are not deformed; if they are considered to predate the folding, there must have been a subsequent period of recrystallization in the absence of directed stress.

Similar differences of opinion have centered around the gold of the Southern Piedmont in the United States; it is not clear whether the emplacement of gold predates or postdates the principal metamorphism. Pardee and Park (1948) noted that the ore is broken and shattered in places but that abundant evidence for postmetamorphic ore deposition can be found. Gold-bearing quartz replaces deformed layers, and mineralization cuts sharply across foliation planes in places. Most of the ore shows little evidence of directional stresses. Other workers have held that the ores were recrystallized completely during metamorphism, and the presence of predeformation quartz veins in the Piedmont rocks of Virginia has been convincingly demonstrated by Cloos and Hietanen (1941).

Schistose sulfide ores have formed apparently through metamorphism and shearing of sulfide bodies and through the replacement of schistose rocks (Newhouse and Flaherty, 1930). Flow banding in sulfide masses has been described from Coeur d'Alene, Idaho, where plastically deformed galena contains streaks of sphalerite, tetrahedrite, and pyrite (Waldschmidt, 1925). This "steel galena" formed along fault zones as a result of shearing, but it was not subjected to high-grade metamorphism. Similar sheared galena has been mined from the Slocan district in British Columbia (Uglow, 1917). In contrast, banded ores from the Mammoth mine, Shasta County, California, inherited their foliation from a sheared, schistose alaskite porphyry (Graton, 1909); the relict foliation was replaced by pyrite, sphalerite, and chalcopyrite.

Galena is especially susceptible to plastic flowage under conditions of stress, and it is not uncommon to find curved cleavage planes on galena within rocks that show no other signs of deformation. The plastic deformation is readily detected both megascopically and microscopically. Bent cleavage planes apparently reflect only minor stress, because continued deformation results in granulation along planes of shear, producing the fine-grained steel galena (Bastin, 1950). The deformation of galena and other sulfides is primarily due to translation, a mechanism whereby movement takes place along crystallographically oriented shear planes without actually rupturing grains.

The mobilization of sulfides under metamorphic conditions may explain many features of ore deposits, but the behavior and stability of sulfides under high temperatures and pressures are essentially unknown. For example, galena melts at 1130°C (Kracek, 1942), and its presence in furnace slags proves that it will form at high temperatures; but its stability range under conditions of dynamothermal metamorphism is a different matter, for which there are no quantitative data. Nor are there quantitative data for most other sulfides. If, as most mining geologists contend, the ore minerals remain in residual magmatic fluids until the waning phases of igneous activity, then it should follow that where metamorphic conditions approach rheomorphism (partial fusion) or anatexis, or where the volatiles are metamorphically activated, the same ore minerals would be the first to be mobilized for migration. It would be expected that the sulfides would migrate much more readily than most silicates. Possibly, the sulfides would split into their chemical parts, in which case the sulfur might be separated from the metallic elements. Such a metamorphic origin has been suggested for the unique zinc oxide deposits of Franklin Furnace and Sterling Hill in New Jersey.

The behavior of native metals during metamorphism closely parallels that of sulfides, but depends, as would be expected, upon the metal. Under ordinary atmospheric conditions, gold is one of the most stable elements; yet the absence of any clearly defined nuggets in Precambrian placer deposits indicates that gold migrates under metamorphic conditions at least for short distances. No characteristic of the gold in Precambrian metamorphic rocks has been found applicable in determining whether the gold was mobilized during metamorphism or introduced hydrothermally after the metamorphic processes had ceased. Metamorphosed deposits of silver and copper are certainly not common, if known at all. Native silver recrystallizes under very mild pressures; even the grinding of polished sections causes a distortion in crystals of the surface layer—an annoying phenomenon that makes the microscopic study of original silver textures a difficult problem (Bastin, 1950). Native copper begins to recrystallize at 450–500°C (Carpenter and Fisher, 1930; Edwards, 1954), although it will not melt until the temperature reaches 1083°C (Kracek, 1942). Platinum, which is found as well-defined nuggets in the Witwatersrand district of South Africa, seems to be comparatively stable under high-grade metamorphism.

Iron oxides are more stable under high temperatures and pressures than are either the sulfides or native metals. In the Lake Superior region, and in other areas of iron formation, the rocks have locally been intensely deformed into hematite schists, yet the amount of metal in the formation is not noticeably lowered. In places, the oxides form iron silicates, and the minerals are completely recrystallized; the composition of the minerals has been rearranged, but the iron content remains about the same.

Many of the other metal oxides originate in high-temperature, high-pressure environments; consequently, they tend to be stable under conditions of high-grade metamorphism. Chromite is characteristically a product of magmatic segregation. Rutile, zircon, and monazite are also common constituents of igneous rocks. Corundum, ilmenite, and the spinels are found in high-grade metamorphic rocks, where they apparently are stable. In contrast, metamorphosed manganese oxide appears to be unusual; the manganese combines with silica to form tephroite (Mn_2SiO_4) and other silicates.

DeVore (1955) has suggested that ore-forming fluids in general result from the mobility of metals and sulfides under metamorphic conditions. Thus the metals are considered to migrate outward from centers of metamorphic activity, and the associated plutonic rocks to represent a further product of rheomorphism. The geosyncline becomes the furnace that generates hydrothermal fluids. This hypothesis is gaining favor among economic geologists, and it is considered the best explanation for certain deposits. The Michigan copper district is a good example, where native copper is found along the tops of Precambrian basaltic flows. Stoiber and Davidson (1959) presented abundant field and laboratory data in support of the argument that metamorphism of the lavas at depth altered the basalt to pumpellyite, releasing the copper and other chemical constituents that formed the native copper deposits associated with albitized wall rock and amygdule fillings of calcite, chlorite, epidote, quartz, prehnite, and laumontite ($CaAl_2Si_4O_{12} \cdot 4H_2O$). If abundant sulfur had been available (for example, from sapropelic rocks within the zone of high-grade metamorphism), perhaps a normal assemblage of sulfide minerals would have resulted.

The concept of a metamorphic origin for all hydrothermal fluids seems a little narrow when considered with reference to the deposits of obvious late-magmatic origin. Moreover, metamorphism in general is believed to be a process of dispersion rather than a process of concentration. Perhaps it would be more realistic to consider several possibilities in the zone of anatexis of a geosynclinal prism of sediments. If avenues of escape are available for the mobilized fractions, these fluids may be expelled from the high-temperature, high-pressure zone, forming veins or replacement ores in a cooler zone. Thus dispersed metals would in effect become concentrated along available channels of escape. The complete fusion of geosynclinal sediments, however, forming a fluid magma, would incorporate all the metals that had not escaped earlier; in fact, in a highly plastic environment, the existence of an open fissure would be prohibited. Therefore the magma produced by anatexis would contain the metals as dissolved ions to be expelled during the waning stages of crystallization, according to the classic concept of hydrothermal fluids. It is conceivable that both of these mechanisms could be operative in a single district. Metallogenetic provinces may result from metamorphic or igneous action involving widespread sedimentary concentrations of the metals. Accordingly, the presence of numerous copper-bearing quartz monzonites in the southwestern United States may conceivably reflect anatexis that involved a bed of sedimentary copper sulfides in the deeper parts of the geosynclinal prism—a bed with copper enrichment similar to that in the Kupferschiefer of Germany.

References Cited

Andrews, E. C., 1922, The geology of the Broken Hill district: Geol. Survey of New South Wales Mem., Geol., no. 8.

Bastin, E. S., 1950, Interpretation of ore textures: Geol. Soc. America Mem. 45.

Betekhtin, A. G., 1958, Structures and textures of ores (translated by E. A. Alexandrov), in Internat. Geol. Rev.: v. 4, no. 8, 1962, p. 940–946.

Carpenter, H. C. H., and Fisher, M. S., 1930, A study of the crystal structures of native copper: Inst. Mining Metallurgy (London) Bull. 306, p. 32.

Cloos, Ernst, and Hietanen, Anna, 1941, Geology of the "Martic overthrust" and the Glenarm Series in Pennsylvania and Maryland: Geol. Soc. America Spec. Paper 35, p. 31–32.

DeVore, G. W., 1955, The role of adsorption in the fractionation and distribution of elements: Jour. Geology, v. 63, p 159–190.

Edwards, A. B., 1954, Textures of the ore minerals and their significance: Melbourne, Australasian Inst. Mining Metallurgy.

Graton, L. C., 1906, Gold and tin deposits of the Southern Appalachians: U.S. Geol. Survey Bull. 293.

———, 1909, The occurrence of copper in Shasta County, California: U.S. Geol. Survey Bull. 430, p. 71–111.

Gustafson, J. K., 1954, Discussion: geology of Australian ore deposits, Broken Hill: Econ. Geology, v. 49, p. 783–786.

———, Burrell, H. C., and Garretty, M. D., 1950, Geology of the Broken Hill ore deposit, N. S. W., Australia: Geol. Soc. America Bull., v. 61, p. 1369–1437.

King, H. F., and Thomson, B. P., 1953, The geology of the Broken Hill district, *in* Edwards, A. B. (ed.), Geology of Australian ore deposits: Australasian Inst. Mining Metallurgy, Melbourne, p. 533–577.

Kracek, F. C., 1942, Melting and transformation temperatures of mineral and allied substances, *in* Handbook of physical constants: Geol. Soc. America Spec. Paper 36, p. 139–174.

Newhouse, W. H., and Flaherty, G. F., 1930, The texture and origin of some banded or schistose sulphide ores: Econ. Geology, v. 25, p. 600–620.

Pardee, J. T., and Park, C. F., Jr., 1948, Gold deposits of the Southern Piedmont: U.S. Geol. Survey Prof. Paper 213.

Ramdohr, Paul, 1950, Die Lagerstätte von Broken Hill in New South Wales im Lichte der neuen geologischen Erkenntnisse und erzmikroskopischer Untersuchungen: Heidelberger Beit. zur Min. und Pet., v. 2, p. 291–333.

———, 1953, Über Metamorphose und sekundäre Mobilisierung: Geol. Rund., v. 42, no. 1, p. 11–19.

Stoiber, R. E., and Davidson, E. S., 1959, Amygdule mineral zoning in the Portage Lake lava series, Michigan copper district: Econ. Geology, v. 54, p. 1250–1277, 1444–1460.

Uglow, W. L., 1917, Gneissic galena ore from the Slocan district, British Columbia: Econ. Geology, v. 12, p. 643–662.

Waldschmidt, W. A., 1925, Deformation in ores, Coeur d'Alene district, Idaho: Econ. Geology, v. 20, p. 573–586.

Index

Page numbers in italic indicate an illustration.